Severity DRGs and Reimbursement: An MS-DRG Primer

James S. Kennedy, MD, CCS

Anita Orenstein, RHIT, CCS
Anne B. Casto, RHIA, CCS
Karen M. Lindemann, RHIT, CCS, CCS-P, CPC

AHIMA
American Health Information
Management Association®

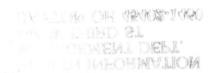

This book is based on the *ICD-9-CM Table and Index to Diseases for Fiscal Year 2008*, effective October 1, 2007, the *ICD-9-CM Official Guidelines for Coding and Reporting*, effective November 15, 2006, and the *Medicare Severity Diagnosis Related Grouper*, version 25, published by the Centers for Medicare & Medicaid Services, effective October 1, 2007.

ISBN: 1-58426-197-8 or 978-1-58426-197-1
AHIMA Product No. AB215107

Kimberly L. Hines, MS, Project Editor
Katie Greenock, Assistant Editor
Melissa Ulbricht, Editorial/Production Coordinator
Ken Zielske, Director of Publications

Rita A. Scichilone, MHSA, RHIA, CCS, CCS-P, CHC, Technical Reviewer
Carol Spencer, RHIT, CCS-P, CCS, Technical Reviewer
Ann M. Zeisset, RHIT, CCS-P, CCS, Technical Reviewer

Any Web sites listed in this book were current and valid as of the date of publication. However, Web page addresses and the information on them may change or disappear at any time and for any number of reasons. The user is encouraged to perform general Web searches to locate any site addresses listed here that are no longer valid.

AHIMA strives to recognize the value of people from every racial and ethnic background as well as all genders, age groups, and sexual orientations by building its membership and leadership resources to reflect the rich diversity of the American population. AHIMA encourages the celebration and promotion of human diversity through education, mentoring, recognition, leadership, and other programs.

American Health Information Management Association
233 North Michigan Avenue, 21st Floor
Chicago, Illinois 60601-5800

Contents

Chapter 3 Secondary Diagnosis—CCs and Major CCs 75

Chapter 4 Other Severity-Adjustment Models (APR-DRGs) 145

Chapter 5 Ready, Set, Implement! 157

Appendix A: MS-DRG Tables 169

Appendix B: 2007 CMS-DRG CC and 2008 MS-DRG CC/MCC Table 171

Appendix C: AHIMA Practice Brief: Developing a Physician Query Process 309

Index 315

Foreword

Dr. Kennedy's experience in training the coding community is vast and keeps him moving throughout the United States on a daily basis. That experience along with his medical background and expertise on current coding issues makes this volume a valuable tool in deciphering the changes that are occurring as a result of the switch to MS-DRGs.

AHIMA Publications has decided to let much of the content in Dr. Kennedy's chapters (chapters 2 and 3) speak for itself and simply reflect that wealth of experience, rather than paring down to specific editorial specifications. Therefore, the two chapters are lengthy but are loaded with extremely useful information that we hope will well serve the needs of the HIM community.

Preface

The October 1, 2007, implementation of Medicare Severity Diagnosis-Related Groups (MS-DRGs) as the primary methodology for Medicare inpatient reimbursement brings home the long-forecasted and long-awaited reality that insurance payers nationwide are reimbursing healthcare services based on the severity of illness sustained by the patient and the intensity of service rendered by the provider. In 2005, the state of Maryland implemented All Patient Refined DRGs (APR-DRGs) as a more highly refined reimbursement methodology; private insurance will be next.

Pay-for-performance is a term applied to incentive programs that provide monetary bonuses to participating entities making progress toward achieving or attaining specific program quality and/or efficiency benchmarks or standards. As these programs develop and use these and other more highly refined methodologies to rank performance and adjust for risk, both physician and health information management professionals must learn, document, and code accordingly, using official language, if they are to thrive in this new environment.

This book is dedicated to bridging the knowledge gaps between physicians and coding or quality professionals in navigating the more highly refined APR-DRG methodologies. The hope is that physicians can describe the nature and severity of illness in compliance with the requirements of the Centers for Disease Control and Prevention. *International Classification of Diseases, 9th Edition, Clinical Modification* (ICD-9-CM), as interpreted by the American Hospital Association's *Coding Clinic for ICD-9-CM*, and that health information management and quality professionals can systematically recognize the nature and severity of illness so they can partner with and query physicians in their mutually beneficial pursuit of data quality. As ICD-9-CM changes and pay-for-performance methodologies develop or become more transparent, this work will be amended to keep pace.

About the Editor

James S. Kennedy, MD, CCS, a native of Oak Ridge, Tennessee, received his undergraduate degree in chemistry and computer science at the University of Tennessee–Knoxville in 1976 and completed his medical school education at the University of Tennessee–Memphis in 1979. Upon completion of his primary care-oriented Internal Medicine residency in Memphis in 1982, he practiced general internal medicine in Williamson County, Tennessee, until his retirement in 1998. Although direct nursing home, hospital, and outpatient care was his occupation, his achievements in community service, such as the implementation of the county's enhanced 911 system and the elimination of intracounty long distance telephone tolls, endure today.

Dr. Kennedy's HIM career began through service on his hospital's Medical Records and Utilization Review Committee and as secretary-treasurer for his group practice, a position from which he advocated CPT billing compliance. Upon his designation as an AHIMA-Certified Coding Specialist in 2001, Dr. Kennedy developed CMS, MS, and APR-DRG–based clinical documentation integrity processes through VP-MA Health Solutions, Healthcare Management Associates, Cambio Health Solutions, and FTI Healthcare, where he is currently a Director.

Living in Smyrna, Tennessee, and married to Monica, Dr. Kennedy has two adult human children and two feline children who think they are human. Dr. Kennedy enjoys traveling and may be winning the war with the weeds in his yard.

About the Contributing Authors

Anita Orenstein, RHIT, CCS, has 21 years of experience in health information management and 5 years of experience working in a clinical laboratory. Anita is currently the Corporate HIM Compliance Manager for Intermountain Healthcare in Salt Lake City, Utah. She has primary responsibility for oversight of the HIM compliance program, including the auditing and monitoring of coding functions and coder education, for their 20 acute care facilities.

Anita has served as a member of the Editorial Advisory Board for *Coding Clinic for ICD-9-CM*, has been a contributing author for several AHIMA publications for the Ambulatory Care Section, and has published a chapter in the text *Effective Management of Coding Services* in which she authored the chapter "Performance Management and Process Improvement." Anita has spoken at numerous AHIMA national and local meetings and has presented several audioconferences relating to coding quality and productivity.

Anita has served as a member of AHIMA's CCS Construction Committee and currently is the Chair of the Council on Certification for AHIMA.

Anne B. Casto, RHIA, CCS, is the President of Casto Consulting, LCC. Prior to founding the firm, Anne was the Program Manager of the HIMS Division at The Ohio State University School of Allied Medical Professions. Anne taught healthcare reimbursement, ICD-9-CM coding, and CPT coding courses for several years. Additionally, she was responsible for curriculum revisions in the areas of chargemaster management, clinical data management, and healthcare reimbursement.

Additionally, Anne was the Vice President of Clinical Information for Cleverley & Associates where she worked very closely with APC regulations and guidelines, preparing hospitals for the implementation of the new Medicare PPS. She was also the Clinical Information Product Manager for CHIPS/Ingenix. Anne joined CHIPS/Ingenix in 1998 and spent the majority of her time developing coding compliance products for the inpatient and outpatient settings.

Anne has been responsible for inpatient and outpatient coding activities in several large hospitals, including Mt. Sinai Medical Center (NYC), Beth Israel Medical Center (NYC), and The Ohio State University Hospitals. She has worked extensively with CMI, quality measures, physician documentation, and coding accuracy efforts at these facilities.

Anne received her degree in health information management at The Ohio State University in 1995. She received her Certified Coding Specialist credential in 1998 from the American Health Information Management Association. Anne recently coauthored an AHIMA-published textbook entitled *Principles of Healthcare Reimbursement*.

Karen M. Lindemann, RHIA, CCS, CCS-P, CPC-P, has more than 25 years of HIM/coding experience, with expertise in outpatient, inpatient, physician office coding, auditing, and case mix analysis. Her experience includes serving as Coding Manager for a community-based hospital and currently serving as the Director of Coding Quality Assurance for a health system that includes seven hospitals. In this position Karen helped analyze case mix data for four Maryland hospitals to assist with their transition to the APR-DRG classification system. She also helped develop an internal coder training program to mentor new professionals into the coding profession and develop coding guidelines to promote consistent quality coding throughout the system's hospitals. Her other experience includes performing coding audits for several major companies.

Karen's professional memberships include AHIMA, MdHIMA, and AAPC. She has served as a member of the MdHIMA board and has been a member of the MdHIMA data quality committee for many years.

Acknowledgments

This work would not have been possible without the love and grace of dedicated individuals willing to sacrifice for this endeavor. First and foremost, allow me to honor my wife, Monica, for her patient endurance. (Thank you, sweetie.) Next, I honor my coworkers at FTI Healthcare, especially Rob Gamble, Bernie O'Neil, and Kathleen Baugh, who allotted time during our work schedules so that this book would be completed. To Anne Casto, Karen Lindemann, and Anita Orenstein, your contributions demonstrate your great worth to our professional practice of HIM. Finally, without the support of my editor, Kimberly Hines, this book would still be on my laptop.

Let me not forget those who encouraged me to learn ICD-9-CM and DRGs in the first place: Dr. Bob Gold, Mr. Lamar Blount, clients of FTI Cambio Health Solutions, and the practice managers of AHIMA, all of whom allowed me to review their medical records, helped me apply ICD-9-CM principles to DRG assignment, and encouraged me to speak to their constituencies about what I had learned. I honor Dr. Gene Stollerman, Dr. Stephen T. Miller, and the late Dr. Gerald Plitman, my professors at the University of Tennessee–Memphis, who taught me to critically and passionately think like an internist. Last, but not least, I thank God for His help.

History of Diagnosis Related Groups

Development of Diagnosis Related Groups

The Diagnosis Related Groups (DRGs) classification system was created at Yale University in the 1970s by researchers Robert Barclay Fetter and John Devereaux Thompson. Their motivation was to create an encounter-based classification system that provided a way to monitor the quality of care and utilization of services provided to patients in the acute care setting.

The DRG system measures the level of resource utilization rendered to a patient during the inpatient confinement period and captures the patient's clinical status (that is, age, patient status, discharge disposition, principal diagnosis, selected secondary diagnoses, and significant procedures). Based on these factors, patients are grouped together into DRGs. Each DRG represents a group of patients with a homogeneous level of complexity and resource consumption.

Prior to DRGs, hospitals used bed size, teaching status, rural/urban location, or a combination of characteristics to explain why patients with similar diagnoses and/or procedures would have significant cost variations. When this approach did not adequately explain the cost differences, hospitals contended that their facilities treated a more complex patient population. The DRG method was the first payment system to explain significant cost variations that exist across hospitals based on patients' resource consumption (Averill et al. 2001, 83).

Each DRG is assigned a relative value, which, when averaged with all the applicable cases, generates a case mix index (CMI) that allows a hospital to compare its resource intensity with that of other hospitals. The relative value or relative weight (RW) is a standardized measure scaled so that a value of 1.0 represents the resource intensity for the typical inpatient case. The case mix index is the weighted average of the RWs of the DRGs and represents the organization's caseload. Case mix index is a single number that compares the overall complexity of the healthcare organization's patient population to the average complexity of all hospitals' patient populations.

Medicare Movement to a Prospective Payment System

In the late 1970s and early 1980s, the Health Care Financing Administration (HCFA), which is now the Centers for Medicare & Medicaid Services (CMS) faced expanding healthcare expenditures. Hospitals were reimbursed based on their costs. Therefore, as utilization of services and cost of providing healthcare services increased, so did the government's financial outlay. Likewise, the copayment amount increased, providing an additional burden for Medicare beneficiaries. CMS was directed to search for a way to control this exponential rise in healthcare costs.

In 1972, Congress authorized CMS to roll out prospective payment demonstration projects. The demonstration projects were examined until 1983. Several states participated in the projects, including Connecticut, Maryland, Massachusetts, New Jersey, New York, Rhode Island, Washington, and Wisconsin (Averill et al. 2001, 106). Each organization implemented prospective payment systems that were based on the following four guiding principles:

- Payment rates are established in advance and remain fixed for the fiscal period for which they apply.

- Payment rates are not automatically determined by the hospital or healthcare providers' past or current actual costs.
- Prospective payment rates are considered to be payment in full.
- The hospital or healthcare provider retains the profit or suffers a loss resulting from the difference between the payment rate and the cost of providing care; thus creating an incentive for cost control.

The New Jersey Department of Health applied DRGs as their prospective payment methodology in the CMS demonstration project. New Jersey reimbursed hospitals a fixed DRG-specific amount for each patient treated. This was the first large-scale application of the DRG methodology (Averill et al. 2001, 83). It later proved to be very successful.

The demonstration projects showed that prospective payment methodologies provided adequate reimbursement for hospital inpatient services but also provided a strong incentive for hospitals to monitor and control healthcare costs. Therefore, the Tax Equity and Fiscal Responsibility Act of 1982 (TEFRA) called for the implementation of a prospective payment system for hospital inpatients. Public Law 98-21 amended sections 1886(d) and 1886(g) of the Social Security Act (the Act) and put into operation DRGs as the prospective payment system for acute care services administered under Medicare Part A (DHHS 2004e, 48920).

DRGs were implemented on October 1, 1983, as the CMS inpatient prospective payment system and have remained in use for over 20 years. The adoption of DRGs forced hospitals to practice cost containment and they had the desired effect, with hospital margins falling from an average of 15 percent to 2 percent within 5 years.

Because of the implementation of DRGs, monitoring hospital inpatient statistics (financials and quality) by DRG has become commonplace. Hospitals continue to use this method to monitor cost, charge, and reimbursement data. Even though components of the DRG system such as RW, length of stay figures, and reimbursement rates are updated each year, major revisions have not occurred to date.

Development of Refined Grouping Systems

DRGs provided a way for hospitals to explain cost variations among their patient population, especially their Medicare population. However, as the healthcare industry progressed, hospitals, healthcare agencies,

consumer groups, and government agencies began to look for a classification system with a higher level of precision for grouping Medicare and non-Medicare patients—a system that adjusts for specific characteristics that impact resource utilization. Specifically, CMS has examined refinements that would allow a hospital to be compensated more equitably for patients with a higher severity of illness. When examining refinement grouping systems, the following concepts should be taken into consideration:

- A reduction of within-group variation
- Improved homogeneity
- A manageable number of DRGs
- Reasonable administrative costs
- A system that is easily understood by hospitals, physicians, patients, etc (Edwards et al. 1994, 2)

The State of New York passed legislation in 1987 that required the use of a prospective payment system for non-Medicare patients. In January 1988, All Patient Diagnosis Related Groups (AP-DRGs) were implemented. The New York Department of Health contracted with 3M™ Health Information Systems to create AP-DRGs (Boucher et al. 2006, 2). AP-DRGs expanded the Centers for Medicare & Medicaid Services Diagnosis Related Group (CMS DRG) system by adding groups for neonates, pediatrics, HIV encounters, transplants, and others. In 1990, New York added a refinement calculation to AP-DRGs by introducing the concept of a major complication or comorbidity (MCC) into the grouping logic. Statistical analysis showed that within a major diagnostic category (MDC), surgical patients with MCCs were similar to each other in terms of resource use (Edwards 1994, 4). This proved true for medical patients as well. Therefore, refinement categories were applied at the MDC level rather than the separate splits being created at the DRG level (Edwards et al. 1994, 4). This allowed for the system to add a refinement level to measure severity of illness without creating a significant increase in the number of DRG groups. The AP-DRG system is still widely used today in a number of Medicaid agencies and third-party payers (Boucher et al. 2006, 2).

In 1989, CMS funded a project at Yale University that resulted in the development of the Refined DRG system (RDRGs) (Boucher et al. 2006, 2). The Health Systems Management Group at Yale incorporated a measurement of severity of illness into the RDRG system. Using the impact of secondary diagnoses on resource consumption, the RDRG system created three subclasses for medical patients (minor/no effect, moderate, and major) and four subclasses for surgical patients (minor/no effect, moderate, major, and catastrophic). The refinement resulted in more than 1,200 RDRGs, some of which represented only a small volume of patients.

CMS introduced Severity DRGs (S-DRGs) in 1993. The S-DRG system uses Complication and Comorbidity (CC) and MCC secondary diagnoses to add a severity of illness refinement to the DRG system. Rather than creating refinement breakouts at the MDC level (AP-DRG) or creating breakouts for every DRG (RDRG), the S-DRG methodology examines the need for a refinement breakout on a DRG-by-DRG basis (Edwards et al. 1994, 3). CMS published the S-DRG system in 1994; however, the system was not adopted for use in the Inpatient Prospective Payment System (IPPS) at that time.

3M Health Information Systems joined with the National Association of Children's Hospitals and Related Institutions (NACHRI) to develop APR-DRG in 1990. The APR-DRG system was created to address the limitations of the RDRG system, which include:

- RDRGs used CMS DRGs and therefore did not address all patient types (for example, pediatric cases).
- The presence of multiple CC conditions had no impact on the level of severity.
- RDRGs used the Medicare list of CCs, which had only minor revisions that were based on code additions and deletions.
- The RDRG structure of subclasses was inconsistent and confusing (Edwards et al. 1994, 5).

Unlike Medicare and AP-DRGs, which for the most part have two and three levels of severity respectively for each base DRG, APR-DRGs incorporate four complexity subclasses: minor or no CC, moderate, major, and extreme. In deriving these complexity subclasses, APR-DRGs take a three-phase approach to assigning patients into a subclass. First, the complexity level of each secondary diagnosis is determined. Second, a base complexity subclass based on the secondary diagnoses is determined. And third, the final complexity subclass for the patient is determined by incorporating the impact of the principal diagnosis, age, nonoperating room procedures, and combinations of categories of secondary diagnoses (Edwards et al. 1994, 5). Like RDRGs, APR-DRGs created a large number of patient groups, some with low patient volume. However, the APR-DRG system enhances the ability to explain differences in resource use across the patient population and creates improved homogeneity among the patient groups. The first version of APR-DRGs was released in 1993.

Since 1974, the Health Service Cost Review Commission (HSCRC) of Maryland has set hospital rates within their state. In 1977, Maryland was granted a waiver by the federal government to test alternative payment approaches, exempting the state from national Medicare and Medicaid reimbursement requirements.

Unlike the rest of the nation, Maryland adopted its own prospective payment system using a modified version of the CMS DRGs, which differed by allowing ventilator care to change the DRG across all MDCs and by providing more discrimination for low birth-weight babies. The Maryland modified-DRG methodology applied to all payers, including Medicare, Medicaid, and private insurers.

To better account for variations in resource utilization among Maryland's tertiary and rural hospitals, the HSCRC approved the nation's first statewide implementation of APR-DRGs for hospital reimbursement in July 2005. Maryland's coders were forced to adjust to a completely different approach to the principal and secondary CC diagnosis query process and DRG sequencing than what they had been using for the previous 20 years. In 2007, Mississippi also implemented APR-DRGs for its Medicaid program. Chapter 4 of this book discusses the details of Maryland's experience with APR-DRGs. Process reviews and outcome analyses can provide valuable information about what worked and what did not work from Maryland's implementation of APR-DRGs, and the lessons the state learned will assist with the large-scale implementation of Medicare Severity Diagnosis Related Groups (MS-DRGs) for Medicare IPPS.

With the development of physician-owned specialty hospitals during the early 2000s and the alleged skimming of lower-resource-intensity patients from community all-purpose hospitals, Medicare recognized a need to further refine its severity model.

To address concerns regarding the cardiac physician hospitals, Medicare created a new CC system for cardiovascular procedures, labeling them Major Cardiovascular Diagnoses (MCVD). For the first time since CMS implemented DRGs, hospital coding professionals had to learn a new CC system and develop closer relationships with cardiothoracic surgeons. Documentation of secondary conditions had to be present in the medical record to assign these codes so that the resulting DRG assignment accurately reflected the patient's severity of illness.

Upon further recommendations of the Medicare Payment Advisory Commission (MedPAC), CMS released for public comment an even more highly refined, severity-adjusted DRG system based on the 3M APR-DRG fiscal year (FY) 2007 IPPS proposed rule. The FY2007 proposed rule is available on the CMS Web site under IPPS Regulations and Notices at: http://www.cms.hhs.gov/AcuteInpatientPPS/IPPS/list.asp#TopOfPage. The proposed system was labeled Consolidated Severity Diagnosis Related Groups (CS-DRG) and was suggested for potential implementation on October 1, 2006. There were numerous public comments, several focusing on concerns that the consolidated DRGs were based on 3M's proprietary APR-DRG system. Additionally, several comments discussed the difficulties Maryland encountered implementing the APR-DRG system in 2005. Therefore, rather than implementing consolidated DRGs for FY2007, CMS opted to further refine the CMS DRGs by adding the following categories: Major Gastrointestinal Diagnoses, Major Esophageal Diagnoses, Major Hematological Diagnoses, and Major Urological Procedures. CMS also commissioned a study of various DRG severity systems for potential implementation in FY2008. The contract was awarded to RAND Corporation.

The following companies provided their severity-adjusted systems for the RAND Corporation study:

- 3M (All Payer Refined DRGs and Consolidated Severity DRGs)
- CMS (Consolidated Severity DRGs using APR-DRG CC methodology)
- Ingenix (All Payer Severity-Adjusted DRGs)
- RDRG (Solucient's version and Health Systems Consultant version)

RAND Corporation found that all of these methodologies measured resource utilization more accurately across most MDCs than did CMS DRGs alone (Wynn et al. 2007).

The RAND Corporation Working Paper, Evaluation of Severity-Adjusted DRG Systems: Interim Report can be downloaded from the CMS Web site at: http://www.cms.hhs.gov/reports/downloads/Wynn0307.pdf

Even though these DRG systems performed favorably against the CMS DRGs, CMS included in the proposed rule for Inpatient Prospective Payment for FY2008 a completely new methodology—the MS-DRG system. In this system, CMS added a more highly refined severity-of-illness component to the CMS DRG system. This refinement process involved the following three steps:

- Consolidation of existing DRGs into base DRGs
- Categorization of each diagnosis as MCC, CC, or non-CC
- Subdivision of each base DRG into subclasses based on the CC categories

This is similar to the process that was used in the development of S-DRGs in 1993. However, instead of updating S-DRGs, CMS began a new development process. The revision of the DRG system really relies on the full evaluation and revision of the CC list. The original CC list was created at Yale University in the early 1980s, and except for a few revisions in 1984 and basic code maintenance, the current CC list is almost identical to the original CC list. But because dramatic changes have occurred in the delivery of healthcare, patient characteristics, and coding practices over the past 20 years or longer, a revision was greatly needed. The revision includes reducing the CC list to 3,343 codes and creating a MCC list of 1,585 codes. Table 1.1 shows the comparison between the FY 2007 CC list and the finalized FY 2008 MCC and CC lists in a case study. The severity refinement is added to the base DRGs in one of the following four ways:

- No refinement category (no subgroup)
- MCC and CC category and non-CC category (two subgroups)
- MCC category and CC and non-CC category (two subgroups)
- MCC category, CC category, and non-CC category (three subgroups)

Table 1.1   The FY 2007 CC List and the Revised FY 2008 CC List

Copy of Table E—Comparison of Current CC List and Revised CC List (page 47154) FY 2008 final rule

	Current CC List	Revised CC List
Codes designated as a CC	3,326	2,583
Percentage of patient with one or more CCs	77.66%	40.34%
Percentage of patients with no CC	22.34%	59.66%
Average charge of patients with one or more CCs	$24,538	$31,451
Average charge of patients with no CCs	$14,795	$16,215

The result of this development process is a severity-adjusted DRG system that includes 745 DRG categories. Chapters 2 and 3 of this book discuss the internal workings of the MS-DRG system. Chapter 2 provides a detailed view of the MS-DRG system MDC by MDC, pointing out the intricacies of this severity-adjusted system. From this chapter, health information management professionals, coders, and physicians will be able to fully understand how coding and improved documentation in the medical record will allow the MS-DRG to capture the patient's severity of illness and provide appropriate reimbursement for the case.

For CMS payments to remain equitable under IPPS, CMS has made strides during the past few fiscal years in implementing a severity-of-illness component to CMS DRGs. Finding the best system for the CMS population is a challenge; however, the healthcare industry is lobbying for change as the need to explain and receive appropriate reimbursement for greater severity-of-illness patients continues to grow.

CMS Movement to a Severity-of-Illness Adjusted DRG System

In March 2005, MedPAC published recommendations for IPPS reform in its Report to the Congress, Physician-Owned Specialty Hospitals. MedPAC recommended that the Secretary of Health and Human Services (HHS) refine the entire DRG system by implementing a severity-of-illness component (FR Vol. 72. No. 85, page 24690). Specifically, MedPAC recommended that CMS refine the current DRGs to more fully capture differences in severity of illness among patients. As noted previously, CMS has funded and evaluated several projects with the goal of incorporating a severity-of-illness component to CMS DRGs. However, given a tight timeframe, CMS was not able to implement a severity-adjusted DRG system for fiscal year 2006. Instead, CMS adopted severity-weighted cardiac DRGs in response to public concerns regarding cardiac surgery DRGs (FR Vol. 72 No. 85 page 24690). On September 1, 2006, CMS contracted with RAND Corporation to evaluate several severity-adjusted DRG systems for use in IPPS. In the FY2007 proposed rule, CMS suggested implementation of the CMS DRG system for FY2008. This proposal was met with mixed reactions from the healthcare community due to the short implementation period, private ownership of the system, and the complexity of the grouping logic. So instead, for fiscal year 2007, CMS made changes to the current DRGs that incorporated a severity-of-illness component in limited areas. The

modifications created 20 new DRGs for 13 clinical areas and altered 32 other DRGs. CMS took these steps as an interim measure while analysis continued for the full adoption of a severity-adjusted DRG system into IPPS.

The MedPAC report also called for refinements in RW calculations. MedPAC recommended that CMS move from charge-based RWs to cost-based RWs. Additionally, MedPAC specified that a RW adjustment be incorporated to account for differences in the prevalence of high-cost outlier cases. CMS addressed cost-based RWs and in the FY2007 final rule implemented a 3-year transition plan for the adoption of cost-based RWs.

As noted previously, on September 1, 2006, CMS contracted with RAND Corporation to evaluate several severity-adjusted DRG systems for use in IPPS. In an effort to aid CMS with determining the most appropriate severity-adjusted DRG system, the RAND Corporation interim report focuses on the following three key questions:

- How well does each classification system explain variation in resource usage?
- How would the classification system affect a hospital's patient mix?
- Are the groupings manageable, administratively feasible, and understandable? (Wynn et al. 2007)

Interestingly, these are similar questions to those used by CMS in 1993 to evaluate S-DRGs. These questions and their answers are extremely important. CMS is evaluating the severity-adjusted DRG system not only in response to MedPAC recommendations but also to avoid creating an incentive for hospitals to avoid treating high-cost cases due to inequity in payments for complex cases (Wynn et al. 2007).

To evaluate a system's ability to explain variation in resource usage, four aspects are measured. First, a key goal of a severity-adjusted DRG system is to reduce the within-DRG cost variation; that is, to reduce the dollar amount between the highest-cost case and lowest-cost case in a particular DRG. Second, a system is evaluated for its explanatory power, or how well the system explains differences in cost across all Medicare discharges (Wynn et al. 2007). This is a measurement of how Medicare payments are distributed across discharges and hospitals. Third, systems are evaluated for their validity. In the DRG system, this means that as the cost per discharge increases, the severity level should increase also. Fourth, systems are evaluated on their stability. Ideally, the best system is one in which the DRG RWs remain stable from year to year.

The RAND Corporation report also addresses each severity-adjusted system's impact on patient mix. To determine the impact on patient mix, the total payment redistribution is examined. Total payment redistribution reflects the impact of the enhancement in explanatory power (Wynn et al. 2007, xv). In a severity-adjusted DRG system the payment should shift away from less-resource-complex cases and to more-resource-complex cases. This impact analysis focuses on the severity-adjusted DRG system's impact on patient mix, not the change in coding practices that may result from the adoption of such a system.

Even though a system explains cost variation and has a positive impact on patient mix, the system's complexity and administrative burden must be taken into consideration. Not only must a severity-adjusted DRG system be complex enough to explain cost variations, redistribute payment adequately, and measure case mix appropriately, but also it must be simple enough for its users to understand. Currently, system users include physicians, allied health clinicians, coding professionals, third-party payers, and others who would like to use the system for purposes other than reimbursement. Likewise, a suitable severity-adjusted DRG system should be feasible for wide-scale implementation. Two areas of cost must be considered. First, training costs must be assessed. Will coding professionals and other data users require extensive training to understand the system and apply required changes to their coding and abstracting procedures? Second, what level of health information system modifications will be necessary to implement the severity-adjusted DRG system? Not only will hospitals require new grouping software, but modifications must be made to all systems housing coded data and DRG information, including patient financial systems and encoders.

The search for the best severity-adjusted DRG system is complex. One system may score high in explanation of cost variance but may score low in understandability and ease of implementation, whereas another system may do just the opposite. The key to a suitable system is balance. A system that is easy to understand and provides improvements to payment equity will allow CMS to successfully add a severity-of-illness component into the prospective payment system for short-term, acute-care hospitals. Chapter 5 of this book provides healthcare professionals with implementation strategies. The chapter discusses the importance of forming an IPPS team and highlights all areas of training that are required for the successful implementation of MS-DRGs.

CMS Adoption of MS-DRGs for Fiscal Year 2008 IPPS

In Proposed Changes to the Hospital Inpatient Prospective Payment Systems and Fiscal Year 2008 Rates; Proposed Rule (HHS 2007, 24690-24712), CMS presents the framework for the proposed MS-DRG system. The final rule adopts the proposed MS-DRG grouping with some modifications to the implementation period. As discussed previously, the MS-DRG system includes a three-subgroup breakout methodology and a complete revision to the CC list. Appendix A provides an impact analysis of all changes proposed in the final rule for FY2008 IPPS. Interestingly, the impact from the implementation of RWs, MS-DRGs, and wage index changes is reported to be 0 percent. The impact for each individual hospital may be significantly higher or lower than zero. The MS-DRG system is designed to reimburse a hospital with a more complex mix of services at a higher rate; therefore, this system will benefit urban teaching hospitals and may penalize smaller rural hospitals. The remainder of this book discusses the details of the MS-DRG system, provides insight and guidance concerning significant coding issues and strategies, and discusses implementation issues that healthcare facilities will encounter when they adopt the system. The implementation of the MS-DRG system is the most significant change in the IPPS payment methodology since the implementation of DRGs in 1983. All healthcare professionals must work together during the implementation phase. Successful implementation of MS-DRGs requires coders to code at the highest level of specificity, physicians to document with greater precision and detail, HIM professionals to accurately abstract all required pieces of information from the healthcare record, and financial professionals to produce a clean Uniform Bill (UB-04) bill for submission. Only when this happens will hospitals be able to report accurate severity-of-illness levels for their patient population and, in turn, CMS will be able to appropriately reimburse hospitals for the services rendered to their beneficiaries.

References

Averill, R. F., N. I. Goldfield, J. Eisenhandler, J. S. Hughes, and J. Muldoon. 2001. Clinical risk groups and the future of healthcare reimbursement and diagnosis-related groups. In *Reimbursement methodologies for healthcare services* [CD-ROM], ed. L. M. Jones, 1-12, 83-116. Chicago: American Health Information Management Association.

Boucher, A., S. Bowman, C. Piselli, and R. Scichilone. 2006. The evolution of DRGs. *Journal of AHIMA* 77(7):68A–C.

Department of Health and Human Services. 2007 (May 3). Medicare Program: Changes to the hospital inpatient prospective payment systems and fiscal year 2008 rates; proposed rule. Federal Register Vol. 72, No. 85, pages 24690-24711.

Department of Health and Human Services. 2007 (August 22). Medicare Program: Changes to the hospital inpatient prospective payment systems and fiscal year 2008 rates; final rule. Federal Register Vol. 72, No. 162, pages 47130-48175.

Edwards, N., D. Honemann, D. Burley, and M. Navarro. 1994. Refinement of the Medicare diagnosis-related groups to incorporate a measure of severity—Medicare payment systems: Moving toward the future. *Health Care Financing Review* (Winter): 1–6.

Wynn, B., M. Beckett, L. Hillborne, M. Scott, and B. Bahney. 2007 (March). Evaluation of severity-adjusted DRG systems: Interim report. Working Paper, RAND Corporation, Santa Monica, CA.

Resource

Casto, A., and E. Layman. 2006. *Principles of Healthcare Reimbursement*. Chicago: AHIMA.

Guterman S, Altman SH, Young DA. Hospitals' Financial Performance in the First Five Years of PPS. *Health Affair*. Spring 1990;9(1):125-134. Available at: http://www.content.healthaffairs.org/cgi/reprint/9/1/125.pdf.

Chapter 2

Principal Diagnosis and Principal Procedures Grouping Changes Under MS-DRGs

Introduction

A diagnosis related group (DRG) is a group of clinically coherent conditions with a similar pattern of resource intensity determined by the principal diagnosis, significant additional diagnoses (and their present-on-admission status), and procedures as reported on the Uniform Bill-04 (UB-04).

The Inpatient Prospective Final Rule FY2008 revises the DRG grouping system used from 1983 until 2007 (referred to as CMS DRGs) to a Medicare-Severity DRG grouping system (MS-DRGs). This chapter highlights diagnoses and procedures grouping to the different major diagnostic categories (MDCs) and DRGs under the MS-DRG system. The secondary diagnoses are classified into three categories: with major complication or comorbidity (MCC), with complication or comorbidity (CC), or without MCC or without CC.

ICD-9-CM states that certain conditions have both an underlying etiology and multiple body systems manifestations due to the underlying etiology (ICD-9-CM 2006). Many conditions categorized in ICD-9-CM have up to five components that, if allowed in ICD-9-CM, should be documented and coded to fully report the severity of illness. These are:

- Manifestation(s)—Manifestations are the specific symptoms, signs, diagnoses, or a constellation thereof (known as a syndrome) alerting the provider that the patient has a disease (ICD-9-CM 2006). Symptoms and signs are acceptable for reporting purposes when a related definitive diagnosis has not been established (confirmed) by the provider. Those that are integral to the

disease process should not be reported. As a general rule, the higher the specificity of the manifestation, the higher the weight of the DRG. For example, altered mental status is assigned to MS-DRG 948 (Signs and symptoms without MCC) (RW 0.6542), whereas psychosis is assigned to MS-DRG 885 (Psychosis) (RW 0.7783) or delirium without CC is assigned to MS-DRG 880 (Acute adjustment reaction and psychosocial dysfunction) (RW 0.6085).

- Underlying etiology—The underlying pathology responsible for the patient's manifestation is the underlying etiology (ICD-9-CM 2006). For the most part, MS-DRGs group underlying etiologies into higher-weighted DRGs than those for manifestations. For example, delirium due to an accidental overdose of a medication taken as prescribed (MS-DRG 880 [Acute Adjustment Reaction and Psychosocial Dysfunction]) (RW 0.6085) is likely due to a toxic encephalopathy (MS-DRG 93 [Other disorders of nervous systems w/o CC/MCC]) (RW 0.7710). To qualify as a principal diagnosis, the toxic encephalopathy must be documented and linked as the underlying etiology of the delirium and must meet principal diagnosis reporting guidelines.

- Severity—The degree of the patient's underlying condition or manifestation is the severity. For example, type 1 diabetes mellitus can be controlled (250.01—not a complication or comorbidity [CC]), uncontrolled (205.03—not a CC), in diabetic ketoacidosis without coma (250.13—a major complication or comorbidity [MCC]), in diabetic ketoacidosis with coma

(250.33—an MCC), or in the hyperosmolar state (250.22—an MCC if stipulated as uncontrolled or 250.20—an MCC if uncontrolled is not stated). Benign hypertension can be controlled (401.1—not a CC) or accelerated/malignant (401.0—a CC). Malnutrition may be mild (263.1—not a CC), moderate (263.0—not a CC), or severe (261—an MCC). Sepsis (SIRS due to infection) associated with organ dysfunction is severe sepsis (995.92—an MCC), while that without organ dysfunction is sepsis (995.91—an MCC).

- Precipitating etiology—Many exacerbations of a patient's underlying condition are precipitated by another acute disease process known as a precipitating or instigating etiology. For example, chronic systolic heart failure due to hypertensive cardiomyopathy (codes 402.91 [Hypertensive cardiomyopathy], 425.8 [Hypertensive Cardiomyopathy], 428.22 [Chronic systolic heart failure]—a CC) may be exacerbated (changing 428.22 to 428.23 [Acute on chronic systolic heart failure]—an MCC) by a pulmonary embolus, sepsis, or an acute myocardial infarction that may fit the definition of principal diagnosis. Because precipitating causes usually are not clinically evident upon admission, their presence may not be documented until later in the patient's admission or linked to the circumstances of admission. Coding professionals may need to query physicians to clarify these circumstances.

- Complications—A complication is defined as an unexpected consequence as a direct result of a disease or treatment (Bronnert 2006). A complication may have precipitated the patient's manifestations or exacerbated the underlying etiology that occasioned the hospital stay. For example, digoxin toxicity in a patient may be complicated by a third-degree heart block, thus warranting hospitalization. In another example, a patient's sepsis may be an unexpected complication of an infected vascular or urinary catheter, necessitating the complication code to be the principal diagnosis. Respiratory failure may be a complication of the patient's exacerbation of chronic obstructive pulmonary disease (COPD) for which the patient could not be treated as an outpatient, thus requiring inpatient admission. Although a complication may have an adverse effect on the patient's health, it does not necessarily indicate poor quality care by the provider.

ICD-9-CM states that consistent, complete documentation in the medical record cannot be overemphasized and that without such documentation, the application of all coding guidelines is a difficult, if not impossible, task (ICD-9-CM 2006). A joint effort between the healthcare provider and the coding professional is essential to achieve complete and accurate documentation, code assignment, and reporting of diagnoses and procedures.

When confronted with a diagnosis or condition, a coding professional develops an overall gestalt for the admission's severity of illness and ascertains that the clinical signs and circumstances support what is documented. Next, a coding professional determines under which component each documented condition is grouped (for example, a manifestation or precipitating etiology) and looks for its other four components. If the physician ambiguously describes the patient's severity of illness (for example, urosepsis instead of sepsis due to urinary tract infection [UTI]) or fails to document any missing components (for example, linkage of sepsis with associated organ dysfunction), especially when supporting clinical signs, circumstances, or treatments are present, the coding professional may query the physician for additional information or clarification prior to coding and submitting the admission for payment. Coding professionals also should query for the clinical significance or specificity of any unexplained ancillary tests (for example, pathology reports) or paraprofessional documentation (for example, dietician or nursing notes) that impact patient severity or resource utilization.

Components of a DRG Assignment

The following metrics govern DRG assignment:

- Principal diagnosis—Defined by the Uniform Hospital Discharge Data Set (UHDDS), the principal diagnosis is "the condition established after study to be chiefly responsible for occasioning the admission of the patient to the hospital for care." The circumstances of admission, the diagnostic approach, and the treatment rendered factor into principal diagnosis selection. Clinical documentation should support that the principal diagnosis is present on admission. When physician documentation is not clear that a potential principal diagnosis is present on admission, as is required for sepsis, concurrent or retrospective query is warranted (ICD-9-CM 2006).

  Another way of viewing the principal diagnosis is that the acute condition established after study is chiefly responsible for why the patient cannot be treated in an outpatient or alternative setting or, in more common terms, why the patient could not go home. For example, if a patient has an acute exacerbation of COPD but has acute respiratory failure (for example, respiratory distress and a pO_2 of 52—a fall in pO_2 of 20 mm from baseline), then acute respiratory failure was the condition for which the patient's acute exacerbation of COPD could not be treated as an outpatient (why the patient could not go home), qualifying it as principal diagnosis.

The ICD-9-CM Official Guidelines for Coding and Reporting and *AHA Coding Clinic for ICD-9-CM* provide official advice for principal diagnosis assignment and other code sequencing. Not only the circumstances of admission, but also the diagnostic approach and the treatment rendered determine the principal diagnosis.

More often than not, the condition present on admission necessitating the need for an operative procedure performed during an inpatient admission governs the principal diagnosis assigned. Supporting this, *Coding Clinic for ICD-9-CM* (3rd Quarter, 2002, 14) cites an example in which a patient with dental caries requiring extraction was admitted as an inpatient to have his anticoagulants adjusted perioperatively. The physician documented that the reason for inpatient admission was to manage the anticoagulants (V58.61). After review of the entire case and applying coding rules, the reason for admission is the surgical procedure to address the dental caries. The anti-coagulant management meets additional diagnosis reporting guidelines as it is a condition being treated and evaluated during the inpatient stay for the dental caries.

In another example, a patient may have sepsis (SIRS) due to acute cholecystitis on admission and undergo a cholecystectomy. Sequencing rules guide the coding professional to report 038.9 (Septicemia) as principal diagnosis rather than acute cholecystitis.

- Significant additional diagnoses—UHDDS defines additional diagnoses as "all conditions that coexist at the time of admission, that develop subsequently, or that affect the treatment received and/or the length of stay. Diagnoses related to an earlier episode that have no bearing on the current hospital stay are to be excluded. ICD-9-CM further specifies that conditions affecting patient care must require clinical evaluation, therapeutic treatment, diagnostic

procedures, extension of the length of the hospital stay, or increased nursing care and/or monitoring.

Some DRGs are based on the secondary diagnosis. For example, a normal newborn is assigned to MS-DRG 795 (Normal newborn) (RW 0.1580), yet one with a secondary diagnosis of urinary tract infection is assigned to MS-DRG 794 (Neonate with other significant problem) (RW 1.1668). Secondary diagnoses of HIV infection and acute myocardial infarction, among others, influence DRG assignment in some circumstances as well.

Cases with an applicable CC or a major CC are assigned to higher-weighted DRGs than their base DRG. This aspect of DRG assignment is discussed in more detail in chapter 3.

- Principal procedure—Defined as the procedure (operating room, diagnostic, or therapeutic service [such as respiratory therapy] recorded on the medical record of discharged patients) that was performed for definitive treatment rather than for diagnostic or exploratory purposes or that was necessary to take care of a complication. If there are two procedures that meet the above definition, then the one most related to the principal diagnosis is selected as the principal procedure.

Procedures are categorized as "operating room procedures" with the rest assigned as "nonoperating room" or "minor" procedures.

Based on the MDC assigned, CMS has established a surgical hierarchy within that MDC that determines if the performed procedure is significant or pertinent to that MDC and which one of multiple surgical procedures within that MDC should be principal. For example, if a patient has an aortic valve replacement and a thyroidectomy performed on the same admission, the valve replacement is the principal procedure if the principal diagnosis (for example, aortic stenosis) is assigned to MDC 5 (Diseases and Disorders of the Circulatory System), whereas the thyroidectomy is a principal procedure if the principal diagnosis (for example, hypokalemia) is assigned to MDC 10 (Endocrine, Nutritional and Metabolic Disorders and Disease).

Most nonoperating room or minor procedures will not affect MS-DRG assignment, although some do within applicable MDCs (for example, ventilator care in MDC 4, administration of tissue plasminogen activator in MDC 1, cardiac catheterization in MDC 5). If a significant operative procedure does not correlate with the assigned MDC, CMS has established MS-DRGs for OR procedures unrelated to the principal diagnosis. For example, if a patient has an aortic valve replacement and no other significant procedures, yet the principal diagnosis does not assign the case to MDC 5, the patient is assigned to MS-DRG 981–983 (Extensive OR procedure unrelated to principal diagnosis with or without CC/MCC).

- Secondary procedures—Some DRGs are determined by a secondary procedure performed in concert with a specific principal procedure. For example, percutaneous transluminal coronary angioplasty (PTCA) without insertion of a drug-eluting stent groups to one set of DRGs (with and without MCC) and one with a drug-eluting stent groups to another. Carotid artery stent procedures require both the percutaneous angioplasty or atherectomy of a precerebral vessel *and* the percutaneous insertion of a carotid artery stent to affect DRG assignment.

- MDC assignment—Every principal diagnosis, influenced by certain secondary diagnoses (for example, 042 [Human immunodeficiency virus, neonatal codes]) assigns the admission to one of 25 MDCs correlating with an organ system (for example, respiratory), condition (for example, burns or HIV), or patient type (for example, newborns and other neonates). Table 2.1 provides a list of the MS-DRG MDCs.

Surgical procedures do not directly affect MDC assignment except under two circumstances:

- The patient receives a CMS-designated high-intensity treatment placing the procedure into a pre-MDC category. The DRG descriptions for these procedures are listed in Table 2.2.
- The patient undergoes a significant operative procedure that is not assigned to the MDC determined by the principal or secondary diagnosis. For example, a patient may be admitted for pneumonia but undergoes a repair of a hip fracture that occurred after admission. These assign a DRG associated with "all MDCs" or "no MDCs" listed in Table 2.3.

Table 2.1   Major Diagnostic Categories

01—Diseases and Disorders of the Nervous System
02—Diseases and Disorders of the Eye
03—Diseases and Disorders of the Ear, Nose, Mouth, and Throat
04—Diseases and Disorders of the Respiratory System
05—Diseases and Disorders of the Circulatory System
06—Diseases and Disorders of the Digestive System
07—Diseases and Disorders of the Hepatobiliary System and Pancreas
08—Diseases and Disorders of the Musculoskeletal System and Connective Tissue
09—Diseases and Disorders of the Skin, Subcutaneous Tissue, and Breast
10—Endocrine, Nutritional, and Metabolic Diseases and Disorders
11—Diseases and Disorders of the Kidney and Urinary Tract
12—Diseases and Disorders of the Male Reproductive System
13—Diseases and Disorders of the Female Reproductive System
14—Pregnancy, Childbirth, and the Puerperium
15—Newborns and Other Neonates With Conditions Originating in Perinatal Period
16—Diseases and Disorders of Blood, Blood-Forming Organs, Immunological Disorders
17—Myeloproliferative Diseases and Disorders, Poorly Differentiated Neoplasm
18—Infectious and Parasitic Diseases, Systemic, or Unspecified Sites
19—Mental Diseases and Disorders
20—Alcohol/Drug Use and Alcohol/Drug-Induced Organic Mental Disorders
21—Injuries, Poisonings, and Toxic Effects of Drugs
22—Burns
23—Factors Influencing Health Status and Other Contacts with Health Services
24—Multiple Significant Trauma
25—Human Immunodeficiency Virus Infections

Patient status is the level of care under which the patient was discharged. Options available in the UB-04 include the following.

- 01 = Discharged to home or self care (routine discharge)
- 02 = Discharged/transferred to another short-term general hospital
- 03 = Discharged/transferred to skilled nursing facility (SNF)
- 04 = Discharged/transferred to an intermediate care facility (ICF)
- 05 = Discharged/transferred to another type of institution
- 06 = Discharged/transferred to home under care of organized home health service organization
- 07 = Left against medical advice

- 08 = Reserved
- 09 = Admitted as an inpatient to this hospital (Medicare outpatient only)
- 20 = Expired (or did not recover—Christian Science patient)
- 21–29 = Reserved
- 30 = Still a patient
- 40 = Expired at home
- 41 = Expired in a medical facility, such as a hospital, SNF, ICF, or free-standing hospice (Medicare hospice care only)
- 42 = Expired–place unknown (Medicare hospice care only)
- 43 = Discharged to federal healthcare facility
- 50 = Hospice–Home
- 51 = Hospice–Medical Facility
- 52–60 = Reserved
- 61 = Discharge to hospital-based swing bed

Table 2.2   CMS DRG Descriptions for Pre-MDC Categories

MS-DRG	MDC	MS-DRG Title	Weights
001	PRE	Heart transplant or implant of heart assist system w MCC	23.1117
002	PRE	Heart transplant or implant of heart assist system w/o MCC	16.2735
003	PRE	ECMO or trach w/ MV 96+ hrs or PDX except face, mouth, and neck w major OR	18.7707
004	PRE	Trach w MV 96+ hrs or PDX except face, mouth, and neck w/o major OR	11.4219
005	PRE	Liver transplant w MCC or intestinal transplant	10.6120
006	PRE	Liver transplant w/o MCC	7.2562
007	PRE	Lung transplant	8.4002
008	PRE	Simultaneous pancreas/kidney transplant	5.1726
009	PRE	Bone marrow transplant	6.4842
010	PRE	Pancreas transplant	3.8902
011	PRE	Tracheostomy for face, mouth, and neck diagnoses w MCC	4.1482
012	PRE	Tracheostomy for face, mouth, and neck diagnoses w/ CC	3.2472
013	PRE	Tracheostomy for face, mouth, and neck diagnoses w/o CC/MCC	2.6760

Table 2.3   All MDCs/No MDCs

MS-DRG	Title	R.W.
981	Extensive OR procedure unrelated to principal diagnosis w MCC	4.5168
982	Extensive OR procedure unrelated to principal diagnosis w CC	3.5417
983	Extensive OR procedure unrelated to principal diagnosis w/o CC/MCC	2.9737
984	Prostatic OR procedure unrelated to principal diagnosis w MCC	2.7217
985	Prostatic OR procedure unrelated to principal diagnosis w CC	2.0865
986	Prostatic OR procedure unrelated to principal diagnosis w/o CC/MCC	1.6706
987	Nonextensive OR proc unrelated to principal diagnosis w MCC	2.8500
988	Nonextensive OR proc unrelated to principal diagnosis w CC	2.0134
989	Nonextensive OR proc unrelated to principal diagnosis w/o CC/MCC	1.6310

- 62 = Discharged to inpatient rehabilitation
- 63 = Discharged to long-term care hospital
- 64 = Discharged to nursing facility
- 65 = Discharged to psychiatric hospital
- 66 = Discharged to critical access hospital

Patient discharge status usually does not affect MS-DRG assignment. Only in death due to myocardial infarction assigned to MDC 5 (Diseases and Disorders of the Circulatory System) in which there is no significant principal procedure (MS-DRG 283), in neonates who died or were transferred to another acute care facility (MS-DRG 789), and in patients with alcohol/drug abuse or dependence who left against medical advice (MS-DRG 894) does the discharge status directly affect the MS-DRG assignment.

Patient status may reduce an inpatient prospective payment system (IPPS) facility's reimbursement as part of the Postacute Care Transfer Policy (PACTP), utilized when patients have a length of stay at least 1 day less than the geometric mean length of stay (GMLOS) and are transferred to another hospital covered by the acute IPPS or, in certain DRGs, are discharged to a postacute care setting (MedPAC 2006).

Under the PACTP, the full prospective payment is made to the final discharging hospital, and payment to the transferring hospital is based on a per diem rate. The per diem rate equals the full prospective payment rate divided by the geometric mean length of stay for the assigned DRG. The first day is paid at double the per diem rate. A second category called "special payment" transfer MS-DRGs (for example, hip replacement or coronary artery bypass surgery without cardiac catheterization) allows payment of 50 percent of the DRG for the first day and then a per diem payment up to the full DRG.

According to the most recent MedPAR data, an MS-DRG qualifies as a PATCP DRG when:

- The total number of discharges to postacute care in the MS-DRG must equal or exceed the 55th percentile for all DRGs, and
- The proportion of short-stay discharges to postacute care to total discharges in the MS-DRG exceeds the 55th percentile for all MS-DRGs. A short-stay discharge is a discharge before the geometric mean length of stay for the MS-DRG.

- If one MS-DRG meets the PATCP criteria, its corresponding MS-DRGs with or without a CC or MCC, are automatically included. By law, the transfer provision rule does not apply to newborns who die or are transferred out.

Appendix A lists all MS-DRGs and whether the transfer provision rule or special payment methodology applies to them. There are 273 transfer DRGs (of which 25 are special payment) with a potential to impact reimbursement; therefore complete and clear documentation and abstracting of the correct patient status is a vital responsibility entrusted to coding professionals in their facility's compliance to Medicare (and other) payment rules and regulations.

- Age—Some CMS DRGs are assigned based on the patient's age at admission. For example, a 20-year-old patient with septicemia as principal diagnosis and no significant procedures is assigned to CMS DRG 576 (Septicemia without ventilator support 96+ hours, age older than 17 years) (RW 1.5953), whereas a 17-year-old patient with the same diagnosis is assigned to CMS DRG 417 (Septicemia) (RW 18734). MS-DRGs removed the 0 to 17 age subgroups and age differentials in diabetes mellitus used in CMS DRGs, consolidating these patients into the adult groups.

Careful consideration of how these definitions and codes interact with each other enables the coding professional to best apply his or her experience, knowledge, and judgment in assigning and sequencing ICD-9-CM codes or for requesting clarifications from the attending or treating physician.

What's Not Different in MS-DRGs Compared With CMS DRGs?

As challenging as any new DRG system may be to a coding professional, two principles remain reassuringly constant:

- The Official ICD-9-CM Guidelines for Coding and Reporting, *AHA Coding Clinic for ICD-9-CM*, advice, and Coding Convention instructions for ICD-9-CM code assignment remain the official resources for code assignment.
- Most of the same principal diagnoses, secondary diagnoses (for example, 042 [HIV]), principal procedures, and secondary procedures governing base CMS DRGs without CCs apply to MS-DRGs. For example, the same principal

diagnoses applicable to CMS DRG 79 (Respiratory infections and inflammation) carry over to the MS-DRG 177 of the same title. Excisional débridements of skin ulcers will still change MS-DRG 594 (Skin ulcer without CC/MCC) (RW 0.9334) to the higher weighted MS-DRG 575 (Skin graft &/or debridement for skin ulcer or cellulites) RW 1.1444.

Furthermore, in its annual update for FY2008, CMS revised some DRG titles, moved principal diagnoses from one MDC to another, allowed some procedures to effect the DRG in the same manner a as MCC, and created some new DRGs based on resource utilization reflected in the MedPAC. These are summarized as follows.

MDC—Specific Issues

To guide the coding professional, each MDC will be examined for diagnoses and procedures that factor into base MS-DRG assignment. Chapter 3 discusses CC and major CC assignment (MCC). Chapter 4 discusses issues pertinent to APR-DRGs.

MDC 1: Diseases and Disorders of the Nervous System

Most diagnoses within MDC 1 relate to underlying neurological etiologies or neurological complications of other underlying illnesses. Severity matters when describing cerebral ischemia; differentiating transient ischemic attack, aborted, and completed stroke; grading the varying levels of mental status (for example, delirium versus stupor versus coma); or differentiating hemiparesis from hemiplegia. Although closed head injury may be the instigating event for the patient's transient loss of consciousness, the underlying pathology was likely a cerebral concussion.

Surgery

For the most part, the base surgical DRGs in CMS DRGs remain the same in MS-DRGs. Carpal tunnel release (DRG 6) has been consolidated into the Peripheral and Cranial Nerve and Other Nervous System Procedure DRGs (CMS 7 and 8; MS-DRG 40, 41, and 42). Tissue plasminogen activator (tPA) given in the setting of aborted or completed stroke as principal diagnosis continues to group to its own unique MS-DRG as it did under CMS DRGs.

Most of the indications for surgery within MDC 1 are clear cut, thus the diagnosis assignment necessitating

surgery is relatively straightforward. Very rarely will a patient have sepsis on admission requiring neurological surgery, yet if the SIRS criteria and a presumed infection are present on admission, the coding professional may wish to query for it.

Prior to the implementation of the pain codes, created effective October 1, 2006, neurostimulator implantation DRGs were primarily assigned to MDC 1. Beginning in FY2007, neurostimulator cases with a principal diagnosis using the pain codes are being assigned to MDC 23 (CMS DRG 461 [O.R. procedure with diagnoses of other contact with health services] [RW 1.5643]). Under MS-DRGs, CMS amended this policy by assigning cases with a principal diagnosis of 338.0 (Central pain syndrome), 338.21 (Chronic pain due to trauma), 338.22 (Chronic post-thoracotomy pain), 338.28 (Other chronic postoperative pain), 338.29 (Other chronic pain), or 338.4 (Chronic pain syndrome) to MDC 1.

ICD-9-CM principal diagnosis sequencing rules sometimes favor MDC 1 assignment. For example, *Coding Clinic* (4th Quarter, 1998, 35) describes a patient with a flexion contracture of the hand caused by a previous stroke who undergoes a tendon release, assigning this patient to MS-DRG 42 (Peripheral and cranial nerve and other nervous system procedure w/o CC/MCC) (RW 1.7012). If the physician had not linked the previous stroke to the flexion contracture, the base DRG would be MS-DRG 229 (Hand or wrist procedures except major thumb or joint procedures) (RW 0.8186).

Most applicable principal procedures within MDC 1 are easily identifiable and readily applied to DRG methodologies. Principal diagnosis assignments should be made carefully and operative reports for spinal procedures should be read carefully to ensure that no combined anterior/posterior, cervical spinal, or other spinal fusion grouping to MDC 8 was performed. Because some MDC 1 pertinent procedures are performed outside the operating room, such as in radiology (for example, carotid stents) or in the emergency department (for example, tPA administration), the entire medical record (not just the surgery operative reports) must be carefully reviewed.

Medicare covers percutaneous transluminal angioplasty (PTA) and stenting of intracranial arteries for the treatment of cerebral artery stenosis in cases in which the extracranial artery stenosis is ≥50 percent in patients with intracranial atherosclerotic disease when furnished in accordance with FDA-approved protocols governing Category B Investigational Device Exemption (IDE) clinical trials. Under CMS DRGs, procedure code 00.62 (Percutaneous angioplasty or atherectomy of intracranial vessel[s]) and code 00.65 (Percutaneous insertion of intracranial vascular stent[s]) are grouped to CMS DRG 533 (Extracranial procedures with CC) and CMS DRG 534 (Extracranial procedures without CC) when the principal diagnosis is grouped to MDC 1.

With MS-DRGs, CMS recognized the similarity of these codes with 39.72 (Endovascular repair or occlusion of head and neck vessels), 39.74 (Endovascular removal of obstruction from head and neck vessel[s]), and 39.79 (Other endovascular repair [of aneurysm] of other vessels). Therefore, CMS moved procedure code 00.62 and code 00.65 to MS-DRGs 025–27 (Craniotomy and endovascular intracranial procedures with and/or without CC/MCC) and MS-DRGs 023 and 024 (Craniotomy with major device implant or acute complex central nervous system principal diagnosis with MCC and without MCC).

Medicine

Challenges in MDC 1 DRG assignment stem from incomplete physician documentation, especially with underlying causes, severity, or complications. Physicians may document a patient as having dementia not otherwise specified (NOS) or multi-infarct dementia, but they will not state whether it is due to Alzheimer's disease, the late effect of a stroke, or a consequence of a neurodegenerative process. Patients with confusion and malignant hypertension requiring nitroprusside therapy may not have their hypertensive encephalopathy described. With the change in the clinical definitions of transient ischemic attack and stroke in 2002 (see the following section on stroke) followed by the new definition and coding of aborted stroke in *Coding Clinic* (1st Quarter, 2007), physicians may not accurately document these conditions using these standards. Emphasis of the underlying cause or treatment for a transient ischemic attack as a cerebral thrombus or embolus without infarction impacts DRG assignment. Respiratory failure may be present on admission during a stroke or transient ischemic attack (TIA) and thus may qualify as a principal diagnosis.

Some of the challenges coding professionals will face include:

- MS-DRGs 61–72—Stroke versus Aborted stroke versus TIA NOS versus Cerebral embolus/thrombosis without Infarction versus Nonspecific cerebrovascular disease

Understanding, coding, and sequencing these conditions is difficult because the medical literature and *Coding Clinic* are inconsistent in defining these terms. Likewise, physicians do not differentiate between these conditions well nor do they always integrate their own definitions into their clinical documentation. Many coding professionals (and some physicians) use old definitions, further confusing the situation.

Using the clinical literature and *Coding Clinic* as a guide, the following definitions are suggested:

- Stroke—A stroke, or cerebrovascular accident, is defined by the abrupt onset of a neurologic deficit attributable to a focal vascular cause. In ICD-9-CM, the term "stroke" equates to cerebral infarction or hemorrhage. The most recent definition of stroke for clinical trials has required either symptoms lasting over 24 hours or imaging of an acute clinically relevant brain lesion in patients with rapidly vanishing symptoms. Even though diffusion-weighted MRI imaging has 95 to 100 percent specificity (a negative study effectively excludes a diagnosis), stroke remains a clinical diagnosis, supported in most but not all cases by an appropriate abnormality on brain imaging. Some experimental biomarkers, such as matrix metalloproteinase-9 (MMP-9), MMP-13, or fibronectin, may indicate stroke in the same manner that troponin or CK-MB assays identify acute myocardial infarction. Physician interpretation and clinical correlation is vital (Montaner 2006). Although cerebral artery embolus, thrombosis, or hemorrhage cause most strokes, cerebral venous thrombosis, migraines, or cerebral vasculitis also are contributing factors.
- Transient ischemic attack—TIA is a brief episode of neurological dysfunction caused by a focal disturbance of brain or retinal ischemia, with clinical symptoms typically lasting less than 1 hour, and without evidence of infarction (Sacco et al 2006). Because most TIAs last less than 1 hour, and because many patients with imaging evidence of stroke have symptoms lasting less than 24 hours, patients with stroke-like symptoms or TIAs lasting over 1 hour should raise clinical suspicion for aborted or completed stroke. Although some may equate the TIAs to mini-strokes, a clinical documentation improvement (CDI) opportunity exists to clarify whether the patient had a stroke.
- Cerebral embolism or thrombosis without infarction—Either the passage of body tissue (for example, cholesterol or bacterial fibrin clumps from heart valves or aortic plaques), foreign objects (for example, air bubbles), blood clots into the cerebral vessels (embolism), or the formation of a clot within a

cerebral blood vessel (thrombosis) whereby a stroke does not occur. Their usual manifestation is a transient ischemic attack; however, they may be asymptomatic.

- Impending stroke, progressive stroke or stroke-in-evolution—An ischemic attack lasting over 1 hour whereby stroke is the likely outcome. ICD-9-CM codes these as 435.9 (Unspecified transient cerebral ischemia).
- Aborted stroke—There is no official definition for "aborted stroke" in the clinical literature; the term "aborted stroke" did not generate any references on the National Library of Medicine's PubMed search engine during May 2007 (http://www.pubmed.gov May 29, 2007). Some physicians or stroke centers may label patients with impending stroke who are successfully treated with alteplase (tPA), resulting in negative imaging studies and significant improvement, as "aborted stroke" rather than as a "transient ischemic attack." *Coding Clinic* (1st and 3rd Quarter, 2007), describing this exact scenario, advises that microscopic changes are present in the presence of negative CT studies (the MRI was normal in this example as well) and directs the coding professional to use a cerebral infarction code (434.91).
- Encephalopathy—A disease of the brain caused by another disease process or external provocation, usually defined by its adjective, manifested as altered mental status, delirium seizures, or loss of neurological function. Options pertinent to MDC 1 include:
  - 437.2 (Hypertensive)—Occurs in the setting of malignant hypertension
  - 348.8 (Metabolic)—Occurs in the setting of metabolic abnormalities such as electrolyte imbalance (hyponatremia, hypercalcemia) or severe sepsis (septic encephalopathy)
  - 349.82 (Toxic)—Occurs in the setting of adverse drug effect
  - 348.3 (Encephalopathy) (etiology) NOS
- Encephalomalacia—Necrotic brain tissue, usually the result of a stroke
- Transient global amnesia—A distinctive syndrome, usually in middle-aged individuals, characterized by anterograde amnesia (inability to retain new information) and a retrograde amnesia (inability to remember the past) for relatively recent events that occurred before the onset. Patients experience sudden disorientation and repeatedly ask who they are, where they are, and what their circumstances are. The syndrome usually resolves within 24 to

48 hours and is followed by the filling-in of the period affected by the retrograde amnesia, although there is persistent loss of memory for the events that occurred during the ictus. Migraines, TIAs in the posterior circulation, and temporal lobe seizures are postulated as underlying etiology (Mesulam 2005).

Example: A patient presents with altered mental status due to digoxin toxicity. The coding professional queries the physician for the effect that toxic amounts of digoxin on the brain had on the altered mental status. The physician responds that the patient had a toxic encephalopathy. The MS-DRG changes from MS-948 (Signs and symptoms w/o MCC) (RW 0.6542) to MS 72 (Nonspecific cerebrovascular disease w/o CC/MCC) (RW 0.9586).

Example: A patient presents with a TIA documented by the physician as probably due to atrial fibrillation, warranting that the patient initially receive heparin and later warfarin during the hospitalization. The coding professional queries for the underlying cause and mechanism of the patient's TIA in light of his atrial fibrillation and the need for heparin. The physician documents in the medical record that the patient probably had a cerebral embolus. Cerebral embolus without infarction (MS-DRG 68 [Nonspecific CVA and precerebral occlusion w/o infarct w/o MCC] [RW 0.9131]) is now assigned rather than MS-DRG 69 (Transient ischemia) (RW 0.7339).

Summary

If a patient presents with acute focal neurological findings (usually asymmetrical), amaurosis fugax (transient loss of vision in one eye), and/or a change in mental status (delirium, stupor, coma, amnesia) from their baseline condition, the coding professional can ascertain the probable underlying cause and possibly the mechanism (for example, cerebral embolus or thrombosis). If the physician rules out seizures, central nervous system infection, or psychiatric cause, alternatives include encephalopathy (toxic, metabolic, septic, or other etiologies) or transient global amnesia. Although cerebral atherosclerosis or other ill-defined cerebrovascular disease are listed as potential principal diagnoses for this MS-DRG group, more specific conditions better fit the criteria for principal diagnosis.

• MS 73–74 Cranial and Peripheral Nerve Disorders—The human nervous system is divided into two parts, the central and peripheral nervous system. The central nervous system includes the brain, the brain stem, and the spinal cord, whereas the peripheral nervous system includes 12 cranial nerves (labeled by roman numerals I–XII) and 31 spinal nerves (labeled from their bony locations and number, such as cervical 8, thoracic 12, lumbar 5, sacral 5, or coccygeal 1) emanating from the central nervous system. See Figure 2.1 for their cutaneous correlations (source: http://www.bartleby.com/107/208.html).

These peripheral nerves have two functions, somatic (motor and sensory) and autonomic (regulating organ function). Autonomic functions are further divided into sympathetic "fight or flight" and parasympathetic "rest and digestion" (see Figure 2.2) (source: http://education.yahoo.com/reference/gray/illustrations/figure?id=839). Somatic nerve dysfunctions include sensory (pain, numbness, tingling, false or impaired sensations of hot and cold, paresthesias) or motor (weakness, paralysis) abnormalities, whereas autonomic dysfunctions include wide swings in blood pressure and pulse, impaired bowel function (diarrhea or constipation), urinary dysfunctions (incontinence or urine retention), erectile dysfunctions, and wheezing.

Peripheral nerve disease can be caused by any disease. Underlying causes include diabetes mellitus, adverse reactions to medications or toxins (for example, alcohol), infections such as herpes simplex or herpes zoster (shingles), nerve injuries, systemic and local effects of neoplasms, and other illnesses with systemic manifestations. Precipitating causes may include accidental overdose, bioterrorism (for example, sarin as the cause of Gulf War syndrome), or a drug-drug reaction. Complications include syncope (for example, autonomic neuropathy), foot ulcers (for example, diabetic neuropathy), asthma (for

Figure 2.1   Spinal-Cutaneous Dermatones

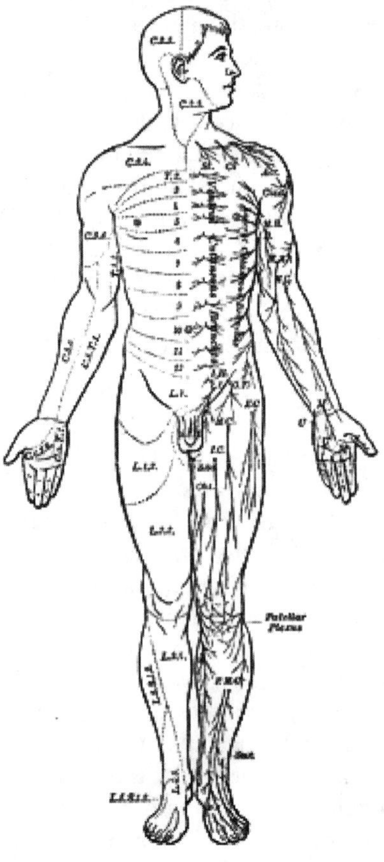

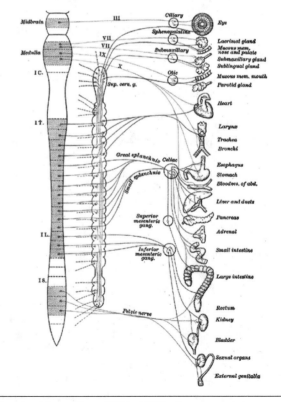

Figure 2.2   Sympathetic Nervous System

Source: Henry Gray (1821–1865). Anatomy of the Human Body. 1910.

Source: Henry Gray (1821–1865). Anatomy of the Human Body. 1910.

example, autonomic neuropathy), or persistent pain (for example, postherpetic neuralgia).

Example: A diabetic patient presents with syncope. Physical examination shows that the systolic blood pressure drops from 140 supine to 80 upon standing. The physician documents orthostatic hypotension as the cause of the syncope. Physician query asked for any potential relation between the patient's orthostatic hypotension and his diabetes. The physician documents that the patient probably has autonomic neuropathy due to diabetes as a contributing cause. The MS-DRG changes from 312 (Syncope and collapse) (RW 0.7197) to 74 (Cranial and peripheral nerve disorders w/o MCC) (RW 0.8954).

Example: A patient presents with long-standing chest pain to rule out a myocardial infarction (MI). The patient has a previous history of herpes zoster to the chest. The physician documents "noncardiac chest pain" or "musculoskeletal pain." The coding professional's query to the physician for the underlying cause of the patient's chest pain in light of the documented previous history of herpes zoster results in physician documentation that it was likely due to postherpetic neuralgia. The MS-DRG changes from 313 (Chest pain) (RW 0.5489) to 74 (Cranial and peripheral nerve w/o MCC) (RW 0.8954).

Summary

Patients can present with multiple symptoms (pain, loss of function, ulcers, syncope, arrhythmias) related to the peripheral nervous system. CDI opportunities for the underlying cause or mechanism behind these symptoms can assign these patients to the most appropriate DRG.

- MS 80–90 (Stupor and coma)—Alterations of mental status are manifestations of underlying illness. In most cases, the underlying cause of the altered mental status is the reason the patient could not be sent home. Not uncommonly, the type and severity of the altered mental status factors into principal diagnosis selection and may qualify as such. Alterations of mental status take the following forms:
  - Confusion—Mental and behavioral state of reduced comprehension, coherence, and capacity to reason
  - Delirium—Confusion accompanied by agitation, hallucinations, tremor, and illusions

- Dementia—deterioration in cognitive abilities that impairs the successful performance of daily living
- Delusional state—Loss of contact with reality that may or may not be associated with delirium or psychosis
- Psychosis—A mental disorder characterized by derangement of personality and loss of contact with reality and causing deterioration of normal social functioning associated with delusional thinking, hallucinations, personality changes, or disorganized thinking
- Vegetative state—An awake but unresponsive state
- Lethargy or drowsiness—Simulates light sleep but is easily aroused, usually associated with some degree of confusion
- Stupor—A lesser degree of arousal whereby the patient responds only by vigorous stimuli
- Coma—A deep sleeplike state from which the patient cannot be aroused

There is considerable overlap between these terms. Physician documentation and coding professional understanding and query of these terms are crucial.

ICD-9-CM and MS-DRGs differentiate concussion from other cerebral laceration and contusion. Concussion groups to MS-DRG 90 (Concussion w/o CC/MCC) (RW 0.7405), whereas cerebral laceration with coma less than 30 minutes groups to MS-DRG 87 (Traumatic stupor and coma w/o CC/MCC) (RW 0.9235) and nontraumatic coma NOS groups to MS-DRG 81 (Nontraumatic stupor and coma w/o MCC) (RW 0.7161). Concussion allows for addition of a CC, whereas coma NOS requires an MCC to change the DRG.

Cerebral concussion is a diffuse brain injury characterized by immediate and transient alteration in brain function, including alteration of mental status and level of consciousness, thought to be caused by acceleration-deceleration injury to the brain. Cerebral concussion is a spectrum of injuries, ranging from mild to severe. Cuts or bruises may be present on the head or face, but in many cases there are no signs of trauma. Many people assume that concussions involve a loss of consciousness; however, in most cases, a person with a concussion does not lose consciousness. CT scans are commonly normal, whereas MRI studies may show axonal damage. Second-impact syndrome is malignant cerebral edema resulting from relatively mild head trauma occurring after a recent concussion.

A cerebral contusion, on the other hand, is a focal brain injury caused primarily by impact of the brain surface and the bony ridges of the inner skull. Cerebral contusions are frequently found in the frontal region, anterior poles skull base, adjacent to the sphenoid ridge, and at the temporal poles. Other locations include the cerebellar hemispheres and the occipital poles. A characteristic pattern of cerebral contusion called the coup and contrecoup injury is frequently seen. The coup contusion occurs at the site of impact and the contrecoup contusion occurs in the brain at the point diametrically opposite the point of impact.

Physician documentation of coma and its duration govern DRG assignment. While a Glasgow Coma Scale score of under 7 clinically indicates coma, the physician still must document coma as a diagnosis and specify its duration if it is to be accurately coded. A CDI opportunity exists when these elements are missing.

Some physicians only document "closed head injury" for patients with head trauma presenting with transient loss of consciousness or altered mental status and do not specify if any brain injury occurred, which represents a CDI opportunity.

Example: An 18-year-old football player sustained mental confusion from a head injury during practice. He is alert and oriented with a Glasgow Coma Scale of 15 in the ER. A CT scan of the head is normal, and he is admitted as an inpatient for overnight observation with the diagnosis of closed head injury. No neurological sequelae occurred. He is advised not to play for 1 week and is discharged with a final diagnosis of closed head injury.

ICD-9-CM code 959.01 (Closed head injury) as the principal diagnosis, groups to MS-DRG 914 (Traumatic injury without MCC) (RW 0.6890). The coding professional queries the physician to determine the etiology of the patient's confusion and the need to refrain from playing football for 1 week; the physician replies that the patient has a probable mild concussion and that he is prohibited from playing to avoid Second Contact Syndrome. The principal diagnosis changes to 850.0 (Concussion with no loss

of consciousness), grouping to MS-DRG 90 (Concussion w/o CC/MCC) (RW 0.7405).

Example: A 50-year-old man is admitted as an inpatient with stupor after a closed head injury that occurred during a motor vehicle accident (MVA). His blood alcohol level is 0.50 mg/dL (legal definition of intoxication is 0.08 mg/dL) and his drug screen was positive for opiates. His CT scan is normal. Upon discharge, his final diagnosis is closed head injury with stupor and alcohol and narcotic abuse with intoxication. Closed head injury with stupor codes to 959.01 and 780.09; alcohol intoxication with abuse as a secondary diagnosis codes to 305.00, and narcotic abuse codes to 350.90, grouping to MS-DRG 914 (Traumatic injury w/o MCC) (RW 0.6890). The coding professional queries the physician to determine the underlying etiology of the patient's stupor and the severity and chronicity of his alcohol and narcotic abuse; the physician documents that the stupor was due to an acute toxic encephalopathy from his high alcohol level and recent inappropriate narcotic abuse and that he is a chronic and currently active alcoholic and drug addict. As a result, 967.9 becomes the principal diagnosis, and 349.89 is one of the secondary diagnoses, resulting in MS-DRG 917 (Poisoning and toxic effect of drugs w/MCC) (RW 1.1717).

Summary

Altered mental status in the setting of head trauma invariably has underlying traumatic or nontraumatic brain pathology. Recognizing the difference between brain concussion and contusion from underlying or contributing encephalopathies allows for more appropriate DRG assignment.

Seizures and Headaches—Seizures are the clinical manifestation of abnormally hyperexcitable cortical neurons. Epilepsy is a chronic disorder characterized by a spontaneous tendency for recurrent seizures. Whereas all patients with epilepsy have seizures, many patients have only a single seizure during their lifetime and are not considered to have epilepsy.

Although in most clinicians' minds there is no difference between convulsions and seizures, the ICD-9-CM coding changes of 2007 directed coding professionals to code convulsive disorders to 780.39, whereas a seizure disorder codes to 345.9. Isolated seizures or convulsions remain at 780.39. Category 345 and code 780.39 group to MS-DRG 100 or 101.

Headache principal diagnoses grouping to headache DRGs do not change in MS-DRGs (MS-DRG 102 [Headaches w/ MCC] [RW 0710]; MS-DRG 103 [Headaches w/o MCC] [RW 0.6677]). Even though hospitals with specialized inpatient headache centers use more resources and have longer lengths of stay than typical medical-surgical hospitals, CMS did not create a special category for these patients.

If a patient's seizure or headache has a secondary underlying cause (for example, brain tumor, metabolic abnormalities, adverse drug reactions, or drug overdoses), the circumstances of admission, the diagnostic approach, and the treatment rendered govern the principal diagnosis assignment.

Meningitis and Other Central Nervous System Infections—Central nervous system infections are serious illnesses requiring intensive hospital treatment, evidenced by their high relative weights. Patients with meningitis present with headache, neck stiffness (nuchal rigidity), fever, or possibly sepsis (fever, elevated white blood cell count, and tachycardia). If altered mental status, immunocompromised state (for example, HIV or chronic steroid use) or new-onset focal neurological signs are present, encephalitis, encephalomyelitis, brain abscess, other brain masses, or other systemic illnesses that invade the brain (for example, lupus, sarcoidosis, or syphilis) also should be considered.

ICD-9-CM did create new codes for human herpes virus 6 affecting MDC 1. See list below.

Most physicians will perform a lumbar puncture, CT scan, and/or MRI if a CNS infection is suspected. Indications of meningitis or encephalitis on lumbar puncture include an elevation of the CSF white count and protein, a possible reduction of the CSF glucose, or possible completely normal studies. Specialized microbiological studies, such as West Nile virus, tuberculosis or fungal cultures, cryptococcal antigens, herpes simplex or varicella zoster, syphilis, DNA probes, or other studies may be performed. Any abnormalities of these tests or the use of antibiotics creates a CDI opportunity.

If no bacteria are immediately isolated on CSF studies, the physician may label the patient as having aseptic meningitis NEC, coding to 047.9 (Unspecified viral meningitis) and grouping to MS-DRG 76 (Viral meningitis w/o CC/MCC) (RW 1.1439). Aseptic meningitis can be caused by fungal illnesses, tuberculosis, tick diseases (for example, ehrlichiosis or Rocky Mountain spotted fever), viral encephalomyelitis, or other brain and spinal cord infections, grouping to MS-DRG 99 (Non-bacterial infection of the nervous system except viral meningitis) (RW. 1.8177). Aseptic meningitis represents a CDI opportunity to better define its probable underlying cause.

Because some test results may not return until after discharge (for example, tuberculosis or fungal cultures, DNA probes, or paired serologies), coding professionals should review the discharge medications for possible etiologies still to be ruled out. Because many of these conditions are reportable to the state and are actively followed by the hospital's infection control nurse, some facilities develop protocols whereby delayed diagnoses or abnormal laboratory results after discharge are reported to the coding manager by the infection control nurse or pathologist.

MS-DRG	MS-DRG Title	Relative Weight
75	Viral meningitis w CC/MCC	1.5369
76	Viral meningitis w/o CC/MCC	1.1439
95	Bacterial and tuberculous infections of nervous system w CC	2.5679
96	Bacterial and tuberculous infections of nervous system w/o CC/MCC	2.3482
97	Nonbacterial infection of nervous system excluding viral meningitis w MCC	2.6665
98	Nonbacterial infection of nervous system excluding viral meningitis w CC	2.0568
99	Nonbacterial infect of nervous system excluding viral meningitis w/o CC/MCC	1.8177

Diagnosis code	Description	CC
58.21	Human herpes virus 6 encephalitis	MCC
58.29	Other human herpes virus encephalitis	MCC

Source: CMS Proposed Rule (Federal Register)

Example: An 80-year-old man is admitted with altered mental status. All studies, including head CT, are normal, except for a mild anemia of chronic disease and mild hyponatremia (serum Sodium level of 130 mg/dL). A lumbar puncture shows some elevated protein but is otherwise normal; it is sent for TB and fungal studies. The patient is transferred to an academic medical center and signed out as altered mental status of unknown etiology with hyponatremia (MS-DRG 948 [Signs and symptoms without MCC] [RW 0.6542]).

Thirty days after referral to the academic medical center, the infection control nurse at the referring hospital received a call from the state microbiology laboratory that the CSF was growing tuberculosis and notified the attending physician who, being late on his records, included this fact in his discharge summary. Given that the record was coded 3 days after discharge, the health information management (HIM) staff never knew that this patient had tuberculosis meningitis until their external compliance auditor noted it on external review after the 60-day time limit for rebilling established by Medicare. If the infection control nurse had notified the HIM staff of the positive culture, and if the physician had agreed that the patient probably had tuberculosis meningitis, the MS-DRG would have changed to 95 (Bacterial and tuberculosis infections of the nervous system with CC) (RW 2.2579), and the record could have been successfully rebilled.

MDC 2: Diseases and Disorders of the Eye

MS-DRGs offer the following changes to the current CMS DRGs:

- Consolidation of the following CMS DRGs into one MS-DRG group:
  - MS-DRGs 116–117 (Intraocular procedures with and without CC/MCC)
    - CMS DRG 36 (Retinal procedures)
    - CMS DRG 38 (Primary iris procedures)
    - CMS DRG 39 (Lens procedure with and without vitrectomy)
    - CMS DRG 42 (Intraocular procedures except retina, iris, and lens)
  - MS-DRGs 124–125 (Other disorders of the eye w and w/o MCC)

- CMS DRG 43 (Hyphema)
- CMS DRGs 46, 47, and 48 (Other disorders of the eye)

Relatively few eye conditions occasion inpatient hospitalization. Many neurological eye diseases, such as diplopia, sudden visual loss, nystagmus, or ptosis, have underlying conditions receiving treatment that usually groups to a higher weighted MS-DRG. Eye surgeries are straightforward. Querying physicians for the manifestations, underlying, and precipitating etiologies of eye diseases and linking these appropriately usually places these patients in the correct DRG group.

MDC 3: Diseases and Disorders of the Ear, Nose, Mouth, and Throat

Surgery

MS-DRGs make the following changes in the CMS DRG structure:

- Most ENT surgical procedures have clear cut indications that should serve as the principal diagnosis if the patient requires inpatient admission. Rarely will sepsis be part of the presentation. Sometimes, hypotension from excessive bleeding may be the reason for ligation of the ethmoidal arteries, grouping these to MDC 5.

Coding Clinic (3rd Quarter, 2002, 14) cites an example of a patient requiring tooth extraction for dental caries who was admitted as an inpatient to manage his anticoagulants prior to surgery. *Coding Clinic* required that dental caries be the principal diagnosis, even though the patient's hematologic disorder prevented his procedure from being performed as an outpatient.

In FY2008, CMS amended the MS-DRG structure to allow the implantation of cochlear devices, previously grouping to CMS DRG 049 (Major health and neck procedures) (RW 1.6654) to count as a major device, creating the new MS-DRG 129 (Major head and neck procedures with CC or MCC or Major Device) (RW 1.7992).

Careful review of the operative and pathology reports are warranted. If the pathology reports show granulomatous inflammation or if the specimen was sent for cultures, physician query is warranted to ascertain the probable underlying diagnosis (for example, sarcoidosis, tuberculosis, or fungal infections).

CMS-DRG Version 24.0	DRG Description	MS-DRG Version 25.0	New Base MS-DRG Description
50	Sialoadenectomy	139	Salivary Gland Procedures
51	Salivary Gland Procedures Except Sialoadenectomy		
52	Cleft Lip & Palate Repair	133	Other Ear, Nose, Mouth & Throat OR Procedures with and without CC/MCC
55	Miscellaneous Ear, Nose, Mouth, & Throat Procedure		
56	Rhinoplasty	131, 132	New DRG—Cranial/Facial Bone Procedures with and without CC/MCC
57, 58	Tonsillectomy & Adenoidectomy Procedure, Except Tonsillectomy and/or Adenoidectomy Only		
59, 60	Tonsillectomy and/or Adenoidectomy Only		
61, 62	Myringotomy with Tube Insertion		
63	Other Ear, Nose, Mouth, & Throat OR Procedures		
67	Epiglottitis	152, 153	Otitis Media & Upper Respiratory Infection with and without MCC
68, 69, 70	Otitis Media & Upper Respiratory Infection		
71	Laryngotracheitis		
72	Nasal, Trauma & Deformity	154, 155, 156	Other Ear, Nose, Mouth & Throat O.R. Diagnoses with MCC, with CC, and without CC/MCC
73, 74	Other Ear, Nose, Mouth, & Throat Diagnoses		
185, 186	Dental & Oral Diseases Except Extractions & Restorations	157, 158, 159	Dental & Oral Disreases with MCC, with CC, and without CC/MCC
187	Dental Extractions & Restorations		

Source: CMS Final Rule (Federal Register)

Medicine

The MS-DRG structure for medical diagnoses in MDC 3 remains essentially the same as in CMS DRGs.

Dizziness is a challenging term related to the various sensations of a person's perception of his or her body's relation to space (Sloane et al 2001). Physicians characterize dizziness as:

- Vertigo—A false sensation that the body or the environment is moving (usually spinning). Vertigo suggests a disturbance of the vestibular system, although psychological states, such as panic disorder, can also produce it.
- Presyncopal lightheadedness—A feeling of lightheadedness that is often described as a sensation of an impending faint. It is episodic and usually results from diffuse temporary cerebral ischemia.
- Disequilibrium—A sense of imbalance (postural instability) that is generally described as involving the legs and trunk without a sensation in the head. Isolated symptoms of disequilibrium are generally attributed to neuromuscular problems; imbalance that accompanies other types of dizziness is generally a secondary symptom.
- Other dizziness—Typically described as vague or floating, or the patient may have difficulty describing the sensation. Such dizziness is generally present much of the time and is most often caused by psychological disturbances. Other dizziness includes dizziness due to acute vision change (such as after cataract surgery) and dizziness described as tilting of the environment, usually due to an otolith disease.

MS-DRG 149 (Disequilibrium) (RW 0.6154) includes vertigo with its peripheral origins and nonspecific central origins, motion sickness, dizziness, and giddiness not otherwise specified. Differentiating alternative causes impacts MS-DRG assignment. These include:

- Orthostatic hypotension—MS-DRG 312 (Syncope and collapse) (RW 0.7197)
- Chronic or other specified hypotension
  - MS-DRG 316 (Other circulatory system diagnoses w/o CC) (RW 0.9075)
  - MS-DRG 315 (Other circulatory system diagnoses w CC) (RW 1.1720)
  - MS-DRG 314 (Other circulatory system diagnoses w MCC) (RW 1.5606)

- Panic Disorder—MS-DRG 880 (Acute adjustment reactions and psychosocial dysfunction) (RW 0.6085).
- Late effect of stroke or other degenerative CNS disorders—MS DRG 57 (Degenerative nervous systems disorders w/o MCC) (RW 0.8951).
- Hyperventilation—MS-DRG 204 (Respiratory signs and symptoms) (RW 0.6252).

Similar to disequilibrium, the etiology of epistaxis is not always straightforward. Multiple disease processes can result in bleeding from the nose. These are divided into two broad categories:

- Local factors include vascular anomalies, infectious/inflammatory states, trauma, iatrogenic injuries, neoplasm, desiccation, and foreign bodies.
- Systemic factors include accelerated hypertension, atherosclerosis, infectious/inflammatory diseases, blood dyscrasias, platelet deficiencies or dysfunction, coagulopathies, and kidney and liver disease.

Because epistaxis and disequilibrium usually have probable underlying causes or complications that prevent their evaluation in an observation or outpatient status, CDI opportunities exist for these (for example, acute blood loss anemia requiring blood transfusion or late effect of stroke causing dizziness) and how they factored into the decision to admit the patient as an inpatient.

Example: A 70-year-old man came to the emergency department because of recurrent epistaxis. The nose bleed was controlled by cautery in the emergency department, and he was admitted as an inpatient. His hematocrit was 25 on admission, which was a precipitous drop from his baseline of 35, for which he received one unit of blood. The discharge diagnosis was epistaxis. Upon physician query, the physician documented that the hemorrhage was controlled in the emergency department, that the patient's blood transfusion was for acute blood loss anemia, and that the anemia factored into the decision to admit the patient. The MS-DRG changed from MS-DRG 151 (Epistaxis w/o MCC) (RW 0.6227) to MS-DRG 812 (Red blood cell disorders w/o MCC) (RW 0.7780).

MDC 4: Diseases and Disorders of the Respiratory System

Although most diseases within MDC 4 are straightforward, physician documentation of illness severity, underlying causes, and complications is necessary for accurate MS-DRG assignment. Because the respiratory system is easily infected, MS-DRGs related to sepsis or HIV are common alternatives for MDC 4 DRGs. Second only to heart failure and total joint replacement, "simple pneumonia" and chronic obstructive pulmonary disease are some of the most common MS-DRGs to be assigned to Medicare patients.

Surgery

There is little change in the base CMS DRGs and base MS-DRGs for surgeries in MDC 4. New ICD-9-CM procedure codes assigned to MDC 4 involve thorascopy and group to the following MS-DRGs.

Caution should be used when assigning MDC 4 surgical DRGs in the following situations:

- Differentiating thorascopic procedures from open procedures. Careful review of the operative note is necessary to determine if the procedure was done through the thorascope or without it. If it is not clear whether the procedure was performed through the thorascope, querying the physician may clarify the circumstance.
- Differentiating endobronchial versus transbronchial biopsy during bronchoscopy. Careful review of the operative note is necessary to determine if the biopsy needle obtaining lung tissue went through the bronchus into the alveoli. For optimum compliance, the physician must describe any transbronchial biopsy in this manner. Although a pathology report showing lung tissue itself is reassuring, it is not necessary.
- Ascertaining whether these patients undergo a tracheostomy during the hospital stay. Tracheostomies in the ambulance or at referring hospitals do not count.
- Ascertaining whether patients have more than 96 uninterrupted hours of mechanical ventilation.

- Ascertaining whether patients admitted or treated for deep venous thrombosis or pulmonary emboli have a vena cava filter placed.
- Reviewing all pathology notes to determine if lymph nodes are biopsied or removed.

Medicine

Manifestations, underlying and precipitating etiologies and complications factor greatly in principal diagnosis assignment in MDC 4 medical diagnoses.

Pulmonary Embolism

Pulmonary embolism is a commonly missed diagnosis by physicians. As the diagnosis is often made after the patient is admitted, physician query to determine whether it is present on admission is crucial. Some patients are labeled as having exacerbations of COPD when it was a pulmonary embolus that caused their symptoms. Pulmonary embolism is one of the causes of noncardiac chest pain.

Although symptoms and signs such as dyspnea, pleuritic chest pain, tachypnea, and tachycardia may raise the suspicion of pulmonary embolism and indicate a need for further evaluation, these findings are inconsistent and nonspecific. Risk factors, such as recent surgery, possible cancers, pregnancy, previous blood clots (the patient may have a primary hypercoagulability syndrome) or prolonged immobilization should be investigated. If present, a CDI opportunity exists to determine whether the patient has a pulmonary embolus or a contributing primary or secondary hypercoagulability syndrome.

Laboratory and simple radiology testing may help. Atelectasis on simple x-rays may render a clue. Hypoxemia (for example, oxygen saturations less than 88 percent, pO_2 less than 60) suggests pulmonary embolus, especially if there are risk factors. A normal D-dimer test eliminates pulmonary embolus in most low probability patients. CT angiography with or without venous-phase

Procedure code	Description	Operative Procedure
32.41	Thoracoscopic lobectomy of lung	Y
32.49	Other lobectomy of lung	Y
33.20	Thoracoscopic lung biopsy	Y
34.06	Thoracoscopic drainage of pleural cavity	Y
34.20	Thoracoscopic pleural biopsy	Y
34.52	Thoracoscopic decortication of lung	Y

Source: CMS Proposed Rule (Federal Register)

multidetector CT venography and lower extremity venous Doppler studies is commonly used for assessment of intermediate or high-risk patients or those with positive D-dimer studies. Pulmonary embolism is treated with anticoagulants (for example, heparin, warfarin); severe cases may receive thrombolytics or require pulmonary embolectomy.

Pulmonary embolism can present as respiratory failure or cardiogenic shock. Septic emboli, such as those from a tricuspid valve with endocarditis in an IV drug abuser, can be a complication from another illness. The circumstances of admission, the diagnostic approach, and the treatment rendered should factor into principal diagnosis assignment.

Pneumonia and Bronchitis

To understand pneumonia, the coding professional must understand basic lung anatomy. The lungs are divided into five parts as shown in Figure 2.3:

- The trachea is a long hollow tube extending down the center of the chest connecting the larynx with the bronchi.
- The bronchi is a hollow tube extending from the trachea to the five different lobes of the lungs.

Figure 2.3   Respiratory System

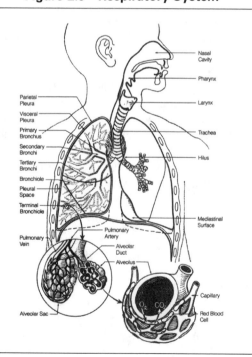

Source: National Cancer Institute Visuals Online. http://visualsonline.cancer.gov/retrieve.cfm?imageid= 1773&dpi=150&fileformat=jpg

- The bronchioles are small hollow tubes connecting the bronchi to the alveoli.
- The alveoli are small sacs of lung tissue where air interfaces with the pulmonary blood vessels.
- The pleura is the tissue that covers the lungs and the surrounding ribs. There are two types of pleura—the visceral pleura that covers the lungs and the parietal pleura that covers the ribs. The space between these is called the pleural space.

Knowing this anatomy and remembering that the suffix "itis" is Greek for "denoting diseases characterized by inflammation," the coding professional should be able to conceptualize the following terms and their manifestations:

- Tracheitis—Inflammation of the trachea alone. Symptoms include cough that is usually productive of purulent sputum. Fever may be present, depending on the cause. The chest x-ray is usually normal.
- Bronchitis—Inflammation of the main bronchitis alone, usually including the trachea. Bronchitis is also usually accompanied by a cough that is productive of purulent sputum and possibly a fever. The chest x-ray is usually normal.
- Bronchiolitis—Inflammation of the bronchioles. Bronchiolitis has the same presentation as tracheitis and bronchitis; however fever is more likely. The x-ray may be positive. If it is, the physician should be queried for the presence of alveolitis (pneumonia).
- Alveolitis—Inflammation of the alveoli. If it is due to an infection, it is usually called pneumonia. It presents with fever, cough, and a positive x-ray. Other symptoms, such pleuritic chest pain from mild pleural inflammation or the systemic inflammatory response syndrome (sepsis), may also be present.

Inflammation of the lungs may not always be due to an infection. For example, asthma is an inflammatory condition of the bronchi resulting in airway hyperactivity, thus the term "asthmatic bronchitis." Some chronic noninfectious lung inflammations leading to fibrosis, sometimes referred to as interstitial lung disease, may be due to rheumatoid arthritis, sarcoidosis, radiation therapy, asbestos, or other diseases. These mimic infectious bronchitis and pneumonia. Physician query is necessary if the underlying etiology is not clear.

MS-DRGs classify bronchitis from infectious pneumonia and interstitial lung diseases without CC.

Infectious Pneumonia

Before coding infectious pneumonia, the patient's presentation must be differentiated from bronchitis. Clinical signs, such as bronchial breath sounds, rales, egophony, or dullness to percussion, and a positive chest x-ray signify pneumonia. If the physician believes the patient has pneumonia, an antibiotic will likely be prescribed.

ICD-9-CM and MS-DRGs classify pneumonia based on their underlying infectious etiology (for example, pneumococcal or tuberculosis) or circumstance (for example, aspiration), not on the location where the pneumonia was encountered. Although many physicians use terms such as "community-acquired pneumonia," "nosocomial pneumonia," "nursing-home acquired pneumonia," "ventilator-associated pneumonia," and "pneumonia in an immunocompromised host," ICD-9-CM does not associate these conditions with any specific etiologic organism. When the physician is not specific in the suspected infectious etiology or circumstance, the coding professional should query for the specific underlying cause based on the appropriate clinical indicators for the type of pneumonia being queried.

Unlike bronchitis, pneumonia has two MS-DRG groups; simple pneumonia (MS-DRGs 193–195) and respiratory infections and inflammations (MS-DRGs 177–179). Underlying etiologies for these DRGs are listed in the table below.

One difficulty in differentiating the various etiologies in pneumonia is that laboratory tests are often not diagnostic for their bacterial cause. Only one out of six patients will have a reliable positive laboratory study that can guide clinical therapy. Although sputum cultures may make logical sense, quite often they are contaminated by the germs in the patient's mouth or suppressed by previous antibiotic administration. Other tests that may be helpful include:

- Blood cultures (if positive, their clinical significance should be ascertained to ensure that they are not contaminants or to determine if they represent a systemic infection)
- Blood serologies (for example, cryptococcal antigen)
- Urine studies (for example, legionella antigen, pneumococcal antigen)
- Cultures obtained by bronchoscopy
- Cultures of pleural fluid
- TB or fungal cultures or other specialized studies (for example, DNA probes)—Often these cultures are sent out to reference laboratories and may not return for weeks. If these laboratory studies are pending, perhaps the hospital's infection control coordinator can be on the lookout for these results and report them back to the coding department.

MS-DRG	MS-DRG Title	Weights
198	Interstitial lung disease w/o CC/MCC	0.9654
179	Respiratory infections and inflammations w/o CC/MCC	1.2754
195	Simple pneumonia and pleurisy w/o CC/MCC	0.8398
203	Bronchitis and asthma w/o CC/MCC	0.6252

MS-DRG 193–195 Simple Pneumonia	MS-DRG 177–179 Respiratory Infections and Inflammation
Community-Acquired Pneumonia	Staphylococcal Pneumonia
Nosocomial Pneumonia	Aspiration Pneumonia
Pneumococcal Pneumonia	Gram-Negative Pneumonia
Haemophilus Influenza Pneumonia	Tuberculosis Pneumonia
Viral Pneumonia	Legionnaire's Disease
Pneumonia Related to Influenza	Histoplasmosis Pneumonia
Pleurisy without Mention of Effusion	Empyema/Lung Abscess

Because it is uncommon for physicians to have a positive laboratory study or to document the suspected underlying bacterial etiology of their patient's "community-acquired" or nosocomial pneumonia, many coding professionals do not know when to query for the probable underlying etiology.

The literature suggests that 60 to 70 percent of community-acquired pneumonias are due to organisms grouping to DRG 193–195 and are commonly treated with a quinolone antibiotic (for example, levofloxacin) alone or a combination of a third-generation cephalosporin (for example, ceftriaxone [Rocephin] and a macrolide [for example, azithromycin]) (Bartlett and Mundy 1995; Mandell et al 2007). If the patient is treated with this combination of antibiotics, and there are no revealing diagnostic studies (for example, positive blood or sputum cultures, serologies, or urinary Legionnaire's antigens), then the query is unlikely to result in a different MS-DRG.

On the other hand, 25 to 30 percent of community acquired pneumonias are due to organisms that group to MS-DRG 177–179 and should be treated with broader-spectrum or more powerful antibiotics than ceftriaxone, azithromycin, or levofloxacin. Because infectious disease physicians are encouraging that these antibiotics not be used unless absolutely necessary to avoid antibiotic resistance, the use of these antibiotics should indicate that the physician suspects a more virulent organism. If the following antibiotics are used, physician documentation of the probable corresponding underlying infectious etiology is appropriate.

Example: A patient is admitted to the hospital from a hospice with lung cancer and "community-acquired" pneumonia. Due the patient's immunocompromised state and to severe malnutrition, the attending physician treats this pneumonia with Zosyn® and clindamycin. The patient dies after admission; the discharge summary lists community-acquired pneumonia, severe malnutrition, and lung cancer as the final diagnosis, resulting in MS-DRG 193 (Simple pneumonia with MCC) (RW 1.2505). Prior to final bill submission, the coding professional queries the physician for the probable organisms targeted by the antibiotics selected, given this patient's documented immunocompromised state and known lung cancer. The attending physician states that the patient probably had a gram-negative pneumonia and documents it in an addendum to the discharge summary. The final MS-DRG assigned is MS-DRG 177 (Respiratory infections and inflammations with MCC) (RW 1.8444).

Pneumonia is commonly complicated by sepsis (the systemic inflammatory response to infection), acute respiratory failure, and complicated pleural effusions. Abnormalities of the white blood cell count, fever, altered mental status, or organ dysfunctions suggest sepsis. Hypoxemia (pO_2 is less than 60, the need for over 30 percent oxygen by Ventimask) or use of BiPAP or mechanical ventilation may suggest respiratory failure. A large pleural effusion on the admission chest x-ray requiring thoracentesis may be the reason that the patient's pneumonia was not treated as an outpatient, especially if it is a complicated pleural effusion or a partially treated empyema. Physician documentation and query are necessary to correctly assign the principal diagnosis.

Other Interstitial Lung Diseases

Not all abnormal x-rays are the result of pneumonia or acute left-sided systolic or diastolic congestive heart failure. Other diseases, such as the late effect of tuberculosis, exposure to asbestos, collagen vascular diseases such as systemic lupus erythematosus or rheumatoid arthritis, acute chest syndromes due to sickle cell anemia, chronic dust exposure, sarcoidosis, or chronic pulmonary fibrosis (also known as diffuse idiopathic pulmonary fibrosis or eosinophilic pneumonia) may mimic bacterial pneumonia. Many of these patients are treated with corticosteroids such as prednisone. If the physician only

Antibiotic	Indicated Organism
Vancomycin (Vancocin®)	Methicillin-resistant *Staphylococcus aureus*
Clindamycin (Cleocin®)	*S aureus*, anaerobes (for example, aspiration pneumonia)
Pipercillin-sulbactam (Zosyn®)	Gram-negative rods, *S aureus*, anaerobes (for example, aspiration pneumonia)
Ampicillin-sulbactam (Unasyn®)	
Cefepime, ceftazidime (Maxipime®, Fortaz®)	Gram-negative rods, probably *Pseudomonas*
Linezolid (Zyvox®)	Methicillin-resistant *Staphylococcus aureus*
Imipenem-cilastin (Primaxin®)	Gram-negative rods, *S aureus*, anaerobes (aspiration)

documents chronic pulmonary infiltrates, especially if they are treated with steroids, it is appropriate to query for its underlying etiology.

Pleural Effusions

A pleural effusion is a collection of fluid between the parietal (next to the ribs) and visceral (next to the lungs) pleura. Although a small amount of fluid is normal, it takes about 300 to 400 milliliters of fluid to be seen on a chest x-ray. This amount of fluid is never normal and should prompt a diagnostic workup or consideration by the physician.

When pleural fluid is associated with fluid overload states and their underlying causes (for example, congestive heart failure, cirrhosis, acute renal failure, or end-stage renal disease), especially if it is present in the right lung, most physicians will consider the pleural effusion to be integral to the underlying condition and monitor it closely. *Coding Clinic* (3rd Quarter, 1991, 19–20) has directed coding professionals not to code pleural effusions in this circumstance separately unless documentation supports additional studies, such as decubitus x-rays, or treatment, such as thoracentesis. In this case, when treated separately, coding of pleural effusion NOS, 511.9, is reported. If the pleural effusion requires additional studies, such as decubitus x-rays, or treatments, such as a thoracentesis, this same *Coding Clinic* allows for 511.9 (Pleural effusion NOS) to be coded as an additional diagnosis.

If a physician performs a thoracentesis, he or she should categorize the fluid to be exudative or transudative. Transudative fluid is caused by fluid overload; no special treatment is necessary other than treating the underlying condition. If the pleural effusion is exudative or complicated, the physician should consider a more serious underlying cause, such as empyema, malignancy, pancreatitis, chronic infections (for example, tuberculosis), or collagen vascular diseases (for example, rheumatoid arthritis or lupus). The coding professional should always query for the clinical significance of an exudative or complicated pleural effusion and its probable underlying etiology.

Example: A 76-year-old white man with a two-pack-a-day smoking history for 50 years and a stable COPD is admitted for dyspnea and a left-sided pleural effusion. A thoracentesis is performed that drained 2 L of fluid from his lung. Preliminary studies demonstrate that the fluid was exudative; studies for TB, fungus, and cancer cytology are pending. The physician thinks that it is safe to discharge the patient and follow these results as an outpatient. Upon coding, the coding professional initially assigns pleural effusion as a principal diagnosis; however, upon noting that the fluid was exudative, she queries for its probable underlying cause. The physician states that he strongly suspects that the patient has lung cancer and that this condition was still to be ruled out. This changes the MS-DRG from MS-DRG 188 (Pleural effusion without CC) (RW 0.9745) (COPD is not a CC in MS-DRGs) to MS-DRG 182 (Respiratory neoplasm w/o CC) (RW 1,1455). The coding professional then notifies the infection control nurse to be on the lookout for the results of the TB-fungal studies and to communicate these results to her if they are positive.

Example: A patient with pneumococcal pneumonia and parapneumonic effusion is admitted for intravenous antibiotics. Upon performance of a thoracentesis, the pH of the pleural fluid is 7.15 and it is thought to be an exudate; the physician documents that the patient will need prolonged antibiotics. The clinical documentation specialist asks the physician for the clinical significance of the pH, and he replies that he believes that it is partially treated empyema. This documentation changes the initial MS-DRG from MS-DRG 194 (Simple pneumonia and pleurisy with CC) (RW 1.0235) to MS-DRG 178 (Respiratory inflammations and infections with CC) (RW 1.5636) because the empyema is thought to have been present on admission and, after study, is found to have occasioned the hospitalization along with the patient's pneumonia.

MDC 5: Diseases and Disorders of the Circulatory System

Surgery

The main change for MS-DRGs in MDC 5 is the substitution of the Major Cardiovascular Diagnoses (MCV) with new CC and MCC system.

Coding professionals should read operative reports carefully so that these procedures are accurately coded. Areas to differentiate include the following:

- Ascertaining that a cardiac catheterization or percutaneous transluminal coronary angioplasty was done during the same admission, especially in the setting of coronary artery bypass surgery or valve surgery.
- Differentiating implantations of simple pacemakers from cardiac resynchronization pacemakers or automatic implantable cardiac defibrillators.

- Determining if a coronary sinus angiogram (mapping) was performed during the implantation of a cardiac resynchronization device. *Coding Clinic* (1st Quarter, 2007, 16), allows for ICD-9-CM code 88.52 (Angiocardiography of right heart structures) to be added.
- Differentiating drug-eluting from nondrug-eluting coronary stents.
- Reading radiology reports to find peripheral vessel angioplasties, especially of carotid, renal, and femoral arteries.

Principal diagnosis remains important because many gastrointestinal (for example, appendectomy, gastrectomy), skin (for example, excisional debridement), and pulmonary (for example, transpleural thoracoscopy, transbronchial biopsy) procedures group to MDC 5 if a cardiovascular principal diagnosis is justified. CMS has eliminated separate DRGs for automatic implantable cardioverter defibrillator (AICD) implantation and cardiac catheterization with acute myocardial infarction, congestive heart failure, and shock as principal diagnoses.

Medicine

CMS eliminated the designations for complex diagnosés for cardiac catheterization (CMS DRGs 125 and 124) and complication diagnoses acute myocardial infarction (CMS DRGs 121 and 122), substituting the requirements for CCs or MCCs.

Coding professionals should be aware of the following areas.

Chest Pain

Chest pain is one of most problematic diagnoses for MDC 5 DRGs due to lack of physician documentation of the probable underlying cause. Because 5 percent of patients evaluated in the emergency department with normal electrocardiograms and cardiac isoenzymes will have a significant myocardial ischemic event, many physicians hospitalize these patients to rule out a myocardial infarction. Not only are physicians unclear about whether to admit these patients as inpatient or observation status, but also chest pain workups are often inefficient unless an organized approach has been implemented. Even after a 2- to 3-day hospital stay, the cardiac workup is commonly negative, prompting physicians to discharge the patient on empiric medications and to label the patient as noncardiac or atypical chest pain (MS-DRG 313 [Chest pain] [RW 0.5550]).

Options for querying physicians about chest pain include:

- Manifestation—What was the nature of the pain—pleuritic, heartburn, angina, radicular, or colicky (for example, biliary colic)—if the pain was described as cardiac, noncardiac, or atypical? Descriptions of these symptoms include:
  - Pleuritic—Sharp "sticking" chest pain usually made worse by a deep breath
  - Angina pectoris—A heaviness, pressure, or squeezing that, while usually retrosternal, may occur or radiate in other parts of the body. It does not have to go to the left arm; sometimes it is located in the stomach or even the knees!
  - Heartburn—A burning feeling in the chest or throat
  - Radicular—A sharp pain radiating along a dermatome
  - Biliary colic—A rather sudden but vague aching or cramping discomfort in the upper abdomen or chest sometimes radiating to the back, reaching its climax within 1 hour and lasting up to 6 hours, leaving no persisting symptoms.
- Underlying etiology—What was the underlying etiology? Was it chest wall pain, costochondritis, Tietze syndrome, rib fractures, gastroesophageal reflux disease, reflux esophagitis, coronary artery atherosclerosis, coronary artery spasm, Syndrome X (for example, impaired coronary flow reserve), hypertrophic cardiomyopathy, aortic stenosis, pericarditis, postmyocardial infarction syndrome, gallstones, acalculous cholecystitis, peptic ulcer disease, pneumonia, pulmonary embolus, dissecting aortic aneurysm, viral pleurisy, herpes zoster, diabetic radiculopathy, psychiatric disease (for example, conversion reaction, panic disorder, posttraumatic stress disorder, anxiety, or a combination thereof)?
- Severity—In the case of angina, was the angina stable, was it at rest (lasting less than 10 minutes), was it progressive or accelerated, or did it result in a non-Q-wave myocardial infarction?
- Precipitating cause—Was there an antecedent trauma? Did the patient receive a medication that could have caused an esophageal ulcer (for example, tetracyclines) or acute esophagitis? Did the patient have recent surgery predisposing him or her to a secondary hypercoagulability syndrome and a possible

pulmonary embolus? Did the patient use cocaine which led to coronary spasm, increased myocardial oxygen demand and accelerated angina?

- Complications/comorbidities—Was there any atelectasis, GI bleeding, jaundice, hypoxemia, or other consequence to this circumstance? Was there another comorbidity requiring inpatient hospitalization other than the chest pain, such as uncontrolled diabetes, an acute exacerbation of COPD, or GI bleeding?

Even clarifying the type of chest discomfort the patient had impacts the MS-DRG, as shown in the table below.

Underlying etiologies have higher relative weights than chest pain alone.

Angina Pectoris/Myocardial Infarction

As mentioned above, angina pectoris is a discomfort in the chest or other part of the body that usually radiates to the neck or arms, occurs with physical or emotional stress, is relieved with rest or nitroglycerin, and is associated with myocardial ischemia.

The etiology of unstable angina and myocardial infarction is characterized as follows (Cannon and Braunwald 2005):

- Plaque rupture or erosion with superimposed nonocclusive thrombus
- Dynamic obstruction or constriction of the small muscular coronary arteries, such as in coronary spasm
- Progressive mechanical obstruction
- Inflammation or infection or both
- Secondary unstable angina related to increased myocardial oxygen demand or decreased supply (for example, anemia)

A patient may have one or more of these conditions.

A normal cardiac catheterization does not necessarily signify that the patient does not have angina. As just noted, not all angina pectoris is due to obstructive atherosclerotic coronary artery disease. In many of these patients, the nuclear study suggests some reversible ischemia, thus the physician should be queried of its clinical significance (for example, possible cardiac syndrome X or coronary vasospasm) if the coronary arteriogram is normal.

Angina severity is stratified in the following manner:

- Stable angina pectoris (413.9) is characterized by chest or arm discomfort that is rarely described as pain, but that is reproducibly associated with physical exertion or stress and is relieved within 5 to 10 minutes by rest and/or sublingual nitroglycerin.
- Angina at rest or angina decubitus (413.0) is stable angina that occurs at rest. It lasts less than 10 minutes, is not progressive, and is easily relieved by one or two nitroglycerin tablets.
- Unstable or progressive angina (411.1) is defined as angina pectoris or equivalent ischemic discomfort with at least one of the following three features: (1) it occurs at rest (or with minimal exertion) usually lasting over 10 minutes, (2) it is severe and of new onset (that is, within the past month), and/or (3) it occurs with a crescendo pattern.
- Acute coronary syndrome is a form of unstable angina in which an acute myocardial infarction is imminent. It may or may not have ST-segment elevation. A myocardial infarction may be aborted by aggressive interventions such as percutaneous transluminal coronary angioplasty or tissue-plasminogen activator (for example, tPA). Both acute coronary syndrome and aborted myocardial infarction code

MS-DRG	Description	R.W.
313	Chest pain	0.5489
303	Atherosclerosis w/o MCC	0.6055
311	Angina pectoris	0.5118
282	Acute myocardial infarction, discharged alive w/o CC/MCC	1.0617
204	Respiratory signs and symptoms	0.6658
392	Esophagitis, gastroent, and miscellaneous digestive disorders w/o MCC	0.7121
395	Other digestive system diagnoses w/o CC/MCC	0.7874
446	Disorders of the biliary tract w/o CC/MCC	0.8521
74	Cranial and peripheral nerve disorders w/o MCC	0.8954

to 411.1 (Intermediate coronary syndrome), and not to myocardial infarction.

- Non-ST segment elevation myocardial infarction (410.81) is established if a patient with the clinical features of unstable angina without ST segment elevation develops evidence of myocardial necrosis, as reflected in elevated cardiac biomarkers. Usually, the serum troponin level is elevated; however, some false-positive troponin elevations may occur due to end-stage renal disease, cardiopulmonary resuscitation, pericarditis, congestive heart failure, or other heart diseases.
- ST segment myocardial infarction is the same as non-ST segment elevation MI except that the ST segments are elevated.

Example: A 70-year-old man is admitted to observation status due to vague chest discomfort with a normal electrocardiogram and serum cardiac biomarkers. At the sixth hour, he has an elevated troponin I level (defined by the hospital's laboratory as indicative of myocardial ischemia) but with a normal CK-MB. The EKG remains normal. The patient's admission is converted to an inpatient admission. He is transferred to the ICU, given aggressive heparin, IV nitroglycerin, morphine sulfate, beta-blockers, calcium channel blockers, and aspirin, and his condition is monitored. The patient refuses a coronary angiogram for religious reasons. His symptoms stabilize on medical treatment. After a 5-day stay, the patient is discharged with a diagnosis of acute coronary syndrome (MS-DRG 311 [Angina pectoris] [RW 0.5118]). The coding professional queries the physician to ask the clinical significance of the elevated troponin levels in light of the standards set by the pathology lab and for the probable underlying cause of this patient's acute coronary syndrome. The physician replies in his dictated addendum to the discharge summary that the patient probably has coronary atherosclerosis and that these enzyme elevations possibly mean that the patient has a non-ST segment or non-Q-wave MI, changing the MS-DRG from 311 to 282

(Acute myocardial infarction, discharged alive, w/o CC or MCC) (RW 1.0617).

Heart Failure

Heart failure is defined as a condition in which an abnormality of cardiac function is responsible for the inability of the heart to pump blood at a rate commensurate with the requirements of the metabolizing tissues and/or allows it to do so only from an abnormally elevated ventricular diastolic pressure. In stating that a patient has heart failure (or congestive heart failure [CHF]), the documenting physician declares that the patient has an abnormal heart.

Coding professionals (and physicians) commonly associate pulmonary edema with congestive heart failure. Although congestive heart failure quite often manifests with pulmonary edema, many patients with normal hearts can also develop pulmonary edema. For example, a renal dialysis patient may miss their dialysis treatments and develop fluid overload with pulmonary edema; this does not mean that he or she has an abnormal heart. Adult respiratory distress syndrome (ARDS) manifests as noncardiogenic pulmonary edema that may resemble CHF. This likewise does not mean that the patient has an abnormal heart. Even a healthy 20-year-old can receive intraoperative fluid overload during surgery, resulting in edema and pulmonary edema. To state that this patient has CHF mislabels them with a disease he or she does not have.

What is new with respect to MS-DRGs is that heart failure will now be assigned to three MS-DRGs rather than one as shown in the following table.

More details on CHF and its CCs/MCCs are provided in chapter 3.

Although an exacerbation of CHF is usually the principal diagnosis when patients are admitted with fluid overload due to heart disease, there are circumstances in which an underlying or precipitating cause or complication may be sequenced as a principal diagnosis. Options for principal diagnosis include:

- Manifestation—Heart Failure
  - Right versus left
  - Systolic versus diastolic
  - Acute versus chronic
  - Decompensated versus compensated

MS-DRG	MS-DRG Title	Weights
291	Heart failure and shock w MCC	1.2585
292	Heart failure and shock w CC	1.0134
293	Heart failure and shock w/o CC/MCC	0.8765

- Underlying Cause
  - Cardiomyopathy (alcoholic, diabetic, hypertensive, ischemic)
  - Old myocardial infarction
  - Pulmonary lung disease (acute versus chronic cor pulmonale)
  - Valve disease
  - Accelerated or malignant HTN
- Severity
  - NYHA association Class I–IV (no ICD-9-CM code currently exists for heart failure severity)
- Precipitating Causes
  - Acute MI
  - Pulmonary embolus
  - Salt indiscretion
  - Medication noncompliance
  - Underlying infection (sepsis)
  - Valvular disease
- Complications
  - Venous stasis ulcers
  - Chronic venous HTN (not venous insufficiency)
  - Chronic kidney disease (needs to be staged)
  - Acute renal insufficiency or failure

Example: A 56-year-old man is admitted with fulminate pulmonary edema and respiratory distress. He has a 20-year history of hypertension; his chest x-ray shows an enlarged heart and pulmonary edema. His EKG shows left ventricular hypertrophy with a left ventricular strain pattern. His admitting arterial blood gases are pH 7.32, pCO_2 52, pO_2 48 on a 40 percent Ventimask. He responds to morphine, oxygen, diuretic, digoxin, and aminophylline, diuresing two liters of fluid; his O_2 saturation was 98 percent on room air on discharge. A myocardial infarction is ruled out; his echocardiogram shows left ventricular enlargement and dilation with an ejection fraction of 32 percent. A workup for other secondary causes for CHF was negative. The physician discharges the patient on the fourth hospital day and signs him out as new onset acute systolic CHF due to newly diagnosed hypertensive congestive cardiomyopathy.

Because the patient's CHF was present on admission and the underlying cause was newly worked up and diagnosed on this admission, both may be considered as principal diagnoses. If the patient's cardiomyopathy was known prior to this admission and the diagnostic approach and treatment rendered was primarily for heart failure, then the underlying cardiomyopathy cannot be considered as a principal diagnosis.

The coding professional also can query for the clinical significance of the arterial blood gases in the setting of acute respiratory distress, knowing that this patient meets clinical criteria for acute respiratory failure.

Syncope

Many patients are admitted with transient total or near loss of consciousness to evaluate for its underlying etiology. Transient loss of consciousness has many possible etiologies, including:

- Vasovagal states (hypotension, bradycardia)
- Postural hypotension (hypotension upon standing)
- Autonomic or peripheral neuropathy
- Hypovolemia due to blood loss, diuresis
- Addison's disease
- Carotid sinus hypersensitivity
- Situational—Cough, micturition, valsalva—cause bradycardia
- Glossopharyngeal neuralgia—cause bradycardia
- Cardiac disorders
- Arrhythmias (especially in patients with heart failure or ischemic heart disease)
- Pulmonary embolus
- Aortic outflow obstruction
- Hypertrophic cardiomyopathy
- Cerebrovascular disorders
- Posterior circulation transient ischemic attack
- Basilar migraine
- Subarachnoid hemorrhage
- Metabolic disorders
- Hypoxia
- Anemia
- Hyperventilation
- Hypoglycemia
- Psychogenic
- Anxiety disorder, hysterical fainting
- Seizures

Syncope is transient loss of consciousness due to a cardiovascular cause. Patients often have more than one contributing factor to their symptoms. Usually, no underlying cause is clearly evident, resulting in physicians documenting that the patient has syncope of unknown etiology. Querying the physician about the possible underlying cause given the circumstances of admission, diagnostic approach, and treatment rendered may be fruitful.

Example: An 80-year-old man with multi-infarct dementia is admitted with transient loss of consciousness and positive cardiac enzymes. He is observed in the hospital on telemetry, which shows the following EKG pattern (see Figure 2.4).

Figure 2.4   Nonsustained Ventricular Tachycardia (3 or more Premature Ventricular Beats in a row)

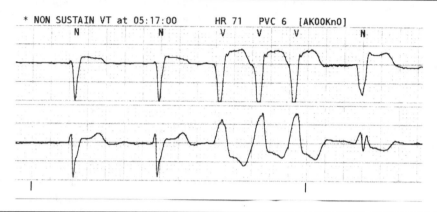

Source: James S. Kennedy, MD, CCS. Personal files.

Procedure Code	Description	Operative Procedure
70.53	Repair of cystocele and rectocele with graft or prosthesis	Y
70.54	Repair of cystocele with graft or prosthesis	Y
70.55	Repair of rectocele with graft or prosthesis	Y

Source: CMS Proposed Rule (Federal Register)

One morning, he is found without vital signs. Because he was "no code," CPR is not instituted. The physician's final diagnosis is syncope (MS-DRG 312 [Syncope] [RW 0.7197]). The coding professional queries the attending physician for the clinical significance of the positive cardiac enzymes and the EKG. Because the coding professional is uneasy with the query and has concerns regarding the quality of the attending physician's documentation, her physician advisor is engaged to discuss this situation with the attending physician. The attending physician subsequently writes that the patient probably had a non-Q-wave myocardial infarction, that the syncope was possibly due to ventricular tachycardia, and that both conditions were probably present on admission. The new MS-DRG was 284 (Acute myocardial infarction w/CC) (ventricular tachycardia is a CC) (RW 1.2074). The attending physician refuses to speculate on whether the patient had ventricular fibrillation as a cause of death.

MDC 6: Diseases and Disorders of the Digestive System

Surgery

New ICD-9-CM procedure codes for rectocele repair affect MDC 6 as shown in the above list.

CMS still differentiates between appendectomy with or without a complicated principal diagnosis, such as abdominal abscess or generalized peritonitis. Coding professionals should read the pathology report to determine if perforation was present and possibly a small abscess. Principal diagnosis assignment issues still center around whether the patient has sepsis present on admission and whether the surgery was necessary to remove infected tissue. If a cholecystectomy is performed, the circumstances of admission determine whether the gallbladder disease or a MDC-6 specific principal diagnosis is assigned. In assigning the principal procedure, consider the following caveats:

- Coding professionals should read operative reports carefully to discern what procedures were actually performed. Oftentimes, the name of the operation may not match the description of the procedure performed. Coding is based on the description of the procedure performed.

- Accurate reporting of procedures allows for coding of lysis of adhesions in abdominal surgery when the physician documents significant time invested in lysing these adhesions.

Example: A 58-year-old man who is an alcoholic is admitted with abdominal pain and an upper GI bleed. His temperature is 101° F, his white blood cell count is 17,000 mm^3 with 8 percent bands and 88 percent segmented neutrophils, his pulse is 100, and his respiration rate is 20; blood cultures are negative. Upper GI endoscopy finds that he has a nonobstructive bleeding duodenal ulcer that requires cauterization; his abdominal ultrasound shows cholelithiasis. After receiving antibiotics, his fever resolves and his white blood cell count returns to a normal level, but he still has abdominal pain. An open cholecystectomy without common bile duct exploration is performed; the initial laparoscopic cholecystectomy is aborted due to an extensive lysis of adhesions that added 30 minutes to the operative procedure. The discharge summary notes duodenal ulcer disease with upper gastrointestinal (UGI) hemorrhage as the first listed diagnosis and acute cholecystitis as the second listed diagnosis.

In this circumstance, the coding professional chooses to sequence acute cholecystitis as the principal diagnosis because this requires an operative procedure, and she initiates a query to the physician for the clinical significance of the temperature and elevated white blood cell count in the setting of the cholecystitis responding to antibiotics. The physician replies that the patient probably has SIRS due to the cholecystitis that was present on admission. Another coding professional thinks that the duodenal ulcer could be a principal diagnosis because it required acute treatment and is a reason that the patient could not be treated as an outpatient.

Medicine

MS-DRG assignment for medical diagnoses within MDC 6 mirrors that of the CMS DRGs. Areas of emphasis include:

Gastrointestinal Hemorrhage

In evaluating gastrointestinal hemorrhage, the following terminology applies:

- Manifestation—Hematemesis, melena, anemia, stool positive for acute blood, high output CHF, accelerated angina pectoris (the last two due to the anemia)
- Underlying Cause—Esophageal, gastric, duodenal, or gastrojejunal ulcer (benign) or cancer; Meckel's diverticulum, Barrett's or reflux esophagitis, Mallory-Weiss tear of the esophagus (after excessive vomiting), ulcerative or Crohn's colitis, diverticulosis, angiodysplasia of the gut, hemorrhoids, foreign body in the GI tract. Although patients may have an acquired coagulopathy due to warfarin or heparin, there is usually an underlying structural abnormality that led the patient to bleed.
- Severity—Was there a small amount of bleeding whereby the stool appeared normal, was there simply bright red bleeding in the stool or hematemesis, or was the bleeding rapid enough to be termed a hemorrhage?
- Precipitating Etiology—Was this a complication of drugs (for example, heparin or aspirin) or a procedure? Does this patient have sepsis leading to stress ulcerations? Was the patient toxic on warfarin or heparin? Were the drugs taken as prescribed?
- Complications—Was there acute or chronic blood loss anemia, congestive heart failure, angina2 at rest or accelerated angina (due to the anemia), transient loss of consciousness, acute renal failure due to hypovolemia, prolonged hypotension or hypovolemic shock? If there was a peptic ulcer, was there GI obstruction or preformation?

How these questions are answered determines the base MS-DRG that these are assigned.

MS-DRG	MS-DRG Title	Weights
335	Peritoneal adhesiolysis w MCC	3.4785
336	Peritoneal adhesiolysis w CC	2.4776
337	Peritoneal adhesiolysis w/o CC/MCC	1.6984
853	Infectious and parasitic diseases w O.R. procedure w MCC	5.1840
854	Infectious and parasitic diseases w O.R. procedure w CC	3.9291
855	Infectious and parasitic diseases w O.R. procedure w/o CC/MCC	3.3662

MS-DRG	MS-DRG Title	Weights
370	Major esophageal disorders w/o CC/MCC	0.9558
376	Digestive malignancy w/o CC/MCC	1.0268
379	G.I. hemorrhage w/o CC/MCC	0.8476
382	Complicated peptic ulcer w/o CC/MCC	0.9662
384	Uncomplicated peptic ulcer w/o MCC	0.8399
387	Inflammatory bowel disease w/o CC/MCC	0.9488
392	Esophagitis, gastroent, and miscellaneous digestive disorders w/o MCC	0.7121
395	Other digestive system diagnoses w/o CC/MCC	0.7874

Esophageal Disorders

Although most coding professionals understand (or probably have experienced for themselves while querying physicians for improved documentation) heartburn or gastroesophageal reflux disease (GERD), these symptoms may indicate other conditions than simple erosive or ulcerative esophagitis resulting from prolonged peptic acid exposure—MS-DRG 392 (Esophagitis, gastroenteritis, and miscellaneous digestive disorders w/o CC/MCC) (RW 0.7121).

Common conditions grouping to major esophageal disorders (MS-DRG 370) (RW 0.9558) include:

- Candidiasis of the esophagus—Suspect if the patient has oral candidiasis and odynophagia (pain while swallowing)
- Esophageal varices—Suspect if the patient has a history of chronic hepatitis C, cirrhosis, chronic alcoholism, or other chronic liver diseases
- Mallory-Weiss ulcers—Suspect if the patient has prolonged retching prior to his upper GI bleed
- Complications of GI procedures

Other esophageal conditions grouping to the higher weighted MS-DRG 382 (Complicated peptic ulcer w/o CC/MCC) (RW 0.9662) or MS-DRG 395 (Other digestive system diagnoses w/o CC/MCC) (RW 0.7874) include:

- Esophageal ulcers—Usually a complication of tetracycline antibiotics
- Barrett's esophagus—A condition in which the lining of the esophagus looks like stomach rather than esophagus, usually caused by prolonged acid reflux. Because this condition is premalignant, patients require frequent surveillance to ensure they do not have esophageal cancer.

Major Gastrointestinal Disorders and Other GI Conditions

CMS retained the classification of Major Gastrointestinal Disorders that was created in FY2007, which now groups to MS-DRG 373 (Major gastrointestinal disorders and peritoneal infections w/o CC or MCC) (RW 1.1109). Conditions that coding professionals should watch for include:

- Diarrhea with elevated white blood cell count—Not uncommonly, this is due to overgrowth of pathological bacteria in the gut and may be a consequence of food poisoning. Antibiotics (especially clindamycin, penicillin, and cephalosporin) can cause an overgrowth of *Clostridium difficile* leading to colitis and diarrhea. If the patient has fever, tachycardia, or evidence of organ dysfunction, a CDI opportunity for sepsis (SIRS due to infection) exists.
- Chronic diarrhea with normal white blood cell count—Although this condition is commonly a result of irritable bowel syndrome or chronic laxative abuse, if Flagyl (metronidazole) is prescribed, a CDI opportunity for *Giardia*, a parasite obtained from well, unfiltered, or unpasteurized bottled water, exists.
- Abdominal pain after foreign travel—While water in civilized countries is relatively pure, patients traveling to or coming from a foreign country may develop chronic intestinal infections (amebiasis or tuberculosis) that coding professionals would not normally encounter in the United States. A CDI opportunity exists if any antibiotic prescribed after a patient has traveled to a foreign country (for example, traveler's diarrhea probably due to enteropathogenic *Escherichia coli*) adds specificity to diagnosis assignment.

MDC 7: Diseases and Disorders of the Hepatobiliary System and Pancreas

Surgery

Surgeries within MDC 7 are fairly straightforward. MS-DRGs did consolidate Hepatobiliary Diagnostic

CMS-DRG Version 24.0	DRG Description	MS-DRG Version 25.0	New Base MS-DRG Description
199	Hepatobiliary Diagnostic Procedure for Malignancy	420, 421, 422	Hepatobiliary Diagnostic Procedures with MCC, with CC, without CC/MCC
200	Hepatobiliary Diagnostic Procedure for Non-Malignancy		

Source: CMS Final Rule (Federal Register)

Procedures for malignancies and nonmalignancies into one MS-DRG group.

Areas of emphasis include the following:

- Unlike many procedures in MDC 6 where lysis of adhesions changes the DRG, lysis of adhesions does not change the DRG for many procedures in MDC 7. Peritoneal adhesiolysis should nevertheless be coded.
- Physicians should clearly describe their performance of liver biopsies surrounding any exploratory laparotomy. *Coding Clinic* (4th Quarter, 1988) states that when a physician documents "laparotomy with needle biopsy of the liver," code 50.11 (Closed liver biopsy) is to be used. Code 50.12 (Open liver biopsy) should be used only if the physician uses a scalpel and obtains a wedge biopsy.
- Do not code biopsies of any organs (for example, liver, pancreas) that are sampled by mistake. *Coding Clinic* (2nd Quarter, 1995, p. 6) cites an example where a biopsy of the gallbladder was scheduled, yet the pathology report identified gallbladder and pancreatic tissue. Because the purpose of the biopsy was for determination of gallbladder pathology, the pancreatic biopsy should not have been reported. Furthermore, this same *Coding Clinic* emphasizes that inadvertent biopsies are not complications of care.
- Cholecystectomy operative reports must be read carefully. CMS differentiates laparoscopies from open cholecystectomies, those with and without common bile duct exploration (an intraoperative cholangiogram or endoscopic removal of biliary stones is *not* a common bile duct exploration), and cholecystectomies associated with other operative procedures. If any bile duct repairs (for example, after an incidental incision) or other operations on the biliary duct are performed, these will likely change the DRG.
- If patients undergo an endoscopic retrograde cholangiopancreatography (ERCP) to evaluate jaundice, elevation of liver enzymes, pancreatitis,

and/or abnormal biliary x-rays, coding professionals should be careful to note if procedures on the papilla of Vater, ampulla of Vater, or the sphincter of Oddi are performed. These terms are quite confusing and are defined as follows:
- Papilla of Vater—Also known as the major papilla of the duodenum, this is an eminence of intestinal mucosa at the location where the pancreatic and common bile duct empties into the duodenum.
- Ampulla of Vater (Santorini)—Also known as the hepatopancreatic ampulla or biliaropancreatic ampulla, this is a dilated confluence where the pancreatic and distal biliary ducts meet before they empty into the duodenum through the major papilla of the duodenum.
- Sphincter of Oddi—This is a thickening of both the longitudinal and circular layers of smooth muscle surrounding the hepatopancreatic ampulla and the pancreatic and biliary ducts as they course through the duodenal wall at the location of the major papilla of the duodenum. It serves to restrict the flow of bile or pancreatic fluids into the duodenum and prevent duodenal contents from entering the biliary system.

Coding professionals should remember that *endoscopic* sphincterotomy of the sphincter of Oddi or the major papilla of the duodenum codes to 51.85, which is not a major operative procedure, whereas performance of these as part of an *open* procedure codes to 51.82 (Pancreatic sphincterotomy), grouping this to MS-DRG 407 (Pancreas, liver, and shunt procedures w/o CC/MCC) (RW 2.2443).

- Quite often, patients with acute cholecystitis or pancreatitis present with the systemic inflammatory response syndrome (generally identified as a constellation of symptoms of elevated white blood cell count, elevated pulse, elevated respiration rate, fever, and/or organ dysfunction) for which surgical intervention (for example, cholecystectomy or drainage of a pancreatic abscess or phlegmon) is necessary. If the patient has SIRS due to an infection that was present on admission and undergoes a pancreatic or biliary procedure, the principal diagnosis will be a septicemia code and the DRG will be MDC 18 (Infectious and parasitic diseases).

Example: A 70-year-old white man with acute cholecystitis and ascending cholangitis is admitted to the hospital. His white blood cell count is 30,000 mm³ with a left shift, his temperature was 103° F., and his blood culture grew *Enterococcus*. An abdominal ultrasound showed cholelithiasis. After receiving antibiotics and nutritional support, he undergoes a laparoscopic cholecystectomy with an intraoperative cholangiogram, which is negative (apparently, he passed his biliary stone). The final diagnosis is acute cholecystitis with cholelithiasis, ascending cholangitis, and bacteremia (MS-DRG 418 [Laparoscopic cholecystectomy w/o c.d.e. w/CC] [RW 1.7104]). Upon physician query, the physician documents that the elevated white blood cell count and fever present on admission indicate that the patient has SIRS, probably due to his acute cholangitis, and that the patient's bacteremia is severe enough to be septicemia, changing the MS-DRG to 854 (Infectious and parasitic diseases with O.R. procedure with CC) (RW 3.9291).

Medicine

Medicine diagnoses within MDC 7 appear straightforward. Areas of emphasis include the following:

- Recognizing liver disease and biliary disease

    Not only is it important to recognize liver disease, given that ICD-9-CM instructs 456.2x (Esophageal varices in diseases classified elsewhere) to code to 571.0–571.9 (Cirrhosis of the liver) or 572.3 (Portal hypertension) first, but also disorders of the pancreas or gallbladder can mimic liver disease and thus must be differentiated.

    The following should be considered in addressing liver disease:
    - Manifestations—Liver disease is recognized by elevations of the liver enzymes (ALT, AST, alkaline phosphatase, bilirubin), possibly by abnormalities of the prothrombin time or liver x-rays, and certainly by clinical signs as symptoms such as ascites, peripheral edema, jaundice, hepatomegaly, and upper GI bleeding.
    - Underlying etiologies—Infections (for example, hepatitis viruses [A, B, C, D, E], cytomegalovirus, HIV, liver abscesses, tuberculosis, syphilis), malignancies (for example, primary hepatomas or metastatic lesions), toxins (for example, alcohol, pharmaceuticals, carbon tetrachloride), passive congestion of blood into the liver (for example, due to chronic right heart failure), other inflammatory diseases (for example, sarcoidosis), biliary duct obstructions or stasis (for example, gallstones, acute pancreatitis, sclerosis cholangitis, AIDS, or cholangiopathy), pregnancy, sepsis, veno-occlusive disease
    - Severity—Differentiating whether or not the liver inflammation has led to cirrhosis (scar tissue within the liver). Usually the Pro-Time® is elevated or the physician ascribe ascites, hepatic encephalopathy, or asterixis to the liver disease.
    - Precipitating causes—Liver disease may be exacerbated by other illnesses. For example, the patient may have continuous chemical dependency to alcohol (a CC) and may not disclose this to the physician due to intense shame, be an IV-drug abuser (again, another individual with continuous chemical dependency), may acquire a new hepatitis B or C infection, or may be accidentally overdosing on over-the-counter medications that have acetaminophen (for example, Nyquil®) that can lead to a toxic hepatitis.
    - Complications—Chronic liver disease can lead to portal hypertension (elevations in the blood vessels between the gut and the liver) resulting in esophageal varices that bleed, enlargement of the spleen that leads to pancytopenia, ascites (fluid in the abdomen) that leads to hypovolemia and chronic kidney disease), delirium (due to a hepatic encephalopathy), or coagulopathies leading to subdural hematomas.

Certain patterns of laboratory value elevation, especially with jaundice (elevations of the bilirubin) indicate whether the pathology primarily involves the hepatic cell itself (for example, hepatitis) or stasis of the bile (cholestasis) within the liver (for example, due to biliary or pancreatic disease). These patterns include the following.

	Hepatocellular (Liver Cell Disease)	Cholestasis (Biliary Disease or Liver Disease)	Pancreatic Disease
Alkaline Phosphatase	↑	↑↑↑	↑
ALT (SGPT) AST (SGOT)	↑↑↑ (if SGPT is near normal and SGOT is elevated, alcohol is likely involved)	↑	↑ or normal
Bilirubin	↑ or normal	↑↑ or normal	Normal
ProTime	↑ or normal	Normal	Normal
Lipase/Amylase	Normal	Normal	elevated

Further laboratory studies that help include:

- Hepatocellular disease
  - Hepatitis studies—(IgM to hepatitis A, hepatitis B antigen, hepatitis C RNA)——Note if an antigen or antibody study is positive and query the physician for the clinical significance.
  - Serum protein electrophoresis—Note if there is beta-gamma bridging consistent with cirrhosis.
  - ProTime—Elevated levels are indicative of severe liver disease or liver failure.
  - Sedimentation rate, ANA—Indicative of autoimmune disease.
  - Acetaminophen level—Acetaminophen overdose can cause acute liver disease.
- Cholestasis
  - Antimitochondrial antibody—Primary biliary cirrhosis
  - Hepatitis studies—Hepatitis A, B, and C antibodies—Chronic disease can have a cholestatic pattern.
  - Drug levels

Radiology studies may help as well. These include:

- Abdominal ultrasound—Able to discern if there is bile duct dilation or obstruction. May show lesions within the liver itself.
- CT scan or MRI—Able to show lesions within the liver, biliary duct obstruction, pancreatitis, or enlargement of the spleen indicative of cirrhosis.
- Liver-spleen scan—Able to show enlargement of the spleen and increased bone marrow uptake consistent with cirrhosis.
- ERCP—Able to show biliary duct disease.

If a cirrhotic patient has hepatic encephalopathy, an encephalopathy code cannot be coded as a secondary diagnosis. Hepatic encephalopathy is integrated into the appropriate hepatic coma codes. If a patient has both alcoholic liver disease and viral hepatitis with hepatic encephalopathy, sequence the viral hepatitis with hepatic coma code first (*Coding Clinic*, 2nd Quarter, 2007, 6–7).

Example: A 70-year-old white man is admitted with jaundice. His bilirubin level is 6.0 mg/dL (normal is less than 1.0 mg/dL), his alkaline phosphatase is markedly elevated at 540 units/L (normal is less than 120), AST (SGOT) is slightly elevated at 58 U/L (normal is less than 35 U/L), and ALT (SGPT) is slightly elevated at 85 U/L (normal is less than 35 U/L), indicative of a cholestatic pattern. A CT scan of the abdomen shows a pancreatic mass at the head of the pancreas and dilated biliary ducts consistent with probable carcinoma of the head of the pancreas, assigned to MS-DRG 437 (Malignancy of the hepatobiliary system or pancreas w/o CC) (RW 1.1709).

Example: A 35-year-old white man is admitted with an upper GI bleed and mild jaundice. Endoscopy is nondiagnostic. The bilirubin is 2.0 mg/dL, the alkaline phosphatase is 200, the AST is 400 U/L, and the ALT is 40 U/L. CT scan of the abdomen showed diffuse fatty liver. The physician's final diagnosis is jaundice due to alcoholic fatty liver and UGI bleed of unknown etiology (MS-DRG 442 [Disorders of liver except malignancy, cirrhosis, and alcoholic hepatitis w/CC] [RW 1.0935]. The coding professional queries the physician for the clinical significance of the normal ALT, given that the AST was normal. The physician responds that the patient probably had a mild acute alcoholic hepatitis, which changes the DRG to MS-DRG 433 (Cirrhosis and alcoholic hepatitis with CC) (RW 1.1431).

Acute pancreatitis is an acute inflammation of the pancreas that releases digestive enzymes into the abdomen, leading to profound abdominal pain, dehydration, hypocalcemia, and even SIRS with its associated acute renal dysfunctions or failure. Invariably, the amylase or lipase will be elevated and CT scans of the abdomen will show pancreatic swelling. Coding professionals should be aware of the most common causes of pancreatitis and query the physician for the underlying cause. Furthermore, physician description of SIRS and the respective organ dysfunctions will add severity to the DRG.

Typical underlying causes for pancreatitis include:

- Biliary disease or gallstones
- ERCP—A common complication of this procedure
- Ethanol
- Radiation
- Vasculitis—autoimmune disease (for example, lupus)
- Oncology—pancreatic tumors, operations
- Metabolic disease (for example, hypertriglyceridemia)
- Idiopathic conditions
- Trauma
- Uremia—end-stage renal disease
- Sphincter of Oddi dysfunction

Example: A 55-year-old woman is admitted with the third bout of acute pancreatitis over the past 3 months. She vows that she does not drink. Abdominal ultrasounds and CT scans of the abdomen show no underlying etiology. An ERCP is nondiagnostic. She does, however, have some mild joint pain and constantly drank water due to dry mouth. The sedimentation rate is elevated and the ANA test is positive. She is started on steroids. The final diagnosis is acute idiopathic recurrent pancreatitis—MS-DRG 440 (Disorders of the pancreas except malignancy w/o CC/MCC) (RW 0.8912). The coding professional queries the physician for the

clinical significance of the elevated sedimentation rate and the positive ANA study. The physician responds that the patient possibly has pancreatic vasculitis due to lupus, which changes the MS-DRG to 546 (Connective tissue disorders with CC [pancreatitis]) (RW 1.2092).

MDC 8: Diseases and Disorders of the Musculoskeletal System and Connective Tissue

Surgery

DRG assignment for MDC 8 remains practically the same between CMS DRGs and MS-DRGs. One revision made for FY2008 is that the ICD-9-CM procedure codes 00.83 (Revision of knee replacement, patellar component) and 00.84 (Revision of total knee replacement, tibial insert [liner]) now group to MS-DRG 485–487 (Knee procedure with principal diagnosis of infection with and without CC/MCC) and MS-DRG 488–489 (Knee procedure without principal diagnosis of infection with and without CC/MCC) instead of grouping to MS-DRG 466–468 (Revision of hip or knee replacement).

Most procedures within MDC 8 have principal diagnoses pertinent to the musculoskeletal system. At times, diabetes mellitus or neurological conditions will make a difference. *Coding Clinic* has suggested some opportunities, as outlined.

Example: A nursing home patient is admitted for a tendon transfer due to severe contractures of the right hand. The past medical history on the H&P states that the past history is "noncontributory." The clinical documentation specialist screens the record and groups this procedure to MS-DRG 514 (Hand or wrist procedure, except major thumb or joint procedure w/o CC) (RW 0.8313). Due to the previous history of stroke noted on the nursing admission paperwork, she queries the physician for the underlying cause

MS-DRG	MS-DRG Title	Relative Weight
466	Revision of hip or knee replacement w MCC	3.5408
467	Revision of hip or knee replacement w CC	2.7523
468	Revision of hip or knee replacement w/o CC/MCC	2.4545
485	Knee procedures w pdx of infection w MCC	2.9362
486	Knee procedures w pdx of infection w CC	2.3382
487	Knee procedures w pdx of infection w/o CC/MCC	1.7771
488	Knee procedures w/o pdx of infection w CC/MCC	1.6584
489	Knee procedures w/o pdx of infection w/o CC/MCC	1.4512

of the contractures. He documents that it was due to the late effect of a stroke. The new MS-DRG is 042 (Peripheral and cranial nerve and other nervous system procedure w/o CC/MCC) (RW 1.8710) (*Coding Clinic*, 4th Quarter, 1998, 40).

Example: A diabetic nursing home patient is admitted for a nonhealing heel ulcer. The physician initially documents that the patient has a diabetic foot ulcer and plans a below-the-knee amputation. The clinical documentation specialist (CDS) initially groups this patient to MS-DRG 618 (Amputation of the lower limb for endocrine, nutritional, and metabolic disease w/o CC/MCC) (RW 1.7554). The CDS remembers *Coding Clinic*, 1st Quarter, 2004, which stated that not all ulcers in diabetic patients are diabetic ulcers, that diabetic ulcers of the foot generally start on the toes and move upward, that diabetic ulcers do not usually start on the heel, and that ulcers of the heel are almost always decubitus ulcers. Upon query, the physician documents that the ulcer is probably due to a pressure sore, which changes the MS-DRG to 581 (Other skin, subcutaneous tissue, and breast procedure w/o CC) (RW 0.8209). Upon performing the amputation, the pathologist notes that the osteomyelitis was probably present in the bone. Given that the patient is diabetic, the osteomyelitis was automatically linked to diabetes, which changes the MS-DRG back to 618 (RW 0.9124). The CDS again asks the physician the etiology of the patient's osteomyelitis. He replies it is due to the pressure sore, which changes the working MS-DRG to 476 (Amputation for musculoskeletal system and connective tissue w/o CC/MCC) (RW 1.6799).

• Spinal fusions and other neck and back procedures cause considerable confusion for coding professionals. Significant changes in relative weight between combined anterior/posterior spinal fusion and other spinal fusions plus changes in MS-DRGs from CMS DRGs require coding professionals to understand this procedure.

CMS made the following changes in spinal fusion DRGs:

• CMS recognized that noncervical spinal fusion involving nine or more vertebra consumes more resources than those involving a smaller number of vertebra. CMS opted to combine spinal fusions of nine or more vertebra into the MS-DRG for fusion with spinal malignancy or scoliosis (MS-DRG 456–458)

• CMS recognized that patients with spinal osteomyelitis or tuberculosis requiring spinal fusion required additional resources. CMS opted to group principal diagnoses for these conditions undergoing spinal fusion to group to MS-DRG 456–458.

• CMS reiterated that the CHARITE™ Artificial Disc is not covered for the CMS population over age 60. CMS also noted that the Corflex/Dysesys/M-Brace, X-stop, and CHARITE™ devices had lower costs than the spinal fusion DRGs but greater costs than the Back and Neck Procedures except Spinal Fusion DRGs, thus they opted not to include these devices in the Spinal Fusion DRGs. What CMS did was to count the insertion of one of these devices as if the patient had an MCC.

MS-DRG	MS-DRG Title	Relative Weight
453	Combined anterior/posterior spinal fusion w MCC	8.4313
454	Combined anterior/posterior spinal fusion w CC	6.5810
455	Combined anterior/posterior spinal fusion w/o CC/MCC	5.7023
456	Spinal fusion except cervical w spinal curvature/malignancy/ infection or 9+ fusion w MCC	6.7669
457	Spinal fusion except cervical w spinal curvature/malignancy/infection or 9+ fusion w CC	5.4650
458	Spinal fusion except cervical w spinal curvature/ malignancy/infection or 9+ fusion w/o CC/MCC	4.9437
459	Spinal fusion except cervical w MCC	4.8679
460	Spinal fusion except cervical w/o MCC	3.4870
461	Bilateral or multiple major joint procs of lower extremity w MCC	3.8345
462	Bilateral or multiple major joint procs of lower extremity w/o MCC	3.0993
463	Wound débridement and skin graft except hand, for musculoconnective tissue disease w MCC	3.9615
464	Wound débridement and skin graft except hand, for musculoconnective tissue disease w CC	2.8821
465	Wound débridement and skin graft except hand, for musculoconnective tissue disease w/o CC/MCC	2.3417
466	Revision of hip or knee replacement w MCC	3.5408
467	Revision of hip or knee replacement w CC	2.7523
468	Revision of hip or knee replacement w/o CC/MCC	2.4545
469	Major joint replacement or reattachment of lower extremity w MCC	2.6664
470	Major joint replacement or reattachment of lower extremity w/o MCC	1.9871
471	Cervical spinal fusion w MCC	3.4723
472	Cervical spinal fusion w CC	2.4819
473	Cervical spinal fusion w/o CC/MCC	1.9446
490	Back & neck proc exc spinal fusion w CC/MCC or disc device/neurostim	1.4912
491	Back & neck proc exc spinal fusion w/o CC/MCC	1.0066

Medicine

CMS consolidated the bone diseases and arthropathies (excluding septic arthritis) into one MS-DRG.

Areas of emphasis include the following:

- Osteopenia—33.6 million Americans, 80 percent of them women, have osteopenia. Coding professionals must understand the difference between 733.90 (Osteopenia), 733.00 (Osteoporosis), and 268.2 (Osteomalacia).
  - Osteopenia—A reduction of bone mass for any reason. A T score that is between –2.5 and –1.0 on a bone density test is indicative of osteopenia.

- Osteoporosis—A chronic, progressive disease characterized by low bone mass, microarchitectural deterioration and decreased bone strength, bone fragility, a consequent increase in fracture risk, and a bone density of 2.5 or more standard deviations (*SD*) below the young normal mean (*T* score of –2.5 or less). Osteoporosis is secondary if it is due to steroids, renal disease, hyperthyroidism, or COPD.
- Osteomalacia—A bone disorder is characterized by low rates of bone turnover, a mineralization defect, and an accumulation of unmineralized osteoid (bone matrix). This can occur in vitamin D deficiency

CMS-DRG Version 24.0	DRG Description	MS-DRG Version 25.0	New Base MS-DRG Description
244, 245	Bone Diseases & Specific Arthropathies	553, 554	Bone Diseases & Arthropathies with and without MCC
246	Non-Specific Arthropathies		

Source: CMS Final Rule (Federal Register)

and aluminum exposure in end-stage renal disease.

- Osteodystrophy—A bone disorder characterized by abnormal bone remodeling and formation. Osteodystrophy is seen in end-stage renal disease (which differs from osteomalacia in dialysis patients), Paget's disease (a bone disease whereby the osteoclast consumes the body's bone and the osteoblast responds in an unorganized manner), or chronic liver disease.
- Pathological Fracture—A pathologic fracture occurs when a bone breaks in an area that is weakened by another disease process. Causes of weakened bone include tumors, infection, osteoporosis, osteodystrophy, osteomalacia, and certain inherited bone disorders. These fractures occur with minimal or no trauma. Another way to view it is to ask, "Would the trauma that occurred with this fracture have caused a fracture in a healthy 25-year-old?"

Most physicians recognize multiple myeloma, metastatic cancer, Paget's disease, and rickets as causes of pathological fractures but frequently do not recognize or document osteopenia or osteoporosis as a pathology that can cause fracture. Because more than 33.6 million Americans have osteopenia (80 percent of them women), and ICD-9-CM refers osteoporotic fractures to the pathologic fractures category, querying the physician for the underlying etiology of an elderly patient's fracture in a setting of minimal trauma (for example, falling out of bed in a nursing home) will help better identify pathological fractures.

- Back Pain—Many patients with back pain admitted to the hospital have vertebral fractures. A CDI opportunity exists to determine to what extent these may represent pathological fractures.
- Falls—Frequently, a patient is admitted to the hospital after a fall; however, there is

no ICD-9-CM index or table code for falls. If no fracture occurs, these patients usually group to MS-DRG 556 (Signs and symptoms of musculoskeletal system and connective tissue) (RW 0.5958). Coding professionals should be alert for underlying causes of the patient's fall and should discuss with the physician to what extent any evaluation or treatment of these conditions were the conditions found after study to have occasioned the hospitalization.

- Septic arthritis—As septic arthritis has its own DRG (for example, 550 [Septic arthritis w/o CC or MCC]), it must be differentiated from other inflammatory arthritic conditions. Most patients with septic arthritis have acute pain (or an acute exacerbation of chronic pain) and an obvious joint effusion. Fifty percent involve the knee, followed in frequency by the hip, shoulder, ankle, and wrist. Most include only one joint; however, gonococcal arthritis can involve multiple joints. Joint aspiration usually shows a white blood cell count over $50,000 \, mm^3$ with a predominance of polymorphonuclear cells; however, gout can mimic these findings. Coding professionals should look at the Gram stain and culture. If the patient receives antibiotics, they should ascertain why these were prescribed. If joint fluid was sent for fungal or tuberculosis culture, the infection control nurse may notify the coding staff if these cultures are later found to be positive.

MDC 9: Diseases and Disorders of the Skin, Subcutaneous Tissue, and Breast

The MS-DRG structure consolidates some CMS DRGs in the following manner.

Surgery

An area of difficulty in MDC 9 is in excisional débridement of pressure sores. CMS's 2006 Status Report on Recovery Audit Contractors (RACs) (http://www.cms.hhs.gov/ RAC/Downloads/RACStatusDocument--FY2006.pdf) reports that RACs collected $17.8 million out of a total of $19.8 million based on incorrect documentation or coding of excisional débridement. As RACs expand their scope of work to other states after the Demonstration Project, excisional débridement will likely be a target.

Coding Clinic (2nd Quarter, 2004, 5) states that excisional debridement occurs when a provider uses a scalpel to remove necrotic tissue beyond the border of the lesion, usually a skin ulcer. Sharp débridement is coded as nonexcisional débridement unless the provider explicitly describes excisional débridement

in the operative note. In hospitals where bylaws or rules and regulations require that all surgically excised tissue be submitted for pathology, a pathology report should support that debrided tissue was indeed excised. If the cutting away of tissue is not described as part of the excisional débridement technique, then a query may be initiated based on the pathology report.

Coding Clinic (1st Quarter, 1999, pp. 8–9) requires that only one code for the deepest layer of débridement be assigned when multiple layers of the same site are débrided. For example, if the fascia, muscle, or bone is excised, this should be the code used. If the principal diagnosis groups to MDC 9 (for example, pressure sore) or MDC 10 (for example, diabetic ulcer), MS-DRGs pertinent to these procedures include:

CMS-DRG Version 24.0	DRG Description	MS-DRG Version 25.0	New Base MS-DRG Description
259, 260	Subtotal Mastectomy for Malignancy	584, 585	Breast Biopsy, Local Excision & Other Breast Procedures with and without CC/MCC
261	Breast Procedures for Non-Malignancy Except Biopsy & Local Excision		
262	Breast Biopsy & Local Excision for Non-Malignancy		

Source: CMS Final Rule (Federal Register)

Procedure Code	MDC 9–MS-DRG	MDC 10–MS-DRG
86.28 (Nonexcisional débridement of wound, infection, or burn)	594 (Skin ulcers w/o CC/MCC) (RW 0.9335)	639 (Diabetes w/o CC/MCC) (RW 0.6742)
86.22 (Excisional débridement of wound, infection, or burn)	575 (Skin graft and/or débridement for skin ulcer or cellulitis w/o CC/MCC) (RW 1.4216)	624 (Skin grafts and wound débridement for endocrine, nutritional, and metabolic disorders w/o CC/MCC) (RW 1.6056)
83.5 (Débridement of bursa)	989 (Nonextensive O.R. procedure unrelated to principal diagnosis w/o CC/MCC) (R. W. 1.6310)	989 (Nonextensive O.R. procedure unrelated to principal diagnosis w/o CC/MCC) (RW 1.6310)
83.39 (Débridement, fascia)	581 (Other skin, subcutaneous tissue, and breast procedure w/o CC/MCC) (RW 0.9124)	630 (Other endocrine, nutritional, and metabolic O.R. procedure w/o CC/MCC) (R.W. 1.7767)
83.45 (Débridement of muscle)	581 (Other skin, subcutaneous tissue, and breast procedure w/o CC/MCC) (RW 0.9124)	983 (Extensive O.R. procedure unrelated to principal diagnosis w/o CC/MCC) (RW 2.9737)
86.75 (Débridement of flap graft)	575 (Skin graft and/or débridement for skin ulcer or cellulitis w/o CC/MCC) (RW 1.4216)	630 (Other endocrine, nutritional, and metabolic O.R. procedure w/o CC/MCC) (RW 1.7767)
77.60 (Débridement of bone)	989 (Nonextensive O.R. procedure unrelated to principal diagnosis w/o CC/MCC) (RW 1.6310)	989 (Nonextensive O.R. procedure unrelated to principal diagnosis w/o CC/MCC) (RW 1.6310)

Diagnosis Code	Description	CC Status
58.81	Human herpes virus 6 infection	No
58.82	Human herpes virus 7 infection	No
58.89	Other human herpes virus infection	No

Source: CMS Proposed Rule (Federal Register)

Principal Diagnosis	MS-DRG
707.15 (Ulcer of other part of the foot) or 707.09 (Decubitus ulcer, other site)	594 (Skin ulcer w/o CC/MCC) (RW 0.9335)
250.70 (Diabetes with peripheral circulatory disorders) + 707.15	639 (Diabetes w/o CC/MCC) (RW 0.6742)
250.60 (Diabetes with neurological manifestations) + 707.15	74 (Cranial and peripheral nerve disorders w/o MCC) (RW 0.8954)
250.80 (Diabetes with other specified complications) + 707.15	301 (Peripheral vascular diseases w/o CC/MCC) (RW 0.7183)

CMS-DRG Version 24.0	DRG Description	MS-DRG Version 25.0	New Base MS-DRG Description
289	Parathyroid Procedures		Thyroid, Parathyroid & Thyroglossal Procedures with MCC, with CC, and without CC/MCC
290	Thyroid Procedures	625, 626, 627	
291	Thyroglossal Procedures		
294	Diabetes Age > 35	637, 638, 639	Diabetes with MCC, with CC, and without CC/MCC
295	Diabetes Age < 35		

Source: CMS Final Rule (Federal Register)

Medicine

Most conditions within MDC 9 are straightforward.

Skin ulcers and cellulitis often coexist, thus physician documentation is critical to ascertain which of these best qualify as a principal diagnosis. Because skin ulcers commonly occur in diabetics, coding professionals should work with their physicians to ascertain if the ulcer is related to decubiti, diabetic angiopathy, or diabetic neuropathy.

MDC 10: Endocrine, Nutritional, and Metabolic Diseases and Disorders

MS-DRGs for endocrine diseases mirror CMS DRGs except for the consolidations listed in the above table.

Diagnosis Code	Description	CC Status
255.41	Glucocorticoid Deficiency	Yes - CC
255.42	Mineralocorticoid Deficiency	Yes - CC
258.01	Multiple endocrine neoplasia [MEN] type I	No
258.02	Multiple endocrine neoplasia [MEN] type IIA	No
258.03	Multiple endocrine neoplasia [MEN] type IIB	No

Source: CMS Final Rule (Federal Register)

Principal Diagnosis	Assigned MS-DRG
Hyperkalemia— Selected because hyperkalemia is what prompted this hospitalization	627 (Thyroid, parathyroid, and thyroglossal procedures w CC) (R.W. 0.8169) (In MDC 10, the thyroidectomy is the principal procedure; angina at rest is the CC.)
Aortic stenosis—Selected because aortic stenosis and the planned aortic valve replacement is what prompted the preoperative laboratory tests to be performed	220 (Cardiac valve and other major cardiothoracic procedure w/o cardiac cath w CC) (RW 5.7278) (In MDC 5, the aortic valve replacement is the principal procedure.)

New ICD-9-CM codes grouping to this MDC are listed above.

Surgery

As discussed in MDC 8 and 9, diabetes can impact MS-DRGs for amputations in lower limbs, skin grafts, and wound débridements. Coding professionals must ascertain whether the principal diagnosis in diabetics undergoing these procedures should be an appropriate diabetes code or the body part that was operated on. In primary diabetes (250.xx), ICD-9-CM automatically links gangrene (250.7x + 785.4) or osteomyelitis (250.8x + 731.8 + 730.20), unless the physician automatically delinks them.

As fluid and electrolyte imbalance (for example, hyperkalemia or dehydration) may occasion a premature hospitalization prior to a planned surgery, clinical documentation and physician query may be necessary to properly assign the principal diagnosis.

Example: A 70-year-old man with mild chronic kidney disease and known aortic stenosis is scheduled to have an aortic valve replacement. Preoperative laboratory tests performed in preparation for this procedure reveals that the patient has a serum potassium level of 7.6 mEq/L, thus the attending surgeon is having the patient admitted to address this condition. Because the patient has angina at rest after his potassium level was corrected, the attending physician is keeping the patient in the hospital over the weekend and is performing the aortic valve replacement during the same hospital stay. During the valve replacement, an incidental thyroidectomy is performed for a multinodular goiter.

Based on UHDDS definition of principal diagnosis as the reason for admission (after study), aortic stenosis is assigned as the principal diagnosis. The secondary diagnosis of hyperkalemia (although present at admission) meets reporting guidelines as an additional diagnosis.

Medicine

New ICD-9-CM codes grouping to this MDC can be seen in the tables above.

Opportunities in DRG assignment in MDC 10 include diabetes. The definition of diabetes mellitus is a group of metabolic diseases characterized by hyperglycemia resulting from insulin secretion, insulin action, or both.

CMS removed the age differentiation between diabetes in patients younger than 35 years of age and older patients; now they all fall into one DRG group—MS-DRG 637–639 (Diabetes with MCC, with CC, or without MCC/CC). Diabetes mellitus (250.xx) with a fourth digit of 0, 1, 2, 3, 8, or 9.groups to these MS-DRGs.

Diagnostic Criteria for diabetes mellitus follows:

- Symptoms of diabetes (weight loss, polyuria, polydipsia) plus random blood glucose concentration above 200 mg/dL. Repeat test required if not unequivocal.
- Fasting (no calories for 8 hours) blood glucose above 126 mg/dl. Repeat test required if not unequivocal.
- Two-hour blood glucose above 200 mg/dL during an oral glucose tolerance test (glucose load of 75 grams of anhydrous glucose—equivalent to 24 oz of Coca-Cola®).

Types of Diabetes

A wise person once said, "The issue at hand is not the issue." Applied to diabetes, not all diabetes is diabetes. The different forms of diabetes are listed here:

- Type 1 diabetes (This is also called juvenile-onset diabetes in ICD-9-CM, even though type 1 diabetes can occur at any age. This term has been abandoned by the American Diabetes Association)—A complete loss of pancreatic beta cell function due to autoantibodies to insulin (IAAs), glutamic acid decarboxylase (GADA), the protein tyrosine phosphataselike molecule (IA–2A), or islet cell cytoplasm, which are found in 85 to 90 percent of patients with type 1 diabetes. c-Peptide levels are low or nonexistent. The individual's complete loss of ability to make insulin predisposes the presence of diabetic ketoacidosis; therefore the individual needs insulin to prevent diabetic ketoacidosis.
- Type 2 diabetes (This is also called adult-onset diabetes by some physicians, even though it can occur at any age. This term has been abandoned by both ICD-9-CM and the American Diabetic Association.)—Diabetics with insulin resistance and relative insulin deficiency have high blood glucose levels. Because Type 2 diabetics do produce insulin, their C-peptide levels are normal or high. Predisposing characteristics of Type 2 diabetes include obesity (BMI above 25 kg/m²), increased waist to hip ratios (0.88 and above in women, 0.95 and above in men), increasing age, lack of physical activity, endothelial dysfunction, or subclinical inflammation. Even though the term "insulin-dependent diabetes mellitus" (IDDM) indicates to many physicians that the patient is

dependent on insulin to prevent ketoacidosis, not to maintain glucose control, ICD-9-CM codes IDDM to 250.0x with a fifth digit of 0 or 2, signifying type 2 or an unspecified type of diabetes. *Coding Clinic* (2nd Quarter, 1997, 14) stipulates that physician query may be necessary to determine the underlying etiology or classification of IDDM. Type 2 diabetics typically do not develop ketoacidosis unless stressed (for example, infection, sepsis, or acute myocardial infarction). A small subgroup of young black patients presenting with new onset diabetic ketoacidosis actually may have type 2 diabetes (Umpierrez 2006). These patients have negative autoantibodies and elevated C-peptide levels. *Coding Clinic* (2nd Quarter, 2006, 19–20) advises to automatically code diabetic ketoacidosis in diabetes not otherwise specified to a fifth digit of 3 unless the physician has documented that the patient is a type 2 diabetic.

Other forms of primary diabetes include:

- Maturity-onset diabetes of the young (MODY), which is an autosomal dominant genetic defect of β-cell function that reduces pancreatic beta-cell responsiveness to glucose or severely impairs insulin release.
- Genetic defects in insulin action, such as type A insulin resistance, leprechaunism, or other genetic syndromes, such as lipoatrophic diabetes
- Uncommon forms of immune-mediated diabetes, such as stiff-man syndrome and anti-insulin receptor antibodies
- Transient neonatal diabetes with manifest disease in the infant

ICD-9-CM directs to code MODY as type 2 diabetes (250.00 or 250.02), dwarfism-obesity syndrome as 258.1, transient neonatal diabetes as 775.1, and stiff-man syndrome as 333.91.

- Gestational diabetes—Any degree of glucose intolerance that first occurs during pregnancy (not to be used with preexisting diabetes). Gestational diabetes uses different diagnostic criteria than regular diabetes as maternal plasma glucose is 15 to 20 mg/dL lower due to use of glucose by the fetus. Gestational diabetes should be suspected if the fasting blood glucose in a pregnant woman is 105 mg/dL or if any blood glucose value is above 165 mg/dL. This condition should not be confused with preexisting diabetes that carries over into the pregnancy, which is coded as 648.0x. (Gestational diabetes is coded as 648.8x.)

- Secondary diabetes—Not all diabetes is due to the mechanisms described in type 1, type 2, or gestational diabetes. Other diseases or surgical procedures can destroy the pancreatic beta cells that make insulin (for example, coxsackie virus infection, hemochromatosis, pancreatectomy, or chronic pancreatitis) or induce a state of insulin resistance (for example, Cushing's syndrome or acromegaly). Certain drugs can likewise destroy beta cells (for example, streptozocin) or induce a state of insulin resistance (for example, prednisone or other corticosteroids causing secondary Cushing's syndrome, beta-blockers, niacin, and thiazide diuretics inducing insulin resistance). Secondary diabetes is differentiated from the primary types of diabetes, as MS-DRG assignment is greatly affected. Examples of how these conditions can change the MS-DRG are listed below.

Linkage of Complications

Many uncontrolled diabetics admitted to control their hyperglycemia have complications which, if documented and linked to diabetes, can affect the principal diagnosis code and the MS-DRG assignment. For example, when a patient with diabetic neuropathy and long-standing blood glucose levels of 400 to 500 mg/dL with a hemoglobin A_{1C} of 12 g/dL (controlled diabetes is less than 7 g/dL) is admitted to control his diabetes, the final diagnosis should be 250.62 rather than 250.02, grouping this patient to MS-DRG 74 (Cranial and peripheral nerve disorders w/o MCC) (RW 0.8954) rather than MS-DRG 639 (Diabetes w/o CC/MCC) (RW 0.6742).

Patients admitted with hypoglycemia due to insulin are coded to 250.8x as a principal diagnosis. Likewise, diabetics admitted with ketoacidosis (250.1x), hyperosmolarity (250.2x), coma (250.3x), or osteomyelitis (250.8x) must have these corresponding codes sequenced as principal according to the ICD-9-CM index *unless* the attending physician explicitly delinks these conditions from the diabetes. Patients admitted with gangrene and diabetes are automatically linked to 250.7x by the same ICD-9-CM index to diseases.

Principal Diagnosis with No Procedure	MS-DRG	Relative Weight
251.3 (Postsurgical hypoinsulinemia)	641 (Nutritional and miscellaneous metabolic disorders w/o MCC)	0.7248
275.0 (Hemochromatosis)	642 (Inborn errors of metabolism)	1.0616
577.1 (Chronic pancreatitis)	440 (Disorders of the pancreas except malignancy w/o CC/MCC)	0.8912
251.8 (Steroid-induced diabetes–dose properly administered)	645 (Endocrine disorders w/o CC/MCC)	0.8310
648.83 (Gestational diabetes)	781 (Other antepartum diagnoses w medical complications)	0.5689
250.(0,1,2,3,8,9)x	639 (Diabetes w/o CC/MCC)	0.6742

Principal Diagnosis with No Procedure	MS-DRG	Relative Weight
250.4x	700 (Other kidney and urinary tract diagnoses w/o CC/MCC)	0.8232
250.5x	125 (Other disorders of the eye w/o MCC)	0.6792
250.6x	74 (Cranial and peripheral nerve disorders w/o MCC)	0.8954
250.7x	301 (Peripheral vascular disorders w/o CC/MCC)	0.7183
250.(0,1,2,3,8,9)x	639 (Diabetes w/o CC/MCC)	0.6742

250.0 (Diabetes, diabetic [brittle, congenital, familial, mellitus, poorly controlled, severe, slight, without complication]) has the following subcategories:

- With coma [with ketoacidosis] 250.3
- Hyperosmolar [nonketotic] 250.2
- Complication NEC 250.9
- specified NEC 250.8
- Gangrene 250.7
- Hyperosmolarity 250.2
- Ketosis, ketoacidosis 250.1
- Osteomyelitis 250.8
- Specified manifestations NEC 250.8

Diabetic Ketoacidosis, Coma, and Hyperosmolarity

Although diabetic ketoacidosis, coma, and hyperosmolarity are more important in the assignment of major CCs since uncontrolled diabetes is no longer a CC. Characteristic clinic signs and symptoms associated with these conditions include the following.

Diabetic Ketoacidosis

Diabetic ketoacidosis usually occurs in type 1 but can occur in type 2 or secondary diabetes. *Coding Clinic* (2nd Quarter, 2006, 19) allows coding professionals to assume that in diabetic ketoacidosis the patient's diabetes is uncontrolled, requiring the use of a fifth digit of 3 unless the physician explicitly specifies that patient has type 2 diabetes for which the fifth digit of 2 is required. If ketoacidosis occurs with secondary diabetes, codes 250.1x or 250.3x should not be used because the patient does not have type 1 or type 2 diabetes. The appropriate secondary diabetes code (251.3 or 251.8) should be used. If the physician's notes are not clear that the diabetes is due to a secondary cause, then the physician may be queried.

Symptoms include the following:

- Hyperglycemia (300–600)
- Ketosis (4+ plasma ketones, 1:8 or greater)
- Profound dehydration on physical examination
- Kussmaul breathing
- Possible fever
- High white blood cell count
- Coma (possible—if present, assign to 250.3x)
- Metabolic acidosis—(pH 6.8–7.3, HCO_3 less than 15 mEq/L, "elevated anion gap")
- Serum potassium level usually high due to acidosis; if normal, patient very depleted

Diabetic Hyperosmolarity

Diabetic hyperosmolarity usually occurs in type 2 diabetics but can occur in type 1 diabetics who have some insulin in their bodies. Results in profound dehydration, hyperglycemia, and hyperosmolality (330–380). Most hospitals do not report a calculated osmolality, yet there is a simple formula whereby this value may be obtained. This formula is:

$$Osmolality = (2 * Na) + Glucose/18 + BUN/2.8$$

A normal osmolality is 285–295. If the calculated osmolality rises above 330, the physician should be queried for its clinical significance. Even so, it is usually not beneficial to query for hyperosmolality if the glucose level is less than 550 mg/dL or if the patient is not profoundly dehydrated.

Symptoms include the following:

- Blood glucose usually over 600, not uncommonly over 1,000
- pH is normal or slightly decreased due to dehydration
- HCO_3 usually normal
- Creatinine moderately elevated due to dehydration.
- Codes to 250.2x. In this case, neither ICD-9-CM nor *Coding Clinic* assumes that the patient's diabetes is uncontrolled, thus the physician must be queried.

Coma

Coma in diabetic patients is automatically linked unless the physician delinks it, coding it to 250.3x. Coma is not stupor or lethargy; there must be a complete loss of consciousness to qualify as coma (refer to MDC 1 for a more complete description). If a patient presents with insulin coma, ICD-9-CM requires this condition to be coded to 250.3x, not just 250.8x, which is applied to diabetic hypoglycemia. Nondiabetic hypoglycemic coma, such as in patients with insulin-secreting tumors, codes to 251.0. Because diabetic coma can occur in patients with secondary diabetes and coma can be due to other causes, physician consultation, query, and clarification is necessary when coma is present in diabetic patients.

Example: A 72-year-old women with rheumatoid arthritis treated with corticosteroids presents to the emergency department with a blood glucose level of 800 mg/dL, profound hypovolemia, and lethargy. There is no evidence of metabolic acidosis, and her urine is negative for ketones. She is treated with aggressive IV hydration, small doses of insulin, and lowering of her steroid dose. She is initially discharged as having diabetic hyperosmolar syndrome, hypovolemia, and rheumatoid arthritis, grouping to MS-DRG 639 (Diabetes w/o CC/MCC) (RW 0.6742) (Hypovolemia is no longer a CC in MS-DRGs and hyperosmolality is integral to 250.20, thus it is not coded separately.) The coding professional queries the physician for the underlying cause of this patient's diabetes, given that she was not diabetic prior to starting corticosteroids. He responds that the diabetes is probably due to the steroids which changes his diagnoses and coding to 251.8 (Steroid-induced diabetes), 276.0 (Hyperosmolarity), and 276.52 (Hypovolemia). The new MS-DRG is 644 (Endocrine disorder with CC) (RW 1.0638), as hyperosmolality is a CC in MS-DRGs.

Example: A 60-year-old man with type 2 diabetes presents to the emergency department in a coma. He is found to have a blood glucose level of 30 mg/dL. The patient responds to $D_{50}W$. He is admitted to the hospital as an inpatient due to recurrent hypoglycemia in the ER requiring ongoing IV $D_{10}W$ with a working diagnosis of diabetic hypoglycemic coma (MS-DRG 639 [Diabetes w/o CC/MCC] [RW 0.6742]) (coma is integral to 250.30 and thus is not coded separately). The clinical documentation specialist asks the physician why this patient's blood glucose level suddenly became so low. Upon questioning the family, the physician discovers that the patient mistakingly took double the dose of prescribed hypoglycemic medication. The new principal diagnosis is 962.3 (Poisoning by insulin and antidiabetic agents) and a secondary diagnosis of 250.30 (Diabetes and coma) are linked unless the physician delinks them), resulting in MS-DRG 917 (Poisoning and toxic effects of drugs w/MCC) (RW 1.1717).

Hyperkalemia

Many patients, especially those with kidney disease, are admitted to the hospital to treat hyperkalemia. When the cause of the hyperkalemia is known on admission, such as end-stage renal disease, and the diagnostic approach and the treatment rendered is primarily to correct the hyperkalemia, *Coding Clinic* (2nd Quarter, 2001, 12–13) says to sequence hyperkalemia as the principal diagnosis. When the cause of the hyperkalemia is not known on admission, the diagnostic workup uncovers a previously unknown underlying cause, and treatment is administered to address this underlying cause, a defense may be made to sequence the underlying cause as the principal diagnosis.

Principal Diagnosis With No Procedure	MS-DRG	Relative Weight
584.9 (Acute renal failure) 585.6 (End-stage renal disease) Warning: This must be a new diagnosis with appropriate workup and treatment to count as a principal diagnosis.	684 (Renal failure w/o CC/MCC) (Hyperkalemia is not a CC.)	0.9835
255.41 (Glucocorticoid deficiency) or 255.42 (Mineralocorticoid deficiency), either primary processes (including Addison's disease or congenital adrenal hyperplasia) or secondary processes (including adverse reactions to ACE-inhibitors, NSAIDs, or heparin).	645 (Endocrine disorders without CC/MCC)	0.8310
276.7 (Hyperkalemia)—In the setting of ESRD (585.6).	640 (Nutritional and metabolic disorders with CC) (In this circumstance, ESRD can be counted as an MCC.)	0.9793
250.40 (Diabetes with renal manifestations)—Associated with type IV renal tubular acidosis (588.89).	700 (Other kidney and urinary tract diagnoses w/o CC/MCC)	0.8232

Hyponatremia

Severe hyponatremia, a serum sodium of less than 125 mEq/L, is not an uncommon reason for inpatient hospitalization. The circumstances of admission, diagnostic approach, and treatment rendered apply in appropriate principal diagnosis and MS-DRG assignment. Options include:

- Manifestations—Weakness, confusion, muscle cramps, lethargy, numbness
- Underlying etiologies—Consider the setting
- Fluid overload—Congestive heart failure, chronic kidney disease or end-stage renal disease, nephrotic syndrome, cirrhosis, overzealous iatrogenic hydration with hypotonic fluids (for example, D_5W, ½ normal saline), psychogenic polydipsia
- Hypovolemia—Diuretics, gastrointestinal fluid loss (vomiting, diarrhea), osmotic diuresis (for example, diabetic ketoacidosis)
- Normal fluid status—Syndrome of inappropriate diuresis (SIAD, sometimes known as SIADH), hypothyroidism, hypoadrenalism (Addison's disease), hypoaldosteronism
- Laboratory error—Occurs when the serum glucose or triglyceride levels are extraordinarily high
- Precipitating cause—Noncompliance with mineralocorticoids (for example, Florinef or prednisone) or overzealous use of diuretics to keep weight down (for example, in patients with bulimia or anorexia nervosa), acute stroke, or recurrence of a predisposing malignancy (leads to SIAD)
- Complications—Metabolic encephalopathy (manifested as confusion, stupor, seizures, and headaches). Inappropriate correction of hyponatremia can lead to cerebral edema.

The syndrome of inappropriate diuresis deserves considerable mention because it is the most common cause of hyponatremia (not diuretics as some coding professionals or physicians may think) (Ellison and Berl 2007). In a study of 172 geriatric patients in a subacute facility, 43 (25 percent) of them had hyponatremia, of which half of them had SIAD/SIADH (Anpalahan 2001). Usually, the patients have low serum osmolality with an inappropriate elevation of the urine osmolality (over 100), and the urine sodium is over 40 mmol/L. Treatment usually consists of fluid restriction, judicious use of hypertonic (3 percent) saline, and/or certain medications (for example, vasopressin-receptor antagonists—intravenous conivaptan and Vaprisol; oral demeclocycline—an antibiotic that has a favorable side effect of reducing urine osmolality and increasing the serum levels). If the physician documents SIAD/SIADH, hyponatremia should not be coded because it is integral to the condition.

Physician query for the etiology of a patient's hyponatremia is appropriate, especially if it is chronic or not associated with diuretic use or other conditions previously noted (SIAD/SIADH is a strong possibility). If the patient is taking Florinef or chronic corticosteroids, coding professionals should query the physician for their indication (for example, hypopituitarism or Addison's disease). If the patient has neurological symptoms, querying for the effect that the hyponatremia had on the brain (seizures, headaches, metabolic encephalopathy) is reasonable.

Example: A 75-year-old man lives in a boarding home and is known to have chronic mild hyponatremia. At the boarding home he developed pneumonia, which was treated with levofloxacin on an outpatient basis. He has become more confused and is admitted to the Pennsylvania hospital with serum sodium of 122 mEq/L and pneumonia. His physician treats him with fluid restriction and a small amount of hypertonic saline for the hyponatremia and intravenous levofloxacin for the pneumonia. His discharge diagnoses state that the patient was admitted for hyponatremia and community-acquired pneumonia, assigning the patient to MS-DRG 640 (Nutritional and miscellaneous metabolic disorders with MCC) (RW 0.9793).

The coding professional queries the physician for the underlying etiology of the patient's hyponatremia, citing that the patient was not on diuretics and received hypertonic saline. She further queries for the underlying brain pathology leading to the patient's confusion. The physician responds that the patient probably has SIADH and that the confusion was consistent with a metabolic encephalopathy that required hypertonic saline. After the physician's dictated addendum is placed on the discharge summary, the MS-DRG is changed to 643 (Endocrine disorders with MCC) (RW 1.3926). Although the addition of metabolic encephalopathy does not change the MS-DRGs, the attending physician is pleased to hear that it likely will have a favorable effect on his Pennsylvania Healthcare Cost Containment Council (PHC4), Solucient, 3M APR-DRG, and Delta Group risk-adjustment and severity-adjustment profiles.

Dehydration and Hypovolemia

Dehydration is a common reason that patients are admitted to the hospital. *Coding Clinic* (July–August, 1984, 19–20) emphasized that dehydration should be sequenced first if it is primarily the reason that the underlying cause (for example, gastroenteritis) could not be treated as an outpatient. Pertinent clinical components include:

- Manifestation—Shock, syncope, hypotension, oliguria
- Underlying etiologies—Hemorrhage, acute pancreatitis, diarrhea (gastroenteritis), GI hemorrhage, prolonged fever (especially in infants), use of diuretics
- Severity—Severity of hypovolemia is usually measured by its effect upon the kidneys and the peripheral vasculature
- Precipitating causes—Adverse reaction to medications (for example, *Clostridum difficile* colitis caused by antibiotics or aspirin in causing a peptic ulcer)
- Complications—Acute renal failure or insufficiency, hypotension, or shock

Coding Clinic (3rd Quarter, 2002, 21–22) recognizes that dehydration (hypovolemia) can lead to acute renal failure and shock. Likewise, dehydration (hypovolemia) can lead to lesser degrees of dysfunction, such as acute renal insufficiency and hypotension. Definitions of these terms follow.

- Acute renal failure—A rapid decline in renal function (glomerular filtration rate) within hours to days (usually less than 2 weeks) to the point of requiring renal replacement therapy (which may be withheld if deemed appropriate by the treating physician). Criteria for this condition have varied over the years. In 2003, a review article in the *Journal of the American Medical Association* defined acute renal failure as the acute rise of the serum creatinine from baseline by at least 0.5 mg/dL (or 20 percent if the baseline creatinine was over 2.5 mg/dL) (Singri et al 2003). More stringent criteria were proposed by the Acute Dialysis Quality Initiative Group and were published in 2004 (Bellomo et al 2004). Known as the RIFLE criteria (R—risk, I—injury, F—failure, L—Loss, E—end-stage renal disease), acute renal failure was defined as a tripling of the baseline serum creatinine or, if the current creatinine level is over 4.0 mg/dL, a recent rise of over 0.5 mg/dL within the previous 2 weeks.

- Acute renal insufficiency—Also known as acute renal injury using the RIFLE criteria. However, there is no ICD-9-CM code for this language. RIFLE defines acute renal injury (insufficiency) as a doubling of the serum creatinine from baseline.

- Hypotension—A symptomatic fall of the systolic blood pressure to less than 90 mm Hg or a significant fall of the systolic blood pressure of 40 mm Hg from baseline

- Shock—sustained hypotension lasting more than 1 hour that is resistant to intravenous hydration and is associated with markers of tissue hypoperfusion (for example, oliguria, lactic acidosis, or delirium).

Any of these conditions can be sequenced first if the physician documents that their presence contributed substantially to why the dehydrated or hypovolemic patient could not receive care outside of the inpatient setting.

Example: An 85-year-old nursing home patient with severe Alzheimer's disease is admitted to the hospital for altered mental status and hypotension. She is found to be severely dehydrated with a serum sodium of 155, a BUN of 120, and a serum creatinine of 2.3 mg/dL. Upon rehydration, her studies return to baseline with a serum sodium of 140 mEq/L, a BUN of 15, and a creatinine level of 1.0 mg/dL. Her physician signs the patient out as having acute renal insufficiency, hypotension, and hypernatremia due to dehydration. Options for principal diagnosis assignment are listed below.

Principal Diagnosis With No Procedure	MS-DRG	Relative Weight
593.9 (Acute renal insufficiency)	699 (Other kidney and urinary tract diagnosis w/CC)	1.0352
276.51 (Dehydration) 276.0 (Hypernatremia)	641 (Nutritional and miscellaneous metabolic disorders w/o MCC)	0.7248
458.9 (Hypotension)	315 (Other circulatory system diagnosis with CC)	1.1720

Procedure Code	Description	Operative Procedure
70.53	Repair of cystocele and rectocele with graft or prosthesis	Yes
70.54	Repair of cystocele with graft or prosthesis	Yes
70.55	Repair of rectocele with graft or prosthesis	Yes

Source: CMS Final Rule (Federal Register)

MS-DRG	MS-DRG Title	Relative Weights
625	Thyroid, parathyroid, and thyroglossal procedures w MCC	1.5928
626	Thyroid, parathyroid, and thyroglossal procedures w CC	1.0183
627	Thyroid, parathyroid, and thyroglossal procedures w/o CC/MCC	0.8169
673	Other kidney and urinary tract procedures w MCC	2.5235
674	Other kidney and urinary tract procedures w CC	2.1024
675	Other kidney and urinary tract procedures w/o CC/MCC	1.7196

Although many coding professionals can effectively argue that hypotension should not be the principal diagnosis as it would be integral to a patient having profound hypovolemia, *Coding Clinic* (3rd Quarter, 2002, 21–22) allows coding professionals to code acute renal failure as principal when it is due to dehydration. Thus acute renal insufficiency due to dehydration may be defendable as a principal diagnosis.

MDC 11: Diseases and Disorders of the Kidney and Urinary Tract

There are practically no changes to MDC 11 in MS-DRGs from the previous CMS DRGs, other than the following new procedure codes for cystocele repair.

Surgery

Usually, the indication for surgery in MDC 11 is underlying urological disease. There are times that sepsis (SIRS due to infection) may be present, necessitating a urological operation, such as with perinephric or renal abscesses, grouping these to MDC 18 (with its associated higher relative weight). CMS still differentiates Major Bladder Procedures from other MDC 11 procedures, thus careful review of the operative report narrative is essential to determine if a cystectomy, bladder reconstruction, fistula repair, or cystourethroplasty and plastic repair of the bladder neck was performed.

Procedures grouping to MS-DRG 673-675 require review for principal diagnosis appropriateness because many of these include vascular, endocrine, or gastrointestinal procedures grouping to a lower or higher weight. To examine this, the relative weights for MS-DRG 673-675 should be reviewed first:

For example, if a parathyroidectomy is performed for renal osteodystrophy or secondary hyperparathyroidism due to renal disease, it groups to the DRGs noted above. If the physician documents that it is due to hyperparathyroidism not otherwise specified, its corresponding MS-DRGs are as follows:

In another example, if a patient presenting with renovascular hypertension due to atherosclerotic renal artery stenosis and worsening chronic kidney disease (Stage 4 at this time) undergoes a renal artery angioplasty, 440.1 (Sequencing renal artery stenosis) first results in the DRGs listed above.

MS-DRG	MS-DRG Title	Relative Weights
252	Other vascular procedures w MCC	2.7564
253	Other vascular procedures w CC	2.2536
254	Other vascular procedures w/o CC/MCC	1.6786

On the other hand, sequencing 405.91 (Renovascular hypertension) elicits the MS-DRGs in the above table.

The circumstances of admission, the diagnostic approach, and the treatment rendered, as well as physician documentation, is critical to properly coding and sequencing these conditions and assigning the correct MS-DRGs.

Medicine

Renal medicine MS-DRGs, although few in number, are some of the most common MS-DRGs used in community hospitals. MS-DRGs retain the basic CMS DRG infrastructure which explains some of the difficulties involved in their use.

- Manifestation—Hematuria, dysuria, pyuria, proteinuria, oliguria (Note: Renal failure does not have to be oliguric.), ureteral colic, abnormal x-rays (for example, cysts or masses seen on renal CT or ultrasound), abnormal laboratory results (for example, elevations of the BUN and creatinine levels are labeled azotemia, hypokalemia, or hyponatremia), abnormal urine color (for example, green urine) or smell, fever, abnormal mental status, or hypertension. Renal failure is a manifestation, not an underlying cause; its severity is discussed in the next paragraphs and must be qualified as acute or chronic and quantified as outlined below.

The underlying etiology is categorized as follows:

- Prerenal—Hypotension, hypovolemia, dehydration, renal artery stenosis (caused by fibromuscular hyperplasia or atherosclerosis), heart failure, liver failure, or sepsis
- Renal—Any form of kidney pathology (for example, nephropathy due to diabetes), toxins (IV contrast, aminoglycosides, ibuprofen), or connective tissue diseases (for example, lupus, systemic sclerosis, rheumatoid arthritis, or vasculitis), emboli (for example, thrombotic, cholesterol), trauma, radiation damage, congenital disorders (for example, polycystic kidney disease or missing kidneys), acute and chronic glomerulonephritis (for example, due to streptococcal infections or rapidly progressive or membranous glomerulonephritis), sepsis, localized infections (for example, pyelonephritis or renal abscess)
- Postrenal—Due to urinary outflow obstruction, seen in complete bladder outlet obstructions due to prostate enlargement, bilateral or possibly unilateral ureteral stones, retroperitoneal fibrosis (for example, as an adverse reaction to certain migraine medications), cystitis, prostatitis
- Severity—As discussed in MDC 9, renal disease is classified according to its chronicity (acute versus chronic) and to the level of renal impairment. Acute renal disease is described as a rapid decline in renal function (glomerular filtration rate) within hours to days (usually less than 2 weeks) to the point of requiring renal replacement therapy, which may be withheld if deemed appropriate by the treating physician.

Criteria for this condition have varied over the years. In 2003, a review article in the *Journal of the American Medical Association* defined acute renal failure as the acute rise of the serum creatinine level from baseline by at least 0.5 mg/dL (or 20 percent if the baseline creatinine was over 2.5 mg/dL) (Singri et al 2003). More stringent criteria were proposed by the Acute Dialysis Quality Initiative Group and were published in 2004 (Bellomo et al 2004). Known as the RIFLE criteria, these are defined as follows:

- Risk—Defined as a 50 percent elevation of the baseline serum creatinine or urine output less than 0.5 mL/kg/h (35 mL/h in a 164 lb individual) for over 6 hours. There is no ICD-9-CM code for acute renal risk. However, coding professionals may wish to query for azotemia or discuss with their nephrologists whether this fits their definition of acute renal insufficiency.

- Injury—Defined as a doubling of the baseline serum creatinine level or urine output less than 0.5 mL/kg/h for over 12 hours. There is no ICD-9-CM code for acute renal injury, thus physician query for an equivalent term (for example, acute renal insufficiency, prerenal azotemia) is necessary.
- Failure—Acute renal failure is defined as a tripling of the baseline serum creatinine or, if the current creatinine is over 4.0 mg/dL, a recent rise of over 0.5 mg/dL within the previous 2 weeks.
- Loss—Attainment of renal injury (failure) without complete recovery. If the loss lasts over 3 months, ICD-9-CM places this in one of the Chronic kidney disease (585.1–585.5) codes based on the resulting glomerular filtration rates.
- End-stage renal disease—Complete loss of renal function, usually with a creatinine clearance (glomerular filtration rate) of less than 15 and requiring permanent hemodialysis.

It is very important for physicians and coding professionals to recognize, document, and treat RIFLE in its earliest stages. Underlying causes, such as hypovolemia or contrast exposure, must be treated urgently and aggressively. Hospital mortality rates in RIFLE increase in an almost linear fashion as follows (Van Biesen et al 2006):

N (normal) = 4.4 percent
R (mild ARF) = 15.1 percent
I (moderate) = 29.2 percent
F (failure) = 41.1 percent

For this reason, accurately documenting, capturing, and coding RIFLE within the first nine diagnoses predicts in-hospital mortality and better explains hospital mortality scores in risk-adjusted methodologies.

Chronic Kidney Disease

Although more applicable to CCs (see chapter 3), chronic kidney disease (CKD) exists when there is renal pathology (for example, known chronic nephritis or transplant status), laboratory (for example, chronic hematuria or proteinuria) or radiological abnormalities (for example, pathological renal cysts or malformations), or a prolonged renal impairment (glomerular filtration rate of less than 60 cc/h) for more than 3 months.

A complete description of CKD is available on the Web (K/DOQI Clinical Practice Guidelines on Chronic Kidney Disease Work Group. Available at: http://www.kidney.org/professionals/KDQI/guidelines_ckd/p4_class_g1.htm published in 2002.)

Sepsis versus Urosepsis

As described in MDC 18, sepsis is a systemic inflammatory response to infection. Sepsis with organ dysfunction is severe sepsis. If a physician uses the term "urosepsis," he or she is stating that the patient has only an isolated urinary tract infection without systemic consequences.

Invariably something caused the kidney manifestations or exacerbated the underlying cause. Common examples include instrumentation (for example, Foley catheters, suprapubic catheters, or double-J stents), contrast nephropathy or nephropathy due to other medications (a CDI opportunity exists to determine to what extent contrast or other medications injured the kidneys), malignant hypertension (causes renal arterioles to contract, reducing renal blood flow), cholesterol emboli from aorta crossclamping as part of a CABG, intracapillary

ICD-9-CM	Label	Criteria GFR	Estimated Serum Creatinine in 65-Year-Old White 70 kg man (mg/dL)	CC?
585.1	CKD—stage 1	>90	<0.9	N
585.2	CKD—stage 2	60–89	1.0–1.3	N
585.3	CKD—stage 3	30–59	1.4–2.5	N
585.4	CKD—stage 4	15–29	2.5–4.5	CC
585.5	CKD—stage 5	<15	>4.5	CC
585.6	End-stage renal disease	Need for chronic dialysis	Need for chronic dialysis	MCC
585.9	CKD NOS chronic renal failure	See above	See above	N

thrombosis from sepsis (known as severe sepsis), over-zealous diuretic use, diabetic ketoacidosis (the osmotic diuresis led to profound hypovolemia and acute renal insufficiency or failure), or a flare up of a female patient's systemic lupus due to her new pregnancy.

While end-stage renal disease or acute renal failure describe the kidney's functionality, the term "uremia" describes the buildup of renal poisons that results from loss of renal function. Uremia can cause a metabolic encephalopathy, pericarditis, or dermatitis. As the kidneys do not function, fluid overload can result, which should *not* be termed "congestive heart failure" unless there is actually a failing heart, as documented by the physician. Hyperkalemia, hyponatremia, hypocalcemia, hyperphosphatemia, anemia of chronic kidney disease (due to loss of erythropoietin), and metabolic bone disease (renal osteodystrophy) can occur. If foreign bodies exist in the urinary system, other urinary tract infections or sepsis may occur.

Areas of risk and opportunities include the following.

- Renal stones—If a patient has renal or bladder stones, associated hematuria is integral to the disorder and cannot be coded as a CC.
- End-stage renal disease (ESRD)—If a patient has known ESRD and is seen by a physician because of a complication of that disease (for example, hyperkalemia, renal osteodystrophy, or anemia of chronic kidney disease), the principal diagnosis is the complication, not ESRD. Furthermore, if a known ESRD patient is hospitalized primarily for dialysis (especially for initiation of their first dialysis), codes from V56.x are the principal diagnosis (MS-DRG 685 [Admit for renal dialysis] [RW 0.8483]). To sequence ESRD as the principal diagnosis,

the physician must reasonably have made the initial diagnosis of this condition during this admission.

- Acute renal failure—Because *Coding Clinic* (3rd Quarter, 2002, 21–22) allows for acute renal failure to be sequenced first if it is due to dehydration, it is reasonable to assume that if the dehydration is severe enough to cause the acute renal insufficiency that led to inpatient hospitalization that this can be the principal diagnosis as well. Likewise, if male patients have bladder outlet obstruction due to prostate disease and present with postrenal azotemia, it is reasonable to query the physician for coexisting acute renal insufficiency or failure.
- Catheter-related disease—If a patient has a urinary tract infection or hematuria and also has an indwelling catheter or stent, it is reasonable to query the physician for any possible relation between the manifestation and these devices.
- Diabetes—If a patient is admitted for uncontrolled diabetes and has evidence of chronic kidney disease, it is reasonable to query the physician for any linkage between the CKD and diabetes.

MDC 12: Diseases and Disorders of the Male Reproductive System

There is little change in MDC 12 for MS-DRGs. CMS did consolidate and change some DRGs.

Some confusion with MDC 11 may occur given that many physicians consider the prostate and urethra to be part of the urinary tract. If clinical documentation is not clear, the physician should be queried.

CMS-DRG Version 24.0	DRG Description	MS-DRG Version 25.0	New Base MS-DRG Description
338	Testes Procedures for Malignancy	711, 712	Testes Procedured with and without CC/MCC
339, 340	Testes Procedures, Non Malignancy		
342, 343	Circumcision	None	Procedure 64.0 changed to non-OR Cases with only this procedure will go to medical DRGs
351	Sterilization, Male	729, 730	Other Male Reproductive System Diagnoses with and without CC/MCC
352	Other Male Reproductive System Diagnoses		

Source: CMS Final Rule (Federal Register)

Example: A 55-year-old white man is admitted with severe abdominal pain, dysuria, oliguria, and prostate tenderness. His serum creatinine level is 3.0 on admission; upon Foley catheterization, there was diuresis of a large volume of urine and his creatinine level returned to baseline at 1.0 mg/dL. The final diagnosis is acute prostatitis, BPH with urinary obstruction, and postrenal azotemia, grouping to MS-DRG 728 (Inflammation of the male reproductive system without MCC) (RW 0.7241). The coding professional queries the physician about the clinical significance of the patient's creatinine level and postrenal azotemia and how it factors into the reason that the patient cannot be treated as an outpatient. The physician documents in his discharge summary that the patient has acute renal insufficiency due to the acute prostatic obstruction caused by the acute prostatitis, thus the patient needs inpatient hospitalization to relieve the obstruction, treat the infection, and monitor his renal status. The MS-DRG changes from MS-DRG 728 to MS-DRG 700 (Other kidney and urinary tract diagnoses w/o CC/MCC) (RW 0.8232).

MDC 13: Diseases and Disorders of the Female Reproductive System

There is little change in MS-DRGs for MDC 13. CMS did consolidate some DRGs as evidenced below. Most MDC 13 diseases are straightforward; invariably their attending physicians will be gynecologists. Reviewing pathology reports is critical because some DRGs are for pelvic malignancies.

MDC 14: Pregnancy, Childbirth, and the Puerperium

There are few changes in MS-DRGs for MDC 14. CMS embraced the CC/MCC strategy for cesarean section. CMS still maintains the diagnosis of vaginal deliveries

with and without complicating diagnoses rather than using CCs or MCCs. Coding professionals must be certain to capture the following diagnoses, complicating diagnoses with delivery, and operating room procedures:

Complicating Diagnoses

- Placenta previa
- Essential and secondary hypertension
- Preeclampsia
- Maternal syphilis, tuberculosis, malaria, rubella, gonorrhea, or other viral diseases
- Maternal diabetes
- Obesity or bariatric surgery status complicating pregnancy
- Epilepsy
- Urine amount and date discrepancy
- Generalized infection (for example, sepsis)
- Postpartum hemorrhage
- Retained placenta
- CNS or pulmonary complications
- Anesthetic complications
- Thrombophlebitis and embolism
- Nipple infection
- Cerebrovascular disease

Operating Room Procedures

- Rectal, vaginal, or cervical repair
- Vulva diagnostic procedure (for example, a simple punch biopsy, which is *not* a significant procedure in other MDCs)
- Hymenectomy
- Repair of current uterine, cervical, bladder, or urethral laceration

CMS also maintained the other antepartum diagnoses with medical complications DRG. Almost any medical condition requiring prescription medications or those associated with the complicating diagnoses listed, liver disease, and drug dependency should be noted.

CMS-DRG Version 24.0	DRG Description	MS-DRG Version 25.0	New Base MS-DRG Description
361	Laparoscopy & Incisional Tubal Interruption	744, 745	D&C, Conization, Laparoscopy & Tubal Interruption with and without CC/MCC
362	Endoscopic Tubal Interruption		
363	D&C, Conization & Radio-Implant for Malignancy		
364	D&C, Conization Except for Malignancy or History of Malignancy with Endoscopy		

Source: CMS Final Rule (Federal Register)

MDC 15: Newborns and Other Neonates With Conditions Originating in the Perinatal Period

CMS made no changes in MDC 15. Differentiating extreme immaturity (weight less than 1,500 grams, under 26 completed weeks of gestation, and respiratory distress of newborns) remains important. Neonates with prematurity (weights less than 2,500g or 36 completed weeks of gestation) receive additional relative weight. Neonates with specified major conditions, such as postauricular fistulas, embolism, cardiac/respiratory arrest, asphyxia, anemia, and bacteremia/septicemia, also receive additional reimbursement.

As in MDC 18, sepsis (SIRS due to infection) has been defined for neonates and children. Previously defined as a positive blood culture, sepsis for children is defined as follows (International Sepsis Forum and the Pediatric Acute Lung Injury and Sepsis Investigative Network 2007). At least two of the following four criteria, one of which must be abnormal temperature or leukocyte count, must be met:

- Core temperature of greater than 38.5° C or less than 36° C
- Tachycardia above 2 *SD* for age OR bradycardia for children under 1 yr old
- Mean RR above 2 *SD* for age or mechanical vent
- Elevated or depressed WBC or above 10 percent bands
- No secondary causes for these criteria

MDC 16: Diseases and Disorders of the Blood and Blood-Forming Organs and Immunological Disorders

CMS made few changes to MDC 16. CMS still differentiates anemia (reduced red blood cell mass) from increased red blood cell mass (polycythemia), white blood cell and platelet disorders, and nonmalignant lymph node disorders. They preserved the Major hematologic and immunologic diagnoses except for Sickle cell crisis and coagulation disorders designations for specific types of anemia (for example, hemolytic diseases or aplastic anemia; pancytopenia

does not count), T cell and B cell diseases leading to immunodeficiency (abnormal T cell function; pathological reductions of immunoglobulins—IgG or IgM). If immunodeficiency is due to HIV, these should be grouped according to MDC 25.

In approaching MDC 16, the hemolytic anemia and neutropenic fever should be understood

Hemolytic anemia is an abnormal destruction of red cells by whatever mechanism. Clinical signs include:

- Anemia—A hematocrit less than 33 and hemoglobin less than 11 should alert the coding professionals to consider anemia. Fluid status can alter these values. Profound dehydration can lead to hemoconcentration and an artificial elevation of hematocrit/hemoglobin levels.
- Elevated reticulocyte count (usually over 3 percent) or reticulocyte production index—An indication that the bone marrow is making blood cells to replace those that have been lysed. Can also be elevated due to anemias of other causes (for example, vitamin B_{12} deficiency, iron deficiency, and acute blood loss) if the bone marrow is able to replace the lost red cells; however, hemolytic anemias tend to have much higher reticulocyte counts.
- Low haptoglobin levels—Due to binding of free hemoglobin and excretion by the kidneys.
- Elevated LDH (due to red cell destruction)—It is very difficult to make a diagnosis of hemolytic anemia with a normal LDH.
- Positive direct or indirect Coombs test (indicates autoimmune anemia)
- Red blood cell fragments on peripheral smear (schistocytes)

If the physician only documents pancytopenia, (combination of anemia, neutropenia (leucopenia), and thrombocytopenia) he should be queried to document all of its associated elements and to outline a probable underlying cause. If it is related to cancer chemotherapy, the physician should document whether this is an acute drop due to myelosuppression from the drugs or if it is a long-term reduction due to the underlying disease.

Neutropenic fever is a difficult dilemma in clinical documentation and coding. In patients with neutropenia due to chemotherapy who develop fever, the standard of practice is to treat with broad-spectrum antibiotics until the patient's absolute neutrophil count is above 500 (or 750) cells/mm^3. A patient receiving an antibiotic does not necessarily have an infection, but physician query is still needed to determine the presence of infection.

The response of fever (or nonresponse of fever) cannot be used to determine the presence or absence of infection because studies have shown that patients with no documented source of fever actually respond more quickly and have more favorable outcomes than those with documented infection.

It is rare for a patient with neutropenia from chemotherapy to have antibiotics discontinued at 72 hours, even if fever resolves, as long as their absolute neutrophil count is very low. These patients are different from those patients with low-risk neutropenia from certain types of chemotherapy whose neutrophil level recovers very quickly and have excellent responses regardless of antibiotic therapy. Even so, physician query will be necessary to determine if there was a probable underlying infection if a full course (over 10 to 14 days) of antibiotics was administered.

For patients with prolonged fever that eventually resolves with a change in antibiotic regimen, a diagnosis of bacterial or fungal infection of undetermined etiology might be an appropriate choice, but many neutropenic patients have transient fevers that resolve quickly, and they are not severely ill, whereas others with prolonged neutropenia may have long-standing and variable fevers without much clinical change.

It is not appropriate to diagnose a bacterial infection without any supporting evidence. The tendency to assume bacterial infections must be present in patients with fevers has resulted in a remarkable overuse of antibiotics in the US with resulting bacterial resistance. Even so, bacterial (or fungal) etiology is more likely to be a consideration in the patient with prolonged fever and neutropenia than in the patient with a short-term illness (lasting 5 to 7 days).

Example: A patient with myelodysplastic disorder is admitted for blood transfusion due to a hematocrit of 20 with a white blood cell count of 3,000 (both levels are low). Because the patient's platelet count is 20,000, the physician opts to transfuse platelets as well. The final diagnosis is pancytopenia and myelodysplastic disorder, grouping to MS-DRG 812 (Red blood cell disorders w/o MCC) (RW 0.7780). Upon physician query, the diagnosis of thrombocytopenia is added. Because the patient also receives a platelet transfusion, the coding professional has the option to assign MS-DRG 813 (Coagulation disorder) (RW 1.3426) as well.

Example: A patient has recently received chemotherapy for known lung cancer and has a white blood cell count of 250, fever (103 °F), and tachycardia (heart rate 105) prompting hospitalization. The patient receives antibiotics and Neupogen, a drug to stimulate bone marrow production of white blood cells. His white blood cell count returns to normal after 5 days and the IV antibiotics are discontinued after 6 days. The patient is discharged on a 14-day course of oral antibiotics to be followed as an outpatient. The final diagnosis was neutropenic fever due to cancer chemotherapy and lung cancer, grouping to MS-DRG 809 (Major hematologic/immunologic diagnoses except sickle cell crisis and coagulation disorders w/CC) (RW 1.2031).

The coding professional wonders if there is a data quality opportunity, given that the patient is discharged on long-term antibiotic treatment. Because the coding professional is not comfortable talking to the oncologist or infectious disease physician about this possibility, they engages the physician advisor to discuss the issue. They discuss options such as neutropenic sepsis and bacterial infection of unknown etiology. The attending physician finally dictates in a discharge summary that the fever was possibly due to a bacterial infection of unknown etiology exacerbated by the patient's neutropenia; however, the physician is not certain if the patient has sepsis. (The attending physician still believes that patients must have positive blood cultures for sepsis to be diagnosed.) The MS-DRG changes to MS-DRG 868 (Other infectious and parasitic diagnoses with CC) (RW 1.5258). If the physician had documented that the patient had neutropenic sepsis, the MS-DRG would have been MS-DRG 872 (Septicemia w/o MV 96+ hours with CC) (RW 1.3783).

The same patient returns to the hospital with a fever while on oral antibiotics. The attending physician restarts IV antibiotics and adds caspofungin to the regimen, this time making a diagnosis of probable fungal sepsis. In this circumstance, code 112.5 is assigned as the principal diagnosis, 995.91 is coded as the secondary diagnosis, and the other diagnoses were coded as well. MS-DRG 867 (Other infectious and parasitic diagnosis with MCC) (RW 2.1971) is assigned.

MDC 17: Myeloproliferative Diseases and Disorders and Poorly Differentiated Neoplasm

MDC 17 underwent significant change, not just with the DRG structure and consolidation but also with new ICD-9-CM codes. MS-DRG consolidations for MDC 17 included classifying personal history of malignancy as a principal diagnosis within the malignancy codes

and eliminating endoscopy as a significant procedure, outlined as follows.

CMS-DRG Version 24.0	DRG Description	MS-DRG Version 25.0	New Base MS-DRG Description
411	History of Malignancy without Endoscopy	843, 844, 845	Other Myeloproliferative Disease or Poorly Differentiated Neoplasm Diagnosis with MCC, with CC, without CC/MCC
412	History of Malignancy with Endoscopy		
413, 414	Other Myeloproliferative Disease or Poorly Differentiated Neoplasm Diagnosis		

Source: CMS Final Rule (Federal Register)

CMS also created a new set of codes applicable to this MDC:

- Marginal zone lymphoma (200.30–200.38)
- Mantle cell lymphoma (200.40–200.48)
- Primary central nervous system lymphoma (200.50–200.58)
- Anaplastic large cell lymphoma (200.60–200.68)

- Large cell lymphoma (200.60–200.68)
- Peripheral T cell lymphoma (202.70–202.78)
- Personal history of cervical dysplasia (V13.22)

For surgical procedures, coding professionals should be certain to capture all operating room procedures, especially those listed in MS-DRGs 820–822 and 826–828. These are grouped to the following DRGs:

MS-DRG	MS-DRG Title	RW
820	Lymphoma and leukemia w major OR procedure w MCC	4.4970
821	Lymphoma and leukemia w major OR procedure w CC	2.6847
822	Lymphoma and leukemia w major OR procedure w/o CC/MCC	1.5989
823	Lymphoma and nonacute leukemia w other OR procedures w MCC	3.5188
824	Lymphoma and nonacute leukemia w other OR procedures w CC	2.5164
825	Lymphoma and nonacute leukemia w other OR procedures w/o CC/MC	1.6201
826	Myeloproliferative disorder or poorly differentiated neoplasm w major OR procedure w MCC	3.9780
827	Myeloproliferative disorder or poorly differentiated neoplasm w major OR procedure w CC	2.4230
828	Myeloproliferative disorder or poorly differentiated neoplasm w major OR procedure w/o CC/MCC	1.5109
829	Myeloproliferative disorder or poorly differentiated neoplasm w other OR procedure w CC/MCC	2.4894
830	Myeloproliferative disorder or poorly differentiated neoplasm w other OR procedure w/o CC/MCC	1.6396
834	Acute leukemia w/o major OR procedure w MCC	3.6361
835	Acute leukemia w/o major OR procedure w CC	2.5626
836	Acute leukemia w/o major OR procedure w/o CC/MCC	2.1785

Coding professionals need to differentiate acute from chronic leukemia as well as leukemia from lymphoma.

Most of the major OR procedures have not changed from FY2007. Although the new thorascopic lung

biopsy code (33.20) is not considered a major OR procedure, the new thorascopic decortication of the lung code (34.52) is.

If a diagnosis of leukemia or lymphoma has already been established and the patient is admitted primarily for chemotherapy, either V58.1x or V67.2 should be the principal diagnosis, grouping the patient to MS-DRG 837–839 or MS-DRG 846–848. Patients presenting primarily for radiotherapy should have V58.0 or V67.1 as principal diagnosis. Aftercare with history of malignancy as a secondary diagnosis has been consolidated with all the other aftercare DRGs into MS-DRG 949–950.

MDC 18: Infectious and Parasitic Diseases

One of the most challenging MDCs in the MS-DRGs is MDC 18. No other MDC has such crossover or confusion with other MDCs. Two classes of principal diagnoses cause the problem—Sepsis and Postoperative/Posttraumatic Infection.

Sepsis

It is *strongly encouraged* that the following references be consulted to understand what sepsis is:

- *Coding Clinic* (4th Quarter, 2003, 79)
- *ICD-9-CM Official Guidelines for Coding and Reporting*
- *Understanding Sepsis,* a booklet from the International Sepsis Forum, available at: http://www.sepsisforum.org/whitebook.htm
- Levy, M.M. et al. 2003. 2001 SCCM/ESICM/ACCP/ATS/SIS International Sepsis Definitions Conference.Critical Care Medicine, 31(4): 1258, available at: http://www.sccm.org/press_room/Documents/sepsis.pdf

The literature states that *sepsis is not an infection* but a systemic inflammatory response to an infection (SIRS). An example is a bruise that is not the trauma but a consequence of that trauma.

The literature states (and ICD-9-CM agrees) that *sepsis is not a positive blood culture.* In a review of sepsis syndrome (now known by physicians as severe sepsis) in eight academic medical centers, only 28 percent of patients had a documented bloodstream infection (Sands et al 1997).

The literature also states (and ICD-9-CM agrees) that *sepsis does not require organ dysfunction.* Many physicians who trained in the 1970s and 1980s were taught that septic patients were so sick that they required admission to the ICU and invariably had acute organ dysfunction. What physicians formerly called "sepsis" is now termed "severe sepsis."

The language and vocabulary of sepsis require review. *Harrison's Principles of Internal Medicine*

(McGraw-Hill Professional Publishing) and *Mandell, Douglas, and Bennett's Principles & Practice of Infectious Diseases* (Churchill Livingstone) provide the following definitions of SIRS-related terminologies (see the comments on how ICD-9-CM views these terms after each definition).

- Bacteremia—Presence of bacteria in blood, as evidenced by positive blood cultures. Stating that a patient has bacteremia does not infer that this bacteremia is pathological or resulted in any systemic illness requiring treatment. A bacteremia can result from flossing one's teeth or from undergoing surgery, hence the need for endocarditis prophylaxis. Septicemia with or without SIRS (sepsis) would be a more appropriate term if illness results from the patient's bacteremia.
- Septicemia—Presence of microbes *or* their toxins in the blood. A positive blood culture is not necessary to make a diagnosis of septicemia, as this definition includes endotoxemia. The patient also may have received antibiotics or may have some other reason for a negative blood culture.
- Systemic inflammatory response syndrome (SIRS)—SIRS may have a noninfectious etiology and must meet two or more of the following conditions:
  - Fever (oral temperature greater than 38°C) or hypothermia (less than 36°C)
  - Tachypnea (greater than 24 breaths per minute)
  - Tachycardia (heart rate greater than 90 beats per minute)
  - Leukocytosis (white blood cell count greater than 12,000/L); 14,000 is suggested as dehydration or other factors may artificially raise the white blood cell count), leukopenia (white blood cell count less than 4,000/L), or greater than 10 percent band/metamyelocytes (left shift) on the leukocyte differential count.
  - Other indications are listed in the Society of Critical Care Medicine and the Institute for Healthcare Improvement's resource Web site, available at: http://ssc.sccm.org/files/Tools/sepsisdefinitionsihitool.pdf

Many clinicians fail to recognize SIRS resulting from noninfectious causes, such as pancreatitis, burns, trauma, or postoperative states. Coding professionals cannot code SIRS unless the physician explicitly states in the documentation "SIRS due to . . ." and links it to acute organ dysfunctions or failures that may occur. This is discussed in further detail in chapter 3.

Other factors can cause fever (for example, drug reaction) or elevations of white blood cell count (for example, dehydration or steroid use), thus relying on these factors alone may cause a coding professional to mistakenly believe a patient has SIRS. A normal white blood cell count and differential suggest that sepsis is unlikely.

- Sepsis—SIRS that has a proven or suspected microbial etiology. Many clinicians believe that fever or leukocytosis is inherent to the underlying infectious process (for example, pneumonia) and will not label a patient as having sepsis unless there is organ dysfunction. Although this may have been clinically correct in the 1970s and 1980s, the new SIRS definitions requires categorization of underlying infections without SIRS, those with SIRS without organ dysfunction (995.91), and those with SIRS-related organ dysfunctions (995.92). A patient does not have to have organ dysfunction to have sepsis; likewise, a significant fever and a significant leukocytosis, which signify the circulating interleukins and other chemicals, meet the SIRS criteria on their own.

Therefore, many patients with pneumonia, urinary tract infection (UTI), skin infections, acute cholelithiasis or cholangitis, diverticulitis, appendicitis, *Clostridum difficile* colitis, and similar conditions meet the SIRS criteria but are not labeled "sepsis due to. . . ." Physicians who treat or surgeons who operate on these patients without stating that these patients have "sepsis due to . . ." reduce their P4P severity levels by 35 to 50 percent.

With ICD-9-CM, the term "urosepsis" codes to UTI; to code sepsis, physicians must clearly document "sepsis due to UTI."

- Severe sepsis (previously known as "sepsis syndrome")—Sepsis with one or more signs of organ dysfunction. Physicians must document these as sepsis-related organ dysfunctions or explicitly describe them as failures (for example, acute respiratory failure versus acute respiratory insufficiency) to count. Although the term "sepsis syndrome" is clinically accurate, ICD-9-CM does not code severe sepsis unless the physician uses the term "severe sepsis" or links an acute organ dysfunction to the sepsis syndrome (for example, "acute renal failure due to sepsis syndrome").

- Septic shock—Sepsis with hypotension (Systolic blood pressure less than 90 mm Hg, mean arterial pressure less than 60 mm Hg, or a fall of systolic blood pressure greater than 40 mm Hg) lasting for at least 1 hour and resistant to adequate fluid resuscitation. Approximately 25 percent of patients admitted with severe sepsis present with septic shock.

Many physicians will describe hypotension and use dopamine and not describe the patient as having shock. Coding professionals cannot assume that a patient has septic shock unless the physician explicitly states that it is present. Coding professionals likewise cannot state that shock is caused by SIRS due to noninfectious causes unless the physician explicitly states this information.

- Multiple-organ dysfunction syndrome (MODS)—Dysfunction of more than one organ, requiring intervention to maintain homeostasis. The physician has to link MODS to the appropriate SIRS terminology if coding is to be correct.

- Postoperative infection—The difficulty here is that the wound must be an unexpected complication of surgery for it to be a complication.

- Surgical procedures are weighted more than their counterparts in other MDCs. Critical to this is deciding whether the patient had SIRS due to infection that was present on admission or whether the admission was due to a complication of surgery or trauma. If SIRS was

MS-DRG	MS-DRG Title	Relative Weights
853	Infectious and parasitic diseases w O.R. procedure w MCC	5.1840
854	Infectious and parasitic diseases w O.R. procedure w CC	3.9291
855	Infectious and parasitic diseases w O.R. procedure w/o CC/MCC	3.3662
856	Postoperative or posttraumatic infections w O.R. procedure w MCC	3.9257
857	Postoperative or posttraumatic infections w O.R. procedure w CC	2.4919
858	Postoperative or posttraumatic infections w O.R. procedure w/o CC/MCC	2.0996

not present on admission, then the case cannot be grouped to MDC 18. Another difficulty is discerning whether a surgical débridement was excisional or not and whether it involved tissue below the skin (for example, fascia, muscle, or bone) or whether or not a bronchoscopy had a transbronchial biopsy.

The SIRS criteria may be applied to screening surgical patients for MDC 18. Clinical indicators include:

- Either a white blood cell count of greater than 12,000/mm^3 (14,000/mm^3 is suggested because dehydration or other factors may artificially raise the white blood cell count) or bandemia (bands greater than 10 percent) associated with fever or hypothermia in the setting of infection, especially if that infection required surgery.
- Positive blood culture for a pathogenic organism
- Unexplained organ dysfunction or failure in the setting of an infection requiring surgery, especially if associated with elevated white count, bandemia, or fever

Example: A 95-year-old white man with Alzheimer's disease who is a resident of an intermediate care facility is admitted through the emergency department with a large pressure sore and fever (temperature of 103°F). His laboratory studies show a white blood cell count of 22,000/mm^3, an albumin of 2.2, and a prealbumin of 10. Blood cultures are sterile. He is treated with vancomycin and Zosyn, intravenous hydration, and enteral hyperalimentation via a nasogastric tube. A surgeon débrides necrotic tissue from the wound at the bedside, documenting on a handwritten progress note that he has performed a sharp débridement. The patient's white blood cell count returns to normal and his wounds begin to heal. He is referred to a long-term acute care hospital for continued treatment of his wounds and for long-term antibiotics.

The coding professional codes the pressure sore as the principal diagnosis and assigns 86.22 (Excisional débridement) as the operative procedure, grouping this to MS-DRG 575 (Skin graft and/or débridement for skin ulcer or cellulitis w/o CC/MCC) (RW 1.4216).

Prior to final billing, another coding professional reviews the record and notes that the patient likely met the SIRS criteria based on clinical indicators in the medical record. The attending physician agrees that the patient probably has SIRS due to the wound infection, while blood cell count of 22,000, and Fever. The physician

documents this as sepsis. Furthermore, with the help of the dietician, the coding professional asks the physician about the low albumin and pre-albumin levels. The physician responds that the patient was severely malnourished and that this played a role in causing the pressure sore. The final DRG for this admission is MS-DRG 853 (Infectious and parasitic diseases with O.R. procedure w MCC) (RW 5.1840). Unfortunately, the recovery audit contractor reviews the record later and determines that the physician's documentation of sharp débridement does not qualify as an excisional débridement, changing the MS-DRG to 871 (Septicemia w/o MV 96+ hours w MCC) (RW 1.7484).

Medicine

As in surgery, many patients with underlying infections are admitted for intravenous antibiotics because they meet the SIRS criteria and are deemed too sick to be treated as outpatients. Coding professionals should query for possible sepsis if they meet the same criteria as in the surgery section:

- Both a white blood cell count above 12,000/mm^3 (14,000/mm^3 is suggested as dehydration or other factors may artificially raise the white blood cell count) or bandemia (bands above 10 percent) associated with fever or hypothermia in the setting of infection, especially if that infection required surgery.
- Positive blood culture for a pathogenic organism. If the coding professional is not sure, then he or she should query the physician for the clinical significance of the cultured organism.
- Unexplained organ dysfunction or failure in the setting of an infection requiring surgery, especially if associated with elevated white blood cell count, bandemia, or fever.

Many patients identified as having sepsis do not meet the SIRS criteria. Although a physician may write "rule out sepsis" on admission, the diagnosis must be supported and carried out throughout the admission, especially the discharge summary, if it is to survive outside scrutiny. Coding professionals or their compliance officers should discuss the SIRS and sepsis criteria with physicians who label patients with infection, mild fever, and normal white blood cell counts as having sepsis. If they do not, then it is likely that CMS's Hospital Payment Monitoring Program, Recovery Audit Contractor, or Office of Inspector General program will do so.

MS-DRGs maintain separate DRGs for ventilator support 96+ hours in sepsis as it did in CMS DRGs.

Refer to MDC 4 for a more complete description of ventilator management.

Septicemia with ventilator support 96+ hours is usually weighted higher than respiratory diagnoses with ventilator support 96+ hours. This is not true, however, for patients with sepsis on the ventilator for under 96 hours as compared with those with respiratory diagnoses on the ventilator for under 96 hours.

In maintaining clinical consistency, the coding department may develop policies and procedures regarding the identification of sepsis to be applied consistently across all patients as allowed in *Coding Clinic* (3rd Quarter, 2000, 6), aiding them in selection records that warrant query. Both the 2000 and 2004 editions of *Coding Clinic* warn that the Medical Executive Committee may not define any clinical syndrome (for example, urosepsis or acute blood loss anemia) as a substitute for physician documentation.

Another area of concern is patients admitted with fever. Fever is a symptom and usually has an underlying cause. It should not be labeled "fever of unknown origin" (FUO) unless it persists for more than 3 weeks and its etiology has not been determined by reasonable inquiry. In light of improvements in imaging modalities and laboratory tests, fewer cases of FUO are being attributed to infectious causes and more are eventually being diagnosed as secondary to noninfectious causes, particularly tumors and connective tissue diseases (for example, lupus erythematosus) (Woolery and Franco 2004). Common infectious causes include tuberculosis, intra-abdominal and pelvic abscesses, and subdiaphragmatic abscesses. However culture-negative endocarditis, toxoplasmosis, perinephric abscess, or other viral infections also can cause fever. Coding professionals are referred to literature outlining a comprehensive approach to fever of unknown origin (Mourad et al 2003).

Coding professionals should work closely with their infection control nurses, microbiologists, and pathologists for assistance in interpreting laboratory studies, especially those that are sent to reference laboratories and may not return until after the patient is discharged. Coding professionals should query physicians for indications of any antibiotic or steroid prescriptions used in the setting of fever. Because ICD-9-CM allows coding professionals to code "still to be ruled out diagnoses" as if they existed, the reasons for the postdiagnostic approach or treatment rendered may shed further light.

Example: A 75-year-old white man who had a gastrectomy and a 2-week history of fever of 103°F and night sweats is admitted to the hospital. Outpatient workup does not uncover a diagnosis. His tuberculosis skin test was positive during the 1960s. He traveled occasionally to the Southwest. Other than his fever, physical examination is normal. His white blood cell count showed leucopenia with 30 percent segmented cells, 14 percent bands, and 10 percent monocytes. His LDH value is normal. He undergoes a bone marrow biopsy and culture and is sent home on empiric antituberculosis therapy pending results. The final diagnosis is fever of unknown etiology, grouping to MS-DRG 864 (Fever of unknown etiology) (RW 0.8240). MS-DRG 864 does not allow for CC or MCC.

One coding professional believes that the physician should be queried about why "tuberculosis still to be ruled out" cannot be included on the physician's diagnostic statement, given that the patient went home on antituberculous medications. The physician does not respond to the query. Eight weeks later, the infection control nurse notifies the coding staff that the cultures grew *Mycobacterium tuberculosis*. Given this information, the physician documents that the patient has miliary tuberculosis, grouping the patient to MS-DRG 869 (Other infectious and parasitic diseases w/o CC/MCC) (RW 1.3611).

MS-DRG	MS-DRG Title	Relative Weights
207	Respiratory system diagnosis w ventilator support 96+ hours	5.1231
208	Respiratory system diagnosis w ventilator support <96 hours	2.2463
870	Septicemia w MV 96+ hours	5.7579
871	Septicemia w/o MV 96+ hours w MCC	1.7484
872	Septicemia w/o MV 96+ hours w/o MCC	1.3783

MDC 19: Mental Diseases and Disorders

There are practically no differences between MS-DRGs and CMS DRGs in MDC 19.

As discussed in MDC 1, coding professional should consider any underlying or precipitating causes for patients presenting with mental diseases and disorders, especially delirium, dementia, anxiety, or confusion, as many physicians do not document their underlying causes (for example, metabolic encephalopathy) or complications (for example, hypokalemia due to overuse of laxatives, commonly seen in patients with anorexia nervosa).

MDC 20: Alcohol/Drug Use and Alcohol/Drug-Induced Organ Mental Disorders

There are practically no differences between MS-DRGs and CMS DRGs in MDC 20. The only difference is that the diagnosis Alcohol or drug abuse without rehabilitation will require a major CC rather than a CC to command a higher relative weight.

As discussed in MDC 1, many patients have a toxic encephalopathy or other complications for which their alcohol or drug addiction could not be treated as an outpatient. Coding professionals should work with their case management departments to determine exactly why patients with alcohol or drug addiction require inpatient hospitalization prior to their transfer to or admission to alcohol/drug treatment centers.

Another area of deficient documentation centers on dementia. Some physicians may use the term "senile dementia" or "multi-infarct dementia" rather than describing its probable underlying cause. Physician query for probable Alzheimer's disease or cognitive dysfunctions as the late effect of a stroke or multiple strokes more accurately describe the patient's circumstances and underlying causes.

MDC 21: Injury, Poisoning, and Toxic Effect of Drugs

There are practically no differences between MS-DRGs and CMS DRGs in MDC 21.

In the MDC 21 surgical DRGs, the injury is usually well documented by the physician. In some cases, a noninfectious process, such as trauma, may lead to an infection that can result in sepsis or severe sepsis. If sepsis or severe sepsis is documented as associated with a noninfectious condition, such as a burn or serious injury, and this condition meets the definition for principal diagnosis, the code for the noninfectious condition should be sequenced first, followed by the code for the systemic infection and either code 995.91 (Sepsis) or 995.92 (Severe sepsis), leaving this patient in MDC 18.

Sometimes patients with sepsis due to the injury may be grouped to the appropriate MDC 18 code. If the patient has sepsis resulting from a postprocedural infection that is a complication of care, 998.59 is the principal diagnosis and it groups to MDC 18.

For patients receiving medicine, ICD-9-CM instructions regarding poisoning and toxic effects of drugs should be considered. When the drug is correctly prescribed and properly administered, both the reaction and the appropriate code from the E930–E949 series should be coded. Errors made in drug prescription or in the administration of the drug by provider, nurse, patient, or another person, or a drug overdose that was intentionally taken or administered and resulted in drug toxicity would be coded as a poisoning (960–979 series), resulting in MDC 21. If a nonprescribed drug or medicinal agent was taken in combination with a correctly prescribed and properly administered drug, any drug toxicity or other reaction resulting from the interaction of the two drugs would be classified as a poisoning. In all of these cases, the appropriate 960–979 code should be sequenced first.

Complications are grouped to MDC 21. To qualify as a complication, two criteria must be met:

1. The condition must not have been expected. For it to be a complication, the physician must say that it is or designate it as "postoperative" for certain terms (for example, postoperative ileus). Impotence after prostate surgery would not be a complication because it is an expected consequence of this operation. Abdominal pain or ileus immediately after bowel surgery is expected. Bleeding after joint replacement surgery is expected in many cases. *Coding Clinic* (second Quarter, 2007, 12) specified that events that are not clinically significant should not be considered as complications.
2. Documentation that the treatment provided caused the condition. If a physician explicitly states that the event is a complication of care, then it should be coded to a complication code.

Complications of drugs that are properly administered do not group to MDC 21 because ICD-9-CM states that when the drug was correctly prescribed and properly administered, both the reaction plus the appropriate code from the E930–E949 series should be coded.

Example: A 28-year-old white man is admitted to the hospital with an acute MI. A coronary arteriogram is normal; however, there is wall motion abnormality associated with his MI. His urine drug screen is positive for cocaine metabolites and the physician links his MI to cocaine abuse. Rather than grouping him to MS-DRG 282 (Acute myocardial infarction, discharge alive w/o CC/MCC) (RW 1.0617), he is grouped to MS-DRG 917 (Poisoning and toxic effect of drugs w/MCC) (RW 1.1717).

MDC 22: Burns

There is little change between CMS-DRGs and MS-DRGs in MDC 22. To group these correctly, coding professionals must understand the various degrees of burns, the difference between extensive and nonextensive burns, and various complications such as inhalation injury or full-thickness burns.

Burns are classified according to their depth. These classifications are:

- A first-degree burn is the least serious type of burn because it injures only the top layers of skin, called the epidermis. Typically, the only clinical finding is redness of the skin, much like sunburn. Sunburn (692.71, 692.76–692.77) has its own codes and should not be coded as a first-degree burn.
- A second-degree burn injures the top layers of skin, labeled the epidermis, and extends down to the deeper layers of skin, labeled the dermis. Frequently, these burns are extremely red and blisters are present. They are more apt to cause complications.
- A third-degree burn injures all layers (epidermis, dermis, and subcutaneous tissue) or the full thickness of the skin. They may appear black, white, or leathery and will cause complications unless aggressively treated.
- Deep necrosis is a third-degree burn that also involves the underlying fascia and muscle.

In addition, inhalation injury is classified as follows:

- Damage from heat inhalation—Usually confined to the upper airways. Inhalation of steam can cause damage to the lower lungs.
- Damage from systemic toxins—Carbon monoxide poisoning is the most common.

- Damage from smoke inhalation—Causes 60 to 80 percent of fatalities due to burn injuries.

The location of the burns should be documented. To estimate the amount of skin burned, the "rule of nines" is used. To approximate the percentage of burned surface area, the body has been divided into eleven sections:

- Head
- Right arm
- Left arm
- Chest
- Abdomen
- Upper back
- Lower back
- Right thigh
- Left thigh
- Right leg (below the knee)
- Left leg (below the knee)

Each of these sections takes about 9 percent of the body's skin to cover it. All together, these sections account for 99 percent of the body. The genitals make up the remaining 1 percent (see Figure 2.5).

Children have different ratios, especially in the face and lower extremities (see photos at http://www.biotel.ws/protocolsHTML/Protocols2004/BurnDiagramBurnFormula.asp).

ICD-9-CM requires that the code reflecting the highest severity of burn be sequenced first if more than one burn is present. If the site of the burn is not specified, the physician may be queried to avoid using a code from the 948 series. These codes are used to provide data for evaluating burn mortality.

Inhalation injury is indicated by codes 518.5 (Pulmonary insufficiency following trauma and surgery), 947.1 (Burn of larynx, trachea, and lung), 987.9 (Toxic effect of unspecified gas, fume, or vapor), 518.81 (Acute respiratory failure), or 518.84 (Acute or chronic respiratory failure). Ventilator use over 96 hours impacts MS-DRG assignment.

When a patient is admitted for burn injuries and other related conditions such as smoke inhalation and/or respiratory failure, the circumstances of admission govern the selection of the principal diagnosis or first listed diagnosis.

According to MS-DRGs, an extensive or full thickness burn is any third-degree or deep necrosis burn. If the site is not specified, the third-degree burn must involve more than 10 percent of the body.

Figure 2.5 Rule of Nines

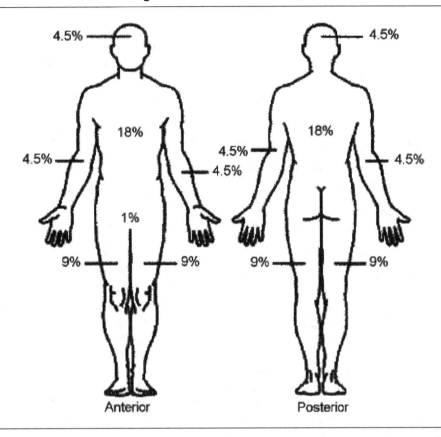

MS-DRG	MS-DRG Title	Relative Weights
189	Pulmonary edema and respiratory failure	1.3660
205	Other respiratory system diagnoses w MCC	1.0636
206	Other respiratory system diagnoses w/o MCC	0.7848
207	Respiratory system diagnosis w ventilator support 96+ hours	5.1231
208	Respiratory system diagnosis w ventilator support <96 hours	2.2463
927	Extensive burns or full thickness burns w MV 96+ hours w skin graft	12.3042
928	Full thickness burn w skin graft or inhalation injury w CC/MCC	4.3956
929	Full thickness burn w skin graft or inhalation injury w/o CC/MCC	2.3533
933	Extensive burns or full thickness burns w MV 96+ hours w/o skin graft	2.6626

Inhalation injury as principal diagnosis groups to MDC 4. A comparison of the MS-DRGs for ventilator use with inhalation injury and burns as principal diagnosis is outlined below.

The circumstances of admission, the diagnostic approach, and the treatment rendered governs principal diagnosis if inhalation injury is present.

Example: A 21-year-old man is injured in an accidental apartment fire and has third-degree burns to 30 percent of his body and smoke inhalation. He is placed on a ventilator but is removed from it after 72 hours.

Sequencing his burns or inhalation injury as principal diagnosis results in the following MS-DRGs:

- Burns—MS-DRG 928 (Full-thickness burns with skin graft or inhalation injury with MCC) (RW 4.3956).
- Inhalation injury—MS-DRG 208 (Respiratory system diagnosis w/ventilator support less than 96 hours) (RW 2.2463).

In the event that the ventilator had been used for more than 96 hours, the following MS-DRGs would be assigned:

- Principal diagnosis—MS DRG 933 (Burns) (RW 2.6626)
- Principal diagnosis—MS-DRG 207 (Inhalation injury) (RW 5.1231)

MDC 23: Factors Influencing Health Status and Other Contacts With Health Services

MDC 23 is one of the least used MDCs, accounting for only 0.4 percent of short-term Medicare admissions in the 2006 MedPAR. On the other hand, MDC 23 is used heavily in long-term acute care and rehabilitation hospitals.

MS-DRGs follow the same principles as CMS DRGs in MDC 23, except for the consolidations listed in the table below.

Assignment to listed in the table below MDC 23 in short-term acute care hospitals should always be questioned. Many of the diagnoses assigned to MDC 23 do not meet medical necessity for admission or usually have underlying causes that have not been adequately described or documented by the attending physician. Coding professionals should query their physicians for any underlying acute conditions requiring the extra level of care inherent to acute or rehabilitative care.

Long-term acute care hospitals should also be aware of MDC 23 DRGs, given that their medical necessity criteria are geared toward acute conditions rather than chronic or rehabilitative conditions.

Many physicians may admit a patient to evaluate a symptom (for example, edema or ascites) and give multiple "rule-out" diagnoses on the discharge statement, forcing the coding professional to group the symptom code as principal. In this event, coding professionals should query the physician to determine which of these conditions best fits the circumstances of admission, diagnostic approach, or treatment rendered so that more accurate MS-DRG assignment may be accomplished.

Pain Codes

Under MS-DRGs, pain codes migrated from MDC 23 to MDC 1. A review of the pain codes is warranted.

Codes in category 338 (Pain, not elsewhere classified), may be used in conjunction with codes from other categories and chapters to provide more detail about acute or chronic pain and neoplasm-related pain. If the pain is not specified as acute or chronic, do not assign codes from category 338, except for post-thoracotomy pain (338.12 or 338.22), postoperative pain (338.18 or 338.28), or neoplasm-related pain (338.3). The default for postthoracotomy and other postoperative pain not specified as acute or chronic is the code for the acute form.

A code from subcategories 338.1 and 338.2 should not be assigned if the underlying (definitive) diagnosis is known, unless the reason for the encounter is pain control/management and not management of the underlying condition.

Category 338 codes are acceptable as principal diagnosis or the first-listed code for reporting purposes:

- When the related definitive diagnosis has not been established (confirmed) by the provider, or
- When pain control or pain management is the reason for the admission/encounter (for example, a patient with displaced intervertebral disc, nerve impingement, and severe back pain presents for injection of steroid into the spinal canal).

The underlying cause of the pain should be reported as an additional diagnosis, if known.

As an example, *Coding Clinic* (2nd Quarter, 2007) cites a patient with known malignancy who was admitted for neoplasm-associated pain. Code 338.3 was recommended to be the principal diagnosis; the neoplasm was to be sequenced as a secondary diagnosis.

As another example in the same *Coding Clinic*, a patient was admitted to the hospital to determine the etiology of excruciating disabling lower back pain. Code 724.4 (Lumbago) was recommended as the

CMS-DRG Version 24.0	DRG Description	MS-DRG Version 25.0	New Base MS-DRG Description
465	Aftercare with History of Malignancy as Secondary Diagnosis	949, 950	Aftercare with and without CC/MCC
466	After without History of Malignancy as Secondary		

Source: CMS Final Rule (Federal Register)

principal diagnosis because the reason for admission described was to assess the etiology of the pain, not primarily to treat or eliminate it.

The sequencing of category 338 codes with site-specific pain codes (including chapter 16 codes), depends on the circumstances of the encounter/admission as follows:

- If the encounter is for pain control or pain management, assign the code from category 338 followed by the code identifying the specific site of pain (for example, encounter for pain management of acute neck pain from trauma is assigned code 338.11 [Acute pain due to trauma], followed by code 723.1 [Cervicalgia] to identify the site of pain).
- If the encounter is for any other reason except pain control or pain management, and a related definitive diagnosis has not been established (confirmed) by the provider, the code for the specific site of pain first should be assigned, followed by the appropriate code from category 338.

Pain associated with devices or foreign bodies left in a surgical site (for example, painful retained suture) is assigned to the appropriate code(s) found in Chapter 17 of *Coding Clinic*, Injury and Poisoning. *Coding Clinic* (2nd Quarter, 2007), cites an example in which the patient's pain was due to a device. *Coding Clinic* recommended that 996.7 (Other complication of internal prosthetic device, implant, and graft) be coded as the principal diagnosis. They clarified that the appropriate code from Category 338 also should be coded.

Postoperative pain not associated with a specific postoperative complication is assigned to the appropriate postoperative pain code in category 338. Postoperative pain associated with a specific postoperative complication (such as a device left in the body) is assigned to the appropriate complication code. As the complication represents the underlying (definitive) diagnosis associated with the pain, no additional code should be assigned from category 338.

Example: A 62-year-old morbidly obese woman is admitted for edema and mild jugular venous distention with Kussmaul's sign. (Kussmaul's sign is the elevation of the jugular veins with inspiration; normally the veins are supposed to go down. This is usually a sign of right heart failure or pericardial disease and should not be confused with Kussmaul's breathing). Her echocardiogram is interpreted as normal with an estimated ejection fraction of 55 percent, but her pericardium seems a little thickened.

Her renal function is normal; there are no ascites or liver abnormalities. She is not hypoxemic and has no nocturnal oxygen desaturations. The attending physician's diagnostic statement is "edema, diastolic heart failure versus possible mild constrictive pericarditis" with tentative plans to refer her to a tertiary referral center for further evaluation, grouping this to MS-DRG 948 (Signs and symptoms w/o MCC) (RW 0.6542). Upon coder query, given that the patient was referred to a tertiary medical center and had abnormal cardiac signs (for example, Kussmaul's sign), the physician amended his diagnostic statement to state that the edema was probably due to new-onset chronic diastolic heart failure and that constrictive pericarditis was still to be ruled out. If chronic diastolic heart failure is the principal diagnosis, the MS-DRG is 292 (Heart failure with CC) (RW 1.0134), while if possible, constrictive pericarditis is sequenced as the principal diagnosis, the MS-DRG is 315 (Other circulatory diagnoses with CC) (RW 1.1720).

MDC 24: Multiple Significant Trauma

There are practically no changes to the MS-DRGs in MDC 24. Coding professionals should be aware of the need to capture CCs and MCCs, as described in chapter 3.

MDC 25: Human Immunodeficiency Virus Infections

There are practically no changes to the MS-DRGs in MDC 25 except that HIV with major related conditions will allow for CC and MCC.

Code assignment for human immunodeficiency virus (ICD-9-CM Code 042) is reported only when a physician explicitly documents and confirms this diagnosis. The provider's documentation confirming that the patient is HIV-positive or has an HIV-related illness is sufficient. This is the only time on inpatient admissions where "possible," "likely," "suspected," "probable," "still-to-be ruled out," or any similar terminology does not allow the coding professional to code the condition as if it existed.

Certain states (for example, California) do not allow coding of asymptomatic HIV infection (V08) or inconclusive HIV serology (795.71) unless the patient has given informed consent.

Not all patients with HIV infection have AIDS. HIV infection is classified into the following three categories that apply to adolescents or adults older than 13 years with documented HIV infection (MMWR 1992):

- Category A consists of one or more of the conditions listed below in an adolescent or adult (age 13 years or older) with documented HIV infection. Conditions listed in Categories B and C must not have occurred.
  - Asymptomatic HIV infection
  - Persistent generalized lymphadenopathy
  - Acute (primary) HIV infection with accompanying illness or history of acute HIV infection
- Category B consists of symptomatic conditions in an HIV-infected adolescent or adult that are not included among conditions listed in clinical category C and that meet at least one of the following criteria: (1) the conditions are attributed to HIV infection or are indicative of a defect in cell-mediated immunity, or (2) the conditions are considered by physicians to have a clinical course or to require management that is complicated by HIV infection. Examples of conditions in clinical category B include, but are not limited to:
  - Bacillary angiomatosis
  - Candidiasis, oropharyngeal (thrush)
  - Candidiasis, vulvovaginal; persistent, frequent, or poorly responsive to therapy
  - Cervical dysplasia (moderate or severe)/cervical carcinoma in situ
  - Constitutional symptoms, such as fever (38.5°C) or diarrhea lasting longer than 1 month
  - Hairy leukoplakia, oral
  - Herpes zoster (shingles), involving at least two distinct episodes or more than one dermatome
  - Idiopathic thrombocytopenic purpura
  - Listeriosis
  - Pelvic inflammatory disease, particularly if complicated by tubo-ovarian abscess
  - Peripheral neuropathy

For classification purposes, category B conditions take precedence over those in category A. For example, someone previously treated for oral or persistent vaginal candidiasis (and who has not developed a category C disease) but who is now asymptomatic should be classified in clinical category B. Patients with HIV-infection and category B illnesses should *not* be coded to 042 (HIV infection) unless the physician *explicitly* links these category B conditions to HIV, documents that these conditions are HIV-related, or labels these patients as "HIV disease, category B."

Category C includes the clinical conditions listed in the AIDS surveillance case definition that follows. For classification purposes, once a person has been diagnosed with a category C condition, the person will remain in category C. *Coding Clinic* (2nd Quarter, 2004) gives coding professionals permission to use ICD-9-CM Code 042 (HIV infection) when a physician describes a patient as having HIV disease, category C.

- Candidiasis of bronchi, trachea, or lungs
- Candidiasis, esophageal
- Cervical cancer, invasive
- Coccidioidomycosis, disseminated or extrapulmonary
- Cryptococcosis, extrapulmonary
- Cryptosporidiosis, chronic intestinal (over 1 month's duration)
- Cytomegalovirus disease (other than liver, spleen, or nodes)
- Cytomegalovirus retinitis (with loss of vision)
- Encephalopathy, HIV-related
- Herpes simplex: chronic ulcer(s) (over 1 month's duration) or bronchitis, pneumonitis, or esophagitis
- Histoplasmosis, disseminated or extrapulmonary
- Isosporiasis, chronic intestinal (over 1 month's duration)
- Kaposi's sarcoma
- Lymphoma, Burkitt's (or equivalent term)
- Lymphoma, immunoblastic (or equivalent term)
- Lymphoma, primary, of brain
- Mycobacterium avium complex or *mycobacterium kansasii*, disseminated or extrapulmonary
- *Mycobacterium tuberculosis*, any site (pulmonary or extrapulmonary)
- *Mycobacterium*, other species or unidentified species, disseminated or extrapulmonary
- *Pneumocystis carinii* pneumonia
- Pneumonia, recurrent
- Progressive multifocal leukoencephalopathy
- Salmonella septicemia, recurrent
- Toxoplasmosis of the brain
- Wasting syndrome due to HIV

Coding professionals must not assume that these conditions are HIV-related unless explicitly documents as so by the physician.

Once a physician has documented that a patient has HIV, qualifying for ICD-9-CM code 042 and MDC 25, MS-DRG's list of HIV-related illnesses is somewhat different than that of the CDC. For example, septicemia, presenile dementia, unspecified psychosis, subacute bacterial endocarditis, and pneumonia due to SARS are listed by MS-DRGs as HIV-related diagnoses.

Surgery

Surgery for patients with HIV-disease (042) is grouped to MDC 25 if it is not listed as one of the procedures assigned to MS-DRGs 987–989. This is discussed further in the section on DRGs Associated with All MDCs and Pre-MDC.

Medicine

Unlike the CDC, MS-DRGs classify HIV-related conditions as Major and Nonmajor. In MS-DRGs, if 042 is the primary or secondary diagnoses, these major and nonmajor conditions group the DRG to MDC 25. Examples of these include:

- Major
  - Septicemia (SIRS due to infection)
  - Candidiasis of the mouth
  - Histoplasmosis
  - Unspecified encephalopathy
  - Most forms of bacterial or viral pneumonia
- Minor
  - Severe malnutrition
  - Nephrotic syndrome
  - Neutropenia
  - Thrombocytopenia
  - Fever
  - Anemia
  - Electrolyte imbalances
  - Weight loss

Given that Minor HIV-related illnesses as principal diagnosis with 042 as a secondary diagnosis group to MDC 25 and usually have a higher weight than their respective MDCs, physicians and coding professionals should ensure that HIV-infected patients are categorized accurately.

Example: A patient with known AIDS is admitted with fever, elevated white blood cell count, and urosepsis and is treated with IV antibiotics. Because urosepsis is not an MS-DRG designated HIV-related

condition, the MS-DRG for this admission is 689 (Kidney and urinary tract infections with MCC) (RW 1.2317). Noting this, the clinical documentation specialist queries the attending physician as to whether the patient has SIRS due to UTI. He responds "yes" and documents this in the medical record and discharge summary. The new MS-DRG is 974 (HIV with major related condition w/MCC) (RW 2.1883).

Example: A 22-year-old patient with HIV category B is admitted with cervical lymphadenopathy for a deep lymph node biopsy. The initial stains show granulomas, but the TB and fungal stains are negative. The final diagnosis is cervical lymphadenitis and AIDS, with the primary procedure being a cervical lymph node excision, initially grouping to MS-DRG 802 (Other OR procedure of the blood and blood-forming organs w/MCC) (RW 2.7940). The culture reports show that the patient has tuberculosis, upon which the infection control nurse notifies the coding department and the physician. The HIM department requests an addendum to the record, to which the physician agrees. Unfortunately, in this circumstance, the MS-DRG changes to 976 (HIV with major related condition w/o CC/MCC) (RW 2.1382) because cervical node excision is not an extensive OR procedure, and the hospital has to refile the claim and send money back to the fiscal intermediary. The HIM director is relieved, however, that she is able to do the right thing, does not have to deal with a Recovery Audit Contractor in the future on this issue, and does not have to send money back with interest.

DRGs Associated With All MDCs and Pre-MDCs

There is no difference between CMS-DRGs and MS-DRGs for circumstances in which an OR procedure unrelated to the principal diagnosis is performed, other than for the allowance of CCs and MCCs. These are listed as follows:

MS-DRG	MS-DRG Title	Relative Weights
981	Extensive O.R. procedure unrelated to principal diagnosis w MCC	4.5168
982	Extensive O.R. procedure unrelated to principal diagnosis w CC	3.5417
983	Extensive O.R. procedure unrelated to principal diagnosis w/o CC/MCC	2.9737
984	Prostatic O.R. procedure unrelated to principal diagnosis w MCC	2.7217
985	Prostatic O.R. procedure unrelated to principal diagnosis w CC	2.0865
986	Prostatic O.R. procedure unrelated to principal diagnosis w/o CC/MCC	1.6706
987	Nonextensive O.R. procedure unrelated to principal diagnosis w MCC	2.8500
988	Nonextensive O.R. procedure unrelated to principal diagnosis w CC	2.0134
989	Nonextensive O.R. procedure unrelated to principal diagnosis w/o CC/MCC	1.6310

MS-DRG	FY2008 Final Rule Postacute DRG	FY2008 Final Rule Special Pay DRG	MDC	TYPE	MS-DRG Title	Weights
001	No	No	PRE	SURG	Heart transplant or implant of heart-assist system w MCC	23.1117
002	No	No	PRE	SURG	Heart transplant or implant of heart-assist system w/o MCC	16.2735
003	Yes	No	PRE	SURG	ECMO or tracheostomy w MV 96+ hours or PDX except face, mouth, and neck w major OR	18.7707
004	Yes	No	PRE	SURG	Tracheostomy w MV 96+ hours or PDX except face, mouth, and neck w/o major O.R.	11.4219
005	No	No	PRE	SURG	Liver transplant w MCC or intestinal transplant	10.6120
006	No	No	PRE	SURG	Liver transplant w/o MCC	7.2562
007	No	No	PRE	SURG	Lung transplant	8.4002
008	No	No	PRE	SURG	Simultaneous pancreas/kidney transplant	5.1726
009	No	No	PRE	SURG	Bone marrow transplant	6.4842
010	No	No	PRE	SURG	Pancreas transplant	3.8902
011	No	No	PRE	SURG	Tracheostomy for face, mouth, and neck diagnoses w MCC	4.1482
012	No	No	PRE	SURG	Tracheostomy for face, mouth, and neck diagnoses w CC	3.2472
013	No	No	PRE	SURG	Tracheostomy for face, mouth, and neck diagnoses w/o CC/MCC	2.6760

Pre-MDC

All DRGs within the pre-MDC are surgical and have not changed significantly from CMS DRGs other than to allow for CCs and MCCs in tracheostomies.

Transplants or ECMO should be obvious. Coding professionals should be certain not to confuse endotracheal intubation with tracheostomy. Tracheostomies carried out elsewhere prior to admission should not be coded; however, if the hospital (for example, a long-term acute care hospital) contracts with and pays another facility to have this procedure performed on their patient as part of their inpatient hospitalization, it may be coded.

Summary

As is true of CMS DRGs, MS-DRGs require accurate principal diagnosis and procedure assignment.

ICD-9-CM Official Guidelines and *Coding Clinic* provide official advice for code assignment. Physician documentation must substantiate all assigned codes. If there is any question, ICD-9-CM and *Coding Clinic* encourage physician query and cooperation.

References

Anpalahan, M. 2001. Chronic idiopathic hyponatremia in older people due to syndrome of inappropriate antidiuretic hormone secretion (SIADH) possibly related to aging. *Journal of the American Geriatric Society*, 49:788–792.

Bartlett, J.G. and Mundy, L.M. 1995. Community-acquired pneumonia. *New England Journal of Medicine* 333(24):1618–1624.

Bellomo R. et al. The Second International Consensus Conference of the Acute Dialysis Quality Initiative (ADQI) Group. 2004.

Acute renal failure—Definition, outcome measures, animal models, fluid therapy and information technology needs. *Critical Care* 8:R204–R212.

Bronnert, J. 2006. Determining surgical complications. *Journal of AHIMA,* 77(7): 76–77.

Cannon, C.P. and Braunwald, E. 2005. Unstable angina and non-ST elevation myocardial infarction. Ch 49 in *Braunwald's heart disease: A textbook of cardiovascular medicine, 7th ed.* Edited by Zipes, D.P. et al. Philadelphia: Saunders.

Ellison, D.H. and Berl, T. 2007. The syndrome of inappropriate diuresis. *New England Journal of Medicine* 356: 2064–2072.

Centers for Medicare & Medicaid Services (CMS) and the National Center for Health Statistics (NCHS). 2006. *ICD-9-CM Official Guidelines for Coding and Reporting.* Available online from www.cdc.gov/nchs/datawh/ftpserv/ftpicd9/ftpicd9.htm Preamble.

Centers for Medicare & Medicaid Services (CMS) and the National Center for Health Statistics (NCHS). 2006. *ICD-9-CM Official Guidelines for Coding and Reporting.* Available online from www.cdc.gov/nchs/datawh/ftpserv/ftpicd9/ftpicd9.htm. Section 1, Subsection A.6.

Centers for Medicare & Medicaid Services (CMS) and the National Center for Health Statistics (NCHS). 2006. *ICD-9-CM Official Guidelines for Coding and Reporting.* Available online from www.cdc.gov/nchs/datawh/ftpserv/ftpicd9/ftpicd9.htm Section 1, Subsection C.1.b. 1) (c).

International Sepsis Forum and the Pediatric Acute Lung Injury and Sepsis Investigative Network. 2005. *Pediatric Critical Care Medicine,* 6(3): S1–S164. Accessed July 5, 2007 at: http://www.sepsisforum.org/activities.htm.

Kasper, D., E. Braunwald, A. Fauci, et al. 2004. *Harrison's Principles of Internal Medicine.* New York: McGraw-Hill Professional Publishing.

K/DOQI Clinical Practice Guidelines on Chronic Kidney Disease Work Group. Part 4. Definition and classification of stages of chronic kidney disease. *American Journal of Kidney Disease,* 39(2): S46–S75. Accessed July 3, 2007 at: http://www.kidney.org/professionals/kdoqi/guidelines_ckd/p4_class_g1.htm.

Mandell, D. 2005. *Bennett's Principles & Practice of Infectious Diseases.* Memphis: Churchill Livingstone.

Mandell, L.A. et al. 2007. Infectious Disease Society of America/American Thoracic Society Consensus guidelines on the management of community-acquired pneumonia in adults.

Clinical Infectious Diseases, 44: S27–S72. Accessed July 31, 2007 at: http://www.journals.uchicago.edu/CID/journal/issues/v44nS2/41620/41620.html.

MedPAC. September 2006. Payment Basic: Hospital Acute Inpatient Services Payment System. Available at: http://www.medpac.gov/publications/other_reports/Sept06_MedPAC_Payment_Basics_hospital.pdf, accessed July 31, 2007.

Mesulam, M.M. Aphasia, memory loss, and other focal cerebral disorders. In Kasper, D.L. et al. 2005. *Harrison's Principles of Internal Medicine* (16th ed.), p. 145.

MMWR 42(No. RR-17), December 18, 1992.

Montaner, J. 2006. Stroke biomarkers: Can they help us to guide stroke thrombolysis? *Drug News Perspective* 19(9):523–532.

Mourad, O, et al. 2003. A comprehensive evidence-based approach to fever of unknown origin. *Archives of Internal Medicine.* 163:545–551.

Sacco, R.L., et al. 2006. Guidelines for prevention of stroke with ischemic stroke or transient ischemic attack. *Stroke.* 37:577.

Sands, K.E., et.al. Academic Medical Center Consortium Sepsis Project Working Group. 1997. Epidemiology of sepsis syndrome in eight academic medical centers. *Journal of the American Medical Association,* 278(3): 234–240. Available at: http://jama.ama-assn.org/cgi/content/abstract/278/3/234.

Singri, N. Ahya, S.N., and Levin, M.L. 2003. Acute renal failure. *Journal of the American Medical Association* 289: 747–751.

Sloane, P.D., Coeytaux, R.R., Beck, R.S., and Dallara, J. 2001. Dizziness: State of the science. *Annals of Internal Medicine,* 134(9) Part 2:823–832.

Umpierrez, G.E., Smiley, D., and Kitabchi. A.E. 2006. Narrative review: Ketosis-prone Type 2 diabetes mellitus. *Annals of Internal Medicine* March(144): 350–357.

Van Biesen, W. et al. 2006. Defining acute renal failure: RIFLE and beyond. *Clinical Journal of the American Society of Nephrology,* 1: 1314–1319. Accessed May 29, 2007 at: http://www.pubmed.gov. Term "aborted stroke" used.

Woolery, W.A. and Franco, F.R. 2004. Fever of unknown origin: Keys to determining the etiology in older patients. *Geriatrics* 59(October):41–45. Available at: http://www.geri.com/geriatrics/data/articlestandard/geriatrics/422004/128364/article.pdf.

Chapter 3

Secondary Diagnoses—CCs and Major CCs

Introduction

Although principal diagnosis and principal procedure coding remain critical to accurate Major Diagnostic Category (MDC) and Diagnosis Related Group (DRG) assignment, the most significant differnce between the Centers for Medicare & Medicaid Services Diagnosis Related Groups (CMS DRGs) and the Medicare Severity-adjusted Diagnosis Related Groups (MS-DRGs) is how secondary diagnoses affect severity levels in each system. Healthcare professionals must learn an entirely new complication and comorbidity (CC) structure and embrace a new concept—that of the Major Complication and Comorbidity (MCC).

Those with experience in other higher-refined, severity-adjusted DRG systems, such as 3M's All Patient Diagnosis Related Groups (AP-DRG), used by Medicaid programs in New York, Indiana, and Kentucky; 3M's All Patient Refined DRG (APR-DRG), used by the state of Maryland and Mississippi's Medicaid; and Ingenix's All-Payer Severity-Adjusted Diagnosis Related Groups (APS-DRG), used in severity and risk adjustment by a number of hospital associations, such as those in Tennessee, Kentucky, and Iowa, have a head start because MS-DRGs closely resemble these methodologies.

The Centers for Medicare & Medicaid Services (CMS) has gradually rolled out the new CC and MCC structures over the past two years with their introduction of Major Cardiovascular Diagnoses (MCVDs) in 2006 and Major Gastrointestinal, Esophageal, and Hematologic Diagnoses in 2007, so the foundations for MS-DRGs are not entirely new. CMS carried forward and standardized the MCC concept throughout all of the MDCs and completely redefined what they consider to be a CC and a MCC.

Learning MS-DRGs requires mastery of the new CC and MCC structure.

Background

The Official Guidelines for Coding and Reporting state that, for reporting purposes, the definition for "other diagnoses" is interpreted as additional conditions that affect patient care in terms of requiring any of the following:

- Clinical evaluation
- Therapeutic treatment
- Diagnostic procedures
- Extended length of hospital stay
- Increased nursing care and/or monitoring

The Uniform Hospital Discharge Data Set (UHDDS) item #11-b defines "other diagnoses" as "all conditions that coexist at the time of admission, that develop subsequently, or that affect the treatment received and/or the length of stay. Diagnoses that relate to an earlier episode which have no bearing on the current hospital stay are to be excluded."

Newborns have an additional condition—implications for future healthcare needs—for which a secondary diagnosis may be assigned. For example, family history of polycystic kidney disease may influence a decision to do a renal ultrasound and thus may qualify as an additional diagnosis.

Not all secondary diagnoses, comorbidities, or complications impact resource utilization, length of stay, or risk of mortality enough to qualify as a CC. When CMS DRGs were developed in 1979, the Yale University researchers created a liberal definition of a CC as any secondary diagnosis that would cause an increase in length of stay in at least 75 percent of patients. Except for new diagnoses, this CC list has remained essentially the same from 1983 to 2007, with 3,226 secondary diagnoses designated as CCs and approximately 77 percent of patients having at least one CC in 2006.

In 2006, CMS deemed this CC capture rate to be too high and revised the CC list to better reflect resource utilization. To develop this list, CMS reviewed each of the 13,549 secondary diagnosis codes to evaluate their assignment as a CC or non-CC using statistical information from the Medicare claims data and applying medical judgment based on current clinical practice. Rather than using length of stay as a primary metric, CMS focused on high hospital resource use (for example, intensive monitoring such as ICU care), expensive and technically complex services (for example, heart transplant), or extensive care requiring a greater number of caregivers (for example, nursing care for a quadriplegic) to qualify a diagnosis as a CC. This process pared down the original list of 3,226 diagnoses to a new "initial revised" CC list of 2,583 diagnoses, reducing the percentage of patients having at least one CC from 77.6 percent to 41.24 percent.

With this new initial revised CC list, CMS then addressed the issue of acute and chronic diagnoses as CCs. According to CMS, many chronic diagnoses did not significantly increase hospital resource utilization unless there was an acute exacerbation present or a significant deterioration in the underlying chronic condition. Therefore, in the initial revised CC list, chronic diseases without a significant acute manifestation (for example, multiple sclerosis) were removed, whereas chronic conditions with codes for acute manifestations remained. For example, for congestive heart failure, the following codes specifying an acute exacerbation of the congestive heart failure were retained as MCCs or CCs.

- 428.1 (Left heart failure)
- 428.20 (Systolic heart failure not otherwise specified)
- 428.21 (Acute systolic heart failure)
- 428.22 (Chronic systolic heart failure)
- 428.31 (Acute diastolic heart failure)
- 428.32 (Chronic diastolic heart failure)
- 428.33 (Acute on chronic diastolic heart failure)
- 428.40 (Combined systolic and diastolic heart failure)
- 428.41 (Acute systolic and diastolic heart failure)
- 428.43 (Acute on chronic systolic heart failure)

However, the following congestive heart failure codes that did not indicate an acute exacerbation were excluded:

- 428.0 (Congestive heart failure not otherwise specified)
- 428.9 (Heart failure not otherwise specified)

As for other major chronic diseases, the stage of the disease was often not clearly specified in the code. Those chronic diseases demonstrating consistency and intensity of the physiologic decompensation and debility were allowed to remain as initial CCs. For example, quadriplegia (codes 344.00 through 344.09), which requires extensive care with a substantial increase in nursing services and more intensive monitoring, remained a CC in the initial revised CC list.

CMS then went on to allow diseases with acute manifestation codes, such as acute myocardial infarction (MI), acute stroke, acute renal failure, acute respiratory failure, pneumonia, and septicemia to remain on the CC list.

Further MS-DRG Refinement

Once CMS determined this initial revised CC list, it analyzed and further revised the list to construct MS-DRGs using the following methodology.

Base DRG Consolidation

CMS reviewed their previous work in the development of other DRG methodologies during the 1980s and 1990s, such as Refined-DRGs (R-DRGs), which included four levels (no CC, moderate CC, major CC, and catastrophic CC), and Severity-DRGs (S-DRGs), which included three levels (no CC, CC, and major CC). Opting to use the S-DRG concept and its infrastructure, CMS consolidated the existing DRGs (with and without CCs) into base DRGs (those without CCs). In addition, CMS consolidated some DRGs that were low volume or were split according to age, complex, or complicating secondary diagnoses into one DRG. These included the following:

- DRGs 121–122—Acute MI with and without complicating diagnoses were consolidated into one DRG.
- DRGs 124–125—MDC 5 principal diagnosis with cardiac catheterization with and without complex diagnosis were consolidated into one DRG.
- Three pairs of burn DRGs associated with significant trauma (CMS-DRGs 506 and 507,

508 and 509, and 510 and 511) were consolidated into one DRG.

- All DRGs based on age (for example, ages 0–17 years; diabetes onset at age 35 years or younger) were consolidated into their base DRGs, given that these base DRGs are low volume in the Medicare population. CMS did, however, leave the maternity and newborn DRGs intact.
- Low-volume DRGs treated mainly on an outpatient basis were consolidated into related DRGs, eliminating separate DRGs for carpal tunnel release, cataract extraction, and laparoscopy.

In addition, CMS created a new DRG for craniofacial procedures—MS-DRG 131–132 (Craniofacial procedures)—that had been previously assigned to CMS DRG 52 and CMS-DRGs 55–63.

Base CC Structure Determination

Once the base DRGs were established using the S-DRG model, CMS established three different levels of CC severity—MCC, CC, and non-CC—into which the applicable diagnosis codes were subdivided. Diagnosis codes classified as MCCs reflected the highest level of severity, while diagnosis codes at the next level of severity were classified as CCs. The lowest level of severity, non-CCs, includes diagnosis codes that do not significantly affect severity of illness and resource utilization.

MCC/CC Determinations

In stratifying MCCs, CCs, and non-CCs, each diagnosis was again evaluated to determine to what extent its presence as a secondary diagnosis increased hospital resource utilization.

CMS applied the initial revised CC list and categorizations just described to those used in 3M's AP-DRGs and the APR-DRGs, opting to select MCCs from the AP-DRG system and the severity levels 3 (major) and 4 (extensive) from the APR-DRG list. CMS designated a non-CC as any diagnosis that was a non-CC in the revised CC list, was a non-CC in the AP-DRG list, and was an APR-DRG default severity level of 1 (minor). Any diagnosis that did not meet either of the above criteria was designated as a CC.

The only exception to CMS's approach was for diagnoses related to newborns, obstetric, and congenital anomalies. These diagnoses are very low volume in the Medicare population and were not reviewed for purposes of creating the revised CC list. CMS used the APR-DRGs to categorize these diagnoses. For newborn, obstetric, and congenital anomaly diagnoses, CMS designated the APR-DRG default severity levels 3 (major) and 4 (extreme) diagnoses as an MCC, the APR-DRG default severity level 2 (moderate) diagnoses as a CC, and the APR DRG default severity level 1 (minor) diagnoses as a non-CC.

CMS then evaluated the interaction of DRG groups without CCs (initially labeled by CMS as C1), with one CC but no MCC (C2), and with one MCC (C3) and studied each individual diagnosis within each class to determine its impact on resource utilization as a ratio of average charges for patients with that individual diagnosis to all of those within that class. The following is a sample formula (Cnt1 means the count of the number of times that diagnosis was found in C1; the others follow suit):

Table 3.1 Examples of Impact on Resource Use of Secondary Diagnoses

Code	Count of C1	C1	Count of C2	C2	Count of C3	C3	CC Subclass
401.1, Benign essential hypertension	12,308	0.955	40,113	1.715	5,297	2.384	Non-CC
530.81, Esophageal reflux	294,673	0.986	917,058	1.639	122,076	2.302	Non-CC
560.1, Paralytic Ileus	10,651	1.466	87,788	2.320	51,303	3.226	CC
491.20, Obstructive chronic bronchitis	7,003	1.416	32,276	2.193	13,355	3.035	CC
410.71, Subendocardial infarction initial episode	1,657	2.245	30,226	2.778	42,862	3.232	MCC
518.81, Acute respiratory failure	5,332	2.096	118,937	2.936	223,054	3.337	MCC

Source: CMS Final Rule (Federal Register)

If the ratio in the C1 group was approximately 1.0, it was designated as a non-CC. If it was approximately 2.0, it was designated as a CC. If it was approximately 3.0, it was designated as an MCC. A complete list of these determinations is available at http://www.cms.hhs.gov/AcuteInpatient PPS/downloads/CCAnalysisdatafiles.zip

Once the list was generated, CMS staff, medical directors, and medical consultants refined it to look for possible additions and deletions to the CC exclusion list. For example, although cardiomyopathy (425.4) is a CC, consultants thought that if the patient was admitted for congestive heart failure, it should not be treated as a CC.

Final Refinement CT: Once the CC and MCC groups had been determined, CMS engaged in a final refinement process. To qualify as a CC or an MCC, the diagnosis had to meet all five of the following criteria:

- A reduction in variance of charges of at least 3 percent within the MS-DRG CC or MCC subgroup.
- At least 5 percent of the patients in the MS-DRG group had to fall within the CC or MCC subgroup.
- At least 500 cases must be in the CC or MCC subgroup.
- There must be at least a 20 percent difference in average charges between subgroups.
- There must be a $4,000 difference in average charge between subgroups.

From these criteria, CMS created four types of DRG splits:

- Those where a base DRG would have no subdivision (for example, MS-DRG 313 (Chest Pain)

- Those where either a CC or an MCC would change the DRG equally, such as MS-DRG 715 (Other male reproductive system OR procedure for malignancy with CC/MCC), corresponding to MS-DRG 716 (Other male reproductive system OR procedure for malignancy w/o CC/MCC)
- Those where only an MCC would change the DRG, such as, MS-DRG 235 (Coronary artery bypass graft w/o cardiac cath w/MCC), corresponding to MS-DRG 236 (Coronary artery bypass graft w/o cardiac cath w/o MCC)
- Those where a three-way subdivision would occur, such as:

  500 Soft tissue procedures w/ MCC
  501 Soft tissue procedures w/ CC
  502 Soft tissue procedures w/o CC/MCC

This process derived 745 MS-DRGs. CMS provides the following comparison for the DRGs listed here.

The final rule modified the CC list based on public comment. For example, Acute posthemorrhagic anemia (285.1) was added as a CC and Coma (780.01) was moved from a CC to an MCC. A list of the CMS DRGs CCs, MS-DRG CCs, and MS-DRG MCCs approved for FY2008 is in Appendix A.

CMS subjected MS-DRGs and this new CC/MCC list to outside review by the RAND Corporation, comparing it with 3M's AP-DRGs, CMS's Consolidated Severity (APR-DRG–based) DRGs and other "off-the-shelf" DRG methodologies. MS-DRGs explained 43 percent of the cost variation, which was a 9.1 percent improvement over the CMS DRGs. Furthermore, the overall explanatory power (adjusted R^2 value—a statistical term denoting the percentage of variation in the dependent variable accounted for by the independent predictor variable—the

Table 3.2   Overall Statistics for CMS DRGs

CC Subclass—Current CMS-DRG	Percent	Average Charges
One or more CCs	77.66	$24,538
Non-CC	22.34	$14,795

Table 3.3   Overall Statistics for MS-DRGs

CC Subgroup	Number of Cases	Percent	Average Charges
MCC	2,607,351	22.2	$44,219
CC	4,298,362	36.6	$24,115
Non-CC	4,826,980	41.1	$18,416

Source: CMS Final Rule (Federal Register)

higher the better) of the MS-DRGs was higher than the AP-DRGs but lower than the other systems analyzed. Of some concern, the MS-DRGs have the lowest adjusted R^2 values, among the severity-adjusted systems in seven MDCs. In three of these MDCs, the R^2 values were actually lower than under the CMS DRGs—MDC 19 (Mental Diseases and Disorders), MDC 20 (Alcohol/Drug Use and Alcohol/Drug Induced Organic Mental Disorders), and MDC 22 (Burns). Although Consolidated Severity DRGs performed the best, the system was not adopted because of its propensity for DRG creep. Further details may be found in the RAND addendum report available at: http://www.cms.hhs.gov/reports/downloads/WR434Z1.pdf

Even though CMS was concerned that MS-DRGs did not perform well in some MDCs, because it is in the public domain, less expensive to implement than the other systems, and strongly supported in the FY2007 comment period, CMS states that MS-DRGs will likely be the system that Medicare uses permanently for the Inpatient Prospective Payment System (IPPS). Although future public comment or industry may change this perspective, MS-DRGs will likely remain as Medicare's primary determinant of inpatient hospital reimbursement. As the other methodologies still apply in many quality and resource utilization ranking programs (for example, Healthgrades®, The Delta Group®, CareScience®, the Pennsylvania Healthcare Cost Containment Council) used in pay-for-performance and public reporting, HIM professionals and their physicians must still understand them to document and code illness severity accurately.

Learning, Understanding, and Differentiating MS-DRG CCs and MCCs

Under MS-DRGs, the numbers of codes assigned to the MCC, CC, and non-CC categories are as follows:

Table 3.4 Distribution of CC and MCC Codes in MS-DRGs

MS-DRG Designation of FY 2008 ICD-9-CM Codes	Number of Codes
MCC	1,584
CC	3,343
Non-CC	8,750
Total	13,677

Source: CMS. Available at http://www.cms.hhs.gov/AcuteInpatientPPS/downloads/CMS-1533-CN2.pdf

DRGs with CCs have a higher weight than DRGs without CCs and, for the most part, DRGs with MCCs have a higher weight than DRGs with CCs.

Following are examples of the three different types of CC splits.

3-way Split

MS-DRG	Title	FY2007 RW
500	Soft tissue procedures w/ MCC	2.4096
501	Soft tissue procedures w/ CC	1.5598
502	Soft tissue procedures w/o CC/MCC	1.0342

2-way Split Where the CC and MCC have Equal Weight

MS-DRG	Title	FY2007 RW
507	Major shoulder or elbow joint procedures w/ CC/MCC	1.4296
508	Major shoulder or elbow joint procedures w/o CC/MCC	1.1330

2-way Split Where Only the MCC Carries Weight

MS-DRG	Title	FY2007 RW
865	Viral illness w/ MCC	1.2074
866	Viral illness w/o MCC	0.7527

Impact of Patient Status on CC Application

Unlike CMS DRGs, where patient status (discharge disposition) has no effect on the CC status, CMS stipulated that the following diagnoses would not count as CCs or MCCs if the patient died on that admission.

- 427.41—Ventricular fibrillation
- 427.5—Cardiac arrest
- 785.51—Cardiogenic shock
- 785.59—Other shock without mention of trauma
- 799.1—Respiratory arrest

New and Deleted CCs

MS-DRGs added and deleted many CCs, compared with CMS DRGs. Many of the CCs that were deleted, such as 250.x2 or 250.x3 (Uncontrolled diabetes), 428.0 (Congestive heart failure) NOS, 427.31 (Atrial fibrillation), and 276.51 (Dehydration) remain CCs in other methodologies (for example, APR-DRGs). Although coders must familiarize themselves with the diagnoses that have been added and deleted as MS-DRG CCs or MCCs, they must not forget to rank CCs in other methodologies within the first nine diagnoses so that quality ranking companies using the MedPAR may include them. Appendix A provides a link to a list of CMS-CCs that are not MS-DRG CCs or MCCs. If physician documentation does not clearly delineate the patient's severity of illness, a clinical documentation improvement (CDI) opportunity exists.

To better understand and implement the new CC system, following is a review of the new changes by ICD-9-CM chapter.

ICD-9-CM Chapter 1: Infectious and Parasitic Diseases 001–139

One of the greatest improvements in the new MS-DRG CC structure is the addition of many infectious diseases that were not CCs under the CMS-DRG system.

Of significance is the inclusion of infectious diarrhea (especially antibiotic-related diarrhea due to *difficile*) and specified food poisonings as new CCs. Most infectious complications of HIV are now counted as CCs (for example, otitis externa from herpes zoster and *Mycobacterium avian-intracellulare*). Diseases usually seen in foreign countries (for example, dengue and kuru) also have been added. Most diseases that must be reported to the public health department will count as CCs, thus the hospital's infection control coordinator may opt to update the coding department regularly to ascertain that these conditions are captured, coded, and reported to fiscal intermediaries as well.

Although CMS added food poisoning, *Clostridium difficile* colitis, gastrointestinal bacterial infections, and giardiasis, which all are common causes of infectious diarrhea, as CCs, viral gastroenteritis does not count as a CC. If only the term "diarrhea due to intestinal infection" is documented, especially if an antibiotic such as Flagyl® (metronidazole), Cipro® (ciprofloxacin), or oral vancomycin is administered, a CDI opportunity exists in physician documentation of its likely underlying etiology.

Deleted CCs include late effect of poliomyelitis and tuberculosis and infections without specified manifestations (for example, histoplasmosis, measles, and mumps).

Sarcoidosis and some of its manifestations (for example, pulmonary fibrosis and pulmonary disease in diseases classified elsewhere) also have been deleted as CCs. CDI opportunities in sarcoidosis include complications of the disease or its treatment (for example, chronic respiratory failure requiring home oxygen and secondary Cushing's syndrome as a consequence of long-term corticosteroid treatment).

CMS determined that brucellosis not otherwise specified is a CC, yet specified versions are not. Protozoal infections such as cryptosporidiosis and giardiasis are CCs, yet balantidiasis, a rare protozoal infection contracted from pigs, which consumes similar resources as the other protozoal infections, is not.

Infectious hepatitis, chronic hepatitis B, and unspecified hepatitis without coma are CCs, whereas the more specified chronic hepatitis C without coma is not. If a patient has known cirrhosis of the liver that could result in hepatic encephalopathy with patient noncompliance with their low-protein diet or medications (for example, oral neomycin or lactulose), a CDI opportunity exists to determine if the patient has hepatic encephalopathy that is controlled on medications and/or diet.

As a general rule, to qualify as an MCC, a physician has to specify that the infection acutely involves the central nervous system, the heart, the bloodstream (for example, septicemia), or the lung parenchyma (not just the bronchi) and/or that it has systemic manifestations involving these organs. Consider the following differentiation of *Candida* and histoplasmosis infections.

ICD-9-CM Code	CC Designation	Title
007.0	Not a CC	Balantidiasis
007.1	CC	Giardiasis
007.2	CC	Coccidiosis
007.4	CC	Cryptosporidiosis
007.5	CC	Cyclosporiasis
007.8	CC	Other specified protozoal intestinal diseases
007.9	CC	Unspecified protozoal intestinal disease
023.0	Not a CC	Brucella melitensis
023.1	Not a CC	Brucella abortus
023.2	Not a CC	Brucella suis
023.3	Not a CC	Brucella canis
023.8	CC	Other brucellosis
023.9	CC	Brucellosis, unspecified
070.0	MCC	Viral hepatitis A with hepatic coma
070.1	CC	Viral hepatitis A without mention of hepatic coma
070.20	MCC	Viral hepatitis B with hepatic coma, acute or unspecified, without mention of hepatitis delta
070.21	MCC	Viral hepatitis B with hepatic coma, acute or unspecified, with hepatitis delta
070.22	MCC	Chronic viral hepatitis B with hepatic coma without mention of hepatitis delta
070.23	MCC	Chronic viral hepatitis B with hepatic coma with hepatitis delta
070.30	CC	Viral hepatitis B without mention of hepatic coma, acute or unspecified, without mention of hepatitis delta
070.31	CC	Viral hepatitis B without mention of hepatic coma, acute or unspecified, with hepatitis delta
070.32	CC	Chronic viral hepatitis B without mention of hepatic coma without or hepatitis delta
070.33	CC	Chronic viral hepatitis B without mention of hepatic coma with hepatitis delta
070.41	MCC	Acute hepatitis C with hepatic coma
070.42	MCC	Hepatitis delta without mention of active hepatitis B, with hepatic coma, and with hepatitis delta with hepatitis B carrier state
070.43	MCC	Hepatitis E with hepatic coma
070.44	MCC	Chronic hepatitis C with hepatic coma

(Continued)

ICD-9-CM Code	CC Designation	Title
070.49	MCC	Other specified viral hepatitis with hepatic coma
070.51	CC	Acute hepatitis C without mention of hepatic coma
070.52	CC	Hepatitis delta without mention of active hepatitis B or hepatic coma
070.53	CC	Hepatitis E without mention of hepatic coma
070.54	Not a CC	Chronic hepatitis C without mention of hepatic coma
070.59	CC	Other specified viral hepatitis without mention of hepatic coma
070.6	MCC	Unspecified viral hepatitis with hepatic coma
070.70	Not a CC	Unspecified viral hepatitis C without hepatic coma
070.71	MCC	Unspecified viral hepatitis C with hepatic coma
070.9	CC	Unspecified viral hepatitis without mention of hepatic coma
112.0	CC	Candidiasis of mouth
112.1	Not a CC	Candidiasis of vulva and vagina
112.2	CC	Candidiasis of other urogenital sites
112.3	Not a CC	Candidiasis of skin and nails
112.4	MCC	Candidiasis of lung
112.5	MCC	Disseminated candidiasis
112.81	MCC	Candidal endocarditis
112.82	CC	Candidal otitis externa
112.83	MCC	Candidal meningitis
112.84	CC	Candidal esophagitis
112.85	CC	Candidal enteritis
112.89	Not a CC	Candidiasis of other specified sites
112.9	Not a CC	Candidiasis of unspecified site
115.00	Not a CC	Histoplasma capsulatum without mention of manifestation
115.01	MCC	Histoplasma capsulatum meningitis
115.02	CC	Histoplasma capsulatum retinitis
115.03	MCC	Histoplasma capsulatum pericarditis
115.04	MCC	Histoplasma capsulatum endocarditis
115.05	MCC	Histoplasma capsulatum pneumonia
115.09	CC	Infection by histoplasma capsulatum, with mention of other manifestation
115.10	Not a CC	Histoplasma duboisii without mention of manifestation
115.11	MCC	Histoplasma duboisii meningitis
115.12	CC	Histoplasma duboisii retinitis

ICD-9-CM Code	CC Designation	Title
115.13	MCC	Histoplasma duboisii pericarditis
115.14	MCC	Histoplasma duboisii endocarditis
115.15	MCC	Histoplasma duboisii pneumonia
115.19	CC	Infection by histoplasma duboisii with mention of other manifestation
115.90	Not a CC	Histoplasmosis NOS without mention of manifestation
115.91	MCC	Histoplasmosis meningitis, unspecified
115.92	CC	Histoplasmosis retinitis, unspecified
115.93	MCC	Histoplasmosis pericarditis, unspecified
115.94	MCC	Histoplasmosis endocarditis
115.95	MCC	Histoplasmosis pneumonia, unspecified
238.5	CC	Neoplasm of uncertain behavior of histiocytic and mast cells
238.6	CC	Neoplasm of uncertain behavior of plasma cells
238.73	CC	High-grade myelodysplastic syndrome lesions
238.74	CC	Myelodysplastic syndrome with 5q deletion
238.76	CC	Myelofibrosis with myeloid metaplasia
238.79	CC	Other lymphatic and hematopoietic tissues

ICD-9-CM Chapter 2: Neoplasms (140–239)

CMS added many primary solid neoplasms to the CC list so that most malignant solid neoplasms invisible to the naked eye are now CCs. Primary malignant neoplasms of the lip, oral cavity, pharynx, spleen, nasal cavities, middle ear, sinuses, larynx, skin, breast (male and female), uterus, uterine adnexa (except the ovary), vagina (and surrounding structures), male genitals, eye, thyroid gland, and other ill-defined sites (for example, pelvis, thorax, abdomen) remain excluded. All malignant neoplasms specified as secondary and those involving the lymphatic and hematopoietic tissue (200–208) are CCs. Of interest, CMS classified the following neoplasms of uncertain nature as CCs.

Myelodysplastic disorders are clonal bone marrow disorders primarily affecting adults. Usually underdiagnosed or passed off as anemia of chronic disease or anemia of chronic kidney disease, The World Health Organization and ICD-9-CM classify myelodysplasia as follows:

Disease	ICD-9-CM	CC Status	Blood Findings	Bone Marrow Findings
Refractory anemia (RA)	238.72	Not a CC	Anemia No or rare blasts	Erythroid dysplasia *only* < 5 percent blasts < 15 percent ringed sideroblasts
Refractory anemia with ringed sideroblasts (RARS)	238.72	Not a CC	Anemia No blasts	Erythroid dysplasia *only* > 15 percent ringed sideroblasts < 5 percent blasts

Disease	ICD-9-CM	CC Status	Blood Findings	Bone Marrow Findings
Refractory cytopenia with multilineage dysplasia (RCMD)	238.72	Not a CC	Cytopenias (bicytopenia or pancytopenia) No or rare blasts No Auer rods <1 × 10_9/L monocytes	Dysplasia in 10 percent of cells in 2 or more myeloid cell lines < 5 percent blasts in marrow No Auer rods < 15 percent ringed sideroblasts
Refractory cytopenia with multilineage dysplasia and ringed sideroblasts (RCMD-RS)	238.72	Not a CC	Cytopenias (bicytopenia or pancytopenia) No or rare blasts No Auer rods <1 × 10^9/L monocytes	Dysplasia in ≥ 10 percent of cells in 2 or more myeloid cell lines ≥ 15 percent ringed sideroblasts < 5 percent blasts No Auer rods
Refractory anemia with excess blasts-1 (RAEB-1)	238.73	CC	Cytopenias <5 percent blasts No Auer rods <1 × 10^9/L monocytes	Unilineage or multilineage dysplasia 5 percent to 9 percent blasts No Auer rods
Refractory anemia with excess blasts-2 (RAEB-2)	238.73	CC	Cytopenias 5 percent to 19 percent blasts Auer rods ± <1 × 10^9/L monocytes	Unilineage or multilineage dysplasia 10 percent to 19 percent blasts No Auer rods ±
MDS associated with isolated del(5q)	238.74	CC	Anemia<5 percent blasts Platelets normal or increased	Normal to increased megakaryocytes with hypolobated nuclei < 5 percent blasts No Auer rodsl isolated del(5q)
Myelodysplastic syndrome, unclassified (MDS-U)	238.75	Not a CC	Cytopenias No or rare blasts No Auer rods	Unilineage dysplasia in granulocytes or megakaryocytes < 5 percent blasts No Auer rods

The primary manifestations of myelodysplastic disorders are anemia, leukopenia, and thrombocytopenia. Although there are some promising therapies that effectively treat myelodysplastic syndrome, such as bone marrow transplant, lineage colony stimulating factor, 5-azacytidine (Vidaza®), decitabine (Dacogen®), antithymocyte globulin, and lenalidomide (Revlimid®), the last of which is particularly effective with myelodysplastic syndrome associated with isolated 5q deletion, blood transfusions remain the main treatment (*Coding Clinic*, First Quarter, 1997, 5–6).

The ICD-9-CM Official Guidelines for Coding and Reporting for chapter 2 require that if a patient has anemia associated with malignancy, and that the treatment is only for the anemia, the appropriate anemia code, such as code 285.22 (Anemia in neoplastic disease), is designated as the principal diagnosis and is followed by the appropriate code for the malignancy.

This instruction does not apply to myelodysplastic syndrome, because *Coding Clinic* (1st Quarter, 1997, 5–6) says to code the appropriate myelodysplasia code first in the setting of pancytopenia, given that blood transfusions are a mainstay of treatment. ICD-9-CM says that when a treatment is directed at the malignancy, the coder should designate the malignancy as the principal diagnosis.

Example: A patient with myelodysplasia was admitted for syncope. The only findings were that she had a hematocrit of 20, for which she received four blood transfusions. There were no other CCs. Because anemia of neoplastic diseases is not a CC, and the physician did not link the anemia to the patient's syncope, the MS-DRG assigned was MS-DRG 312 (Syncope and Collapse) (RW 0.7197). If the syncope had been linked to the patient's anemia caused by the myelodysplastic syndrome, the MS-DRG would have changed to MS-DRG 812 (Red Blood Cell disorders without MCC) (RW 0.7780). The presence of an MCC, such as 042 (HIV infection), would have changed the MS-DRG to 811 (Red Blood Cell Disorder with MCC) (RW 1.0006).

Example: A patient with a 5-year history of myelodysplasia is admitted with community-acquired pneumonia treated with levofloxacin alone. Because the patient's anemia is due to myelodysplasia, she received a blood transfusion. The final diagnosis was pneumonia, myelodysplasia, and anemia, grouping to MS-DRG 195 (Simple pneumonia and pleurisy without CC/MCC) (RW 0.8398). The coder queried the physician for the exact stage of the patient's myelodysplastic syndrome, and the physician replied that the patient had refractory anemia with excess blasts. Upon documentation of this comment in the discharge summary, the MS-DRG changed to MS-DRG 194 (Simple pneumonia and pleurisy with CC) (RW 1.0235).

ICD-9-CM Chapter 3: Endocrine, Nutritional and Metabolic Diseases and Immunity Disorders (240–279)

Following are the most significant changes to the CC structure in chapter 3 of the ICD-9-CM :

- Deletion of diabetes (except for diabetic ketoacidosis, diabetic hyperosmolarity, and diabetic coma), hypoparathyroidism, hyperthyroidism (except for when the patient is described as having thyrotoxic storm), volume depletion, fluid overload, hyperkalemia, and nonspecific electrolytes and fluid disorders as CCs.
- Addition of other and unspecified anterior pituitary hyperfunction, other disorders of the neurohypophysis (for example, Syndrome of Inappropriate Diuretic Hormone (SIADH)), beriberi, other and unspecified manifestations of thiamine deficiency, ariboflavinosis (vitamin B_2 deficiency), active rickets, uric acid nephrolithiasis, disorders of porphyrin metabolism (porphyria), amyloidosis, and the mucopolysaccharidosis as CCs.

Chapter 3 emphasizes the following areas:

Diabetes

As stated in chapter 2 of the ICD-9-CM, codes 250.1x, 250.2x, and 250.3x are classified as follows:

Diabetic Ketoacidosis MCC   Primarily occurring in type 1 diabetes but can occur in type 2 or secondary diabetes. Usually presents with hyperglycemia (300–600 mg/dl), ketosis (4+ plasma ketones, serum acetone of 1:8 or greater), profound dehydration on physical examination, Kussmaul's respiration, coma (if present, assign to 250.3x), and elevated anion gap metabolic acidosis (pH 6.80–7.30, HCO_3 under 18 meq/L, "elevated anion gap"). The serum potassium level is usually high due to acidosis; if normal, the patient's potassium stores are almost depleted.

Diabetic Hyperosmolarity MCC   Usually occurring in type 2 diabetes but can occur in type 1 diabetics who have some insulin in their bodies. Results in profound dehydration, hyperglycemia, and hyperosmolality (330–380) without evidence of metabolic acidosis. A blood glucose level above 550 mg/dL correlates with a serum osmolality of more than 330.

Coma

Coma in diabetic patients is automatically linked unless the physician negates the cause and effect relationship of the coma to the diabetes, coding to 250.3x. Coma is not stupor or lethargy; a complete loss of consciousness must occur to qualify. If a patient presents with insulin coma, ICD-9-CM requires a code assignment of 250.3x, not just 250.8x, which is applied to diabetic hypoglycemia. Nondiabetic hypoglycemic coma, such as in patients with insulin-secreting tumors, codes to 251.0. Because diabetic coma can occur in patients with secondary diabetes or can be due to other causes, a CDI opportunity exists when coma is present in diabetic patients.

Although uncontrolled diabetes by itself is no longer a CC, some chronic complications of diabetes include the following:

- Diabetic autonomic neuropathy (250.7x + 337.1)
- Diabetic nephropathy with chronic kidney disease, Stage 4 or higher (250.4x + 585.x (4th digit of 4, or 5). In these patients, the serum creatinine is usually above 2.5 mg/dL.
- Diabetic cardiomyopathy (250.80 + 425.8). Usually it is associated acute or chronic systolic or diastolic heart failure is a CC or MCC as well.

Hyperthyroidism (Thyrotoxicosis)

Thyrotoxicosis is a state of excessive thyroid hormone. Hyperthyroidism is thyrotoxicosis resulting from a disease of the thyroid itself. Some physicians use these terms interchangeably. Thyrotoxicosis has many manifestations, including the following:

- General—Weight loss fatigue and weakness hyperactivity, irritability, apathy, depression

(especially in elderly people), thirst, polyuria, heat intolerance, sweating
- Cardiovascular—Palpitations, dyspnea, angina, tachycardia, atrial fibrillation, heart failure, thyrotoxic cardiomyopathy (which may manifest as high output congestive acute systolic heart failure)
- Neuromuscular—Tremor, agitation, chorea, psychosis, emotional liability, proximal myopathy, bulbar myopathy periodic paralysis
- Reproductive—Loss of libido, gynecomastia, oligomenorrhea, infertility
- Gastrointestinal—Nausea, vomiting, diarrhea, steatorrhea, hepatomegaly, splenomegaly
- Dermatological—Pruritus, thinning of hair, palmar erythema, spider naevi
- Bone—Osteopenia, osteoporosis

A diagnosis of thyrotoxicosis is made with an appropriate history and physical examination and is confirmed with elevated free serum thyroxine (T_4) and free serum triiodothyronine (T_3) levels, and/or suppression of the thyroid stimulating hormone (TSH) level (rarely—the TSH can be elevated if a TSH-secreting pituitary tumor is present). Underlying causes include:

- Primary hyperthyroidism
  - Graves' disease—thyroid overactivity caused by immune-mediated thyroid receptor stimulation
  - Overactive thyroid nodules or multinodular goiters
  - Functioning thyroid cancer metastatasis
- Secondary hyperthyroidism
  - Pituitary tumors secreting TSH

- Gestational thyrotoxicosis (in pregnancy)
- Other tumors
- Thyrotoxicosis without hyperthyroidism
  - Accidental or intentional overdose of thyroid replacement medications, which some people misuse in a misguided attempt to lose weight. Thyroid hormones induce muscle loss, not fat loss.
  - Subacute thyroiditis
  - Thyroid gland destruction from radiation or amiodarone

Increased uptake of radioactive iodine on thyroid scan may indicate hyperthyroidism due to Graves' disease or a hyperfunction thyroid nodule; however, acute or subacute thyroiditis or external administration of thyroid hormone will have reduced iodine uptake.

ICD-9-CM classifies thyrotoxicosis into those with thyroid crisis (storm) and those without. Thyroid storm, also referred to as thyrotoxic crisis, is an acute, life-threatening, hypermetabolic state induced by excessive release of thyroid hormones. Clinical presentations include fever, tachycardia, hypertension, and neurologic and gastrointestinal abnormalities. Hypertension may be followed by congestive heart failure that is associated with hypotension and shock. Because thyroid storm is almost invariably fatal if left untreated, rapid diagnosis and aggressive treatment are critical. A patient is not in thyroid storm unless hyperthyroidism causes encephalopathy, respiratory distress, heart failure, hypotension, or shock requiring intensive care. Thyroid storm codes are a CC.

Although acute thyroiditis remains a CC, it is rare and unlikely to be diagnosed in hospital inpatients.

ICD-9-CM Code	CC Designation	Title
242.01	MCC	Toxic diffuse goiter with mention of thyrotoxic crisis or storm
242.11	MCC	Toxic uninodular goiter with mention of thyrotoxic crisis or storm
242.21	MCC	Toxic multinodular goiter with mention of thyrotoxic crisis or storm
242.31	MCC	Toxic nodular goiter, unspecified type, with mention of thyrotoxic crisis or storm
242.41	MCC	Thyrotoxicosis from ectopic thyroid nodule with mention of thyrotoxic crisis or storm
242.81	MCC	Thyrotoxicosis of other specified origin with mention of thyrotoxic crisis or storm
242.91	MCC	Thyrotoxicosis without mention of goiter or other cause, with mention of thyrotoxic crisis or storm
245.0	CC	Acute thyroiditis

Hyperkalemia

Hyperkalemia is no longer a CC, yet many of its underlying causes are, including:

- End-stage renal disease (585.6)— MCC
- Chronic kidney disease–Stage V (585.5)—CC
- Chronic kidney disease–Stage IV (585.4)—CC
- Addison's disease (255.41)—CC
- Hypoaldosteronism (255.42)—CC

Special note should be made of patients with hyperkalemia due to aldosterone antagonists (for example, spironolactone), angiotensin-converting enzyme (ACE) inhibitors (for example, captopril, ramipril, and enalapril), and angiotensin receptor blockers (ARBs) (for example, losartan and valsartan).

Spironolactone impairs urinary potassium excretion by blocking aldosterone's effect on the distal tubule of the kidney. ACE inhibitors and angiotensin receptor blockers impair urinary potassium excretion by inhibiting the creation of aldosterone or interfering with the stimulatory effect of angiotensin II on aldosterone secretion in the adrenal gland (Palmer 2004). Because angiotensin II stimulates aldosterone production, a relative state of hypoaldosteronism occurs in predisposed patients. If the physician does not describe the mechanism of the patient's hyperkalemia due to these medications, a CDI opportunity exists to describe the hypoaldosteronism induced by these medications.

Example: A 70-year-old white man with hypertensive kidney disease, chronic kidney disease–stage 3, was admitted for community-acquired pneumonia without evidence of systemic inflammatory response syndrome (SIRS) and generalized weakness. His current medications include Diovan HCT® (a combination of valsartan and hydrochlorothiazide). His serum sodium was 134 mEq/dL (normal 134–144 at this hospital), his serum potassium was 6.5 mEq/dL (normal 3.5–5.0 at this hospital), his blood urea nitrogen was 60 and his serum creatinine was 2.2 mg/dL (normal less than 1.2 mg/dL at this hospital). Upon hydration and discontinuation of the Diovan HCT, his sodium and potassium levels normalized and his creatinine level fell to 1.4 mg/dL, consistent with his stage 3 chronic kidney disease. His pneumonia resolved with levofloxacin. The final diagnosis was community-acquired pneumonia, dehydration, and hyperkalemia due to Diovan HCT® and hypertensive kidney disease, stage 3, grouping him to MS-DRG 195 (Simple pneumonia and pleurisy without CC/MCC) (RW 0.8398). The coder queried the physician for the underlying etiology of the patient's hyperkalemia and the mechanism by which Diovan HCT® caused the hyperkalemia. The physician explained in his progress note that the valsartan induced a state of hypoaldosteronism in the patient. Given this information, the coder added the additional diagnosis of hypoaldosteronism, resulting in MS-DRG 194 (Simple pneumonia and pleurisy with CC) (RW 1.0235).

Thiamine Deficiency (Beriberi)

A common complication of prolonged alcohol abuse or alcoholism is malnutrition along with thiamine deficiency. Up to 80 percent of alcoholics have thiamine deficiency, otherwise known as beriberi. Chronic alcohol consumption can cause thiamine deficiency and thus reduced enzyme activity through several mechanisms, including inadequate dietary intake, malabsorption of thiamine from the gastrointestinal tract, and impaired utilization of thiamine in the cells (Martin, Singleton, and Hiller-Sturmhöfel 2004). Thiamine deficiency is classified as follows:

- Wet beriberi—Cardiovascular symptoms of high-output congestive heart failure
- Dry beriberi—Neurologic symptoms, especially brain disease in alcoholics. Some forms include Wernicke's encephalopathy, an acute condition of mental confusion, impairment of eye movement, or impaired coordination of the lower extremities; Korsakoff's psychosis, a chronic neuropsychiatric syndrome with behavioral abnormalities, the inability to remember new facts (anterograde amnesia), and cerebellar degeneration.

Beriberi, or thiamine deficiency, is diagnosed by measurement of blood thiamine and whole-blood or erythrocyte transketolase activity, measurement of urinary thiamine excretion, or clinical response to administered thiamine (symptoms improve after the person is given thiamine supplements). Most physicians do not order these tests and, for the most part, simply routinely administer parenteral thiamine to severely ill alcoholics, assuming that they are thiamine deficient.

Thiamine deficiency and beriberi are now a CC. If thiamine is administered to a patient, a CDI opportunity exists to determine if the patient is possibly thiamine deficient.

Malnutrition

For FY2008, CMS designated severe malnutrition as an MCC and malnutrition not otherwise specified as a CC. Mild and moderate malnutrition were deleted from the CC list.

ICD-9-CM Code	CC Designation	Title
260	MCC	Kwashiorkor
261	MCC	Nutritional marasmus
262	MCC	Other severe protein-calorie malnutrition
263.0	Not a CC	Malnutrition of moderate degree
263.1	Not a CC	Malnutrition of mild degree
263.2	CC	Arrested development following protein-calorie malnutrition
263.8	CC	Other protein-calorie malnutrition
263.9	CC	Unspecified protein-calorie malnutrition
799.4	CC	Cachexia

Degree of Malnutrition	Normal	Mild	Moderate	Severe
Albumin (g/dL)	3.5–5.0	3.0–3.4	2.1–2.9	< 2.1
Transferring (mg/dL)	176–315	134–175	117–133	< 117
Prealbumin (mg/dL)	18–45	10–17	5–9	< 5
Total lymphocyte count (cells/mm^3)	1,801–3,500	1,501–1,800	900–1,500	< 900

Patients are at risk for malnutrition if they meet one or more of the following criteria:

- Unintentional loss of more than 10 percent of usual body weight in the preceding 3 months
- Body weight less than 90 percent of ideal for height
- Body mass index (BMI) (weight in kilograms [kg] divided by height [m^2]) less than 18.5

With regard to varying levels of severity of malnutrition, the following rules apply:

- Body weight less than 90 percent of ideal for height represents risk of malnutrition (not a CC)
- Body weight less than 85 percent of ideal for height constitutes *malnutrition* (a CC),
- Body weight less than 70 percent of ideal represents *severe malnutrition* (an MCC)
- Body weight less than 60 percent of ideal is usually incompatible with survival

V85.0 (Body Mass Index under 19, adult) and V85.4 (Body Mass Index 40 and over) have been designated as CCs. *Coding Clinic* (4th Quarter, 2005, (pp. 97–98) does allow for the BMI to be coded from dietician documentation. If the BMI is less than 16, a CDI opportunity exists for the presence and severity of malnutrition.

Body Mass Index (kg/m^2)	Nutritional Status
< 16.0	Severely malnourished
16.0–16.9	Moderately malnourished
17.0–18.4	Mildly malnourished
18.5–24.9	Normal
25.0–29.9	Overweight
30.0–34.9	Obese (class I)
35.0–39.9	Obese (class II)
≥ 40	Obese (class III)

Source: World Health Organization and the National Institutes of Health

Laboratory studies may substantiate malnutrition and its severity (Seidner 2006). Because malnutrition contributes significantly to surgical risk and mortality and affects physicians' risk-adjusted morality scores, such as those of California cardiac surgeons profiled by the State of California during July 2007, physicians are becoming more interested in having this risk factor quantified and reported (California Office of Statewide Health Planning and Development 2007).

Nutritional assessments are difficult, which is why some physicians do not perform them or do not perform them well. The guidelines above only estimate nutritional status. In many cases, measurement of skin folds, performing intricate calculations of body mass, laboratory, and other data, and considering the patient's clinical circumstances (for example, bedridden status) apply to nutritional assessment. An evaluation by a registered dietician is necessary to accurately determine a patient's nutritional status in concert with the attending physician.

One hospital implemented a dietary assessment sheet completed by the hospital's dietician identifying and quantifying nutritional status that required physician cosignature. Once the physician validated the findings, the coding staff was able to code the comorbid conditions. Their criteria for malnutrition are as follows:

Figure 3.1   Sample Nutritional Assessment Tool

☐ Nutritional Marasmus/Severe Malnutrition (all criteria met)

☐ Albumin: more than 3.0 g/dL or Prealbumin: more than 10 mg/dL

☐ Overt muscle wasting

☐ BMI less than 16

☐ Poor intake of clear liquids or nothing by mouth for 5 or more days

☐ Weight less than 80 percent of ideal body weight and/or significant history of weight loss of over 10 percent in last 6 months

---

☐ Other Severe Protein Calorie Malnutrition (all criteria met)

☐ Albumin: less than 2.7 g/dL or prealbumin: less than 10 mg/dL

☐ Weight less than 60 percent of ideal body weight

☐ BMI less than 16

☐ Weight loss of over 10 percent of usual body weight in last 6 months with muscle wasting

---

☐ Moderate Protein Calorie Malnutrition (two criteria met)

☐ Albumin: 2.1 g/dL to 2.7 g/dL or prealbumin: 5 to 10 mg/dL

☐ BMI between 16 and 17

☐ Weight: 70–79 percent of ideal body weight or 75–84 percent of usual body weight

---

☐ Mild Protein Calorie Malnutrition (two criteria met)

☐ Albumin: 2.8 to 3.5 g/dL or prealbumin: 10 to 15 mg/dL

☐ BMI between 17–18.5

☐ Weight: 80–89 percent of ideal body weight or 85–95 percent of usual body weight

---

☐ Unspecified Protein-Calorie Malnutrition (one criteria met)

☐ 7 or more days with no nutrition support

☐ Overt muscle and adipose tissue wasting

☐ Other: _____

☐ Kwashiorkor Protein Malnutrition—(all criteria met)

☐ Albumin: less than 2.7 g/dL or prealbumin: less than 10 mg/dL

☐ Weight maintenance

☐ Protein intake less than requirement

☐ Weight maintenance

Nutrition Recommendations:

_____

_____

_____

_____

RD Signature: _____ *Date* _____

Physician Comments:

☐ I agree with the above.   ☐ I agree except for:

_____

_____

_____

_____

_____

Physician

Signature: _____ *Date* _____

Example: A chronic alcoholic developed acute coronary syndrome without an acute MI, which required coronary angioplasty with insertion of a drug-eluting stent. He was at 82 percent of his predicted body weight and had a prealbumin level of 5 mg/dL. After the stent implantation, he was started on enteral hyperalimentation and referred to a long-term acute care hospital for refeeding and nutritional support prior to his entry into an alcohol rehabilitation program. The final diagnoses were acute coronary syndrome, chronic continuous alcohol dependence, and moderate malnutrition, resulting in MS-DRG 247 (Percutaneous cardiovascular procedure w/drug-eluting stent w/o MCC) (RW 2.1255). The coder queried the physician regarding the severity of the patient's malnutrition, citing a note from the dietician stating that the patient was severely malnourished. The cardiologist amended his discharge summary to reflect that the patient had severe malnutrition, resulting in MS-DRG 246 (Percutaneous cardiovascular procedure w/drug-eluting stent w/MCC) (RW 2.9046).

Amyloidosis

CMS added amyloidosis to the CC list. Amyloidosis is the accumulation of a protein (called amyloid) in the body's tissues, as delineated below as adapted from the *New England Journal of Medicine* (Rajkuman and Gertz 2007). CMS made these CCs, thus if the patient is on chronic colchicine, melphalan, or dexamethasone therapy or has a bone marrow, liver, or renal transplant, amyloidosis can be a CDI consideration.

Morbid Obesity

CMS chose not to designate morbid obesity (BMI over 40) as a CC. Alternatively, if a dietician or physician document a BMI over 40 (for example, weights of over 250 pounds in a 5'6" individual) in an adult, then V85.4 (Body Mass Index 40 and over, adult) may be assigned, which is a CC. *Coding Clinic* (4th Quarter, 2005, 97–98) does allow for the BMI to be coded from dietician documentation.

Immunocompromised Host

CMS removed 279.8 (Other specified disorders involving the immune mechanism), which usually covered complement deficiencies, and 279.9 (Unspecified disorder of immune mechanism) as CCs yet retained many of the other more specified conditions of compromised immunity.

Type of Amylodosis	Amyloid Protein Component	Usual Treatment
AL or AH (primary)	AL—light chain immunoglobulin Sometimes AH—heavy chain	Melphalan plus dexamethasone Sometimes stem cell transplant
AA—secondary to chronic inflammation or familial Mediterranean fever	Serum amyloid protein	Treatment of the underlying cause
Mutant ATTR	Mutant forms of transthyretin	Liver transplantation
Senile amylodosis	Wild type of transthyretin	None
Other familial types	Various	None or transplantation

ICD-9-CM Code	CC Designation	Title
279.00	CC	Hypogammaglobulinemia, unspecified
279.01	CC	Selective IgA immunodeficiency
279.02	CC	Selective IgM immunodeficiency
279.03	CC	Other selective immunoglobulin deficiencies
279.04	CC	Congenital hypogammaglobulinemia
279.05	CC	Immunodeficiency with increased IgM
279.06	CC	Common variable immunodeficiency

ICD-9-CM Code	CC Designation	Title
279.09	CC	Other deficiency of humoral immunity
279.10	CC	Immunodeficiency with predominant T-cell defect, unspecified
279.11	CC	DiGeorge syndrome
279.12	CC	Wiskott-Aldrich syndrome
279.13	CC	Nezelof syndrome
279.19	CC	Other deficiency of cell-mediated immunity
279.2	CC	Combined immunity deficiency
279.3	CC	Unspecified immunity deficiency

Physicians may describe patients as being immuno-compromised hosts, especially if they have fever. The Centers for Disease Control and Prevention (CDC) defines patients with the following conditions to be immunocompromised (CDC 2007).

- Severe immunocompromise (non-HIV)
  - Active leukemia or lymphoma
  - Generalized malignancy
  - Aplastic anemia
  - Graft versus host disease
  - Congenital immunodeficiency
  - Persons who have received current or recent radiation therapy
  - Solid organ transplant
  - Bone marrow transplant within 2 years of transplantation
  - Persons whose transplants are of longer duration but who are still taking immunosuppressive drugs. For solid organ transplants, much higher risk of infection occurs within the first year of transplant, so high-risk travel might be postponed until after that time.
  - Medications that cause severe immunosuppression, including:
    - High-dose corticosteroids
      —The immunosuppressive effects of steroid treatment vary, but most clinicians consider a dose equivalent to either more than 2 mg/kg of body weight or 20 mg/day of prednisone or equivalent for persons who weigh more than 10 kg when administered for 2 weeks or longer as sufficiently immunosuppressive to raise concern about the safety of vaccination with live-virus vaccines.
    - Alkylating agents (for example, cyclo, phosphamide)
    - Antimetabolites (for example, azathioprine, 6-mercaptopurine)
    - Transplant-related immunosuppressive drugs (for example, cyclosporine, tacrolimus, sirolimus, and mycophenolate mofetil)
    - Mitoxantrone (used in multiple sclerosis)
    - Most cancer chemotherapeutic agents (excluding tamoxifen)
    - Methotrexate, including low-dose weekly regimens
    - Tumor necrosis factor (TNF)-blocking agents such as etanercept, adalimumab, and infliximab
- Severe immunocompromise due to symptomatic HIV/AIDS
  - HIV-infected persons with CD4 counts lower than 200
  - Persons with history of an AIDS-defining illness
  - Clinical manifestations of symptomatic HIV
- Chronic diseases with limited immune deficits
  - Asymptomatic HIV-infected persons with CD4 counts from 200–500
  - Asplenia
  - Chronic renal disease
  - Chronic hepatic disease (cirrhosis and alcoholism)
  - Diabetes
  - Nutritional deficiencies
    - Drugs—Patients taking ribavirin and interferon for hepatitis C infection are at risk for neutropenia.

A CDI opportunity may exist to determine the immune status of patients with these conditions, especially if they develop fever, require antibiotics, or receive therapy, such as intravenous gamma globulin, to support their immune system.

Dehydration/Hypovolemia

CMS deleted dehydration and hypovolemia from the CC list. Only when acute renal failure (evidenced by a tripling of the serum creatinine level from baseline) or shock (hypotension lasting more than 1 hour resistant to fluid resuscitation and associated with end organ dysfunction or lactic acidosis) is documented can hypovolemia or dehydration possibly lead to a CC or an MCC.

ICD-9-CM Chapter 4: Diseases of the Blood and Blood-Forming Organs (280–289)

CMS eliminated thrombocytopenia NOS, qualitative platelet defects NOS, thalassemia without crisis, and many of the anemias as CCs. They did leave sickle cell or thalassemia disease with crisis, hemolytic anemias, pancytopenia, aplastic anemias, and coagulopathies as CCs.

Anemia

CMS maintained 285.1 (Acute blood loss anemia) as a CC but eliminated 280.0 (Chronic blood loss anemia). In the final rule, 282.69 (Other sickle cell disease with crisis) was added as an MCC. CMS also left 998.11 (Hemorrhage complicating a procedure) and 998.12 (Hematoma complicating a procedure) as CCs.

Interestingly, 790.01 (Precipitous drop in hematocrit) is a new CC. This code was added to ICD-9-CM in 1998 to substantiate signs and symptoms necessitating visits to renal dialysis centers (ICD-9-CM Coordination and Maintenance Committee 1998). When described in *Coding Clinic* 4th Quarter, (2000, p. 46), no definition or parameters were given of what constituted a "precipitous drop in hematocrit."

The hematocrit level can fall precipitously as a result of blood loss, hemodilution, or hemolysis. The medical literature defines major blood loss as a loss of 20 percent of total blood volume or more (Mannucci and Levi 2007). Provided that hemodilution or laboratory error has been ruled out, it would be reasonable to assume that a 20 percent decline in baseline hematocrit (a fall of the hematocrit by 8 points in an individual with a baseline hematocrit of 40) constitutes a "precipitous fall in hematocrit level," creating a CDI opportunity.

Hemolytic anemia should be recognized as a potential cause of anemia to assign it as a CC. As discussed in ICD-9-CM chapter 2, hallmarks of hemolytic anemia include the following:

- Anemia (hematocrit less than 33; hemoglobin less than 11)

- Elevated reticulocyte count (usually over 3 percent) or reticulocyte production index over 2.0
- Elevated LDH (due to red cell destruction)
- Positive direct or indirect Coombs test (indicates autoimmune anemia)
- Red cell fragments on peripheral smear (schistocytes).

Thrombocytopenia

Although thrombocytopenia not otherwise specified is not a CC, specified primary thrombocytopenias (for example, immune thrombocytopenia) or Evans syndrome (thrombocytopenia associated with hemolytic anemia) remain as CCs. Secondary thrombocytopenias, even those caused by sepsis or as an adverse drug reaction (for example, heparin-induced thrombocytopenia) are not CCs. If anemia, thrombocytopenia, and leucopenia all are present at the same time, a CDI opportunity exists for pancytopenia, which is a CC. If thrombocytopenia occurs in the setting of an elevated prothrombin time (PT); activated partial thromboplastin time (aPTT); and systemic inflammatory response syndrome (SIRS) due to infection (sepsis), trauma, pancreatitis, or burns, a CDI opportunity exists to determine if the patient has Disseminated Intravascular Coagulation—286.6 (Defibrination syndrome), which is an MCC.

Code 283.11 (Hemolytic uremic syndrome), a disorder characterized by microangiopathic hemolytic anemia, thrombocytopenia, renal failure, and sometimes central nervous system symptoms, is an MCC. This disease usually occurs in children younger than 5 years of age. Adults with a similar condition often are identified as having 446.6 (Thrombotic microangiopathy), which is also an MCC.

Coagulation Defects

Most coagulation defects remain CCs. Congenital deficiencies of clotting factors VIII and IX are MCCs, whereas congenital deficiencies of other specified clotting factors are CCs.

Acquired coagulation defects from drug use, except those that are supposed to induce a coagulation defect, such as heparin and warfarin (Coumadin), are CCs. An example is vitamin K depletion that occurs with the prolonged use of broad-spectrum antibiotics. Another example is excessive bleeding that can occur after major surgery, such as coronary artery bypass surgery or from massive transfusions after major trauma. Physicians may administer cryoprecipitate or factor VII to these individuals to stop the bleeding or prevent the need for futher operations. If a physician has to prescribe vitamin K, fresh-frozen plasma, cryoprecipitate, or other blood clotting factors, he or she should be queried for the coagulation defect requiring the use of these agents.

As noted previously, disseminated intravascular coagulation (DIC), a complex systemic thrombohemorrhagic disorder involving the generation of intravascular fibrin and the consumption of procoagulants and platelets, is an MCC. DIC is caused by SIRS, malignancies, leukemias (especially promyelocytic leukemias), obstetric complications (for example, preeclampsia, placental abruption), snake bites, blood transfusion or their reactions, acute liver failure, or a number of other conditions. Laboratory tests suggesting DIC include:

- Low platelet counts
- Low fibrinogen counts
- Elevated PT and aPTT (low sensitivity)
- Elevated PT
- Elevated "fibrin degradation products"
- Elevated D-dimer
- Prothrombin fragment 1 and 2
- Decreased antithrombin III levels
- Positive protamine sulfate test

Although qualitative platelet defects not otherwise specified are not CCs, von Willebrand's disease is. von Willebrand's disease is a disorder of the von Willebrand factor, a large protein necessary for platelet adhesion and for proper function of factor VIII. Laboratory tests usually show a prolonged bleeding time and possibly an elevated aPTT. Specific assays are necessary to make the diagnosis.

Hypercoagulable States

If a patient has an unexpected thrombus formation, such as a deep venous thrombus in the veins, a CDI opportunity exists for hypercoagulable syndrome, which is a CC. Predisposing factors for deep venous thrombosis are summarized as Virchow's triad, which includes:

- Alterations of blood flow (stasis)
- Injury to the vascular endothelium (for example, thrombophlebitis)
- Alterations in the constitution of the blood (for example, hypercoagulability)

Hypercoagulable states are either primary or secondary. They include:

- 298.81 (Primary hypercoagulability states)
  - Activated protein C resistance
  - Antithrombin III deficiency
  - Factor V Leiden mutation

- Lupus anticoagulant—The patient doesn't have to have systemic lupus erythematosus for this condition to be present.
- Protein C deficiency
- Protein S deficiency
- Prothombin gene mutation
- 298.82 (Secondary hypercoagulability state), such as those caused by the following:
  - Recent surgery
  - Known or suspected malignancy
  - Pregnancy
  - Chronic inflammation
  - Antiphospholipid syndrome
  - Estrogen use
  - Nephrotic syndrome

Example: A 48-year-old woman was admitted for deep venous thrombosis (DVT) while taking estrogen replacement therapy for menopause. No pulmonary embolus was present on admission. She was treated with low molecular weight heparin and was started on warfarin. She was discharged on the third hospital day after arrangements were made for home healthcare workers to administer heparin while the warfarin dose was being adjusted. Prior to discharge, however, the clinical documentation specialist (CDS) noted that a number of tests were ordered and pending, such as protein C, protein S, and antithrombin III levels. The CDS, therefore, initiated a query to determine what factors contributed to the patient's DVT. The physician replied that because the patient has no family history of unusual clots, the DVT is probably due to her estrogen use. Remembering Virchow's triad, the CDS asked the physician to document these elements in his discharge summary. The physician documented that the patient probably had a mild thrombophlebitis with DVT along with secondary hypercoagulability due to estrogen, but that primary hypercoagulability was still to be ruled out. The MS-DRG changed from 301 (Peripheral vascular disorder w/o CC) (RW 0.7183) to 300 (Peripheral vascular disorder w/CC) (RW 0.9451).

ICD-9-CM Chapter 5: Mental Disorders (290–319)

In ICD-9-CM chapter 5, CMS deleted alcoholism (including continuous dependency on alcohol), noncontinuous chemical dependency (oddly, chemical dependency to marijuana has never been nor is it now a CC), drug abuse, and some drug-induced mood disorders as CCs, yet they added many (if not most) specified conditions involving delirium, dementia, psychosis, or delusion to the CC list. CMS also added complicated bipolar disorders and widened major depressive disorders in the CC list. None of the diagnoses in chapter 5 serve as major CCs, yet their manifestations, underlying causes, or complicating factors may.

Addiction

To understand ICD-9-CM's definitions of drug use, abuse, dependence, and addiction, coders should consider the following:

Alcohol and Drug Use

Alcohol or drugs (tobacco is a drug) are used legally according to their recommended dosages or under the direction of a physician. Consuming a glass of wine once a day or every now and then when permitted by a physician constitutes alcohol use. Drug use is generally not coded unless it leads to an adverse effect while taken as prescribed. One exception is V15.82 (History of tobacco use), whereas 305.1 is Tobacco Dependence. It is possible that an individual may become intoxicated while using alcohol legally; however, more often than not, this is categorized as alcohol abuse.

Alcohol and Drug Abuse

Abuse is defined as the use of an illegal substance (for example, methamphetamines or heroin), the use of a legal substance in an illegal manner (for example, driving while intoxicated or inebriated or obtaining oxycodone through fraudulent means), or the use of a legal substance in such a manner that it causes personal harm (for example, simple drunkenness) but has not yet progressed to dependency.

Tolerance is a state of adaptation in which exposure to a drug induces changes that result in a diminution of one or more of the drug's effects over time. An alcoholic may find it takes more and more alcohol to produce the same mood-altering effect that he or she initially felt.

Alcohol and Drug Physical Dependence

Physical dependence is a state of adaptation manifested by a drug-class-specific withdrawal syndrome that can be produced by abrupt cessation, rapid dose reduction, decreased blood level of the drug, and/or administration of an antagonist. This occurs not only with alcohol or illegal drugs but also with those prescribed by physicians, such as benzodiazepines (for example, Ativan®, Valium®, Klonopin®), beta-blockers (for example,

Inderal®, Tenormin®, Coreg®), some antidepressants (for example, Paxil®), and narcotics (for example, OxyContin®) If a patient demonstrates symptoms of withdrawal from these substances, a CDI opportunity exists to determine whether these patients were physically dependent on these substances.

Alcohol and Drug Addiction

Addiction is a primary, chronic, neurobiologic disease, with genetic, psychosocial, and environmental factors influencing its development and manifestations. It is characterized by behaviors that include one or more of the following: impaired control over drug use, compulsive use, continued use despite harm, and craving (American Pain Society 2007). *Coding Clinic*, second Quarter, 1991, page 10 reiterates that there is a compulsion to take the drug, experience its psychic effects, or avoid the discomfort of its absence, resulting in continued use despite strong incentives. Examples of alcohol and drug addiction include multiple driving while intoxicated (DWI) offenses, multiple job/relationship losses as a result of drinking, multiple admissions for methamphetamine and cocaine detoxification, and continued tobacco smoking despite personal consequences or chronic respiratory failure.

One aspect of drug use, abuse, tolerance, dependence, and addiction is that nonpharmaceutical and nonalcoholic substances may have the same effect on the brain as drugs and alcohol. For example, food such as chocolate, sugar, and foods high in fat can affect the brain in the same manner as nicotine or cocaine, thus patients may develop dependency or addiction to these "mood-altering" substances and incur consequences from overuse or underuse, such as morbid obesity and type 2 diabetes mellitus. Certain behaviors, such as attachment to or avoidance of shopping, romances, relationships, work, and their associated activities can stimulate neural pathways in the same way as drugs, alcohol, or foods, leading to dependent or addictive behavior. ICD-9-CM classifies these as:

- 300.21 (Agoraphobia with panic disorder)
- 300.23 (Social phobia)
- 302.7x (Psychosexual dysfunction)
- 307.1 (Anorexia nervosa)—a CC
- 307.51 (Bulimia nervosa)—a new CC
- 312.3x (Disorders of impulse control, not elsewhere classified)

CMS removed drug use and abuse category 305 (Nondependent use of drugs) as a CC; however, drug-associated consequences or withdrawal are CCs as follows:

ICD-9-CM Code	CC Designation	Title
291.0	CC	Alcohol withdrawal delirium
291.2	CC	Alcohol-induced persisting dementia
291.3	CC	Alcohol-induced psychotic disorder with hallucinations
291.81	CC	Alcohol withdrawal
291.89	CC	Other alcohol-induced mental disorders
291.9	CC	Unspecified alcohol-induced mental disorders
292.0	CC	Drug withdrawal (Note: This does *not* have to be an illegal drug or narcotic.)
292.11	CC	Drug-induced psychotic disorder with delusions
292.12	CC	Drug-induced psychotic disorder with hallucinations
292.81	CC	Drug-induced delirium
292.82	CC	Drug-induced persisting dementia
303.01	Not a CC	Acute alcoholic intoxication, continuous
303.91	Not a CC	Chronic alcoholism, continuous
304.01	CC	Opioid type dependence, continuous use
304.11	CC	Sedative, hypnotic or anxiolytic dependence, continuous
304.21	CC	Cocaine dependence, continuous use
304.31	Not a CC	Cannabis dependence, continuous use
304.41	CC	Amphetamine and other psychostimulant dependence, continuous use
304.51	CC	Hallucinogen dependence, continuous use
304.61	CC	Other specified drug dependence, continuous use
304.71	CC	Combinations of opioid-type drug with any other drug dependence, continuous use
304.81	CC	Combinations of drug dependence, excluding opioid type drug, continuous use
304.91	CC	Unspecified drug dependence, continuous use

CMS removed alcohol and drug-induced "pathologic intoxication" and sleep, amnestic, and mood disorders from the CC list. These may be better described as "toxic encephalopathy," coded to 349.82, which is an MCC.

Regarding drug dependency (which in ICD-9-CM is the same as addiction), the CC designations are as follows:

Physicians will have to specify that their patients' drug addictions or physical dependencies qualify as diagnoses for category 304 (Drug dependence) to be coded,. Furthermore, ICD-9-CM has the following fifth digits for category 304 (Drug Dependence):

- 0—Unspecified (never a CC)
- 1—Continuous (a CC except for 304.31 and 303.91)
- 2—Episodic
- 3—In remission

Physicians must differentiate continuous drug dependency from episodic chemical dependency, *Coding Clinic* 2nd Quarter, 1991, page 11, classifies these as follows:

1. Continuous:
   Alcohol: Refers to daily intake of large amounts of alcohol or regular heavy drinking on weekends or days off from work.
   Drugs: Refers to daily or almost daily use of drugs.
2. Episodic:
   Alcohol: Refers to alcoholic binges lasting weeks or months followed by long periods of sobriety.
   Drugs: Refers to short periods between drug use or use on weekends.
3. Remission:
   Alcohol/Drug: Refers to either a complete cessation of alcohol or drug intake or to the period during which a decrease toward cessation is taking place.

Coders may not code these patterns without explicit provider documentation. CDI opportunity may exist in the following circumstances:

- Patients in an active relapse may be considered as having continuous chemical dependency.
- Patients taking medications indicated to prevent relapse, such as Antabuse®, methadone, levo-alpha-acetylmethadol (LAAM), naltrexone, or similar drugs should be considered to be continuously drug dependent because they would likely relapse if they were to stop taking their medications. Antidepressants or antianxiety medications do not qualify because these address underlying mood disorders, personality disorders, or posttraumatic stress disorders that predispose a person to chemical dependency or relapse behavior.
- Many physicians do not believe that chemical dependency is in remission unless the patient has not used the offending chemical for at least 1 to 3 years and is actively engaged in a good program of recovery; however, this is subject to interpretation.

Altered Mental Status

As discussed in ICD-9-CM chapter 2, altered mental status (not a CC) has many manifestations and underlying etiologies. In most cases, the underlying cause of the altered mental status is the reason the patient could not be sent home. Frequently, the type and severity of the altered mental status factors into principal and secondary diagnosis selection and may qualify as such. Such altered mental statuses include:

- Confusion—Mental and behavioral state of reduced comprehension, coherence, and capacity to reason
- Delirium—Confusion accompanied by agitation, hallucinations, tremor, and illusions
- Delusional state—A form of confusion or psychosis whereby the patient fixates on an erroneous thought. ICD-9-CM codes the paranoid state as a delusion.
- Dementia—An acquired deterioration in cognitive abilities that impairs the successful performance of daily living
- Psychosis—A mental disorder characterized by derangement of personality and loss of contact with reality that causes deterioration of normal social functioning associated with delusional thinking, hallucinations, personality changes, or disorganized thinking
- Vegetative state—An awake but unresponsive state
- Lethargy or drowsiness—Simulates light sleep but is easily aroused; usually associated with some degree of confusion
- Stupor—A lesser degree of unarousability whereby the patient is only aroused by vigorous stimuli
- Coma—A deep sleeplike state from which the patient cannot be aroused

There is considerable overlap between these terms.

MS-DRGs significantly expanded the CC list for delirium, delusion, and dementia with behavioral disturbances, including the following:

Physicians will have to specifically document these conditions for accurate coding. Documenting underlying causes, such as Alzheimer's disease, late effect of stroke, Lewy body dementia, anoxic encephalopathy, or other pathologies also support a higher severity of illness.

Affective Disorders

CMS expanded the CC coverage for mania, major depression single episode, major depression recurrent episode, and bipolar disorders with MS-DRGs, allowing those that are unspecified, mild, moderate, or severe without psychosis to qualify. This expansion applies to the following codes ("x" specifies the fifth digit):

ICD-9-CM Code	CC Designation	Title
290.11	CC	Presenile dementia with delirium
290.12	CC	Presenile dementia with delusional features
290.13	CC	Presenile dementia with depressive features
290.20	CC	Senile dementia with delusional features
290.21	CC	Senile dementia with depressive features
290.3	CC	Senile dementia with delirium
290.41	CC	Vascular dementia with delirium
290.42	CC	Vascular dementia with delusions
290.43	CC	Vascular dementia with depressed mood
290.8	CC	Other specified senile psychotic conditions
290.9	CC	Unspecified senile psychotic conditions
293.0	CC	Delirium due to conditions classified elsewhere
293.1	CC	Subacute delirium
293.81	CC	Psychotic disorder with delusions in conditions classified elsewhere
293.82	CC	Psychotic disorder with hallucinations in conditions classified elsewhere
293.9	CC	Unspecified transient mental disorder in conditions classified elsewhere
294.11	CC	Dementia in conditions classified elsewhere with behavioral disturbance

- 296.0x (Bipolar I disorder, single manic episode) (fifth digit 0–3)
- 296.1x (Manic disorder, recurrent episode) (fifth digit 0–3)
- 296.2x (Major depressive disorder, single episode) (fifth digit 0–4)
- 296.3x– (Major depressive disorder, recurrent episode) (fifth digit 0–3)
- 294.4x (Bipolar I disorder, most recent episode [or current] manic) (fifth digit 0–3)
- 294.5x (Bipolar I disorder, most recent episode [or current] depressed) (fifth digit 0–3)
- 295.6x (Bipolar I disorder, most recent episode [or current] mixed) (fifth digit 0–3)
- 296.89 (Other and unspecified bipolar disorders, other)
- 296.99 (Other specified episodic mood disorder)

Physician must document the severity of the patient's depression as major to qualify it as a CC. To qualify, the patient must have five of the following conditions for over a 2-week period. In addition, the conditions must cause significant distress or impairment, not be related to substance abuse or a medical condition, or not be better accounted for by bereavement:

1. Depressed mood most of the day
2. Markedly diminished interest or pleasure in all, or almost all, activities most of the day
3. Significant weight loss when not dieting, weight gain, or decrease or increase in appetite nearly every day
4. Insomnia or hypersomnia
5. Psychomotor agitation or retardation nearly every day
6. Fatigue or loss of energy nearly every day
7. Feelings of worthlessness or excessive or inappropriate guilt
8. Diminished ability to think or concentrate
9. Recurrent thoughts of death, recurrent suicidal ideation without a plan, or a suicide attempt

Mild forms of mania, hypomania, are included in 296.0, which is a CC; mild forms of depression, dysthymia, are included in 300.4, which is not a CC.

The following medications suggest bipolar disorder, major depression, or mania. If the patient is on these medications or has no history of a seizure disorder, the attending physician should be queried.

- Valproic acid (Depakote®)—Mania, bipolar disorder
- Lithium—Mania or bipolar disorder
- Carbamazepine—Mania or biploar disorder
- Olanzapine (Zyprexa®)—Mania or major depression with psychosis
- Haloperidol (Haldol®)—Mania with psychosis
- Risperidone (Resperdal®)—Mania or major depression with psychosis
- Lamotrigine (Lamictal®)—Hypomania or bipolar disorder
- Bupropion (Wellbutrin®), paroxetine (Paxil®), sertraline (Zoloft®), venlafaxine (Effexor®), or citalopram (Celexa®) plus lithium—Major depression

Other Psychiatric Disorders

CMS added autistic disorder, severe and profound mental retardation, and bulimia to the CC list.

Most cases of schizophrenia, a heterogenous disease manifested by disorders of language, perception, thinking, social activity for which no single finding is unilaterally characteristic, are CCs. CMS added schizoaffective disorders, patients with symptoms of schizophrenia, and independent periods of mood disorders, to the CC list. Clozapine (Clozaril®) is effective in treating schizophrenia, thus a CDI exists if the physician had not indicated why this drug is being used.

ICD-9-CM Chapter 6: Diseases of the Nervous System and Sense Organs (320–389)

CMS deleted the following CCs from ICD-9-CM chapter 6:

- 358.00 (Myasthenia gravis without [acute] exacerbation)
- 377.02 (Papilledema associated with decreased ocular pressure)
- 383.20 (Unspecified abscess of mastoid)
- 383.81 (Postauricular fistula)

Patients with myasthenia gravis due to an identifiable secondary cause, such as a thymoma or oat-cell lung cancer (for example, Eaton-Lambert syndrome) are still classified as a CC. Patients with primary myasthenia gravis, a disease of the neuromuscular junction whereby the acetylcholine receptors are reduced through immunologic mechanisms, must have acute exacerbations of their illnesses to qualify as an MCC.

Chronic myasthenia patients are treated with anticholinesterase medications, which inhibit the metabolism of acetylcholine, or immunosuppressive medications such as steroids, azathioprine, cyclosporine, and mycophenolate mofetil. If these medications are increased due to worsening neurologic symptoms (for example, double vision, ptosis of the eyelids, difficulty swallowing, softness of voice, or dyspnea with effort), or the patient receives plasmapheresis or intravenous immunoglobulin, the physician should be queried for confirmation of acute exacerbation of the illness.

CMS added many CCs to ICD-9-CM chapter 6, including the following.

323 Encephalitis, Myelitis, and Encephalomyelitis

These include those due to infection, vaccinations, toxins (for example, mercury, lead, and thallium), chronic transverse myelitis, and acute necrotizing hemorrhagic encephalopathy, all of which qualify as MCCs. Acute transverse myelitis codes to 341.2, which is a CC.

330 Cerebral Degenerations Usually Manifested in Children

These degenerations include leukodystrophy, such as Krabbe disease; cerebral lipidoses, such as Tay-Sachs disease; and degenerations associated with Gaucher's, Fabry's, Niemann-Pick's, and Hunter's disease.

331.3 Communicating Hydrocephalus and 331.5 Idiopathic Normal Pressure Hydrocephalus

These conditions were added as CCs. Although only obstructive hydrocephalus has been a CC under CMS-DRGs, all of these conditions are now CCs under MS-DRGs. Hydrocephalus, an enlargement of the cerebral ventricles, is usually apparent on CT scan or MRI. Normal pressure hydrocephalus presents as a triad of dementia, gait ataxia or apraxia, and urinary incontinence in older individuals. Both of these conditions are treated with ventricular shunting.

331.81 Reye's Syndrome

Usually encountered in children, this MCC is manifested by acute fatty liver, encephalopathy, and hypoglycemia occurring after an upper respiratory tract infection, influenza, or chickenpox. Aspirin use has been associated with this condition. It is treated with high-glucose fluids, fresh-frozen plasma, and mannitol.

332.1 Secondary Parkinson's

Although primary Parkinson's disease is not a CC, Parkinson's disease due to medications (for example, Reglan®, neuroleptics, or other drugs) is counted as a CC. If the patient has any known psychiatric history for which neuroleptics were administered or gastroesophageal reflux disease for which Reglan® (metochlorproamide) or cisapride was administered, a CDI opportunity exists.

333.0 Other Degenerative Diseases of the Basal Ganglia and 333.4 Huntington's Chorea

Both of the new CCs also may manifest themselves as Parkinson's disease, including Parkinson's disease with orthostatic hypotension (for example, Shy-Drager syndrome). If the patient's systolic blood pressure drops more than 20 mm/Hg upon standing, if he or she has symptoms of orthostatic dizziness or syncope, or if the patient takes medications that purposefully retain fluid (for example, Florinef®, nonsteroidal anti-inflammatory drugs, or salt tablets), a CDI opportunity-exists.

Example: An 80-year-old man with Parkinson's disease was admitted for syncope. His supine blood pressure was 150/80, whereas his standing blood pressure was 100/60. No etiology of his syncope was found. The final diagnosis was syncope probably due to orthostatic hypotension and Parkinson's disease, resulting in MS-DRG 312 (Syncope and collapse) (RW 0.7197). When the coder queried the physician for the etiology of the orthostasis, given that the patient was not on diuretics, the physician replied that it was due to autonomic dysfunction, which changed the MS-DRG to 57 (Degenerative nervous systems disorders w/o MCC) (RW 0.8951). Further query linked the Parkinson's disease to the autonomic dysfunction. However, because 332.1—Secondary Parkinsonism—is only a CC, it did not change the DRG.

333.7x Acquired Torsion Dystonia

Some drugs, such as neuroleptics, can cause acute muscle dystonia, usually treated with anticholinergic medications such as Artane® or Benadryl®. Long-term effects, such as tardive dyskinesia, are not CCs; however, 333.90 (Unspecified extrapyramidal disease and abnormal movement disorder), which includes medication-induced movement disorders, is a CC.

333.91 Stiff-Man (Person) Syndrome

Stiff-man syndrome, also called Moersch-Woltmann syndrome, is a rare, severe autoimmune (positive anti-glutamic acid decarboxylase antibodies are commonly seen) neurologic disease involving the central nervous system. Characterized by a progressive rigidity or stiffness of the muscles caused by a diffuse hypertonia (excess muscular tension or pressure) involving the voluntary muscles of the neck, shoulders, trunk, arms, and legs with some muscle spasm, symptoms abate while the patient is asleep. Sometimes, diabetes mellitus or cancer may be associated with this condition. Most physicians will document this condition and the only treatment is antispasmodics (for example, baclofen).

333.92 Neuroleptic Malignant Syndrome

An inherited condition whereby patients exposed to halothane, succinylcholine, or neuroleptics and with withdrawal of dopamine agonists (for example, Sinemet®) develop very high fever, muscle metabolism and rigidity, muscle death, cardiac instability, and death.

334.x Spinocerebellar Disease and 336.x Other Diseases of the Spinal Cord

These two illnesses have been added as CCs along with almost all of the degenerative conditions of the cerebellum and spinal cord, including those due secondary to other illnesses, such as vitamin B_{12} deficiency or neoplastic disease. Although 341.x (Other demyelinating diseases of the central nervous system), such as acute transverse myelitis and central pontine myelinosis, are now CCs, 340 (Multiple sclerosis) is no longer a CC.

337.0 Idiopathic Peripheral Autonomic Neuropathy, 337.1 Peripheral Autonomic Neuropathy in Disorders Classified Elsewhere, 357.81 Chronic Inflammatory Demyelinating Polyneuritis, and 357.82 Critical Illness Polyneuropathy

These conditions are now added as CCs. Most diabetics have peripheral neuropathy manifested as foot ulcers, gastroparesis, chronic constipation, erectile dysfunction, Charcot's joints, or absent ankle reflexes; however, only if the physician describes their neuropathy as autonomic will it count as a CC. So even though the diabetes may be currently well controlled, a CDI opportunity for this diagnosis in appropriate circumstances may result in a CC. Critical illness polyneuropathy usually occurs as a result of SIRS and thus should prompt the addition of 995.92 (SIRS due to infection with acute organ dysfunction), or 995.94 (SIRS due to noninfectious origins with acute organ dysfunction), both of which are MCCs.

337.2x Reflex Sympathetic Dystrophy

Also known as complex regional pain syndrome (CRPS) and causalgia in the medical literature (causalgia codes to 335.9, 335.71, or 335.4, all of which are not CCs), reflex sympathetic dystrophy (RSD) is a chronic pain syndrome in the upper or lower extremities occurring after tissue (CRPS type 1) or nerve (CRPS type 2) trauma. It is commonly associated with vasomotor symptoms, swelling, or sweat abnormalities. CMS designated RSD as a CC. Patients with chronic pain who are treated with calcium channel blockers (for example, nifedipine), alpha or beta blockers (for example, labatolol), phenytoin, or similar drugs may identify CRPS or RDS as a potential CC.

Hemiplegia and Paraplegia

As stipulated in the final rule, CMS has designated paretic and paralyzed extremities as CCs. These include 342.x (Hemiplegia and hemiparesis), 343.0 (Congenital diplegia), 343.1 (Congenital hemiplegia), 343.4 (Infantile hemiplegia), 344.1 (Paraplegia), 344.2 (Diplegia of upper limps), 344.6x (Cauda equina syndrome), and 438.2x (Late effect of cerebrovascular disease), which is the appropriate late effect of stroke codes.

Hemiplegia/Hemiparesis

CMS designated quadriplegia as an MCC. One special type of quadriplegia, 344.81 (Locked-in state), is an unfortunate consequence of brainstem stroke, usually in the pons. These patients are completely paralyzed except for their ability to blink. Because the cerebral cortex is not affected, they are fully cognizant.

Seizure Disorders and Epilepsy

ICD-9-CM classifies seizure terminology as follows:

- Isolated seizure (780.39)—A paroxysmal event due to abnormal, excessive, hypersynchronous discharges from CNS neurons. An acute condition; such as cocaine intoxication, may induce one seizure, not qualifying the patient as having epilepsy
- Seizure disorder (345.9x)

- Recurrent seizure disorder (345.9x)—Also known as epilepsy, with this condition a patient has recurrent seizures due to a chronic, underlying process.
- Convulsive disorder NOS (780.39)—Because most physicians equate convulsive and seizure disorders, a CDI opportunity exists to differentiate the two.
- Recurrent convulsive disorder (780.39)—Because most physicians equate convulsive and seizure disorders, a CDI opportunity exists to differentiate the two.
- Grand mal status (epilepsy and recurrent seizures) (345.3x)—Continuous seizures or repetitive seizures with impaired consciousness in the interictal period, both of which generally last more than 15 to 30 minutes. Grand mal status presents as generalized overt seizures.
- Petit mal status (epilepsy and recurrent seizures) (345.2x)—Absence seizures are characterized by brief lapses of consciousness without loss of postural control and usually last only seconds. If they last more than 15 to 30 minutes, they are considered to be petit mal status seizures.

CMS eliminated 780.39 as a CC under MS-DRGs (345.9x was not a CC under CMS-DRGs), while adding the following:

- 345.40 (Localization-related epilepsy and epileptic syndromes with complex partial seizures, without mention of intractable epilepsy)
- 345.50 (Localization-related epilepsy and epileptic syndromes with simple partial seizures, without mention of intractable epilepsy)
- 345.60 (Infantile spasm, without mention of intractable epilepsy)
- 345.70 (Epilepsia partialis continua, without mention of intractable epilepsy)
- 345.80 (Other forms of epilepsy and recurrent seizures, without mention of intractable epilepsy)

As a result, seizure/convulsive disorders and epilepsy NOS are not CCs unless the physician specifies that they are intractable, in status, or a specific localization-related, focal, or partial epileptic syndrome. Definitions of these terms include:

- Intractable seizures—Refractory patients are defined in patients typically requiring more than one drug to control their epilepsy. Medically intractable epilepsy has been defined as persistent seizure activity, which, despite maximal medical treatment, remains sufficiently debilitating to warrant the risks of surgery. Approximately 20 to 33 percent of patients fall into this category. A CDI opportunity exists if a patient requires more than two drugs to control seizures.

- Status epilepticus (see above)—345.3 (Grand mal) and 345.2 (Petit mal) qualify as MCCs. Petit mal status may degenerate into grand mal status. Thus if tonic clonic activity is seen, a CDI opportunity exists.
- Localization-related or focal seizures— Otherwise known as partial seizures or partial complex seizures, these occur in a discrete region of the brain. If consciousness is preserved, it is a partial seizure; if consciousness is impaired during an event, it is a partial complex seizure.

Encephalopathy

One of CMS's most significant additions to the CC structure are the encephalopathy codes, many of which are MCCs. Simply stated, encephalopathy is a disease of the brain, much like cardiomyopathy is a disease of the heart muscle, neuropathy is a disease of the peripheral nerves, and angiopathy or vasculopathy is a disease of the blood vessels. In ICD-9-CM and the medical literature, encephalopathy is broadly categorized according to its etiology. Its manifestations are the various forms of altered mental status (for example, coma, stupor, delirium, or confusion), cognitive defects, myoclonus, muscle twitches, or even a seizure. They can include:

- 348.31 (Metabolic encephalopathy) (MCC)— Occurs when a disorder of endogenous metabolism, such as electrolyte imbalance (for example, hyponatremia, hypocalcemia, or hypercalcemia), severe azotemia or uremia (for example, elevation of blood urea nitrogen), chemicals related to SIRS (for example, interleukins or tumor necrosis factors) caused by sepsis or pancreatitis, or other by-products of metabolism affect the brain.

ICD-9-CM Code	CC Designation	Title
345.3	MCC	Grand mal status, epileptic
345.01	CC	Generalized nonconvulsive epilepsy, with intractable epilepsy
345.11	CC	Generalized convulsive epilepsy, with intractable epilepsy
345.2	MCC	Petit mal status, epileptic
345.40	CC	Localization-related (focal) (partial) epilepsy and epileptic syndromes with complex partial seizures, without mention of intractable epilepsy
345.41	CC	Localization-related (focal) (partial) epilepsy and epileptic syndromes with complex partial seizures, with intractable epilepsy
345.50	CC	Localization-related (focal) (partial) epilepsy and epileptic syndromes with simple partial seizures, without mention of intractable epilepsy
345.51	CC	Localization-related (focal) (partial) epilepsy and epileptic syndromes with simple partial seizures, with intractable epilepsy
345.60	CC	Infantile spasms, without mention of intractable epilepsy
345.61	CC	Infantile spasms, with intractable epilepsy
345.70	CC	Epilepsia partialis continua, without mention of intractable epilepsy
345.71	MCC	Epilepsia partialis continua, with intractable epilepsy
345.80	CC	Other forms of epilepsy and recurrent seizures, without mention of intractable epilepsy
345.81	CC	Other forms of epilepsy and recurrent seizures, with intractable epilepsy
345.91	CC	Epilepsy, unspecified, with intractable epilepsy

- 348.31 (Septic encephalopathy) (MCC)—A specific type of metabolic encephalopathy due to the mediators of SIRS. Manifestations include stupor, coma, myoclonus, or any alterations of mental status. It shares the same ICD-9-CM code as metabolic encephalopathy and should prompt the assignment of ICD-9-CM code 995.92 (SIRS due to infection with acute organ dysfunction) an indicator of higher severity of illness or risk of mortality with sepsis or septicemia.
- 572.2 (Hepatic encephalopathy) (MCC)—A specific type of metabolic encephalopathy due to an accumulation of metabolic by-products (for example, ammonia) as a result of liver failure. Code 572.2 is the same as for hepatic coma and should not be used if other codes, such as 070.41 (Acute hepatitis C with hepatic coma), incorporate this in their definition.
- 348.1 (Anoxic encephalopathy) (CC)—Damage to the brain caused by lack of oxygen, usually occurring after cardiac arrest or oxygen deprivation from other sources (for example, drowning or carbon monoxide poisoning), which codes to 348.1 (Anoxic brain damage), which is a CC.
- 349.82 (Toxic encephalopathy) (MCC)—Occurs when toxins such as pharmaceuticals, alcohol, snake venom, heavy metals, or other outside exogenous agents affect mental status. If a more specific code is available, such as 948.9 plus 323.71 (Lead encephalopathy) (MCC) or 291.2 (Alcoholic encephalopathy) (CC), it should be used.
- 437.2 (Hypertensive encephalopathy) (CC)—Cerebral injury caused by vascular ischemia induced during accelerated or malignant hypertension.
- 251.2 (Hypoglycemia encephalopathy) (not a CC)—Altered mental status induced by hypoglycemia.
- 310.2 (Posttraumatic encephalopathy) (not a CC)—Brain disease as a result of head trauma or a concussion.

Other Brain Diseases

Conditions such as 348.4 (Compression of brain) (MCC) and 348.5 (Cerebral edema) (CC) have been added as well. Compression of the brain usually occurs in the brainstem from the cerebral cortex herniating through the skull as a result of an underlying epidural or subdural hematoma, leading to papillary changes and centrally mediated respiratory arrest. Cerebral edema can occur from any structural or metabolic injury to the brain, such as in stroke, head trauma, rapid correction of severe hyponatremia, or fulminant encephalitis. Cerebrospinal fluid rhinorrhea (through the nose) remains a CC, whereas 388.61 (Cerebrospinal fluid otorrhea) (through the ear) has been added.

356.3 Refsum's Disease

Refsum's disease, a rare autosomal recessive disorder with onset in childhood or adolescence, was added to the CC list. Symptoms of this condition include night blindness (the earliest symptom), progressive nerve deafness, atypical retinitis pigmentosa, progressive peripheral neuropathy, an accumulation of phytanic acid in the blood and tissues, progressive concentric constriction of visual fields, lenticular opacity, peripheral polyneuropathy, absent or diminished deep tendon reflexes, cerebellar ataxia, loss of sense of smell, unsteady gait, loss of position sense, intention tremor, nystagmus, heart disease with ECG changes, ichtyosis, hyperkeratosis palmaris et plantaris, epiphyseal dysplasia, syndactyly, hammer toe, pes cavus, urinary sphincter impairment, and osteochondritis. Patients with Refsum's disease are treated with dietary restrictions of phytanic acid and with plasmapheresis.

Myopathies

CMS added several secondary muscle diseases to the CC list, including 359.4 (Toxic myopathy), 359.6 (Symptomatic inflammatory myopathy in diseases classified elsewhere), and 359.81 (Critical illness myopathy). These conditions demonstrate proximal muscle weakness, elevations of the CK-MM isoenzyme or aldolase. Toxic myopathies occur most commonly as adverse reactions to prescribed medications, such as the cholesterol-lowering medications, or possibly due to toxic quantities of alcohol. Symptomatic inflammatory myopathy in diseases classified elsewhere includes systemic vasculitis; it does *not* include primary polymyositis (not a CC) unless the physician designates it as secondary to another condition. Critical illness myopathy occurs in the setting of SIRS and, like critical illness neuropathy, should elicit a 995.92 or 995.94 code (both MCCs) as well.

Eye Diseases

CMS expanded the CC list to cover many acute eye conditions, including:

- 360.0x (Purulent endophthalmitis) (Note: Chronic endophthalmitis is *not* a CC.)
- 360.1x (Other endophthalmitis) (Note: 360.14 [Ophthalmia nodosa] is *not* a CC.)
- 361.2 (Serous retinal detachment), 361.8x (Other forms of retinal detachment), *and* 361.9 (Unspecified retinal detachment)
- 362.3x (Retinal vascular occlusion) (Note: 362.36 [Venous tributary occlusion] and 362.37 [Venous engorgement] are *not* CCs.) plus 362.84 (Retinal ischemia)
- 362.40 (Retinal layer separation, unspecified), 362.42 (Serous detachment of retinal pigment epithelium), 362.43 (Hemorrhagic detachment of retinal pigment epithelium)
- 363.1x (Disseminated chorioretinitis) *or* 363.20 (Chorioretinitis, unspecified)
- 363.63 (Choroidal rupture) *and* 363.7x (Choroidal detachment)
- 364.0x (Acute and subacute iridocyclitis) (Note: 364.04 [Secondary iridocyclitis, noninfectious] and 364.05 [Hypopyon] are not CCs), as well as 364.22 (Glaucomatocyclitic crisis) and 364.3 (Unspecified iridocyclitis)
- 364.22 (Acute open-angle glaucoma) (not chronic open angle glaucoma)
- 368.11 (Sudden vision loss) *or* 368.12 (Transient vision loss)
- 376.01 (Orbital cellulitis)
- 376.02 (Orbital periostitis) *or* 376.03 (Orbital osteomyelitis)
- 377.30 (Optic neuritis, unspecified), 377.31 (Optic papillitis), 377.32 (Retrobulbar neuritis), *or* 377.39 (Other optic neuritis)
- 377.5x (Disorders of the optic chiasm) *or* 377.6x (Disorders of other visual pathways), which are usually seen in pituitary tumors. Code 377.7x (Disorders of visual cortex) is also a CC (which may be a late effect of a stroke); however, code 377.75 (Cortical blindness) is *not* a CC. A CDI opportunity exists if the physician documents cortical blindness to determine its underlying cause and the exact pathophysiology or pathology associated with it.

No eye diseases are designated as MCCs.

Ear Diseases

CMS added the following ear conditions to the CC list:

- 380.14 (Malignant otitis externa)
- 383.0x (Acute mastoiditis)
- 388.61 (Cerebrospinal fluid otorrhea)

But CMS deleted the following ear conditions from the CC list:

- 383.20 (Unspecified abscess of mastoid)
- 383.81 (Postauricular fistula)

No ear diagnoses qualify as MCCs.

ICD-9-CM Chapter 7: Diseases of the Circulatory System (390–459)

Consistent with other chapters, CMS eliminated many diagnoses from ICD-9-CM that only marginally impacted resource utilization or length of stay, including the following:

Cardiac Valve Disorders

CMS eliminated *all* codes referring to noncongenital valvular insufficiency or stenosis as CC. Documentation of the effect the valve disease has upon the heart or the rest of the body, such as systolic or diastolic heart failure, may result in a CC. For example, critical aortic stenosis can cause a hypertrophic cardiomyopathy, result in chronic systolic or diastolic heart failure, or lead to angina-at-rest or accelerated angina. Mitral insufficiency can lead to a dilated cardiomyopathy with resultant systolic heart failure, whereas mitral stenosis can lead to acute or chronic left heart failure, for which 428.1 (Left heart failure) is a CC whereas 428.0 (Congestive heart failure NOS) is not. Severe pulmonic or tricuspid insufficiency can lead to right heart failure, thus the physician will need to document chronic systolic right failure to qualify this diagnosis as a CC.

CMS eliminated the Major Cardiovascular Diagnosis (MCVD) category for interventional cardiology and cardiac surgery as well, substituting MCCs as necessary to change the DRG to the next level (there are no MS-DRGs for these procedures with only a CC).

CMS emphasized that physicians need to document greater acuity in their cardiac patients, evidenced by the following:

Hypertension

CMS maintains that only accelerated or malignant hypertension is a CC. As discussed in chapter 2, many physicians use the terms "hypertensive crisis," "hypertensive urgency," or "hypertensive emergency,"—language that they learned from the National Institutes of Health—which code to 401.9 (Unspecified essential hypertension) (not a CC)

(NIH 2007). ICD-9-CM crosswalks to these terms are as follows:

- 401.0 (Malignant hypertension) (Hypertensive emergency according to the NIH)—Blood pressure of over 180/120 with evidence of progressive end-organ damage (for example, acute congestive heart failure, hypertensive encephalopathy, acute renal insufficiency (risk or injury according to RIFLE criteria), or acute renal failure). Immediate treatment is necessary for these conditions.
- 401.0 (Accelerated hypertension) (Hypertensive urgency according to the NIH)—Blood pressure of over 160/100 without evidence of progressive end-organ damage but perhaps presenting with milder symptoms such as epistaxis, severe anxiety, headaches, or shortness of breath.

If the patient has an altered mental status in the setting of accelerated hypertension, Hypertensive encephalopathy (437.2) should be considered as a CDI opportunity for the principal or secondary diagnosis. Chronic systolic or diastolic congestive heart failure is often acutely exacerbated by accelerated hypertension, thus a CDI opportunity for acute on chronic systolic or diastolic heart failure exists in this circumstance.

Angina Pectoris

Angina pectoris, not otherwise specified, is now eliminated as a CC. On the other hand, 413.0 (Angina decubitus) and 411.1 (Progressive/unstable angina) remain as CCs, whereas 410.81 (Non-Q wave or non-ST segment elevation MI) is classified as an MCC. As discussed in chapter 2, these are differentiated by the following:

- 413.9 (Stable angina pectoris) is characterized by chest or arm discomfort that is rarely described as pain but that is reproducibly associated with physical exertion or stress and is relieved within 5 to 10 minutes by rest and/or sublingual nitroglycerin.
- 413.0 (Angina-at-rest or Angina decubitus) is stable angina that occurs at rest. It lasts less than 10 minutes, is not progressive, and is easy relieved by nitroglycerin. If a patient has to take nitroglycerin sublingually while in the hospital (or even at a referring hospital), he or she likely did not take it during exertion. A CDI opportunity exists in this circumstance.
- 411.1 (Unstable or progressive angina) is defined as angina pectoris or equivalent ischemic discomfort with at least one of the following three features: (1) it occurs at rest (or with minimal exertion) usually lasting more then 10 minutes, (2) it is severe and of new onset (that is, within the past month), and/or

(3) it occurs with a crescendo pattern. A CDI opportunity exists if there has been any change in the patient's angina pattern within the past month.
- Acute coronary syndrome is a form of unstable angina whereby an acute myocardial infarction is imminent. It may have ST-segment elevation or it may not. A myocardial infarction may be aborted by aggressive interventions, such as percutaneous transluminal coronary angioplasty or tissue-plasminogen activator (for example, tPA). Both acute coronary syndrome and aborted MI code to 411.1 (Intermediate coronary syndrome) and not to MI.
- 410.81 (Non-ST segment elevation myocardial infarction) is established if a patient with the clinical features of unstable angina without ST segment elevation develops evidence of myocardial necrosis, as reflected in a new left bundle branch block or elevated cardiac biomarkers. Usually, the troponin levels are elevated; however, some false-positive troponin elevations may occur due to end-stage renal disease, cardiopulmonary resuscitation, pericarditis, congestive heart failure, or other heart diseases.
- ST segment myocardial infarction is the same as non-ST segment elevation MI except that the ST segments are elevated.

If the patient has had a previous coronary artery bypass surgery (CABG) or heart transplant and their angina is stable, CMS did add the following diagnoses to the CC list:

- 414.02 (CAD of autologous vein bypass graft)
- 414.03 (CAD of nonautologous biological bypass graft)
- 414.04 (Coronary atherosclerosis of artery bypass graft)
- 414.06 (Coronary atherosclerosis of native coronary artery of transplanted heart)
- 414.07 (Coronary atherosclerosis of bypass graft of transplanted heart)

Evidence that the patient has stable angina includes taking the following medications:

- Nitrates—Imdur®, Isordil®, sublingual nitroglycerin, nitroglycerin patches
- Calcium channel blockers—Norvasc®, Calan® (verapmil), Procardia® (nifedipine). However, these may be used for hypertension.
- Beta-blockers—Tenormin® (atenolol), Lopressor® (metropolol). However, these may be used for hypertension.

A CDI opportunity exists if these medications are used, especially the nitrates.

Arrhythmias and Heart Blocks

CMS eliminated many of the abnormalities seen on telemetry or routine electrocardiograms as CCs, including the following:

- 424.13 (Other second-degree atrioventricular block)
- 426.6 (Other heart block)
- 426.7 (Anomalous atrioventricular excitation), also known as preexcitation syndrome or WPW syndrome
- 426.81 (Lown-Ganong-Levine syndrome)
- 426.9 (Conduction disorder NOS)

427.0 Paroxysmal Supraventricular Tachycardia

This category includes a number of tachycardias that originate in the atrium, the AV node, or the bundle of His. These include multifocal atrial tachycardia, inappropriate

Figure 3.2   Atrial Fibrillation

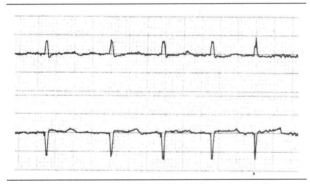

Source: James S. Kennedy, MS, CCS. Personal files.

Figure 3.3   Atrial Flutter   Note the "Saw Tooth" Baseline

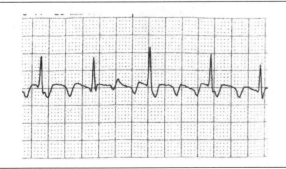

Source: James S. Kennedy, MS, CCS. Personal files.

sinus tachycardia, sinus nodal reentrant tachycardia, AV nodal tachycardia, AV reentrant tachycardia, or junctional ectopic tachycardia. These are sometimes present on telemetry but not commented upon or documented by the physician. Telemetry may appear as in Figure 3.2.

Although many patients now receive cardiac ablation as a permanent cure for these arrhythmias, some still take medications chronically, such as digoxin (Lanoxin), Verapmil (Calan®), beta-blockers (for example, atenolol, metropolol), or sometimes other antiarrhymics such as propafenone (Rhythmol®), flecanide (Tambocor®), sotolol (Betapace®) or amiodarone (Cordarone®). A CDI opportunity exists for patients on these medications without explicit documentation of their indication.

Atrial Fibrillation

CMS eliminated 427.31 (Atrial fibrillation) as a CC but left 427.32 (Atrial flutter) as a CC. Not uncommonly, atrial fibrillation and atrial flutter coexist, but they are differentiated by atrial fibrillation having an irregular ventricular response and atrial flutter having a regular ventricular response. Both are difficult to treat. Patients may be on amiodarone or other antiarrhythmics as to maintain normal sinus rhythm. Atrial fibrillation has an irregular rhythm and lack of "P" waves before the "QRS" wave.

Atrial flutter, as shown below, is reflected by a saw-tooth atrial activity and regular intervals between the QRS. All of the intervals are not the same due to varying degrees of conduction through the AV node. Yet there is regularity with atrial flutter whereas atrial fibrillation has no regularity at all.

Because atrial fibrillation and flutter can coexist, if a physician documents "atrial fib/flutter," a CDI opportunity exists to clarify which of these is the predominant rhythm.

Other Arrhythmias

Other arrhythmias qualify as CCs and may be present on nursing and telemetry notes or treated with medications without explicit physician documentation. These include.

427.1 (Ventricular Tachycardia) (CC)—Ventricular tachycardia is defined as a salvo of three or more premature ventricular beats in a row on an electrocardiogram or telemetry strip at a rate of over 120 beats per minute.

If this rhythm is present on telemetry or if the patient is on medications, such as amiodarone, to suppress this rhythm, the physician should be queried to interpret the strip, discuss its impact on length of stay or patient monitoring, and/or provide the indication for the use of the medication.

427.41 Ventricular Fibrillation or 427.42 Ventricular Flutter both MCCs—If these rhythms occured during hospitalization, the medical staff likely performed advanced cardiac life support. On the other hand, many patients have automatic implantable cardiac defibrillators and take cardiac medications (for example, amiodarone) for known spontaneous ventricular fibrillation or flutter. If these interventions were to be discontinued, these arrhythmias would return, much like a type 1 diabetic patient's blood glucose levels would rise if she stopped taking her insulin.

Cardiac Arrest (MCC)

Coding Clinic (3rd Quarter, 1995), emphasized that 427.5 (Cardiac arrest) is used as a secondary diagnosis when the patient arrives at the hospital in a state of cardiac arrest, is resuscitated, and the underlying cause of the cardiac arrest (for example, ventricular fibrillation or ventricular flutter) is known, or if the patient has a cardiac arrest after admission and is successfully resuscitated. If the patient dies during admission after the cardiac arrest is successfully resuscitated, while it may be coded, it will not count as a CC. A CDI opportunity exists for the underlying circumstances surrounding cardiac arrest if a patient has a cardiac arrest for unknown etiology.

Some patients receiving end-of-life or "no code" care in an acute care setting will have ventricular tachycardia, ventricular flutter, or ventricular fibrillation surrounding their death; some may have even had a pulmonary embolus or a non-Q-wave myocardial infarction that the physician failed to consider or document. A CDI opportunity for these diagnoses exists when patients die in the hospital. Appropriate coding of V66.7 (End of life care or terminal care) within the first nine diagnoses allow for hospital quality monitoring companies, such as Healthgrades® or Solucient®, to know that the death was expected.

Heart Failure

CMS eliminated 428.0 (Congestive heart failure, unspecified) and 428.9 (Heart failure, unspecified) as CCs yet maintained the other codes within 428 as CCs or MCCs. Unfortunately, ICD-9-CM does not robustly categorize the severity heart failure in the same manner as it categorizes the chronic kidney disease codes, even with the improvements to ICD-9-CM made in 2003. For example, ICD-9-CM's code for "compensated" or "decompensated" heart failure, 428.0 (Congestive heart failure NOS) (not a CC), does not differentiate the different New York Heart Association or Canadian Cardiovascular Society stages for heart failure, nor does it indicate if it is acute (an MCC if described) or chronic (a CC if described). ICD-9-CM classifies right heart failure with 428.0 (not a CC) yet separated left heart failure out at 428.1 (a CC). Although ICD-9-CM did well to differentiate systolic versus diastolic failure and acute versus chronic heart failure in 2003, many physicians still do not routinely document these terms in their day-to-day admissions.

Complicating matters further are some time-honored traditions in documentation of pulmonary edema and heart failure. For example, most physicians (including radiologists) will label all radiographic evidence of pulmonary edema on chest x-ray as "CHF," even if there is no demonstrated pathology or failure of the heart or pericardium. Renal dialysis patients with completely normal hearts who miss their dialysis treatments and present in fluid overload with pulmonary edema will be labeled "CHF," causing difficulties for the quality manager who struggles to determine why the CHF core measures were not implemented in this circumstance. Physicians will label well-compensated patients with heart failure as "CHF" (428.0—not a CC), even if they are not fluid congested.

As discussed in the proposed and final rule, CMS wants to differentiate patients whose heart failure is acutely decompensated (deserving an MCC but not applicable since 428.0 [Congestive heart failure NOS] is not a CC) from those who are chronically controlled (deserving a CC) or nonspecific (no CC granted), thus the following CC table is authorized:

ICD-9-CM Code	CC Designation	Title
428.21	MCC	Acute systolic heart failure
428.23	MCC	Acute on chronic systolic heart failure
428.31	MCC	Acute diastolic heart failure
428.33	MCC	Acute on chronic diastolic heart failure
428.41	MCC	Acute combined systolic and diastolic heart failure
428.43	MCC	Acute on chronic combined systolic and diastolic heart failure
428.0	Not a CC	CHF NOS; compensated or decompensated CHF
428.1	CC	Left heart failure
428.20	CC	Unspecified systolic heart failure
428.22	CC	Chronic systolic heart failure
428.30	CC	Unspecified diastolic heart failure
428.32	CC	Chronic diastolic heart failure
428.40	CC	Unspecified combined systolic and diastolic heart failure
428.42	CC	Chronic combined systolic and diastolic heart failure
428.9	Not a CC	Heart failure NOS
429.4	Not a CC	Functional disturbances after surgery—includes heart failure occurring following heart surgery or after valve replacement
997.1	CC	Cardiac complications, not classified elsewhere; heart failure during or as a result of a procedure

It must be emphasized that to have heart failure, the heart must have pathology. Such evidence may include:

- Meeting the Framingham Heart Study or the Cardiovascular Health Study criteria for heart failure (Schellenbaum et al. 2004). The Framingham Heart Study criteria require that from the following lists the patient meet two major criteria or one major and two minor criteria.

Major Criteria
Bilateral moist rales
Paroxysmal nocturnal dyspnea and/or orthopnea
Pulmonary edema by radiography
Neck vein distention in the semirecumbent position
Enlarging heart by radiography
S3 gallop
Hepatojugular reflux
Peripheral venous pressure greater than 16 cm H_2O

Arm-to-tongue circulation time 25 seconds or greater
Weight loss of 4.5 kg or greater in 5 days with treatment

Minor Criteria
Ankle edema
Pleural effusion
Hepatomegaly
Tachycardia (120 beats per minute or greater)
Dyspnea on exertion
Night cough

- Cardiac silhouette enlargement on chest x-ray
- Abnormalities on the electrocardiogram, such as left ventricular enlargement, interventricular conduction delays (for example, left bundle branch blocks), or evidence of old myocardial infarctions
- Left ventricular ejection fraction of less than 35 percent on echocardiogram

- Elevated left ventricular end-diastolic pressure or pulmonary artery wedge pressure on cardiac catheterization
- Evidence that the patient is taking medications or receiving treatment for heart failure, including:
  - Digoxin (Lanoxin®)
  - ACE inhibitors (for example, enalapril [Vasotec®])
  - Angiotensin-receptor blockers (for example, losartan [Diovan®])
  - Low-dose beta-blockers (for example, metropolol [Lopressor®])
  - Diuretics (for example, furosemide [Lasix®])
  - Cardiac resynchronization therapy

Signs of acute CHF include:

- Increasing symptoms of heart failure (edema, dyspnea on exertion, orthopnea [inability to lie flat], angina at rest or progressive angina) or even overt acute respiratory distress and failure
- Increasing brain natriuretic peptide (BNP) levels from baseline.
- Increasing pulmonary edema on chest x-ray, provided other causes have been excluded (for example, hypoalbuminemia or fluid overload from other causes)

Even if the attending physician only documents 428.0 (CHF) or 428.9 (Heart failure NOS) (both not CCs) as a secondary diagnosis, these are often associated with hypertension or with an underlying cardiomyopathy that may serve as a CC (the CC exclusion list including these diagnoses does not apply if 428.0 is not the principal diagnosis), creating a physician CDI opportunity. The final rule removed 402.11 (Hypertensive heart disease, benign, with heart failure) and 402.91 (Hypertensive heart disease, unspecified, with heart failure) to be consistent with the deletion of 428.0 (CHF NOS) and 428.9 (Heart failure NOS). Those serving as CCs include:

ICD-9-CM Code Designation	CC	Title
402.01	CC	Malignant hypertensive heart disease with congestive heart failure
403.91	CC	Hypertensive chronic kidney disease, unspecified, with chronic kidney disease stage V or end-stage renal disease
404.00	CC	Hypertensive heart and chronic kidney disease, malignant, without heart failure and with chronic kidney disease stage I through stage IV, or unspecified
404.01	CC	Hypertensive heart and chronic kidney disease, malignant, with heart failure and with chronic kidney disease stage I through stage IV, or unspecified
404.02	CC	Hypertensive heart and chronic kidney disease, malignant, without heart failure and with chronic kidney disease stage V or end-stage renal disease
404.03	CC	Hypertensive heart and chronic kidney disease, malignant, with heart failure and with chronic kidney disease stage V or end-stage renal disease
404.11	CC	Hypertensive heart and chronic kidney disease, benign, with heart failure and with chronic kidney disease stage I through stage IV, or unspecified
404.91	CC	Hypertensive heart and chronic kidney disease, unspecified, with heart failure and with chronic kidney disease stage I through stage IV, or unspecified
404.93	CC	Hypertensive heart and chronic kidney disease, unspecified, with heart failure and chronic kidney disease stage V or end-stage renal disease

ICD-9-CM Code Designation	CC	Title
425.0	CC	Endomyocardial fibrosis
425.1	CC	Hypertrophic obstructive cardiomyopathy
425.2	CC	Obscure cardiomyopathy of Africa
425.3	CC	Endocardial fibroelastosis
425.4	CC	Other primary cardiomyopathies
425.5	CC	Alcoholic cardiomyopathy
425.7	CC	Nutritional and metabolic cardiomyopathy
425.8	CC	Cardiomyopathy in other diseases classified elsewhere
425.9	CC	Secondary cardiomyopathy, unspecified

ICD-9-CM Code	CC Designation	Title
506.1	MCC	Acute pulmonary edema due to fumes and vapors
518.4	MCC	Acute edema of lung, unspecified
514	CC	Pulmonary congestion and hypostasis

ICD-9-CM Code	CC Designation	Title
391.0	CC (new)	Acute rheumatic pericarditis
393	CC	Chronic rheumatic pericarditis
420.0	CC	Acute pericarditis in diseases classified elsewhere
420.90	CC	Acute pericarditis, unspecified
420.91	CC	Acute idiopathic pericarditis
420.99	CC	Other acute pericarditis
423.1	CC	Adhesive pericarditis
423.2	CC	Constrictive pericarditis
423.3	CC (new)	Cardiac tamponade
423.8	CC (new)	Other specified diseases of pericardium
423.9	CC (new)	Unspecified disease of pericardium

Although 414.8 (Ischemic congestive cardiomyopathy) is not on the CC list, 425.4 (Congestive cardiomyopathy) by itself is.

A CDI opportunity for the probable underlying cause of the patient's heart failure exists in all cases of CHF, assuming that the patient has some sort of heart pathology to qualify as a CC. If there is no heart pathology and the patient had pulmonary edema, then a CDI opportunity exists to determine if the appropriate code from ICD-9-CM chapter 8 should be used.

Other CDI opportunities in CHF include complications of heart failure, such as venous hypertension that can lead to lower extremity stasis ulcers, acute or chronic respiratory failure, or cardiogenic shock. Like cardiac arrest and respiratory failure, 785.51 (Cardiogenic shock) and 785.59 (Other shock) count as MCCs only if the patient is discharged alive from the hospitalization.

Pericarditis—CMS expanded the types of pericarditis that qualify as a CC. Beforehand, only acute pericarditis was considered a CC or a MCVD.

Cerebrovascular Disease

CMS added 435.x—transient ischemic attack (TIA) – as a CC in MS-DRGs and designated cerebral infarction (stroke/CVA) and cerebral hemorrhage as MCCs. Chapter 2 discusses the differentiating factors in these diagnoses. Cerebral embolus without infarction is not a CC, thus if a transient ischemic attack is likely to have occurred, the physician should be queried.

Code 437.1 (Other generalized ischemic cerebrovascular disease), which includes chronic cerebral ischemia and acute cerebrovascular insufficiency NOS, was also added as a CC. Because these terms are vague, a CDI opportunity exists to determine a more specific manifestation and their underlying or instigating cause.

As noted before, hemiplegia and hemiparesis as a late effect of stroke is now a CC.

Various Arterial and Venous Inflammations—CMS eliminated 446.5 (Giant cell arteritis) and 451.2 (Phlebitis and thrombophlebitis, lower extremities unspecified) from the CC list. They maintained 451.81 (Phlebitis and thrombophlebitis of the iliac vein) and 451.11 (Phlebitis and thrombophlebitis, femoral [deep] [superficial] as CCs. Usually, these conditions have deep venous thrombosis, so if there is significant extremity edema, a CDI opportunity exists.

CMS added the following diagnoses to the CC list:

- 454.2 (Varicose veins of lower extremities with ulcer and inflammation)
- 456.1 (Esophageal varices without mention of bleeding)
- 456.21 (Esophageal varices in diseases classified elsewhere, without mention of bleeding)
- 459.11 (Postphlebetic syndrome with ulcer)
- 459.13 (Postphlebetic syndrome with ulcer and inflammation)
- 459.2 (Compression of vein)
- 459.31 (Chronic venous hypertension with ulcer)
- 459.33 (Chronic venous hypertension with ulcer and inflammation)

Stasis ulcers of the lower extremity with inflammation are considered CCs, whereas those without inflammation, the postphlebetic syndrome, or chronic venous hypertension are not. If the physical exam demonstrate any redness, swelling, or pain surrounding the ulcer, a CDI opportunity exists to determine if inflammation is present. Underlying causes such as chronic venous hypertension, which can be due to chronic right heart failure, or postphlebetic syndrome may be considered as well.

Most vascular embolic events and vasculitis conditions count as CCs. The vasculitis codes include:

ICD-9-CM Code	Designation CC	Title
446.6	MCC	Thrombotic microangiopathy
446.0	CC	Polyarteritis nodosa
446.1	CC	Acute febrile mucocutaneous lymph node syndrome (MCLS)
446.20	CC	Hypersensitivity angiitis, unspecified
446.21	CC	Goodpasture's syndrome
446.29	CC	Other specified hypersensitivity angiitis
446.3	CC	Lethal midline granuloma
446.4	CC	Wegener's granulomatosis
446.7	CC	Takayasu's disease

Thrombotic microangiopathy (an MCC), otherwise known as thrombotic thrombocytopenic purpura, is a syndrome of microangiopathic hemolytic anemia, thrombocytopenia, and organ failure that is sometimes associated with enteropathogenic *Escherichia coli* infections (for example, O157:H7, which is encountered at fast-food restaurants). Its counterpart in children, 283.11 (Hemolytic uremic syndrome) is also an MCC.

Hypotension is not a CC. Its most common cause, hypovolemia, is not a CC. Potential CCs with hypotension include autonomic neuropathies or shock. A CDI opportunity exists if the clinical documentation suggests orthostasis or prolonged hypotension requiring dopamine or norepinephrine (Levophed®).

ICD-9-CM Chapter 8: Diseases of the Respiratory System (460–519)

CMS removed nonspecific chronic pulmonary diagnoses from the CC system, requiring them to be acutely exacerbated to qualify as CCs. Significant deletions include:

- 478.3x (Paralysis of the vocal cords) (Note: 478.34 [Complete bilateral paralysis of vocal cords] will remain a CC.)
- 490.20 (Obstructive chronic bronchitis without exacerbation)
- 491.8 (Other chronic bronchitis)
- 491.9 (Unspecified chronic bronchitis)
- 492.8 (Other emphysema)
- 493.20 (Chronic obstructive asthma w/o mention of status asthmaticus or acute exacerbation or unspecified)
- 495.x (Extrinsic allergic alveolitis) (Note: 495.7 ["Ventilation" pneumonitis], 495.8 [Other specified allergic alveolitis and pneumonitis], and 495.9 [Unspecified allergic alveolitis and pneumonitis]will remain CCs.)
- 496 (Chronic airway disease–NEC)
- 515 (Postinflammatory pulmonary fibrosis)
- 517.8 (Lung involvement in diseases classified elsewhere)
- 518.1 (Interstitial emphysema)

CMS added the following CCs:

- 464.01 (Acute laryngitis with obstruction)
- 464.30 (Acute epiglottis without mention of obstruction)
- 464.51 (Supraglottitis unspecified with obstruction)
- 466.1x (Acute bronchiolitis)
- 478.71 (Cellulitis and perichondiritis of larynx)
- 480.0 (Pneumonia due to adenovirus)
- 480.1 (Pneumonia due to respiratory syncytial virus)
- 480.2 (Pneumonia due to parainfluenza virus)
- 480.8 (Pneumonia due to other virus not elsewhere classified)
- 480.9 (Viral pneumonia, unspecified)
- 518.3 (Pulmonary eosinophilia)

CMS designated that all infectious pneumonias are now included as MCCs.

Pertinent differentiating factors in ICD-9-CM chapter 8 include:

Exacerbations of COPD and Asthma

To qualify as a CC, physicians must demonstrate that the condition of their patients with COPD and asthma has recently exacerbated. Coders may suspect this if the patient's medications are changed, if they are receiving aerosol breathing treatments in the hospital when metered-dose inhalers were used as an outpatient, or if there is evidence of respiratory insufficiency, respiratory distress, hypoxemia, or respiratory failure (see chapter 2 for definitions of these terms).

Status asthmaticus is a CC; however, if the patient develops acute respiratory failure, evidenced by normalization or elevation of the pCO_2, respiratory acidosis, or hypoxemia (oxygen saturations less than 88 percent, pO_2 less than 60 mm Hg), then a CDI opportunity exists for acute respiratory failure (an MCC).

Pneumonia

All pneumonias are MCCs in MS-DRG. Coders should be on the alert for sepsis or acute respiratory failure as well. If these are present on admission, pneumonia becomes the secondary diagnosis and maintains its MCC status. Hypoxemia alone is no longer a CC.

For compliance purposes, patients with pneumonia should have a chest x-ray that demonstrates an infiltrate; otherwise outside auditors may suspect that the patient only has bronchitis. If the chest x-ray shows no infiltrate, the physician should document the reason for the lack of infiltrate (for example, extreme dehydration) or show, by conducting a very thorough pulmonary examination that reveals bronchial breath sounds, egophony, and/or whispered pectoriloquy, that the patient does have pneumonia.

Many patients with pneumonia present in acute respiratory distress or acute respiratory insufficiency (518.82) that does not meet the criteria for acute respiratory failure. Although these are integral to exacerbations of COPD (*Coding Clinic*, 2nd Quarter, 1991), they are not necessarily integral to pneumonia.

Pleural effusions are CCs when they qualify as an additional diagnosis. Insignificant pleural effusions as a result of surgery or fluid overload should not be coded unless the physician especially considers it (for example, ruling out empyema) or performs a thoracentesis. Physicians should always be queried for the underlying cause of any pleural effusion, especially if the fluid is labeled as an exudate or as "complicated."

Tuberculosis can present as a pleuritis and pleural effusions. Because cultures are frequently negative, pleural fluid adenosine deaminase, interferon-gamma, or polymerase chain reaction tests may be performed when the physician strongly suspects tuberculosis. A CDI opportunity exists because these tests are difficult to interpret. Pleural effusion due to tuberculosis is an MCC.

Partially treated empyemas, also an MCC, may be considered if the patient has a parapneumonic (fluid around the pneumonia) effusion. Usually the white blood cell count in the fluid is elevated with a predominance of segmented cells. The Gram stain and culture may or may not show an organism because these patients usually have been treated with antibiotics. Physicians will usually label this fluid as exudative. Pleural fluid pH (performed on a blood gas machine, not in the laboratory) less than 7.20 strongly suggests empyema (Light 2002).

Pulmonary Fibrosis

As noted earlier, chronic pulmonary fibrosis is no longer a CC. There are some exceptions, including the following:

If a patient has an interstitial pattern on a chest x-ray or is described as having chronic pulmonary fibrosis, a CDI opportunity exists to determine its exact etiology and complications (such as chronic respiratory failure requiring home oxygen or chronic pulmonary edema).

Acute Pulmonary Edema and Respiratory Failure

As mentioned earlier, not all acute pulmonary edema is due to congestive heart failure. Pulmonary edema can occur as a result of toxic fume inhalation, hypoalbuminemia, postoperative fluid overload, or the acute respiratory distress syndrome. Some physicians may use the term "acute lung injury" to describe this circumstance. A CDI opportunity exists to ascertain the underlying pathology or possible complicating acute respiratory insufficiency or failure.

As discussed in chapter 2, acute respiratory failure should meet at least two of the following three criteria:

- Acute respiratory distress or acute respiratory insufficiency
- Significant hypoxemia—*Coding Clinic* 3rd Quarter 1998 definition is pO_2 less than 60 (oxygen saturation less than 88 percent) or a fall in pO_2 of 10 to 15 mm from baseline.
- Hypercapnia (pCO_2 greater than 50), preferably in the setting of respiratory acidosis (pH less than 7.35).

Note that arterial blood gases or oximetry only support the diagnosis of acute respiratory failure. Although intensive care unit admission or use of a ventilator is not necessary to diagnose acute respiratory failure, these patients should receive intensive treatment with

ICD-9-CM Code	CC Designation	Title
516.0	CC	Pulmonary alveolar proteinosis
516.1	CC	Idiopathic pulmonary hemosiderosis
516.2	CC	Pulmonary alveolar microlithiasis
516.3	CC	Idiopathic fibrosing alveolitis
516.8	CC	Other specified alveolar and parietoalveolar pneumonopathies
516.9	CC	Unspecified alveolar and parietoalveolar pneumonopathy
517.1	CC	Rheumatic pneumonia
517.2	CC	Lung involvement in systemic sclerosis

frequent monitoring and respiratory therapy. Because hypoxemia is no longer a CC, a CDI opportunity exists to determine if the clinical circumstances surrounding hypoxemia meets a generally accepted definition of acute respiratory failure.

Chronic respiratory failure is the inability of the lung to exchange gases over the long term. The pH is usually normal because the kidneys compensate for the respiratory acidosis. Usually these patients maintain pCO_2 levels greater than 45 to 50 mm/Hg or may be on home oxygen. Patients with emphysema may be labeled as "blue bloaters" as opposed to the "pink puffers," who do not retain carbon dioxide. If patients require home oxygen, a CDI opportunity exists to determine the lungs' capacity to exchange gases and for the presence of chronic respiratory failure.

Respiratory arrest as a symptom code is an MCC, whereas impending respiratory arrest cannot be coded. The patient must have completely stopped breathing and undergone a successful resuscitation to qualify.

Respiratory arrest is not counted as an MCC if the patient dies.

Chronic Ventilator Dependency and Tracheostomy Complications

CMS added V-codes to the CC list as shown in the table below.

A CDI opportunity exists for respirator dependent patients for the presence of chronic respiratory failure. Note that ICD-9-CM stipulates that v46.12 and v46.13 can only be principle diagnoses. v46.11 can only be a secondary diagnosis, and v46.14 can be either. Patients admitted with a principal diagnosis of v46.11 cannot have v46.13 as a secondary.

Coders should be aware that the tracheostomy complications listed below qualify as CCs.

Dental Diagnoses

CMS added some of the following mouth dental diagnoses to the CC list. Coders should be aware of these.

ICD-9-CM Code	CC Designation	Title
V46.11	CC	Dependence on respirator, status
V46.12	CC	Encounter for respirator dependence during power failure
V46.13	CC	Encounter for weaning from respirator (ventilator)
V46.14	CC	Mechanical complication of respirator (ventilator)

ICD-9-CM Code	CC Designation	Title
519.00	CC	Tracheostomy complication, unspecified
519.01	CC	Infection of tracheostomy
519.02	CC	Mechanical complication of tracheostomy
519.09	CC	Other tracheostomy complications

ICD-9-CM Code	CC Designation	Title
522.0	CC	Pulpitis
522.4	CC	Acute apical periodontitis of pulpal origin
527.3	CC	Abscess of salivary gland
527.4	CC	Fistula of salivary gland
528. 3	CC	Cellulitis and abscess of oral soft tissues

ICD-9-CM Chapter 9: Diseases of the Digestive System (520–579)

CMS removed the following chronic digestive system diseases from the CC list:

- 536.40 (Gastrostomy complications, unspecified)
- 571.2 (Alcoholic cirrhosis of liver)
- 571.49 (Other chronic hepatitis)
- 571.5 (Cirrhosis of liver without mention of alcohol)
- 571.6 (Biliary cirrhosis)
- 573.3 (Hepatitis, unspecified)
- 574.50 (Calculus of the bile duct without obstruction)
- 574.90 (Calculus of the gallbladder and bile duct without obstruction)

CMS added multiple chronic conditions to the CC list, such as inflammatory bowel disease (for example, Crohn's disease and ulcerative colitis) and other acute conditions, such as acute esophagitis or diverticulitis.

The new CCs are summarized as below:

- 530.12 (Acute esophagitis)
- 530.20 (Ulcer of esophagus without bleeding)
- 531.30 (Acute gastric ulcer without hemorrhage, perforation, or obstruction)
- 532.30 (Acute duodenal ulcer without hemorrhage, perforation, or obstruction)
- 533.30 (Acute peptic ulcer of unspecified site without hemorrhage, perforation, or obstruction)
- 533.40 (Acute gastrojejunal ulcer without hemorrhage, perforation, or obstruction)
- 538 (Gastrointestinal mucositis [ulcerative])

- 555.x (Regional enteritis)
- 556.x– (Ulcerative colitis)
- 557.1 (Chronic vascular insufficiency of the intestine)
- 557.9 (Unspecified vascular insufficiency of the intestine)
- 562.01 (Diverticulitis of the small intestine)
- 562.11 (Diverticulitis of the colon)
- 564.7 (Megacolon, other than Hirschsprung's)
- 564.81 (Neurogenic bowel)
- 569.41 (Ulcer of anus and rectum)
- 569.81 (Fistula of intestine, excluding rectum and anus)
- 569.82 (Ulceration of intestine)
- 572.3 (Portal hypertension)
- 577.1 (Chronic pancreatitis)
- 579.1 (Tropical sprue)
- 579.2 (Blind loop syndrome)
- 579.4 (Pancreatic steatorrhea)
- 579.8 (Other specified intestinal malabsorption)
- 579.9 (Unspecified intestinal malabsorption)

ICD-9-CM chapter 9 emphasizes the following areas.

Esophagus Disease

To qualify as a CC, physicians must document acute esophageal diseases or hemorrhages. Two areas require attention. First, ulcerative esophagitis is *not* an esophageal ulcer. Esophageal ulcers are rare complications of acid-reflux disease but may result from an adverse effect of medications (for example, tetracycline or nonsteroidal anti-inflammatory drugs), infections (for example, *Candida*, herpes, or HIV), or caustic injury (for

ICD-9-CM Code	CC Designation	Title
530.21	MCC	Ulcer of esophagus with bleeding
530.4	MCC	Perforation of esophagus
530.7	MCC	Gastroesophageal laceration-hemorrhage syndrome
530.82	MCC	Esophageal hemorrhage
530.84	MCC	Tracheoesophageal fistula
530.12	CC	Acute esophagitis
530.20	CC	Ulcer of esophagus without bleeding
530.86	CC	Infection of esophagostomy
530.87	CC	Mechanical complication of esophagostomy

example, acid or lye) (Higuchi, Sugawa, Shah, Tokioka, and Lucas). Second, acute esophagitis must be differentiated from chronic esophagitis, reflux esophagitis, or gastroesophageal reflux disease (GERD). Acute esophagitis usually occurs from a known stimulus, such as radiation therapy, adverse effect of recently administered medications or toxins (for example, tetracycline, nonsteroidal anti-inflammatory drugs, cancer chemotherapy, or lye), or infections (for example, *Candida*, cytomegalovirus, HIV, or herpes) and presents with odynophagia (pain upon swallowing) along with the typical heartburn symptoms seen in chronic injury.

Peptic Ulcer Disease

Peptic ulcers (stomach and duodenum) are CCs; those that have hemorrhage (for example, melena or hematemesis) or cause gastrointestinal obstruction are MCCs. Physicians should always be queried for the results of any biopsies or brushing performed on stomach ulcers because these may be malignant; duodenal ulcers are rarely malignant.

Gastritis is not a CC unless there is evidence of hemorrhage. A CDI opportunity exists if the stool is positive for occult blood and there is no other description of GI bleed (for example, melena or hematemesis). The remaining 3 CCs are listed below.

If the "gastritis" is caused by cancer chemotherapy or radiation therapy, a CDI opportunity exists for "mucositis." Code 538 (Gastrointestinal mucositis [ulcerative]) is a term used to refer to damage to the body's mucous membrane following cytotoxic cancer therapy, which is a CC. Symptoms include pain, nausea, heartburn, ulceration, abdominal pain, bloating, vomiting, diarrhea, and constipation. Code 558.1 (Gastroenteritis and colitis due to radiation) also qualifies as a CC.

Gastrointestinal Tubes

Although 536.40 (Gastrostomy complications, unspecified) has been removed as a CC, the following codes for gastrointestinal tubes apply.

Appendicitis

Appendicitis is an MCC unless there is no evidence of peritonitis, which would be highly unusual because the appendix is located directly next to the peritoneum. Symptoms of peritonitis include involuntary abdominal guarding (the patient pushes the doctor away when he gently examines the right lower quadrant) and rebound tenderness (pain is worse when the physician relieves pressure in the right lower quadrant). Peritonitis is invariably described in the operative report. A CDI opportunity exists if peritonitis is not described in the setting of appendicitis.

ICD-9-CM Code	CC Designation	Title
578.0	CC	Hematemesis
578.1	CC	Blood in stool
578.9	CC	Hemorrhage of gastrointestinal tract, unspecified

ICD-9-CM Code	CC Designation	Title
V55.1	CC	Attention to gastrostomy
530.86	CC	Infection of esophagostomy
530.87	CC	Mechanical complication of esophagostomy
536.41	CC	Infection of gastrostomy
536.42	CC	Mechanical complication of gastrostomy
569.62	CC	Mechanical complication of colostomy and enterostomy
569.69	CC	Other colostomy and enterostomy complication

Hernia

Hernias are CCs if they cause gastrointestinal obstruction and MCCs if they are gangrenous or strangulated.

Intestinal Vascular Insufficiency

CMS expanded the intestinal vascular insufficiency codes to allow chronic intestinal vascular insufficiency codes to be CCs. Chronic intestinal vascular insufficiency is a cause of lower gastrointestinal bleeding. Typical findings are usually seen on colonoscopy or barium enema. Acute intestinal vascular insufficiency, usually presenting with increasing abdominal pain, microscopic GI bleeding, and vague physical findings, is an MCC. Because acute intestinal vascular insufficiency is frequently misdiagnosed, only to be discovered after the patient's bowel has infracted or after the patient has been transferred to a tertiary facility, coders should be aware of this possibility for patients transferred to other hospitals for abdominal pain of uncertain etiology.

Diverticulitis

Diverticulosis is usually asymptomatic but often presents as lower gastrointestinal hemorrhage or diverticulitis. Diverticulitis, now added as a CC, is an inflammation of a pocket in the patient's colon, known as diverticulosis. These patients have abdominal pain, fever, and may present with SIRS (for example, sepsis). Diverticulosis may also present with GI hemorrhage.

Liver Disease

CMS has limited the liver diagnoses qualifying as CCs, as listed in the table below.

Jaundice, as a symptom, remains as a CC, as does malignant ascites or other ascites that may be a complication of cirrhosis. Please refer to the infectious hepatitis codes discussed earlier for a more complete discussion.

ICD-9-CM Code	CC Designation	Title
562.02	MCC	Diverticulosis of small intestine with hemorrhage
562.03	MCC	Diverticulitis of small intestine with hemorrhage
562.12	MCC	Diverticulosis of colon with hemorrhage
562.13	MCC	Diverticulitis of colon with hemorrhage
562.01	CC	Diverticulitis of small intestine (without mention of hemorrhage)
562.11	CC	Diverticulitis of colon (without mention of hemorrhage)

ICD-9-CM Code	CC Designation	Title
570	MCC	Acute and subacute necrosis of liver
572.0	MCC	Abscess of liver
572.1	MCC	Portal pyemia
572.2	MCC	Hepatic coma
572.4	MCC	Hepatorenal syndrome
572.3	CC	Portal hypertension
573.4	MCC	Hepatic infarction
573.1	CC	Hepatitis in viral diseases classified elsewhere
573.2	CC	Hepatitis in other infectious diseases classified elsewhere

Gallbladder Disease

All of the cholelithiasis codes are CCs except for calculus of gallbladder without mention of cholecystitis. Acute cholecystitis, even without demonstrated gallstones, is a CC. If the gallstone obstructs the cystic or common bile duct, it is classified as an MCC. Clinical evidence of cystic duct obstruction includes lack of gallbladder visualization on oral cholecystograms or evidence in the operative report. Common bile duct obstruction should be suspected if the patient is jaundiced, has elevations of the serum alkaline phosphatase or gamma-glutamyl transpeptidase (GGTP), or recently sustained gallstone-related pancreatitis. Gallbladder and bile duct perforations are MCCs. These may occur as surgical complications.

Malabsorption

CMS added intestinal malabsorption and one of its common causes, chronic pancreatitis, to the CC list, including the following codes:

- 577.1 (Chronic pancreatitis)
- 579.1 (Tropical sprue)
- 579.2 (Blind loop syndrome)
- 579.4 (Pancreatic steatorrhea)
- 579.8 (Other specified intestinal malabsorption)
- 579.9 (Unspecified intestinal malabsorption)

Malabsorption is associated with diarrhea and fat in the stool (steatorrhea). A CDI opportunity exists to determine any coexisting malnutrition.

Chronic pancreatitis is associated with chronic alcoholism. Often, these patients have calcification of their pancreas on CT scans or pseudocysts (which are CCs). As chronic pancreatitis has chronic pain, some hospitalizations will occur for pain control, thus principal and secondary diagnosis selection should be carefully considered.

Acute Pancreatitis

Acute pancreatitis, an acute inflammation of the pancreas, qualifies as an MCC. Diagnostic criteria usually include elevated serum amylase and lipase levels; invariably there is pancreatic swelling on abdominal CT scan or ultrasound.

As pancreatitis is associated with SIRS due to noninfectious cause, proper capture of the SIRS codes support severity of illness as well. As a review, these are listed below. Coders are encouraged to recognize the acute organ dysfunctions associated with pancreatitis, such as acute renal insufficiency, acute lung injury (with possible adult respiratory distress syndrome or acute respiratory failure), severe hypocalcemia, or metabolic encephalopathy, so they can properly query for and assign the 995.93 or 995.94 code.

ICD-9-CM Chapter 10: Diseases of the Genitourinary System (580–629)

CMS removed the following CCs:

- 585.1 (Chronic kidney disease, stage 1)
- 585.2 (Chronic kidney disease, stage 2)
- 585.3 (Chronic kidney disease, stage 3)
- 585.9 (Chronic kidney disease, unspecified [Chronic renal insufficiency])
- 590.9 (Unspecified infection of kidney)
- 595.1 (Chronic interstitial cystitis)
- 595.2 (Other chronic cystitis)
- 595.4 (Cystitis in diseases classified elsewhere)
- 595.81 (Cystitis cystica)
- 595.89 (Other specified types of cystitis) (Note: 595.82 [Irradiation cystitis remains] a CC.)
- 595.9 (Unspecified cystitis)
- 596.0 (Bladder neck obstruction)
- 596.4 (Atony of bladder)
- 597.0 (Urethral abscess)

ICD-9-CM Code	CC Designation	Title
995.90	CC	Systemic inflammatory response syndrome, unspecified
995.91	MCC	Sepsis (SIRS due to infection)
995.92	MCC	Severe sepsis (SIRS due to infection with acute organ dysfunction)
995.93	CC	Systemic inflammatory response syndrome due to noninfectious process without acute organ dysfunction
995.94	MCC	Systemic inflammatory response syndrome due to noninfectious process with acute organ dysfunction

- 598.1 (Traumatic urethral stricture)
- 598.2 (Postoperative urethral stricture)
- 599.4 (Urethral false passage)
- 599.6x (Urinary obstruction)
- 599.7 (Hematuria)
- 601.3 (Prostatocystitis)

All glomerulonephritis conditions are now CCs.

- 582.x (Chronic glomerulonephritis)
- 583.0 (Proliferative glomerulonephritis)
- 583.1 (Membranous glomerulonephritis)
- 583.2 (Membranoproliferative glomerulonephritis)
- 583.7 (Renal medullary necrosis)
- 588.1 (Nephrogenic diabetes insipidus)
- 588.81 (Secondary hyperparathyroidism [of renal origin])
- 590.01 (Chronic pyelonephritis with lesions of renal medullary necrosis)
- 593.4 (Other ureteric obstruction)
- 593.81 (Vascular disorders of the kidney)
- 593.82 (Ureteral fistula)
- 599.1 (Urethral fistula)
- 607.3 (Priapism)
- 607.82 (Vascular disorders of the penis)
- 608.2x (Torsion of testis)

Chronic Kidney Disease

Chronic kidney disease (CKD) is defined according to the presence or absence of kidney damage and level of kidney function, irrespective of the underlying type of kidney disease (diagnosis). Criteria to diagnosis CKD include (National Kidney Foundation 2007) the following.

- Kidney damage for more than 3 months, as defined by structural or functional abnormalities of the kidney, with or without decreased glomerular filtration rate (GFR)
- Pathological abnormalities
- Markers of kidney damage, including abnormalities in the composition of the blood or urine, or abnormalities in imaging tests
- GFR less than 60 mL/min/1.73 m^2 for more than 3 months, with or without kidney damage

Markers of kidney damage include proteinuria, microalbuminuria, hematuria, or congenital anomalies or cysts seen on x-ray. Transplanted kidneys are always considered to have CKD.

GFR also qualifies as a criteria if it is less than 60 mL/min/1.73 m^2 for more than 3 months. GFR can be estimated from measuring a 24-hour urine collection for creatinine clearance or by measuring the serum creatinine in relation to the patient's sex, race, and body mass. Many hospitals now place calculated GFR next to the serum creatinine on their laboratory results; if a hospital does not do this, the coding department or medical staff may collaborate with the pathologist or laboratory director to implement a change in the laboratory reporting system. If the patient is on chronic dialysis, 585.6—end-stage renal disease (ESRD)—should be used instead of 585.5 (chronic kidney disease, stage 5), as this is an administrative term indicating the need for chronic dialysis. Only CKD stages 4 and 5 are CCs, whereas ESRD is an MCC.

Chronic kidney disease should be differentiated from acute renal failure, as discussed in chapter 2. Acute renal failure can occur in the setting of chronic kidney disease; however, it should not occur with ESRD except for very rare exceptions. A possible scenario is one in which a patient was started on chronic

ICD-9-CM	Label	Criteria GFR	Estimated Serum creatinine (mg/dl) in 65-year-old white 70 kg male	CC?
585.1	CKD, stage 1	>90	<0.9 mg/dL	N
585.2	CKD, stage 2	60–89	1.0–1.3	N
585.3	CKD stage 3	30–59	1.4–2.5	N
585.4	CKD, stage 4	15–29	2.5–4.5	CC
585.5	CKD, stage 5	<5	>4.5	CC
585.6	End-stage renal disease	Need for chronic dialysis	Need for chronic dialysis	MCC
585.9	CKD NOS chronic renal failure	See above	See above	N

dialysis when their GFR was 20 (qualifying the patient for stage 4) and sustains an acute renal injury resulting in acute renal failure. Physician documentation must clearly substantiate this circumstance.

Most of the other CCs and MCCs within this chapter are straightforward. A CDI opportunity exists if a patient has urosepsis or a urinary tract infection, especially in the presence of SIRS, or sepsis due to that urosepsis or urinary tract infection.

Bladder and Ureter Disorders (Including Urinary Tract infection)

CMS maintained most of the same urinary tract CCs in the new MS-DRGs except that they now require greater specificity from physicians. For example, 590.9 (Infection of kidney NOS) and 595.2 (Chronic cystitis NEC) were deleted as CCs, yet 590.10 (Acute pyelonephritis), 595.0 (Acute cystitis), and 599.0 (Urinary tract infection NOS) were maintained as CCs. Chronic interstitial cystitis is now deleted as a CC.

With urinary tract infections, many physicians will perform a CT scan or ultrasound of the kidney to search for an anatomical etiology, especially in men. Some that qualify as CCs include:

- 590.2 (Renal or perirenal abscess) (MCC)
- 591 (Hydronephrosis) (CC)
- 592.1 (Calculus of ureter) (CC) (Note: Physicians cannot just list kidney stone. This must be specified as being present in the ureter.)
- 593.4 (Ureteric obstruction) (CC) (Note: Urinary obstruction NOS is no longer a CC.)
- 593.5 (Hydroureter)
- 601.0 (Acute prostatitis) (but not chronic prostatitis)
- 788.8 (Urinary extravasation)

Some of the anatomic disorders or consequences deleted as CCs include:

- Most urethral disorders (except urethral abscess)
- Hematuria (integral to kidney stones but not integral to urinary tract infections)
- Urinary retention

If the serum creatinine level rises in the setting of a urinary tract infection, the physician should be queried for the underlying cause and severity. In patients with acute pyelonephritis, especially due to *Staphylococcus aureus*, renal medullary necrosis (an MCC) can be the culprit. Depending on the physician's definition of acute renal failure—either a creatinine rise of only 0.5 mg/dL within the past 2 weeks (as described in the 2003 JAMA article) or a tripling from baseline used in the RIFLE criteria (Bellomo et al. 2004)—acute renal failure (also an MCC) may be present as well.

With any urinary tract infection, sepsis (SIRS due to infection) may occur. As most coders know, many physicians document sepsis due to urinary tract infections as "urosepsis" which, according to ICD-9-CM and *Coding Clinic*, is only a urinary tract infection (599.0), a CC. On the other hand, sepsis (SIRS due to infection) is an MCC for both the septicemia (038.xx) and the SIRS (995.91 or 995.92) codes, thus differentiation of the two is vital. The SIRS criteria, adapted from the 2001 International Sepsis Definitions Conference, included infection, documented or suspected, such as some of the following: (Levy et al 2003)

- General variables—995.91 (SIRS due to infection without organ dysfunction), including:
  - Fever (core temperature greater than 38.3°C)
  - Hypothermia (core temperature less than 36°C)
  - Heart rate greater than 90 beats/min or greater than 2 SD above the normal value for age
  - Tachypnea
  - Altered mental status
  - Significant edema or positive fluid balance (20 mL/kg over 24 hours)
  - Hyperglycemia (plasma glucose 120 mg/dL or 7.7 mmol/L) in the absence of diabetes
- Inflammatory variables—SIRS due to infection without organ dysfunction
  - Leukocytosis (WBC count greater than 12,000/μL)
  - Leukopenia (WBC count less than 4,000/μL)
  - Normal WBC count with greater than 10 percent immature forms
  - Plasma C-reactive protein greater than 2 SDs above the normal value
  - Plasma procalcitonin greater than 2 SDs above the normal value

Hemodynamic variables—SIRS due to infection with organ dysfunction

- Arterial hypotension (systolic blood pressure less than 90 mm Hg, mean arterial pressure less than 70 mm Hg, or a systolic blood pressure fall of greater than 40 mm/Hg in adults)
- Arterial hypoxemia (pO$_2$ less than 60)
- Acute oliguria (urine output less than 30 mL/hour)

- Serum creatinine increase of greater than 0.5 mg/dL
- Coagulation abnormalities (INR greater than 1.5 or an activated partial thromboplastin time (aPTT) greater than 60 s)
- Ileus (absent bowel sounds)
- Thrombocytopenia (platelet count less than 100,000/μ/L)
- Hyperbilirubinemia (plasma total bilirubin greater than 4 mg/dL
- Tissue perfusion variables
- Hyperlactatemia (greater than 1 mmol/L)

Documentation of all precipitating causes, such as a urinary catheter or device, and whether this device was present on admission, is critical as well. Not only is this pertinent to principal diagnosis assignment, as discussed in chapter 2, but also the urinary tract infection may not count as a CC (or alteratively, may be counted as a complication of care) if it was not designated as present on admission. Usually the emergency room note or admitting nursing assessment ascertains whether any urinary device or catheter was present on admission.

Male Genital Diseases

Although most of the male genital diseases designated as CCs remain, some changes have occurred. Acute prostatitis and prostatic abscess remain as CCs; however, the vague terms "prostatic congestion" and "prostatocystitis" are no longer CCs. Male patients with acute prostatitis will have many white blood cells in their urinalysis, thus a CDI opportunity exists when pyuria is present and the acuity of the prostate infection is not well documented. Any associated urinary retention has been deleted as a CC.

New CCs for MS-DRGs include:

- 607.3 (Priapism)—Priapism is a persistent, usually painful, erection that lasts for more than 4 hours and occurs without sexual stimulation. The condition develops when blood in the penis becomes trapped and is unable to drain.
- 607.82 (Vascular disorder of the penis)—These include nontraumatic hematomas, hemorrhage, or thrombosis of the penis. Erectile dysfunction due to vascular causes should be coded to 607.84 (Impotence of organic origin).
- 608.2x (Torsion of the testis)—This is a twisting of the testicle upon itself, causing intense pain and swelling. This is a true medical emergency that usually occurs in men younger than 30 years of age, and immediate urologic consultation is necessary to salvage the testicle.

Female Genital Disorders

Few female genital disorders qualify as CCs. CMS removed breast lumps or masses and 620.7 (Hematoma of the broad ligament) as CCs. They added 616.81 (Mucositis of the cervix, vulva, and vagina) as a CC. Mucositis is a consequence of radiation treatments and cancer chemotherapy and thus should only be coded in patients receiving these treatments.

619.x (Urogenital fistulas) and 620.5 (Torsion of the ovary or tube) (much like testicular torsion) were added as CCs.

Chronic pelvic inflammatory disease (PID) remains a CC under MS-DRGs; however, acute PID is an MCC. PID is a spectrum of infections of the female genital tract that includes endometritis, salpingitis, tubo-ovarian abscess, and peritonitis. Sexually transmitted organisms, especially *Neisseria gonorrhoeae* and *Chlamydia trachomatis*, are implicated in many cases. However, microorganisms that comprise the vaginal flora (for example, anaerobes, *Gardnerella vaginalis*, *Haemophilus influenzae*, enteric gram-negative rods, and *Streptococcus agalactiae*) also have been associated with PID.

Acute PID is difficult to diagnose because of the wide variation in the symptoms and signs. Many women with PID have subtle or mild symptoms. Acute PID should be strongly suspected if there is any pain with movement of the cervix or any tenderness in the adnexa (for example, fallopian tubes or ovaries) or uterus in a sexually active woman. Other clinical signs may include:

- Oral temperature greater than 101°F (greater than 38.3°C)
- Abnormal cervical or vaginal mucopurulent discharge
- Presence of abundant numbers of WBC on saline microscopy of vaginal secretions
- elevated erythrocyte sedimentation rate
- Elevated C-reactive protein
- Laboratory documentation of cervical infection with *N gonorrhoeae* or *C trachomatis*

Given that acute PID is an MCC, coders should be aware of these circumstances, especially if antibiotics are administered or there is a strong suspicion of venereal disease.

Menorrhagia and metrorrhagia still do not count as CCs. However, if they are acute and severe, usually requiring blood transfusion, they may lead to a precipitous drop in hematocrit (790.01—arbitrarily defined as a loss of 20 percent of blood volume, corresponding to a drop in hematocrit to 8 in a woman with a baseline hematocrit of 40) or an acute blood loss anemia, which is a CC (Mannucci and Levi 2007).

ICD-9-CM Chapter 11: Complications of Pregnancy, Childbirth, and the Puerperium (630–677)

One of the most extensive revisions of the CC structure in MS-DRGs occurs in ICD-9-CM chapter 11, Complications of Pregnancy, Childbirth, and the Puerperium. In devising MS-DRGs, CMS opted to use the APR-DRG CC structure in assigning CC and MCC status to ICD-9-CM codes. Although these changes are unlikely to affect the Medicare population, many Medicaid payers or private insurance companies have used CMS DRGs for their private plans and may use MS-DRGs as well, given that CMS will not maintain or update CMS-DRGs in the future. Hospitals with a significantly higher-risk obstetric population are likely to benefit from these revisions.

Codes from chapter 11 have sequencing priority over codes from other chapters. Additional codes from other chapters may be used in conjunction with chapter 11 codes to further specify conditions if necessary.

Fetal conditions, codes from category 655 (Known or suspected fetal abnormality affecting the management of the mother) are assigned only when the fetal condition is actually responsible for modifying the management of the mother; that is, it requires diagnostic studies, additional observation, special care, or termination of pregnancy.

ICD-9-CM 650 (Normal delivery) should never be a principal diagnosis when codes from chapter 11 are needed to describe a current complication of the antenatal, delivery, or perinatal period.

In reviewing the revised CC list, CMS made the following very clear:

- Under most circumstances, conditions related to pregnancy that are unspecified as to the episode of care or where the condition is not applicable (fifth digit of 0 for codes 640 to 677) are not CCs.
- Additional resources for the circumstances of pregnancy negatively influencing maternal or fetal health are to be provided.

Deletions from the CC list include:

- Uncomplicated spontaneous, legal, and illegal abortions and those complicated only by hemorrhage (ICD-9-CM codes 634, 635, and 636 with a fourth digit of 1). This fourth digit of 1 includes defibrination syndromes, disseminated intravascular coagulation (DIC), and intravascular hemolysis, which are considered MCCs or CCs in other chapters. 639.1, Postabortion hemorrhage, DIC, and hemorrhage, however, does count as a CC.
- Specified hemorrhage of early pregnancy (ICD-9-CM codes 640.8x—Other specified hemorrhage of early pregnancy). Early pregnancy is defined as less than 22 weeks of gestation. On the other hand, 640.93, unspecified antepartum hemorrhage of early pregnancy, is a CC.
- Other antepartum hemorrhages of pregnancy after 22 weeks, (ICD-9-CM codes 641.8x, Other antepartum hemorrhage and 641.9x, Unspecified antepartum hemorrhage. Those associated with coagulation disorders (for example, hemophilia) specified as antepartum or postpartum were designated as MCCs.
- Anemia of pregnancy—ICD-9-CM code 648.2x). If applicable, a CDI opportunity may exist for the pertinent hemorrhage code.
- Many conditions related to pregnancy and the puerperium ending with fifth digit of 0. Coders should avoid using these codes because more specific codes that are CCs are available.
- All of the codes for category 668 (Complications of the administration of anesthetic or other sedation in labor and delivery)

Additions to the CC list include:

- Legal, illegal, unspecified, and attempted abortions with complications (other than hemorrhage, including DIC and intravascular hemolysis listed above). Oliguria (urine output less than 30 cc/h), acute renal failure, chronic renal failure, shock, and any form of embolism will count as major CCs. Postabortion hemorrhage will be a CC. The conditions counting as MCCs in abortion qualify in postabortion cases.
- Abdominal, tubal, and any form of ectopic pregnancies
- Premature separation of the placenta
- Underlying maternal health issues, such as:
  - Essential and renovascular hypertension
  - Transient hypertension during delivery
  - Early onset of delivery, defined as before 37 completed weeks of gestation
  - Any form of renal disease (look for protein in the urine)
  - Habitual abortion, delivered on that admission
  - Genitourinary infections
  - Liver disorders (jaundice during pregnancy, hepatorenal syndrome)

- Maternal syphilis (positive VDRL, RPR, or FTA test, usually treated with penicillin)
- Maternal gonorrhea or other venereal diseases (look for DNA probe studies or cultures)
- Other maternal infections such as HIV, tuberculosis, malaria, rubella, hepatitis C (common in inner city hospitals or in patients with a history of drug abuse), viral warts, even unspecified viral or chlamydial infections. The entire list of conditions between 50 and 79.99 is included as well.
- Bone and back disorders, including ankylosing spondylitis, neck pain, low back pain, spinal disc disorders, and many disorders of the extremities
- Coagulation disorders
- Epilepsy (See the section on seizures. Conditions referable to the symptom codes do not count.)

- Multigestational deliveries
- Multigestational antepartum care except for twins
- Fetal loss antepartum care except for twins
- Cervical incompetency (an MCC)
- Poor fetal growth, fetal distress, and intrauterine death–delivered
- Oligohydramnios and polyhydramnios –delivered
  - The major source for amniotic fluid is fetal urine, of which fetal swallowing is the main source for resorption. The volume of amniotic fluid increases from 250 to 800 mL between the 12th and 32nd week of gestation, remains stable through the 39th week of gestation, and then falls to 500 mL by the 42nd week (Gabbe 2002). Physicians estimate amniotic fluid volume by determining the amniotic fluid index (AFI), a measurement of amniotic fluid

Progression of Spontaneous Labor at Term

Parameter	Mean	Fifth Percentile
Nulliparas		
Total duration of labor	10.1 hr	25.8 hr
Stage of labor		
Duration of the first stage	9.7 hr	24.7 hr
Duration of the second stage	33.0 min	117.5 min
Duration of latent phase	6.4 hr	20.6 hr
Rate of cervical dilation during active phase	3.0 cm/hr	1.2 cm/hr
Duration of the third stage	5.0 min	30.0 min
Multiparas		
Total duration of labor	6.2 hr	19.5 hr
Stage of labor		
Duration of the first stage	8.0 hr	18.8 hr
Duration of the second stage	8.5 min	46.5 min
Duration of latent phase	4.8 hr	13.6 hr
Rate of cervical dilation during active phase	5.7 cm/hr	1.5 cm/hr
Duration of the third stage	5.0 min	30.0 min

Data from Friedman E.A. 1978. *Labor: Clinical Evaluation and Management*, 2nd ed. Norwalk, CT: Appleton-Century-Crofts.

depth (in centimeters) by ultrasound in four quadrants of the mother's uterus. An AFI of 5 cm or less is oligohydramnios, whereas an AFI of 20 cm or more is polyhydramnios (Phelan et al 1987).

- Fetal malposition–prior to delivery
- Prolonged delivery—not to be confused with prolonged pregnancy. CMS allows prolongation of delivery NOS as a CC but yet does not allow prolongation of the latent or active stages as a CC. These are categorized as:
  - Prolonged latent phase—The time from when the amniotic sac leaks or breaks to the initiation of labor
  - Stage 1—The time from the initiation of labor prior to full dilation of the cervix
  - Stage 2—The time from full dilation of the cervix to delivery of the infant
  - Stage 3—The time from delivery of the infant to delivery of the placenta and its associated membranes

The average time of each phase differs for the primagravida and multigravida delivery (see following table). (Gabbe 2001). Other miscellaneous additions to the MS-DRG CC list include the following:

- Delivery with third- and fourth-degree lacerations or anal sphincter tear, other lacerations such as at the cervix, in the vagina, or other pelvic trauma
- All of category 671 (Venous complications of delivery)
- Obstetrical shock and hypotension
- Puerperal fever

Conditions that remain or that are commonly missed include the following.

Chemical Dependency

648.3x—Drug dependency in pregnancy—remains a CC in MS-DRGs. This condition must be differentiated from drug abuse which does not involve physicial withdrawal or addiction. If there is any evidence of drug withdrawal symptoms or use or replacement therapy (for example, PRN benzodiazepines) to treat withdrawal, a CDI opportunity exists to determine if the patient has drug abuse or drug addiction.

Eclampsia and Hypertension

Maternal hypertension is now included as a CC. Coders should be aware of the definitions for the various types

of these conditions. Chronic hypertension in pregnancy is mild if systolic blood pressure is less than 160 mm Hg and diastolic pressure is less than 110 mm Hg. Hypertension is severe if either systolic pressure is greater than 160 mm Hg or diastolic pressure is greater than 110 mm Hg. Superimposed preeclampsia is defined as exacerbation of hypertension of at least 30 mm Hg in systolic blood pressure or at least 15 mm Hg in diastolic blood pressure, together with the development of proteinuria during the course of the pregnancy (at least 500 mg/day) or exacerbation of preexisting proteinuria (at least 5 g/day) and elevation of serum liver enzymes, low platelets, or development of symptoms. (Gabbe 2001) Hypertension predisposes the patient to placenta abruption, fetal demise, or acute renal failure. A CDI opportunity exists if these circumstances are not well documented in the medical record.

Postpartum Hemorrhage

Normal blood loss during different types of pregnancies is as follows: 500 mL during a normal pregnancy, 1,000 mL after a cesarean section, 1,500 mL after an elective cesarean section with hysterectomy, and 3,000 mL after an emergency cesarean section with hysterectomy. Patients will not show symptoms with a blood loss of 1,000 cc as the arteries and veins constrict to preserve blood flow to the vital organs. Postpartum hemorrhage is nevertheless defined according to the amount of blood lost as summarized below. (Gabbe 2001).

By definition, given the normal amount of blood loss associated with this procedure, most patients who have had a cesarean section, with or without hysterectomy, would qualify as having peripartum or postpartum hemorrhage. Most physicians underestimate the volume of blood loss during obstetrical procedures, sometimes by up to 50 percent. Physician documentation of postpartum hemorrhage and its underlying cause is necessary to code this condition.

Patients tolerate some blood loss due to the 30 percent increase in red cell blood mass that normally

Hemorrhage Class	Acute Blood Loss (mL)	Percentage Lost
1	900	15
2	1,200–1,500	20–25
3	1,800–2,100	30–35
4	2,400	40

Source: Adapted from Rheman, KS, Johnson TRB

occurs in pregnancy (the hematocrit may be low due to hemodilution). Patients do not have symptoms until they have lost more than 1,200 mL of blood, usually manifested as orthostatic hypotension (drop in systolic blood pressure of more than 20 mm Hg when the patient is standing), an increase in the pulse rate to over 100, or a precipitous drop in hematocrit (drop in hematocrit of more than 8 from baseline, correlating the other definitions of major blood loss of more than 20 percent of volume referenced in other sections of this book). Because the baseline hematocrit is difficult to determine, the physician should be queried for hemorrhage when there is any precipitous drop of hematocrit of 5 or more points, any postpartum pulse of over 100, any orthostatic hypotension or transient blood pressure readings under 90 mm Hg, or any blood transfusion in the peripartum or postpartum period. The underlying cause of the hemorrhage (for example, bladder atony, placenta previa, coagulopathy) also should be determined.

Obstetric Shock

The most common cause of obstetric death, obstetric shock is a clinical condition when intravascular capacity is insufficient to perfuse vital organs. Obstetric shock is difficult to diagnose given the marked hemodynamic changes surrounding pregnancy. The blood pressure may be high, normal, or low, given the underlying circumstance. The best indicator is the presence of oliguria and a strong clinical suspicion. Hypovolemic shock from blood loss is the most common cause of obstetric shock, with septic shock the second most common cause. A CDI opportunity exists when oliguria or rapid pulse is found or when large fluid challenges, dopamine, norepinephrine, or other vasoactive drugs are administered.

Obstetric Tears

Because third and fourth degree vaginal tears are now CCs, a CDI opportunity exists in their differentiation, which is defined as follows:

- First-degree injury to the vaginal epithelium and vulval skin only
- Second-degree injury to the perineal muscles, but not the anal sphincter
- Third-degree injury to the perineum involving the anal sphincter complex
- Fourth-degree injury to the perineum involving the anal sphincter complex and rectal mucosa

Other Conditions

Any thrombophlebitis or probable embolus should be captured as a CC. Pregnant patients can develop a peripartum cardiomyopathy, resulting in heart failure. Peripartum and postpartum breast abscesses are also CCs.

ICD-9-CM Chapter 12: Diseases of the Skin and Subcutaneous Tissue (680–709)

CMS eliminated carbuncles, impetigo, psoriatic arthropathy, and ulcers of other parts of the foot besides the heel and midsection as CCs, while adding cellulitis of the hand, pyoderma gangrenosum, and erythema multiforme to the CC list. The only MCCs in this chapter are pressure sores of the back, hip, buttock, ankle, and heel. Thus, recognition of these commonly underdocumented conditions is vital.

Pressure Ulcer (or Sore)

A pressure ulcer is a localized area of soft-tissue injury resulting from compression between a bony prominence and an external surface. They are classified into four stages (Smith 1995).

> Stage 1, nonblanchable erythema—In this circumstance, when the nurse or physician presses on the skin, it stays red instead of turning white.
> Stage 2, partial-thickness skin loss
> Stage 3, full-thickness skin loss
> Stage 4, full-thickness skin loss with extensive destruction

As noted previously, pressure sores on the back, hip, buttock, ankle, and heel are major CCs, thus their identification and differentiation from other pressure sores and nonpressure ulcers is crucial to correct coding and CC capture. Even skin redness not attributable to cellulitis should be considered as a CDI opprotunity for possible pressure ulcer.

Coding Clinic, 1st Quarter, 2004, page 14–15, states that heel ulcers in diabetes are likely pressure sores rather than diabetic ulcers, whereas diabetic ulcers tend to be more distal, involving the toes, or the webs between the toes. Diabetic ulcers involving these distal locations, coding to 707.15, do not qualify as CCs under MS-DRGs.

Physicians commonly do not document skin conditions upon their admission history and physical examination, leaving the diagnosis of pressure sores to the nursing assessment or the hospital's skin team. The ICD-9-CM Official Guidelines for Coding and Reporting for FY2008 cites an example whereby the hospital identified a pressure sore not documented by the attending physician, requiring coders to query the physician to determine if the pressure sore was present on admission. Coders should not code these conditions as present on admission unless they have been explicitly documented by their physicians as such, given that CMS is not likely to allow pressure sores not documented to have been present on admission to serve as CCs or MCCs during FY2009.

Pyoderma Gangrenosum

Pyoderma gangrenosum is an uncommon ulcerative condition of the skin of uncertain etiology that is usually associated with other systemic illnesses, such as malignancies, diabetes, or systemic lupus. They can either be deep purple ulcers, usually located on the lower extremities, or blistery pustular lesions involving the hands or the face. Even though no therapy is uniformly efficacious, physicians still may use topical steroids or other anti-inflammatory medications. If patients have an ulcerative rash meeting these descriptions in the setting of a known systemic illness, especially if any medications or creams are prescribed during the hospital stay, a CDI opportunity exists for the underlying etiology and any precipitating causes.

Erythema Multiforme

Erythema multiforme (EM) (Code 695.1) is an acute self-limited skin eruption composed of spots that are red welts, sometimes with purple or blistered areas in the center that are sometimes associated with mucosal lesions, blisters, or skin detachment. It is considered to be a hypersensitivity reaction to an underlying stimulus. There are several types of EM.

- Erythema multiforme—Typically targeted or raised, edematous papules distributed distally on the hands, shin, or feet, lasting about 1 to 2 weeks, and leaving a brown pigment residual. Usually triggered by the herpes virus (EM minor), other infections, or medications.
- Erythema multiforme major—Lesions of EM associated with epidermal detachment involving less than 10 percent of total body surface area.
- Stevens-Johnson syndrome—EM with widespread blisters predominant on the trunk and face, presenting with erythematous or pruritic macules and one or more mucous membrane erosions. Epidermal detachment is less than 10 percent total body surface area.

- Toxic epidermal necrolysis—EM with the same presentation as Stevens-Johnson syndrome, except that over 30 percent of the total body surface area is affected.

Other CCs in this chapter include cellulitis and pemphigus (a blistering disease). If the patient has cellulitis, the coder should determine if any associated ulcer is present and determine if it is related to pressure necrosis typical of ICD-9-CM category 707.

ICD-9-CM Chapter 13: Diseases of the Musculoskeletal System and Connective Tissue (710–739)

CMS deleted systemic lupus, scleroderma (systemic sclerosis), complications of rheumatoid arthritis (except juvenile rheumatoid arthritis), postlaminectomy syndrome, brachial neuritis, and torticollis as CCs, yet they added some serious conditions as CCs. Following are descriptions of these and others CCs.

Arthritic Conditions Associated with Infection

All the arthritic conditions associated with infection are now CCs. These include the following:

- 711.0x (Pyogenic infection)—A bacterial infection within the joint. Usually the orthopedist has performed an arthrocentesis and finds bacterium on Gram stain or culture. Joint infections are sometimes confused with bursitis or tendinitis (inflammation of the structures surrounding the joint), cellulitis (bacterial infection of the skin around the joint), or crystal-induced disease (for example, gout or pseudogout); thus, caution is advised. Pyogenic infections usually require joint drainage and prolonged antibiotics; a CDI opportunity exists to ensure that these are not complications of procedures or that the patient is not immunocompromised.
- 711.1x (Reiter's syndrome) (Reactivearthritis)—A syndrome of conjunctivitis, urethritis (or cervicitis in females), arthritis, and characteristic mucocutaneous lesions in patients with likely chlamydial infections, but it can also occur as a result of other infections. Also called reactive arthritis, it usually occurs in young men described as being HLA-B27 positive; however, this is not always the case. These patients

usually have an arthritis starting in the lower extremities (for example, knees, feet) and may develop swelling of the fingers or toes ("sausage digits"), a vesicular skin lesion termed as *keratoderma blenorrhagica*, and conjunctivitis or uveitis that may progress to blindness.

- 711.2x (Behçet's syndrome)—A syndrome of arthritis associated with aphthous ulcers of the mouth.
- Other infections—Multiple infections are associated with arthritis, including Lyme's disease, *Salmonella*-induced diarrhea, tuberculosis, Fungi, and possibly even sarcoidosis (once it is proven that it is related to a mycobacterium). ICD-9-CM does give exceptions to coding these to category 711, such as with *Neisseria meningitidis* and gonorrhea and rubella. Often the underlying cause is coded first, allowing the 711 category code to become the CC.
- 719.1x (Hemarthrosis)—This condition is not uncommon in trauma patients or those on anticoagulants. The joint fluid will be visibly bloody.
- Spinal fractures with myelopathies all are CCs. CT scans or MRIs should be inspected with any spinal disease to determine that the spinal cord is not impinged. Usually edema or increased signal uptake will be seen on the MRI, signifying a possible myelopathy.

- Osteomyelitis—As a welcome change, all osteomyelitis infectionions are now CCs, not just acute osteomyelitis.
- Pathological fractures are now CCs. Because osteoporosis is the most common cause of pathological fracture, any fracture occurring with minor or no trauma, such as if a 20-year-old fractures a bone, creates a CDI opportunity for possible pathological fracture and its underlying cause.
- Aseptic necrosis—Necrotic bone not due to infection is now a CC. Patients with systemic illnesses (for example, lupus, rheumatoid arthritis, or sickle cell anemia) and those chronically treated with steroids may have this condition. A CDI opportunity exists if these patients have surgical procedures (for example, hip replacement or core decompression) to determine if aseptic necrosis is still active.
- Nonunion of fractures is now a CC. These are usually well-documented.

ICD-9-CM Chapter 14: Congenital Anomalies (740–759)

CMS removed spina bifida as a CC but added a number of new conditions to the CC list, including those listed here.

Code	Short Title	MS-DRG CC/MCC Designation
740.0	Anencephalus	MCC
740.1	Craniorachischisis	MCC
740.2	Iniencephaly	MCC
742.0	Encephalocele	CC
7422	Reduction deformation, brain	MCC
7424	Brain anomaly NEC	CC
7455	Secundum atrial septal defect	CC
74561	Ostium primum defect	CC
74600	Pulmonary valve anomaly NOS	CC
74609	Pulmonary valve anomaly NEC	CC
74685	Coronary artery anomaly	CC
74687	Malposition of heart	CC
7470	Patent ductus arteriosus	CC
74720	Congenital anomaly of aorta NOS	CC
74721	Anomalies of aortic arch	CC
74729	Congenital anomaly of aorta NEC	CC
7473	Pulmonary artery anomaly	MCC
74740	Great vein anomaly NOS	CC
74741	Total anomaly pulmonary ventricular connection	CC
74742	Partial anomaly pulmonary ventricular connection	CC
74749	Great vein anomaly NEC	CC

Code	Short Title	MS-DRG CC/MCC Designation
74781	Cerebrovascular anomaly	MCC
74782	Spinal vessel anomaly	CC
74783	Persistent fetal circulation	MCC
74789	Circulatory anomaly NEC	CC
7479	Circulatory anomaly NOS	CC
7483	Laryngotracheal anomaly NEC	CC
7503	Congenital esophageal fistula/atres	MCC
7504	Esophageal anomaly NEC	CC
7511	Atresia small intestine	CC
7512	Atresia large intestine	CC
7513	Hirschsprung's disease	CC
7514	Intestinal fixation anomaly	CC
7515	Intestinal anomaly NEC	CC
75160	Biliary and liver anomalies NOS	CC
75161	Biliary atresia	MCC
75162	Congenital cystic liver disease	CC
75169	Biliary and liver anomaly NEC	CC
7517	Pancreas anomalies	CC
7530	Renal agenesis	CC
75310	Cystic kidney disease NOS	CC
75311	Congenital renal cyst	CC
75312	Polycystic kidney NOS	CC
75313	Polycystic kidney, autosomal dominant	CC
75314	Polycystic kidney, autosomal recessive	CC
75315	Renal dysplasia	CC
75316	Medullary cystic kidney	CC
75317	Medullary sponge kidney	CC
75319	Cystic kidney disease NEC	CC
75320	Obstructive Defect of the Renal Pelvis and Ureter NOS	CC
75321	Congenital Obstruction of the Ureteropelvic Junction	CC
75322	Congenital Obstruction of the Ureterovescicular Junction	CC
75323	Congential ureterocele	CC
75329	Obstructive Defect of Renal Pelvis and Ureter NEC	CC
7535	Bladder exstrophy	CC
7536	Congenital urethral stenosis	CC
7542	Congenital postural deformity	CC
75489	Noniteratogenic anomaly NEC	CC
75555	Acrocephalosyndactyly	MCC
75613	Congenital absence of vertebra	CC
7563	Rib and sternum anomaly NEC	CC
75651	Osteogenesis imperfecta	CC
75652	Osteopetrosis	CC
7566	Anomalies of diaphragm	MCC
75670	Congenital anomaly of abdominal wall NOS	MCC
75671	Prune belly syndrome	MCC
75679	Congenital anomaly of abdominal wall NEC	MCC
75683	Ehlers-Danlos syndrome	CC
7581	Patau's syndrome	CC
7582	Edwards' syndrome	CC

(Continued)

Code	Short Title	MS-DRG CC/MCC Designation
75831	Cri-du-chat syndrome	CC
75832	Velo-cardio-facial syndrome	MCC
75833	Microdeletions NEC	CC
75839	Autosomal deletions NEC	CC
7590	Anomalies of spleen	CC
7593	Situs inversus	CC
7594	Conjoined twins	MCC
7595	Tuberous sclerosis	CC
7596	Hamartoses NEC	CC
7597	Multiple congenital anomalies NEC	CC
75981	Prader-Willi syndrome	CC
75982	Marfan syndrome	CC
75989	Specified congenital anomaly NEC	CC

There is no substitute for a well-documented history and physical examination in these conditions.

Common areas of clinical documentation improvement opportunity include the following:

- Congenital heart disease—Heart surgery for structural abnormalities in relatively young individuals creates a CDI opportunity for underlying congenital heart disease. Congenital atrial septal defects—holes in the wall separating the left and right atria—may be a cause for transient ischemic attacks or strokes. Congenital valve abnormalities may lead to endocarditis. A CDI opportunity exists if the patient receives endocarditis prophylaxis.
- Congenital aortic artery disease—Interruptions of the aorta are a correctable cause of hypertension in the young.
- Vascular malformations—Some vascular malformations are congenital and may lead to strokes or hemorrhage.
- Polycystic kidney disease and medullary sponge kidney disease can be congenital. In the author's personal private practice, a diagnosis of congenital absence of the kidney, which is a CC, was made in a 50-year-old man.

ICD-9-CM Chapter 15: Certain Conditions in the Perinatal Period (760–779)

Although MS-DRGs are more likely to be applied to the hospital's Medicare population, many private insurance companies use Medicare DRGs to reimburse hospitals for inpatient care rendered to their members.

Codes from the perinatal chapter should not be assigned unless the provider has established a definitive diagnosis. However, if the physician documents "possible," "probable," "likely," "suspected," or "still to be ruled out," these can still be coded as if they existed if they meet the definition for additional diagnosis. For example, if a neonatologist treats probable neonatal sepsis with antibiotics and intensive care, this may be coded as 771.81.

Diagnoses that have implications for future healthcare needs also should be coded. For example, if a physician observes a condition, such as transient bradycardia or an abnormal laboratory test, and declares that these conditions should be followed up in the future, this meets secondary diagnosis reporting guidelines.

CMS eliminated extreme immaturity, many of the perinatal jaundice diagnoses (except newborn kernicterus and fetal/neonatal hepatitis), and many of the newborn hemolytic diseases as CC but added many of the serious comorbidities associated with immaturity. Changes are listed in the following table.

ICD-9-CM	Title	CMS CC Designation	MSDRG CC Designation
767.0	Cerebral hematoma at birth	CMS CC	MS MCC
767.11	Epicranial subaponeurotic hemorrhage	CMS CC	MS CC
768.5	Severe birth asphyxia	CMS CC	MS MCC
768.7	Hypoxic-ischemic encephalitis		MS MCC
769	Respiratory distress syndrome	CMS CC	MS MCC
770.0	Congenital pneumonia	CMS CC	MS MCC
770.12	Meconium aspiration with respiratory symptoms	CMS CC	MS MCC
770.14	Amniotic aspiration with respiratory symptoms	CMS CC	MS MCC
770.16	Blood aspiration with respiratory symptoms	CMS CC	MS MCC
770.18	Newborn aspiration with respiratory symptoms NEC	CMS CC	MS MCC
770.2	Newborn interstitial emphysema	CMS CC	MS MCC
770.3	Newborn pulmonary hemorrhage	CMS CC	MS MCC
7704	Primary atelectasisCMS CC	MS CC	
7705	Newborn atelectasis NEC/NOS	CMS CC	MS CC
7707	Perinatal chronic respiratory distress	CMS CC	MS MCC
77081	Primary apnea of newborn		MS CC
77082	Other apnea of newborn		MS CC
77083	Cyanotic attack of newborn		MS CC
77084	Respiratory failure of newborn	CMS CC	MS MCC
77086	Aspiration of postnatal stomach contents with respiratory symptomsCMS CC	MS MCC	
77087	Newborn respiratory arrest		MS MCC
7710	Congenital rubellaCMS CC	MS CC	
7711	Congenital cytomegalovirus infection	CMS CC	MS MCC
7712	Congenital infection NEC		MS MCC
7713	Tetanus neonatorumCMS CC	MS MCC	
7714	Omphalitis of newborn		MS CC
7715	Neonatal infectious mastitis		MS CC
77181	Newborn septicemia (SEPSIS)	CMS CC	MS MCC
77182	Newborn urinary tract infection		MS CC
77183	Bacteremia of newborn	CMS CC	MS CC
77189	Perinatal infection NEC		MS CC
77210	Newborn intraventricular hemorrhage, NOS	CMS CC	MS CC
77211	Newborn intraventricular hemorrhage, grade I CMS CC	MS CC	
77212	Newborn intraventricular hemorrhage, grade II CMS CC	MS CC	
77213	Newborn intraventricular hemorrhage, grade III CMS CC	MS MCC	
77214	Newborn intraventricular hemorrhage, grade IV CMS CC	MS MCC	
7722	Newborn subarachnoid hemorrhage	CMS CC	MS MCC
7724	Newborn gastrointestinal hemorrhage	CMS CC	MS MCC
7725	Newborn adrenal hemorrhage	CMS CC	MS CC
7733	Hydrops fetalis due to isoimmunization	CMS CC	MS MCC
7734	Newborn kernicterus due to isoimmunication CMS CC	MS MCC	
7744	Fetal/neonatal hepatitis	CMS CC	MS MCC
7747	Newborn kernicterusCMS CC	MS MCC	
7751	Neonatal diabetes mellitus	CMS CC	MS CC

(Continued)

ICD-9-CM	CMS CC Title	MSDRG CC Designation	Designation	
7752	Neonatal myasthenia gravis	CMS CC	MS CC	
7753	Neonatal thyrotoxicosis	CMS CC	MS CC	
7754	Hypocalcemia and hypomagnesium of newborn	CMS CC	MS CC	
7757	Late metabolic acidosis of newborn	CMS CC	MS MCC	
77581	Newborn acidosis NEC		MS CC	
77589	Neonatal endocrine and metabolic disorders, NEC	MS CC		
7760	Newborn hemorrhagic disease	CMS CC	MS CC	
7761	Neonatal thrombocytopenia	CMS CC	MS MCC	
7762	Disseminated Intravascular coagulation of newborn	CMS CC	MS MCC	
7763	Other neonatal coagulation disorders	CMS CC	MS CC	
7765	Congenital anemia	MS CC		
7766	Anemia of prematurity		MS CC	
7767	Neonatal neutropenia	MS MCC		
7774	Transitory ileus of newborn		MS CC	
7775	Necrotizing enterocolitis of newborn	CMS CC	MS MCC	
7776	Perinatal intestinal perforation	CMS CC	MS MCC	
7780	Hydrops fetalis not due to isoimmunication	CMS CC	MS MCC	
7781	Sclerema neonatorum	MS CC		
7785	Edema of newborn, NEC/NOS		MS CC	
7790	Convulsions in newborn	CMS CC	MS MCC	
7792	Cerebral depression, coma, and other abnormal cerebral signs	MS MCC		
7794	Newborn drug reaction/intoxic	CMS CC	MS CC	
7795	Newborn drug withdrawal syndrome		MS CC	
7797	Periventricular leukomalacia	CMS CC	MS MCC	
77985	Newborn cardiac arrest	CMS CC	MS MCC	

771.81: Newborn Sepsis

The definition of sepsis in newborns changed in 2005. In the past, many neonatologists would not document that a newborn was septic without a positive blood culture. With the initiation of the SIRS criteria for adults, pediatricians and neonatologists could not apply them to newborns given their different physiology and pathophysiology.

Because of the need to clarify sepsis criteria for the study of activated protein C (Xigris) in newborns, in 2005, the International Pediatric Sepsis Definitions Conference convened and reported their findings, which are adapted and outlined below (Goldstein et al 2005).

- *Systemic Inflammatory Response Syndrome (SIRS):*
  The presence of at least two of the following four criteria, **one of which must be abnormal temperature or leukocyte count:**
  - Core temperature of greater than 38.5°C or less than 36°C.
  - Tachycardia, defined as a mean heart rate greater than 2 SD above normal for age in the absence of external stimulus, chronic drugs, or painful stimuli; or otherwise unexplained persistent elevation over a 30-minute to 4-hour time period OR for children younger than 1 year: bradycardia, defined as a mean heart rate less than the 10th percentile for age in the absence of external vagal stimulus, β-blocker drugs, or congenital heart disease; or otherwise unexplained persistent depression over a 30-minute time period.
  - Mean respiratory rate greater than 2 SD above normal for age or mechanical ventilation for an acute process not related to underlying neuromuscular disease or the receipt of general anesthesia.
  - Leukocyte count elevated or depressed for age (not secondary to chemotherapy-induced leukopenia) or greater than 10% immature neutrophils.
- *Sepsis* - SIRS in the presence of or as a result of suspected or proven infection.

- *Severe sepsis* - Sepsis plus one of the following: cardiovascular organ dysfunction OR acute respiratory distress syndrome OR two or more other organ dysfunctions.

Coders are encouraged to obtain this reference because this contains all of the age-dependent variables necessary to define pediatric SIRS and organ dysfunction.

Although there are no differentiations between newborn septicemia, sepsis and severe sepsis in ICD-9-CM, coders should be certain to code the organ dysfunctions associated with neonatal sepsis. These include:

- 779.9 plus 785.2 (Septic shock)—A CDI opportunity exists if the patient has the cardiovascular components previously noted or if vasoactive drugs are used.
- 779.85 (Cardiac arrest of newborn)
- 770.84 (Respiratory failure of newborn) plus the underlying cause, such as 769 (Respiratory distress of newborn)
- 775.81 (Other acidosis of newborn)
- 776.2 (Disseminated intravascular coagulation in newborn)
- 772.0x (Fetal or neonatal hemorrhage), which may be a consequence of thrombocytopenia or coagulation defections

- 774.4 (Perinatal jaundice due to hepatocellular damage)
- 779.0 (Convulsions in newborn)
- 779.2 (Cerebral depression, coma, and other abnormal cerebral signs)

Underlying causes should be coded as well. These include:

- 770.0 (Congenital pneumonia)
- 770.14 (Aspiration of clear amniotic fluid with respiratory symptoms)
- 770.18 (Aspiration of blood with respiratory symptoms)
- 777.5 (Necrotizing enterocolitis in fetus or newborn) (SIRS can occur as a result of pseudomembranous colitis)
- 771.x (Infections specific to the neonatal period)
- 779.89 (Other infections specific to the perinatal period)

Special care should be taken to differentiate 771.83 (Bacteremia of newborn) (a CC) from 771.81 (Newborn septicemia [sepsis] (an MCC). Code 771.81 will meet the SIRS criteria or will be considered significantly more severe than bacteremia alone. A CDI opportunity exists if it is not clear.

Code	Description	CMS CC Status	MS-DRG CC Status	Description
772.10	Newborn intravenous hemorrhage NOS	CMS CC	MS CC	Not otherwise specified
772.11	Newborn intraventricular hemorrhage, grade I	CMS CC	MS CC	Confined to the germinal matrix or subependymal region or involving less than 10 percent of the ventricle. The germinal matrix is a highly cellular and highly vascularized region from which cells migrate during brain development, mainly between 22 and 30 weeks gestation. The ependyma are cells that line the walls of the ventricle
772.12	Newborn intraventricular hemorrhage, grade II	CMS CC	MS CC	Involving 10 to 50 percent of the ventricle
772.13	Newborn intraventricular hemorrhage, grade III	CMS CC	MS MCC	Greater than 50 percent involvement with dilated ventricles
772.14	Newborn intraventricular hemorrhage, grade IV	CMS CC	MS MCC	Stage III hemorrhage plus hemorrhage within the brain parenchyma

Intraventricular Hemorrhage

Intraventricular hemorrhage is associated with prematurity and low birth weight. The diagnosis is made clinically and by imaging studies (ultrasound, CT, or MRI). ICD-9-CM and MS-DRGs differentiate neonatal cerebral intraventricular hemorrhage as follows:

A CDI opportunity exists when intraventricular hemorrhage is diagnosed and it is not staged as listed above.

Birth Asphyxia

All babies undergo a limited amount of asphyxia, defined as the impaired exchange of oxygen and carbon dioxide as a result of a ventilatory defect, as they pass through the birth canal.

ICD-9-CM classifies 768.5 (Severe birth asphyxia) (an MCC) from 768.6 (Mild or moderate birth asphyxia) (not a CC) based on the presence of neurologic involvement. Corresponding symptoms include hypoxic-ischemic encephalopathy, infarction, intracranial hemorrhage, seizures, cerebral edema, hypotonia, and hypertonia. Should the neonate develop hypoxic-ischemic encephalopathy, 768.7 (Hypoxic-ischemic encephalopathy) (a new MCC) should be used.

Significant asphyxia occurs in infants with fetal acidosis (pH less than 7.0), a 5-minute Apgar score of 0 to 3, hypoxic-ischemic encephalopathy (altered tone, depressed level of consciousness, seizures), and other multiorgan system signs (Behrman). As outlined in *Coding Clinic* (November–December, 1986, pp. 3–4), asphyxia may not be assumed from any of these findings unless the physician explicitly documents it.

Apnea and Respiratory Distress

Apnea is a pause in respiration that lasts 3 SDs beyond the mean age-appropriate breath time. Some controversy exists in its definition; all human beings may pause their breathing while asleep. Serious apnea is defined in preterm infants as lasting more than 20 seconds or associated with bradycardia or cyanosis.

Apnea can occur on its own or as a consequence of asphyxia. Nonasphyxic apnea may occur without corresponding disease as a disease of brainstem respiratory control—770.81 (Primary apnea of newborn), as a consequence of oropharyngeal obstruction such as pharyngeal instability (770.82 [Other apnea of newborn]) or as a consequence of other illness (for example, intraventricular hemorrhage). Apnea is treated with neural stimulants, such as aminophylline or caffeine.

CMS added primary apnea of newborn, other apnea of newborn, and cyanotic attack of newborn to the CC list. If a child develops respiratory arrest (770.87 [Newborn respiratory arrest]), this may be coded as well.

Code 769 (Respiratory distress syndrome) is an acute lung disease of immature newborns caused by lack of surfactant. Infants present with acute respiratory distress usually within 8 hours after birth. Hypoxemic or hypercapnic respiratory failure and classic radiologic findings confirm the diagnosis. If symptoms occur after an infant is 8 hours old, another diagnosis (for example, fetal aspiration syndrome, transient tachypnea of newborns, neonatal pneumonia) may be considered.

ICD-9-CM Chapter 16: Symptoms, Signs, and Ill-Defined Conditions (780–799)

Many of these codes are discussed in other chapters. Because symptoms and signs are integral to underlying conditions, it is preferred to code the underlying condition over its manifestation. For example, a patient may be in a persistent vegetative state that is a manifestation of anoxic encephalopathy. Hallucinations may be a manifestation of toxic encephalopathy (for example, as a result of the patient abusing the drug LSD).

Some manifestations, however, are not integral to the underlying cause. For example, hypoxemia, which was removed as a CC, is not integral to asthma. Hemoptysis (a CC) is not integral to pneumonia or bronchitis, even though these are the most common causes of hemoptysis. *Coding Clinic* discusses many of these manifestations. If coding professionals are uncertain, they should query the attending physician to determine whether the manifestation is integral or not.

The following CCs were deleted from ICD-9-CM, chapter 16:

Although these are discussed in other sections of the book, special consideration should be given to the following:

- Meningismus—A stiffness of the neck that may indicate meningitis. Usually a lumbar puncture is performed for this symptom, not uncommonly in the emergency room.
- Precipitous drop in hematocrit—Although not defined in ICD-9-CM or *Coding Clinic*, because major blood loss is defined as a blood

Code	Description
780.39	Convulsions NEC
786.03	Apnea
788.20	Retention urine NOS
788.29	Other specified retention urine
799.02	Hypoxemia

Code	Title	CC Designation
781.4	Transient limb paralysis	New MS-DRG (CC)
781.6	Meningismus	New MS-DRG (CC)
781.8	Neurologic neglect syndrome	New MS-DRG (CC)
782.4	Jaundice NOS	New MS-DRG (CC)
784.3	Aphasia	New MS-DRG (CC)
788.8	Extravasation of urine	New MS-DRG (CC)
790.01	Precipitous drop in hematocrit	New MS-DRG (CC)

loss of greater than 20 percent, a CDI opportunity exists if the hematocrit falls 20 percent or more below baseline.

- Aphasia—A common consequence of stroke. Neurologic neglect syndrome is similar to aphasia. As a result of a stroke, the patient appears to ignore a part of his or her body.
- Transient limb paralysis—Can be a consequence of TIA

ICD-9-CM Chapter 17: Injury and Poisoning (800–899)

CMS totally revamped the CC structure for chapter 17. Very few deletions were made. The deletions that did occur include the following:

Code	Title
838.19	Dislocated foot NEC, open
850.0	Concussion w/o coma
850.9	Concussion NOS
851.00	Cerebral cortex contusion
851.01	Corten contusion—no coma
851.09	Cortex contusion-concussion NOS
851.40	Cerebellum/brainstem contusion
851.41	Cerebellum contusion w/o coma
851.49	Cerebellum contusion-concussion
854.00	Brain injury NEC
854.01	Brain injury NEC, no coma
854.09	Brain injury NEC, concussion
871.4	Laceration of eye NOS
873.9	Open wound of head NEC, complications

Special emphasis includes:

Fractures

Care should be taken to differentiate fractures in healthy bones (800–829) from fractures in pathological bone.

- Skull fractures—All codes remain CCs. Closed fractures with unspecified duration of coma and coma lasting less than 1 hour with unspecified duration of concussion or loss of consciousness *and* without specified brain or surrounding tissue laceration or hemorrhage are CCs; the rest are MCCs. Brain injury alone does not mean brain hemorrhage or laceration, thus a CDI opportunity exists with this term.
- Vertebral fractures—All codes remain CCs. Those that are open or injure the spinal cord are MCCs.
- Rib and sternal fractures—Unlike CMS-DRGs, any number of closed rib fractures are CCs. All open fractures, as well as a flail chest, are MCCs. If they cause a pneumothorax, they are CCs; if they cause a tension pneumothorax, they are MCCs.
- Tracheal and laryngeal fractures—These are MCCs.
- Pelvic fractures—All are now CCs; those that are open are MCCs.
- Clavicle fractures—Open clavicle fractures are now CCs; closed clavicle fractures are not.
- Scapula fractures—Open scapular fractures are now CCs; closed scapular fractures are not.
- Humerus fractures—All humeral fractures are now CCs; those that are open are MCCs.
- Arm fractures—Open radius and ulna fractures are now MCCs. Closed upper-end fractures are not CCs; however, closed fractures involving the shaft and lower end are CCs. Fractures without specification of their location within the bone are not CCs.
- Wrist fractures—Only open fractures are now considered CCs (not MCCs).

- Hand fractures—Open fractures of the metacarpal and phalangeal bones are now CCs.
- Femur fractures—CMS added fractures to the lower end as CCs. Femur fractures are MCCs except for closed fractures involving the lower end, which are CCs.
- Tibia fractures—Tibial fractures are now CCs; those that are open are MCCs.
- Fibula fractures—Open fibula fractures are now MCCs; closed and torus fractures are now CCs.
- Ankle fractures—Open ankle fractures are now CCs, not MCCs.
- Foot fractures—Open foot fractures are now CCs, not MCCs.
- Multiple fractures—Multiple fractures involving both lower limbs, lower with upper limbs, and lower limbs with ribs and sterum all are MCCs, whether they are open or closed.

Dislocations

CMS added open dislocations of most joints as CCs. Closed hip dislocations are now CCs, whereas open hip dislocations are MCCs. Dislocated cervical vertebrae are CCs, whereas open dislocations of cervical vertebrae are MCCs. Other vertebral dislocations must be open to qualify as CCs or MCCs.

Organ Trauma

Cerebral Concussion, Contusion, and Laceration

Concussion NOS is not a CC, whereas those with defined loss of consciousness are CCs and those with prolonged loss of consciousness (over 24 hours) not returning to preexisting consciousness levels are MCCs. Cerebral contusion (except those without a defined loss of consciousness) or cerebral lacerations all are MCCs. CT or MRI scans should differentiate these. Brain injury NOS is not a CC unless it has a specified loss of consciousness.

Traumatic Pneumothorax

Traumatic pneumothoras is a CC unless it is open, in which case it is an MCC. Any description of flail chest or tension pneumothorax also qualifies it as an MCC.

Cardiac Contusion/Laceration

Cardiac contusion/laceration is a CC unless it is open, then it is an MCC. Cardiac contusions are diagnosed with elevated cardiac isoenzymes or cardiac MRI. Cardiac lacerations are MCCs and are diagnosed on cardiac MRI, in surgery, or possibly by cardiac catheterization.

Pulmonary Contusion/Laceration

Lung injury is a CC, whereas open injury or closed lacerations are MCCs. Any bronchial injury is an MCC.

Abdomen

All internal injuries are now CCs. Those qualifying as MCCs include the following:

Code	Title	MS-DRG CC Designation
863.1	Stomach injury, open	MS MCC
863.30	Small intestinal injury NOS, open	MS MCC
863.31	Duodenum injury, open	MS MCC
863.39	Small intestine injury, open	MS MCC
863.50	Colon injury NOS, open	MS MCC
863.51	Ascending colon injury, open	MS MCC
863.52	Transverse colon injury, open	MS MCC
863.53	Descending colon injury, open	MS MCC
863.54	Sigmoid colon injury, open	MS MCC
863.55	Rectum injury, open	MS MCC
863.56	Colon injury multiple site, open	MS MCC
863.59	Colon injury NEC, open	MS MCC
863.90	Gastrointestinal injury NOS, open	MS MCC
863.91	Pancreas, head injury, open	MS MCC
863.92	Pancreas, body injury, open	MS MCC
863.93	Pancreas, tail injury, open	MS MCC
863.94	Pancreas injury NOS, open	MS MCC

Code	Title	MS-DRG CC Designation
863.95	Appendix injury, open	MS MCC
863.99	Gastrointestinal injury NEC, open	MS MCC
864.03	Liver laceration, moderate	MS MCC
864.04	Liver laceration, major	MS MCC
864.10	Liver injury NOS, open	MS MCC
864.11	Liver hematoma/contusion, open	MS MCC
864.12	Liver laceration, minor, open	MS MCC
864.13	Liver laceration, moderate, open	MS MCC
864.14	Liver laceration, major, open	MS MCC
864.15	Liver laceration unspecified, open	MS MCC
864.19	Liver injury NEC, open	MS MCC
865.03	Spleen parenchyma laceration	MS MCC
865.04	Spleen disruption, closed	MS MCC
865.10	Spleen injury NOS, open	MS MCC
865.11	Spleen hematoma, open	MS MCC
865.12	Spleen capsular tear, open	MS MCC
865.13	Spleen parenchymal laceration, open	MS MCC
865.14	Spleen disruption, open	MS MCC
865.19	Spleen injury NEC, open	MS MCC
866.03	Kidney disruption, closed	MS MCC
866.10	Kidney injury NOS, open	MS MCC
866.11	Kidney hematoma, open	MS MCC
866.12	Kidney laceration, open	MS MCC
866.13	Kidney disruption, open	MS MCC
867.1	Bladder/urethra injury, open	MS MCC
867.3	Ureter injury, open	MS MCC
867.5	Uterus injury, open	MS MCC
867.7	Pelvic organ injury NEC, open	MS MCC
867.9	Pelvic organ injury NOS, open	MS MCC
868.10	Intra-abdominal injury NOS, open	MS MCC
868.11	Adrenal gland injury, open	MS MCC
868.12	Biliary tracheal injury, open	MS MCC
868.13	Peritoneum injury, open	MS MCC
868.14	Retroperitoneum injury, open	MS MCC
868.19	Intra-abdominal injury NEC, open	MS MCC
869.1	Internal injury NOS, open	MS MCC

Open Wounds (870–897)

The list of the deleted, current, and new CCs/MCCs follows:

Code	Title	CMS CC Designation	MS-DRG CC Designation
870.2	Laceration of the eyelids involving the lacrimal passages		MS CC
870.3	Penetrating wound of orbit, without mention of foreign body	CMS CC	MS CC
870.4	Penetrating wound of orbit with foreign body	CMS CC	MS CC
870.8	Other specified open wounds of ocular adnexa	CMS CC	MS CC

(Continued)

Code	CMS CC Title	MS-DRG CC Designation	Designation
870.9	Other specified open wounds of ocular adnexa, NOS	CMS CC	MS CC
871.0	Ocular laceration without prolapse	CMS CC	MS CC
871.1	Ocular laceration with prolapse	CMS CC	MS CC
871.2	Rupture of eye with tissue loss	CMS CC	MS CC
871.3	Avulsion of eye	CMS CC	MS CC
871.5	Penetration of eyeball with magnetic foreign body		MS CC
871.6	Penetration of eyeball with (nonmagnetic) foreign body		MS CC
871.9	Open wound of eyeball NOS	CMS CC	MS CC
872.12	Open wound of auditory canal, complications		MS CC
872.61	Open wound of eardrum		MS CC
872.62	Open wound of ossicles		MS CC
872.63	Open wound of eustachian tube		MS CC
872.64	Open wound of cochlea		MS CC
872.69	Open wound of ear NEC		MS CC
872.71	Open wound eardrum, complications		MS CC
872.72	Open wound of ossicles, complications	CMS CC	MS CC
872.73	Open wound of eustachian tube, complications	CMS CC	MS CC
872.74	Open wound, cochlear, complicated	CMS CC	MS CC
872.79	Open wound, other specified parts of ear, complicated, other and multiple sites		MS CC
873.23	Open wound, nasal sinus		MS CC
873.33	Open wound, nasal sinus, complicated	CMS CC	MS CC
874.00	Open wound, neck, larynx with trachea	CMS CC	MS MCC
874.01	Open wound of larynx	CMS CC	MS MCC
874.02	Open wound of trachea	CMS CC	MS MCC
874.10	Open wound of larynx with trachea, complicated	CMS CC	MS MCC
874.11	Open wound of larynx, complicated	CMS CC	MS MCC
874.12	Open wound of trachea, complicated	CMS CC	MS MCC
874.2	Open wound of thyroid gland		MS CC
874.3	Open wound of thyroid gland, complicated	CMS CC	MS CC
874.4	Open wound of pharynx		MS CC
874.5	Open wound of pharynx, complicated	CMS CC	MS CC
875.0	Open wound of chest	CMS CC	MS CC
875.1	Open wound of chest, complicated	CMS CC	MS CC
88020	Opn wnd shouldr w tendon		MS CC
88021	Opn wnd scapula w tendon		MS CC
88022	Open wnd axilla w tendon		MS CC
88023	Open wnd up arm w tendon		MS CC
88029	Mlt opn wnd shldr w tend		MS CC
88120	Open wnd forearm w tendn		MS CC
88121	Opn wound elbow w tendon		MS CC
88122	Opn wound wrist w tendon		MS CC
8822	Open wound hand w tendon		MS CC
8832	Open wnd finger w tendon		MS CC
8842	Opn wnd arm nos w tendon		MS CC
8870	Amput below elb, unilat	CMS CC	MS CC
8871	Amp below elb, unil-comp	CMS CC	MS CC
8872	Amput abv elbow, unilat	CMS CC	MS CC
8873	Amput abv elb, unil-comp	CMS CC	MS CC
8874	Amputat arm, unilat NOS	CMS CC	MS CC

Code	Title	Designation	Designation
8875	Amput arm, unil nos-comp	CMS CC	MS CC
8876	Amputation arm, bilat	CMS CC	MS MCC
8877	Amputat arm, bilat-compl	CMS CC	MS MCC
8902	Opn wnd hip/thigh w tend		MS CC
8912	Opn wnd knee/leg w tendn		MS CC
8922	Open wound foot w tendo–		MS CC
8932	Open wound toe w tendon		MS CC
8942	Opn wnd leg nec w tendon		MS CC
8960	Amputation foot, unilat	CMS CC	MS CC
8961	Amput foot, unilat-compl	CMS CC	MS CC
8962	Amputation foot, bilat	CMS CC	MS MCC
8963	Amputat foot, bilat-comp	CMS CC	MS MCC
8970	Amput below knee, unilat	CMS CC	MS CC
8971	Amputat bk, unilat-compl	CMS CC	MS CC
8972	Amput above knee, unilat	CMS CC	MS CC
8973	Amput abv kn, unil-compl	CMS CC	MS CC
8974	Amputat leg, unilat NOS	CMS CC	MS CC
8975	Amput leg, unil nos-comp	CMS CC	MS CC
8976	Amputation leg, bilat	CMS CC	MS MCC
8977	Amputat leg, bilat-compl	CMS CC	MS MCC

Injury to Blood Vessels (900–904)

All injuries to blood vessels are now CCs. Those serving as MCCs include the following:

Code	Title	CMS CC Designation	MS-DRG CC Designation
9010	Injury thoracic aorta	CMS CC	MS MCC
9011	Inj innomin/subclav art	CMS CC	MS MCC
9012	Inj superior vena cava	CMS CC	MS MCC
9013	Inj innomin/subclav vein	CMS CC	MS MCC
90140	Inj pulmonary vessel NOS		MS MCC
90141	Injury pulmonary artery	CMS CC	MS MCC
90142	Injury pulmonary vein	CMS CC	MS MCC
90183	Inj mult thoracic vessel	CMS CC	MS MCC
9020	Injury abdominal aorta	CMS CC	MS MCC
90210	Inj infer vena cava NOS	CMS CC	MS MCC
90211	Injury hepatic veins	CMS CC	MS MCC
90219	Inj infer vena cava NEC	CMS CC	MS MCC
90220	Inj celiac/mesen art NOS	CMS CC	MS MCC
90221	Injury gastric artery		MS MCC
90222	Injury hepatic artery	CMS CC	MS MCC
90223	Injury splenic artery	CMS CC	MS MCC
90224	Injury celiac axis NEC	CMS CC	MS MCC
90225	Inj super mesenteric art	CMS CC	MS MCC
90226	Inj brnch sup mesent art	CMS CC	MS MCC
90227	Inj infer mesenteric art	CMS CC	MS MCC
90229	Inj mesenteric vess NEC	CMS CC	MS MCC
90231	Inj superior mesent vein	CMS CC	MS MCC
90232	Inj inferior mesent vein	CMS CC	MS MCC

(Continued)

Code	Title	CMS CC Designation	MS-DRG CC Designation
90233	Injury portal vein	CMS CC	MS MCC
90234	Injury splenic vein	CMS CC	MS MCC
90239	Inj port/splen vess NEC	CMS CC	MS MCC
90240	Injury renal vessel NOS	CMS CC	MS MCC
90241	Injury renal artery	CMS CC	MS MCC
90242	Injury renal vein	CMS CC	MS MCC
90249	Injury renal vessel NEC	CMS CC	MS MCC
90250	Injury iliac vessel NOS	CMS CC	MS MCC
90251	Inj hypogastric artery	CMS CC	MS MCC
90252	Injury hypogastric vein	CMS CC	MS MCC
90253	Injury iliac artery	CMS CC	MS MCC
90254	Injury iliac vein	CMS CC	MS MCC
90259	Injury iliac vessel NEC	CMS CC	MS MCC
90287	Inj mult abd/pelv vessel	CMS CC	MS MCC
90300	Inj axillary vessel NOS		MS MCC
90301	Injury axillary artery		MS MCC
90302	Injury axillary vein		MS MCC
9040	Inj common femoral arter	CMS CC	MS MCC
9041	Inj superfic femoral art		MS MCC
9042	Injury femoral vein		MS MCC
90440	Inj popliteal vessel NOS		MS MCC
90441	Injury popliteal artery		MS MCC
90442	Injury popliteal vein		MS MCC

Other Injuries (905–939)

CMS maintained and added the following codes to the CC list.

Code	Title	CMS CC Designation	MS-DRG CC Designation
9251	Crush inj face scalp	CMS CC	MS CC
9252	Crush inj neck	CMS CC	MS CC
92800	Crushing injury thigh		MS CC
92801	Crushing injury hip		MS CC
9340	Foreign body in trachea		MS CC
9341	Foreign body bronchus		MS CC
9348	Fb trach/bronch/lung NEC		MS CC
9405	Burn w eyeball destruct		MS CC

Burns (940–949)

To be a CC, the burn must be a third-degree burn or involve the larynx, esophagus, gastrointestinal tract, or vagina. Burns specified as involving over 20 percent of the body with over 10 percent of the body having a third-degree burn are MCCs.

Injuries to Nerves and Spinal Cord (950–957)

Cranial nerve injuries are CCs whereas spinal cord injury is an MCC. Other nerve injuries are not CCs.

Certain Early Complications of Trauma (958)

CMS added compartment syndromes to the CC list. Others are listed in the following table:

Code	Title	CMS CC Designation	MS-DRG CC Designation
9580	Air embolism	CMS CC	MS MCC
9581	Fat embolism	CMS CC	MS MCC
9582	Secondary/recur hemorr	CMS CC	MS CC
9583	Posttraum wnd infec NEC	CMS CC	MS CC
9584	Traumatic shock	CMS CC	MS MCC
9585	Traumatic anuria	CMS CC	MS MCC
9587	Traum subcutan emphysema	CMS CC	MS CC
95890	Compartment syndrome NOS		MS CC
95891	Trauma comp synd up ext		MS CC
95892	Trauma comp synd low ext		MS CC
95893	Trauma compart synd abd		MS CC
95899	Trauma compart synd nec		MS CC

Other Traumas

CMS has added the following to the CC list

Code	Title	CMS CC Designation	MS-DRG CC Designation
9910	Frostbite of face		MS CC
9911	Frostbite of hand		MS CC
9912	Frostbite of foot		MS CC
9913	Frostbite NEC/NOS		MS CC
9914	Immersion foot		MS CC
9920	Heat stroke & sunstroke		MS CC
9933	Caisson disease		MS CC
9941	Drowning/nonfatal submer		MS CC
9947	Asphyxiation/strangulat		MS CC

Anaphylaxis

Anaphylactic shock and shock due to anesthesia are now CCs, as evidenced here. Physicians must document hypertension or shock to qualify these as CCs.

Code	Title	CMS CC Designation	MS-DRG CC Designation
9950	Anaphylactic shock		MS CC
9954	Shock due to anesthesia	CMS CC	MS CC
99560	Anaphylactic shock food NOS		MS CC
99561	Anaphylactic shock peanuts		MS CC
99562	Anaphylactic shock crstacns		MS CC
99563	Anaphylactic shock frts veg		MS CC
99564	Anaphylactic shock tr nts seed		MS CC

(Continued)

Code	Title	CMS CC Designation	MS-DRG CC Designation
99565	Anaphylactic shock fish		MS CC
99566	Anaphylactic shock food addtv		MS CC
99567	Anaphylactic shock milk prod		MS CC
99568	Anaphylactic shock eggs		MS CC
99569	Anaphylactic shock ot spf food		MS CC

Abuse

Abuse codes are now CCs as evidenced below.

Code	Title	CMS CC Designation	MS-DRG CC Designation
99550	Child abuse NOS		MS CC
99551	Child emotnl/psych abuse		MS CC
99552	Child neglect-nutrition		MS CC
99553	Child sexual abuse		MS CC
99554	Child physical abuse		MS CC
99555	Shaken infant syndrome		MS CC
99559	Child abuse/neglect NEC		MS CC

SIRS

The systemic inflammatory response syndrome codes are CCs. CMS requires that these codes be sequenced after their underlying cause and will likely exclude them as CCs should pancreatitis or other systemic infections serve as the principal diagnosis.

Codes 995.91 and 995.92 (SIRS due to infection) and 995.94 (SIRS due to noninfectious causes with organ dysfunction) are MCCs. On the other hand, 995.93 (SIRS due to noninfectious causes without organ dysfunction) (for example, burns or pancreatitis) is only a CC.

Complication Codes (996–999)

Most of the complication codes are CCs except the following:

99631	Malfunc urethral cath
99632	Malfunction IUD
99670	Comp-unsp device/graft
99700	Nervous syst complc NOS
9975	Surg compl-urinary tract
99760	Amputat stump compl NOS
99761	Neuroma amputation stump
99769	Amputat stump compl NEC
99791	Surg comp - hypertension
99881	Emphysema rsult frm proc
99882	Ctrct frgmt frm ctr surg
99889	Oth spcf cmplc procd NEC
9989	Surgical complicat NOS
999.31	Infection due to central cath
999.39	Infection fol infus/inj/vac
999.9	Complic med care NEC/NOS

None of the complication codes are MCCs except for air embolism.

Although many of the major cardiovascular diagnoses coded by coders in the past, such as 996.72 (Complication of other cardiac device), are CCs, because MS-DRGs require MCCs to change the cardiac surgery MS-DRGs, they will have no effect on reimbursement.

To qualify as a complication, two conditions must be met:

- The condition must be linked to the procedure. For example, a patient may have had fever prior to his coronary artery bypass graft surgery. If it recurs after surgery and the physician states that it was due to another condition, it should not be coded as a complication. A CDI opportunity exists if this is not clear.
- The condition must not be integral to or expected of the surgery. For example, impotence is expected after prostate surgery. Lymphedema is expected after mastectomy. An incidental tear of the gut during a difficult lysis of adhesions not requiring repair is not a complication if the physician states that this is integral to performing the procedure. A CDI opportunity exists in this circumstance to determine whether any condition or incidental event should be considered by the physician as a complication of the procedure.

For example, *Coding Clinic* (1st Quarter, 2006) states that incidental tears of the dura during spinal surgery are always clinically significant due to the potential of cerebrospinal fluid leak (*Coding Clinic*, 2nd Quarter, 2007, pp. 11–12). ICD-9-CM states that using the term "postoperative" as an adjective to certain conditions, such as postoperative fever or postoperative ileus, requires assignment of the complication code unless the physician explicitly documents that it is not.

The medical literature does not view ICD-9-CM codes as an accurate measure of poor medical care, yet public "report card" companies use them as such (Shahian et al. 2007; Glance et al. 2006). Recognizing that these complication codes may result in negative

publicity for their facilities, hospitals must work with their coders and physicians to ascertain whether a postoperative condition meets the definition for a complication and whether it was present on admission (Dayton Business Journal 2005).

V-Codes

As mentioned throughout this chapter, CMS has changed some of the V-codes qualifying as CCs.

Those deleted include:

Code	Title	CMS CC Designation
V23.7	Insufficient prenatal care	CMS CC
V23.81	Supervision elderly primigravida	CMS CC
V23.82	Supervision elderly multigravida	CMS CC
V2383	Supervision young primigravida	CMS CC
V23.84	Supervision young multigravida	CMS CC
V23.89	Supervision high-risk preg NEC	CMS CC
V23.9	Supervision high-risk preg NOS	CMS CC
V42.2	Heart valve transplant	CMS CC
V42.89	Transplant status organ NEC	CMS CC
V45.1	Renal dialysis status	CMS CC
V49.83	Await organ transplant status	CMS CC

Those that remain or are added include:

Code	Title	CMS CC Designation	MS-DRG CC Designation
V42.0	Kidney transplant status	CMS CC	MS CC
V42.1	Heart transplant status	CMS CC	MS CC
V42.6	Lung transplant status	CMS CC	MS CC
V42.7	Liver transplant status	CMS CC	MS CC
V42.81	Transplant status, bone marrow	CMS CC	MS CC
V42.82	Transplant status, peripheral stem cells	CMS CC	MS CC
V42.83	Transplant status, pancreas	CMS CC	MS CC
V42.84	Transplant status, intestines	CMS CC	MS CC
V43.21	Heart assist device replacement	CMS CC	MS CC
V43.22	Artificial heart replacement	CMS CC	MS CC
V46.11	Respirator dependence status	CMS CC	MS CC
V46.12	Encounter for respirator dependence during power failure	CMS CC	MS CC
V46.13	Weaning from respirator	CMS CC	MS CC
V46.14	Mechanical complications of respirator	CMS CC	MS CC
V55.1	Attention to gastrostomy		MS CC
V62.84	Suicidal ideation		MS CC
V85.0	BMI less than 19, adult		MS CC
V85.4	BMI 40 and over, adult		MS CC

Conclusion

CMS has extensively amended the CC and MCC list with MS-DRGs to capture resource utilization and severity of illness. Even though many CCs were deleted, they may still apply to other DRG methodologies, such as APR-DRG, AP-DRG, and CMS DRGs, thus coders should strive to capture them. Data quality depends upon a collaborative relationship between physicians and coders that accurately documents illness severity in ICD-9-CM language as captured by the coding staff. MS-DRGs or other DRG methodologies cannot improve without a high level of data quality.

References

Alcoholism of the National Institute of Health. 2004. Available at http://pubs.niaaa.nih.gov/publications/arh27-2/134-142.htm.

American Pain Society. *Definitions Related to the Use of Opoids in the Treatment of Pain—A Consensus Document from the American Academy of Pain Medicine, the American Pain Society, and the American Society of Addiction Medicine.* Available at: http://www.painmed.org/productpub/statements/pdfs/definition.pdf. Accessed July 16, 2007.

Behrman, Richard, Kliegman, R.M., Jenson, H.B. 2003. *Nelson Textbook of Pediatrics*, 17th edition. Philadelphia: Saunders, an Imprint of Elsevier Science.

Bellomo, R., et al. 2004. Acute renal failure—definition, outcome measures, animal models, fluid therapy and information technology needs: the Second International Consensus Conference of the Acute Dialysis Quality Initiative (ADQI) Group. *Critical Care* 8:R204–R212. Available at: http://ccforum.com/content/8/4/R204, Accessed July 22, 2007.

California Office of Statewide Health Planning and Development. Coronary Artery Bypass Graft Surgery in California. 2003–2004 Hospital & Surgeon Data. Released July 2007. Available at: http://www.oshpd.ca.gov/HQAD/Outcomes/Studies/cabg/200304HospSurgReport/fullreport.pdf.

Centers for Disease Control and Prevention. 2008. The immunocompromised traveler. In *CDC Health Information for the International Traveler.* Available at: http://wwwn.cdc.gov/travel/yellowBookCh9-Immunocompromised.aspx. Accessed July 14, 2007.

Gabbe, Steven G., 2001. *Obstetrics: Normal and Problem Pregnancies*, 4th ed. Nashville: Churchill Livingstone.

Glance, L.G., Dick, A.W., Osler, T.M., Mukamel, D.B. 2006. Accuracy of hospital report cards based on administrative data. *Health Services Research* 41:1413–1437.

Healthgrades salutes Good Sam. *Dayton Business Journal,* January 24, 2005. Available at: http://www.bizjournals.com/ dayton/stories/2005/01/24/daily5.html. Accessed July 23, 2007.

Goldstein, B., Giroir, B., Randolph, A. and the Members of the International Consensus Conference on Pediatric Sepsis. 2005. International pediatric sepsis consensus conference: Definitions for sepsis and organ dysfunction in pediatrics. *Pediatric Critical Care Medicine* 6(1): 1. Available at: http://www.pccmjournal.org/pt/re/pccm/abstract.00130478-200501000-00002.htm. Accessed July 22, 2007.

Higuchi, D., Sugawa, C., Shah, S.H., Tokioka, S., and Lucas, C.E. 2003. Etiology, treatment, and outcome of esophageal ulcers: A 10-year experience in an urban emergency hospital. *Journal of Gastrointestinal Surgery* 7(7): 836–842.

ICD-9-CM Coordination and Maintenance Committee Meeting Minutes, June 4, 1998. Available at: http://www.cdc.gov/nchs/data/icd9/icdp698.pdf.

ICD-9-CM and Vardiman J.W., Harris N.L., and Brunning, R. 2002. The World Health Organization (WHO) classification of the myeloid neoplasms. *Blood* 100(7):2292–2302.

Levy, M.M. et al. 2003. 2001 SCCM/ESICM/ACCP/ATS/SIS International Sepsis Definitions Conference. Critical Care Medicine 31(4): 1250. Available at: http://sccmwww.sccm.org/press_room/Documents/sepsis.pdf. Accessed July 22, 2007.

Light, R.W. 2003. Pleural effusion. *New England Journal of Medicine* 346(25): 1971–1977.

Mannucci, P.M. and Levi, M. 2007. Prevention and treatment of major blood loss. *New England Journal of Medicine* 356(22): 2301–2311.

Martin, P.R., Singleton, C.K., and Hiller–Sturmhöfel, S. The role of thiamine deficiency in alcoholic brain disease. The National Institute of Alcohol Abuse and Alcoholism of the National Institute of Health, July 2004. Available at: http://pubs.niaaa.nih.gov/publications/arh27-2/134-142.htm.

National Institutes of Health. *The Seventh Report of the Joint National Committee on Prevention, Detection, Evaluation, and Treatment of High Blood Pressure—Complete Report.* Available at: http://www.nhlbi.nih.gov/guidelines/hypertension/jnc7full.pdf. Accessed July 20, 2007.

National Kidney Foundation. K/DOQI Clinical Practice Guidelines for Chronic Kidney Disease: Evaluation, Classification, and Stratification. Available at: http://www.kidney.org/professionals/KDOQI/guidelines_ckd/p4_class_g1.htm. Accessed July 20, 2007.

Palmer, B.F. 2004. Managing hyperkalemia caused by inhibitors of the renin–angiotensin–aldosterone system. *New England Journal of Medicine* 351:585–592.

Phelan, J.P., Smith, C.V., Broussard, P. Small, M. 1987. Amniotic fluid volume assessment using the four-quadrant technique in the pregnancy between 36 and 42 weeks gestation. *Journal of Reproductive Medicine* 32:540.

Rajkumar, S.V. and Gertz, M.A. 2007. Advances in the treatment of amyloidosis. *New England Journal of Medicine* 356(23): 2413–2415.

Schellenbaum, G.D. et al. 2004. Survival associated with two sets of diagnostic criteria for congestive heart failure. *American Journal of Epidemiology* 160(7): 628–635.

Seidner, D.L. 2006. Nutritional issues in the surgical patient. *Cleveland Clinic Journal of Medicine* 73(1): s77–81. Available at: http://www.ccjm.org/PDFFILES/Seidnersuppl1_06.pdf.

Shahian, D.M., Silverstein, T., Lovett, A.F., Wolf, R.E., Normand, S.L. 2007. Comparison of clinical and administrative data sources for hospital coronary artery bypass graft surgery report cards. *Circulation* 115(12): 1518–1527.

Singri, N., Ahya, S.N., Levin, M.L. 2003. Acute renal failure. *JAMA* 289: 747–751. Available at: http://jama.ama-assn.org/cgi/content/full/289/6/747. Accessed July 22, 2007.

Smith, D.M. 1995. Pressure ulcers in the nursing home. *Annals of Internal Medicine* 123(6):433–438.

Chapter 4

Other Severity-Adjustment Models (APR-DRGs)

Transition from the Maryland DRGs to APR-DRGs

Maryland hospitals began using the 3M All Patient Refined Diagnosis Related Groups (APR-DRG) Version 20 as the grouper system for measuring case mix on July 1, 2005. (Averill 2003, 1) After three Maryland hospitals had used the APR-DRG Version 15 grouper for several years, the Maryland Rate Regulatory Agency, the Health Service Cost Review Commission (HSCRC) made the decision to move from the Centers for Medicare and Medicaid Services Diagnosis Related Groups (CMS-DRG) grouper to the APR-DRG grouper for all Maryland hospitals. The HSCRC approved the use of a severity-adjusted grouper for several reasons. Maryland hospitals, clinicians, and payers supported this move as a better classification system that would accurately reflect the patient acuity and better reflect resources used for their patients. Also, the use of the ad hoc case mix adjustment process needed to be discontinued. This process created alternate methods of groupings for special situations as deemed necessary by the hospitals and by HSCRC. An example of such an ad hoc adjustment was using a separate grouping system for newborns and special ventilation DRGs to account for DRGs with use of mechanical ventilation therapy. Data collected from FY 2005 was used for the base year, and Maryland-specific relative weights (RW) were assigned to all APRs and the four severity-of-illness subclasses associated with each APR. The risk of mortality (ROM)

subclass is not used to measure case mix. Maryland hospitals began the process of analyzing their data during FY 2005 to determine the financial impact as well as the changes and improvements needed in the coding and documentation processes.

Fundamental Differences Between CMS-DRGs and APR-DRGs

The CMS-DRG classification system differs from the APR-DRG classification system in several ways. First, the CMS-DRG system focuses on the Medicare population and subdivides select base DRGs into two categories: with complication/comorbidity (CC) or without CC. Many of the CMS-DRGs, such as DRG 143 (Chest pain) and DRG 316 (Renal failure), have no subdivisions.

Second, the APR-DRG classification system accounts for all payors, patients, ages, and comorbidities. It classifies patients into clinically similar groups and subdivides all APR-DRGs into the following four severity-of-illness (SOI) subclasses and four risk-of-mortality subclasses: (1) minor, (2) moderate, (3) major, or (4) extreme SOI ROM. All secondary diagnoses are used to determine the SOI and ROM levels, and the classification system includes social and personal risk factors as well as specific nonoperating room procedures to define the SOI and ROM. The presence of several

---

*Please note that all comparison of information contained in chapter 4 is based on CMS-DRG Version 24 and the APR-DRG Version 20 grouper. CMS-DRG Version 24 grouper was effective for October 1, 2007 inpatient data and APR-DRG grouper Version 20 was used by Maryland Hospitals for July 1, 2005 to September 30, 2007 inpatient data. The information contained in this chapter was presented to share the differences between these two grouping systems based on these versions.

comorbid conditions may increase a patient's SOI. The CMS-DRG system does not recognize multiple CCs, and the logic for the CC subdivision is the presence or absence of diagnoses determined to be complications and comorbidities. The APR-DRG system uses an 18-step process to determine the final SOI subclass modifying the standard SOI level based on age, principal diagnosis, specific APR, and non-OR procedures.

Other differences between the two classification systems are that, whereas the CMS-DRG system recognizes complications of care as CCs, in the APR-DRG system, complications of care have little or no impact on the SOI subclass.

Rerouting is another process used in the APR-DRG system that is not used in the CMS-DRG system. The rerouting process may reclassify an APR-DRG based on the presence of certain secondary diagnoses assigned to the case. An example of this process is the principal diagnosis of chest pain with a secondary diagnosis, such as coronary artery disease, atherosclerotic cardiovascular disease, old myocardial infarction, or documented treatment for angina. The presence of any one of these secondary diagnoses combined with 786.50 (Chest pain NOS), 786.51 (Precordial chest pain), 786.59 (Chest pain NEC), or 733.6 (Costochondritis) as the principal diagnosis will reclassify the APR-DRG from an APR-DRG 203 (Chest pain) to an APR-DRG 198 (Angina pectoris and coronary atherosclerosis). The CMS-DRG would remain as 143 (Chest pain). This process also can occur in areas such as skin ulcers in diabetic patients. A patient who is admitted for Diabetic hypoglycemia (250.8x) and also has a Decubitus ulcer of the sacrum (707.03) as a secondary diagnosis will reroute from an APR-DRG 420 (Diabetes) to an APR-DRG 380 (Skin ulcer), even though the reason for admission was the diabetic condition and the ulcer is unrelated to the diabetes.

One of the first steps the Maryland hospitals took when preparing to transition to APR-DRGs was to analyze the current depth of coding of the individual hospitals. The depth of coding has a major impact on assigning the correct APR-DRG and SOI subclass to the patient. The depth of coding impacts the final SOI subclass because of the interaction of all additional secondary codes assigned to the case. This is a major change from the CMS-DRG system. Documentation issues and accurate coding practices also were analyzed because they are the two key components for correct APR-DRG and SOI assignment. The Maryland hospitals analyzed data to understand the differences in how the two grouping systems classify patients. Some of the differences are described in the following sections.

Complex Pneumonia

The CMS-DRG system classifies pneumonia patients into DRGs 079/080/081 (Respiratory infections and inflammation with CC, without CC, or age 0 to 17) or DRGs 089/090/091 (Simple pneumonia and pleurisy with CC, without CC, or age 0 to 17). The APR-DRG system classifies pneumonia patients into APR-DRG 137 (Major respiratory infections and inflammations), APR-DRG 138 (Bronchiolitis and RSV pneumonia), and APR-DRG 139 (Other pneumonia). There are several changes in the CMS-DRG and APR-DRG systems that occur with common principal diagnoses that are assigned to these respiratory DRGs. *Haemophlus influenzae* pneumonia (482.2) is classified as 089/090/091 (Simple pneumonia) in the CMS-DRG system, whereas in the APR-DRG system it is classified as 137 (Major respiratory infections), which is considered to be the optimal DRG for pneumonia patients and carries the higher RW for case mix measurement. Respiratory syncytial virus (RSV) pneumonia (480.1), which would be classified to the CMS-DRG groupings of 089/090/091 (Simple pneumonia), is placed into an APR-DRG grouping of 138 (Bronchiolitis). Pleurisy (511.0), which is classified in the CMS-DRG grouping 089/090/091, is placed in the APR-DRG grouping 144 (Respiratory signs and symptoms), and bronchiolitis (466.19) is placed in grouping 138 (Bronchiolitis) in the APR-DRG, whereas it is assigned to grouping 096/097/098 (Bronchitis and asthma with CC or without CC, or age 0 to 17) in the CMS-DRG.

One versus Three Levels of CCs

APR-DRGs have four subclasses for SOI. When comparing this classification system with CMS-DRGs, subclass 1 can be considered without CC, subclass 2 can be considered with CC, and subclasses 3 and 4 contain multiple interacting CCs. Understanding the interaction and effects of additional secondary diagnosis while following the Official Coding Guidelines will impact the SOI and case mix.

V-Codes that Matter

In general, V-codes had little impact under the CMS-DRG system; however, this is not the case for APR-DRGs. Coding specialists quickly became aware of certain V-codes that could impact patients' SOIs. Coders began frequently using certain codes from this section of the ICD-9-CM code books that they had been ignoring for years. Some coders were struggling with the appropriate use of these codes and, in most instances, the *Coding Clinic* provided limited information due to the infrequent use of the codes. The Official Coding Guidelines do provide some guidance regarding when it is appropriate to use V-codes representing a "status" and "history of" code. Per the official coding guidelines, status codes indicate that a patient is either a carrier of a disease or has the sequelae or residual of a past disease or condition. A status code is informative because the status may affect the course of treatment and its outcome. Also, the official coding guidelines state that a status code should not be used with a diagnosis code from one of the body system chapters if the diagnosis code includes the information provided by the status code (AHA. 2005, 4).

V-codes, such as V15.1 (Surgery to heart and great vessels) and V15.2 (History of surgery to other major organ) are codes that coders have begun to use more frequently. Both of these codes are assigned with a base severity level of 2. The addition of either one of these V-codes could impact many cases by moving the cases from a level 1 to a level 2 or, in some cases, from a level 2 to level 3. The question became what vessels are considered great vessels and what are major organs. Facilities within Maryland now needed to establish internal guidelines on the correct usage of these codes and define internally what types of procedures and surgeries would be considered surgery. Examples include the question: Is the carotid artery considered a great vessel? Another question: Is the procedure of a carotid endarterectomy considered surgery to a great vessel? Facilities also began to contact the *Coding Clinic* for guidance on whether it was appropriate to use code V15.1 and a more specific V-code, such as V45.81 (history of aortocoronary bypass), in combination. V-codes such as V07.0 (Prophylactic isolation) and V46.2 (Dependence supplemental oxygen), assigned a base severity level of 2, also became important secondary diagnoses to capture as additional secondary codes because of their impact on SOI.

Certain V-codes were determined to have impact within specific APRs. For obstetrical cases V-codes such as V23.41 (Pregnancy with history of preterm labor) and V23.49 (Pregnancy with poor obstetrical history NEC) were determined to move cases from SOI level 1 to level 2 in patients with vaginal deliveries. For psychiatric cases, V15.81 (History of past noncompliance with medications) is assigned a base level of severity 2 and V-codes indicating status amputation of shoulder, elbow, knee, or hip would impact APR-DRG 860 (Rehabilitation).

The new V-codes for Body mass index (V85.x) also could impact the final severity level assigned to a case. Per the *Coding Clinic* (Fourth Quarter, 2005),

these V-codes can be assigned based on the dietician's documentation. Therefore, when the medical record documentation is lacking the physician's documentation of the dietitian's diagnosis for which the consultation is being performed, the use of the V-code could help increase the SOI and case mix assigned to the case. This can be seen in the example of a patient admitted for a Cholecystectomy (51.22) due to Chronic cholecystitis (575.11). If the physician orders a nutritional consultation and the dietician documents a body mass index (BMI) of over 40, code V85.4 can be assigned as a secondary diagnosis. The addition of this secondary diagnosis will change the SOI from a subclass 1 to a subclass 2. The final APR-DRG assignment is 262 (Cholecystectomy except laparoscopic). The CMS-DRG 198 (Cholecystectomy except by laparoscope without CDE w/o CC) is not affected by the addition of this secondary code.

Symptom Codes: Are They Integral?

Symptom codes can have a significant impact on APR-DRGs, which is another difference from the CMS-DRG system. The assignment of symptom codes as additional secondary diagnoses had little effect on CMS-DRGs and, in fact, this system eliminated some symptoms as complications and comorbidities in association with the principal diagnosis. The official coding guidelines play a crucial role in the assignment of symptom codes as secondary diagnosis codes. Symptom codes that were not classified as complications/comorbidities under the CMS-DRG system are now impacting SOI under the APR-DRG system. Symptom codes such as Syncope (780.2), Abnormality of gait (781.2), Dysphagia (787.2), and Urinary incontinence (788.30) are not classified as CCs but could impact SOI. These symptom codes could have an impact on patient reimbursement because many of the symptom codes have a base severity level of 2 (moderate). In some instances the addition of a symptom code in combination with other level-2 secondary diagnoses could raise the final SOI subclass to 3 (major). Because of the reimbursement impact, understanding the Uniform Hospital Discharge Data Set (UHDDS) definition of secondary diagnosis reporting and the Official Coding Guidelines is essential to symptom coding. The UHDDS definition of secondary diagnosis includes only those conditions that affect the episode of hospital care in terms of any of the following: clinical evaluation, therapeutic treatment, further evaluation, extended length of stay, or increased nursing care and/or other monitoring. The UHDDS also states that conditions that *are* an integral part of a disease process *should not* be reported as additional diagnoses, and conditions that *are not* an integral part of a disease process *should be* coded when present. It has become essential for coders to have a strong knowledge of disease processes to determine when additional symptom codes are an integral part of the disease process and should be added.

An example of symptom codes impacting the SOI under the APR-DRG system, but not under the CMS-DRG system, is the case of a male presenting with benign hypertrophy of the prostate (BPH) with urinary obstruction and other lower urinary tract symptoms and urinary incontinence. The Coding Guidelines instruct the coder to use code 600.01 for the prostate hypertrophy with urinary obstruction and other lower urinary tract symptoms and to use the additional codes 788.30 to identify the symptom of urinary incontinence and 599.69 for the obstruction. The CMS-DRG assignment for this patient is 349 (Benign prostatic hypertrophy w/o CC), and the APR-DRG assignment is 501 (male reproductive system dx). The difference occurs in the SOI assignment. The case will be assigned to SOI 1 without the presence of urinary incontinence and to SOI 2 with the addition of code 788.30 for the urinary incontinence. The presence of the secondary diagnosis code for the urinary incontinence has no impact on the CMS-DRG.

An example of a symptom that is not integral to the disease process can be seen in a pediatric asthma case. When a pediatric patient is admitted with an Acute exacerbation of asthma (493.92), the CMS-DRG will be 098 (Bronchitis and asthma age 1 to 17), and the APR-DRG assignment will be 141 (Asthma) with an SOI subclass of 1. After reviewing many pediatric asthma cases it was identified that many of these patients also develop tachycardia. These situations were discussed with physicians and the physicians clarified that the tachycardia was associated with the drugs administered for the treatment of the asthma. The albuterol that patients were receiving to correct the acute exacerbation of asthma was affecting the patients by causing tachycardia, and this additional diagnosis needed to be monitored and evaluated. The additional secondary diagnosis of tachycardia will impact the SOI subclass, changing the case from SOI 1 to SOI 2.

It also is important to determine when symptom codes are clinically significant and when they meet the UHDDS definition for reporting. Coding guidelines indicate that abnormal findings should be assigned only when the physician has not been able to arrive at a related diagnosis but also indicate that by listing the abnormal finding in the diagnostic statement, the finding is considered to be clinically significant.

Symptom codes such as Hepatomegaly (789.1) and Splenomegaly (789.2) have a base severity level of 2. When the attending physician records these symptoms in the History and Physical (H&P) or progress notes, the coder will need to determine if these symptoms meet the UHDDS definition for reporting and are considered to be clinically significant.

Examples of Deleted CCs

Some secondary codes that are designated as complications/comorbidities for CMS-DRG are considered base severity level 1 for APR-DRG. Secondary diagnoses assigned to a base severity level of 1 have little impact on the final SOI assignment in APR-DRGs and generally will not help to move a case to a higher SOI subclass. Some commonly eliminated CCs are 413.9 (Stable angina), 518.0 (Atelectasis), 424.0 (Mitral valve prolapse), and 491.9 (Chronic bronchitis). Other secondary diagnoses such as Alcohol and drug abuse (for example, codes 305.00 and 305.60) or Alcohol and drug dependence (for example, codes 303.00 and 304.00) were eliminated as impacting SOI based on the specified fifth digit assignment. In general, alcohol and drug abuse and/or dependence diagnoses are assigned a base severity level of 1 if the fifth digit indicates unspecified use, episodic use, or if in remission. Only a fifth digit of 1 (continuous use) affects SOI and is assigned to a base severity level of 2. This difference demonstrates the need for improved documentation to assign APR-DRGs and SOIs that accurately reflect the severity of the patient population.

Complications of surgery and medical care ICD-9-CM codes that were generally CCs under the CMS-DRG system also were eliminated from impacting SOI. This includes not only codes from the 996 through 999 category of complications, but also includes codes such as 536.4x (Gastrotomy complications) and 569.6x (Colostomy and enterostomy complications), which are assigned a base severity level of 1 in the APR-DRG system. An example of this is a patient who is admitted with Dehydration (276.51) and is also treated for an Infection of the gastrostomy (536.41). Under the CMS-DRG system, this patient will be assigned a DRG 296 (Nutritional & miscellaneous metabolic disorders age older than 17 years with CC); however, under the APR-DRG system, this patient will be assigned a DRG 422 (Hypovolemia/electrolyte disorder) and a SOI subclass of 1. The final SOI is not impacted by the additional secondary code of 536.41, even though additional resources were used to treat this condition.

Secondary diagnosis codes for most primary malignancies were also eliminated from impacting SOI for APR-DRGs. Many of the codes for primary malignancies are assigned a base severity level of 1 but are considered CCs for CMS-DRG. For example, a patient admitted for dehydration due to chemotherapy for primary lung cancer would be assigned to APR-DRG 422 (Hypovolemia/electrolyte disorder) with a SOI subclass of 1 (minor). However, the CMS-DRG would be 296 (Nutritional & miscellaneous metabolic disorders age older than 17 years with CC), reflecting the additional secondary condition of the lung cancer. Another change from the CMS-DRG system is the specificity of chronic obstructive pulmonary disease (COPD). The code for COPD (496) is a CC and impacts SOI by the base severity level of 2, but the specificity of COPD with bronchitis without exacerbation (491.20) is a CC under the CMS-DRG system, whereas under the APR-DRG system, it is assigned a base severity level of 1 for all patients younger than 70 years.

Interdependency of CCs—Secondary Diagnoses

In the APR-DRG system, high SOI or ROM is primarily determined by the interaction of multiple diseases. Patients with multiple comorbid conditions involving multiple organ systems are usually difficult to treat and tend to have poor outcomes. APR-DRGs and the associated SOI subclass are dependent on the interaction of all secondary diagnoses. The interaction of specific combinations of secondary diagnoses makes treatment more difficult. APR-DRGs contain 83 core secondary diagnosis categories for which all ICD-9-CM diagnosis codes are classified. The interaction of these categories affects the final SOI assignment. Because of the extensive logic behind this interaction, it becomes difficult to impossible to easily recognize which combination of secondary diagnoses will impact final SOI assignment. For the most part, the more secondary diagnoses that appear on an inpatient record, the greater the chance of increasing the final assigned SOI subclass. Because of this interaction and the tendency to code more completely, it again becomes imperative that coders understand the official coding guidelines. Only those conditions that impact the patient care during the current hospital stay should be assigned as secondary diagnoses.

An example of an increased SOI subclass based on multiple secondary diagnoses is a 56-year-old patient admitted with Esophageal stricture (530.3). This patient also has Hypotension (458.9), Morbid obesity (278.01), COPD (496), and a Lower limb ulcer (707.10). Each of these secondary diagnoses has a base severity level of 2 (moderate); however, the combination of all of these secondary diagnoses will move the final SOI subclass to 3 (major). The removal of any one of

these secondary diagnoses will lower the final SOI subclass back to 2.

Age Impact

Final APR-DRG assignment and SOI subclasses are impacted by age. The change in the final APR-DRG assignment can be seen in the major diagnostic category for newborns and other neonates (MDC 15). To be assigned to MDC 15, a patient must be 0 to 7 days old, 8 to 14 days old with a birth weight less than 1,000g, 8 to 14 days old with a birth weight of 1,000 to 1,999g and a major OR procedure, or 8 to 14 days old with a birth weight of 1,000 to 1,999g and requiring mechanical ventilation (96.71). Therefore, if a patient is 8 days old and requires readmission to the hospital for Jaundice (774.6) and Phototherapy (99.83), the APR-DRG assigned to the case will be 283 (Other disorders of liver), whereas the CMS-DRG would be 391 (Normal newborn).

SOI subclass is also impacted by age. If a 55-year-old patient is admitted with a Urinary tract infection (599.0) and has Chronic obstructive bronchitis without exacerbation (491.20), this patient will be assigned to CMS-DRG 320 (Kidney and urinary tract infection age older than 17 years with CC). The APR-DRG assignment is 463 (Kidney/urinary tract infection) with a SOI subclass of 1. Using the same scenario in a patient who is older than age 70 years will change the SOI subclass to 2.

Procedure Impact

The two DRG classification systems differ on how the procedure codes impact the DRG assignment. The assignment of the final APR and final SOI on each case is based on a process that consists of 18 steps. Six of these steps involve the process of modifying the OR and non-OR procedures assigned to the individual case. These steps include modifications of the standard SOI of specific secondary diagnoses based on non-OR procedures; modification of the SOI subclass for the patient based on combinations of APR-DRG and non-OR procedures; modification of the SOI subclass based on combinations of APR-DRG and OR procedures; modification of the SOI subclass based on combinations of APR-DRG and pairs of OR procedures; modification of SOI subclass based on a combination of APR-DRG for extracorporeal membrane oxygenation (ECMO) and the presence or absence of certain OR procedures; and modification of the SOI subclass based on combinations of APR-DRG, principal diagnosis and non-OR procedure. This extensive logic demonstrates the importance of complete and accurate code assignments for all patients.

The following examples illustrate the importance of modifications to the SOI subclass and complete and accurate coding. A patient is admitted for Coronary artery disease (CAD) (414.01) and is having a coronary artery bypass graft (CABG) procedure. If the CABG is performed on one to three arteries (36.11 to 36.13), the patient will be classified to APR-DRG 166 (Coronary bypass w/o cardiac cath), and the SOI assigned will be 1 (minor). If the CABG is performed on four or more coronary arteries (36.14) the case will be classified to APR-DRG 166 and the SOI assigned will be 2 (moderate). The SOI subclass was modified based on the combination of the APR-DRG assigned and the OR procedure. The 36.14 procedure is indicative of higher SOI relative to the other OR procedures in the APR-DRG.

Chemotherapy and radiotherapy can also impact SOI subclass. Therefore, coders must review medical records thoroughly to capture these additional procedures. When a patient is admitted with a principal diagnosis of malignancy in APR-DRG 041 (Nervous system neoplasm) and receives radiation therapy during the inpatient stay, the final SOI assignment is increased by one level up to a maximum subclass of 3 (major).

Other differences between the APR-DRG and the CMS-DRG classification systems are seen when bilateral procedures are performed. The CMS-DRG system recognizes and groups separately cases in which bilateral procedures of the same joint are performed. The CMS-DRG for bilateral replacement of hips or knees is 471 (Bilateral or multiple major joint procedures of lower extremity). The APR-DRG assignment for this same condition is 301 (Hip joint replacement), but neither the assignment nor the SOI subclass is impacted by the performance of the bilateral procedures performed on the same joint. No additional case mix is recognized in this instance. The APR-DRG system does, however, modify SOI subclass 301 (Hip joint replacement) when the hip joint replacement is performed in combination with a knee replacement, knee or lower leg procedure, foot and toe procedure, or shoulder and arm procedure.

The CMS-DRG classification system recognizes and groups separately hernia cases with extensive lysis of peritoneal adhesions, whereas under the APR-DRG system, no additional case mix is assigned to these cases. A patient is admitted for repair of an Incisional hernia (553.21 to 53.51) and also has extensive Lysis of peritoneal adhesions (568.0 to 54.59). The APR-DRG assigned to this scenario is 227 (Hernia procedures except inguinal, femoral, and umbilical) and SOI level 1 (minor). The CMS-DRG for this same scenario would change from a 160 (Hernia procedure except inguinal

and femoral age older than 17 years w/o CC) to a 151 (peritoneal adhesiolysis w/o CC). The CMS-DRG classification system provides for additional revenue and case mix for the additional procedure.

Excisional Débridement

A major difference occurs with excisional débridement. Under the CMS-DRG system, Excisional débridement (86.22) is classified to a surgical procedure that will move the DRG from a medical CMS-DRG to a surgical CMS-DRG. Under the APR-DRG system, the addition of the procedure excisional débridement will not have the same effect and move the classification from a medical APR-DRG to a surgical APR-DRG. So a patient admitted with a Urinary tract infection (599.0) who is taken to the operating room for Excisional débridement (86.22) for a Lower extremity heel ulcer (707.14) during the hospital stay will remain in medical APR-DRG 463 (Kidney/urinary tract infection). The hospital will receive an additional case mix for the presence and treatment of the ulcer by the increase in SOI subclass from minor to moderate but will not receive the additional case mix for the OR procedure.

Non-OR Procedures

Although the APR-DRG classification system eliminates some procedures from the surgical APR-DRG assignment, there are also some non-OR procedures that are considered in the final SOI assignment process. Procedures such as total parenteral nutrition (TPN), ECMO, renal dialysis, temporary pacemakers, and ventilation therapy longer than 96 hours can impact the final SOI assignment when used in combination with specific diagnosis codes.

The non-OR procedure of TPN will increase the final severity assignment of patients with regional enteritis and ulcerative colitis. The procedure of renal dialysis is used to increase the severity level of patients with nephritis, and the insertion of a temporary pacemaker with heart block diagnoses, such as trifascicular block, will increase the final severity level.

The correct coding assignment for a patient on mechanical ventilation is extremely important in the APR-DRG system. Mechanical ventilation longer than 96 hours (96.71) is used to increase the standard severity level of a secondary diagnosis by one increment to a 3 (major), and mechanical ventilation longer than 96 hours is used to increase the standard severity level of a secondary diagnosis by two increments to a 4 (extreme). The following is an example of such incremental increases. A patient is admitted with an Acute inferoposterior myocardial infarction (410.31), develops Acute respiratory failure (518.81) after admission and is placed on mechanical ventilation for less than 96 hours (96.71). The CMS-DRG assignment for this case will be 121 (Circulatory disorder w/ AMI and major complication, discharged alive). The final APR-DRG assignment will be 190 (acute MI) with a SOI subclass of 3. However, if this patient was on mechanical ventilation for longer than 96 hours, the final APR assignment would be 190 (acute MI) with a SOI subclass of 4. The CMS-DRG would remain the same.

The use of code 96.71 versus 96.72 can also change the final APR-DRG assigned to a patient when the patient is admitted with a respiratory system diagnosis. This logic is somewhat consistent with the CMS-DRG classification system in which a patient admitted with Status asthmaticus (493.91) and placed on mechanical ventilation for less than 96 hours is assigned to CMS-DRG 566 (Respiratory system diagnosis with ventilation support less than 96 hours. The APR-DRG assignment for this same situation would be 141 (Asthma). If this same patient receives ventilation support for longer than 96 hours, then the CMS-DRG becomes 565 (Respiratory system diagnosis with ventilation support longer than 96 hours), and the APR-DRG assignment is changed to 130 (Respiratory system diagnosis with ventilation support for 96 or more hours).

Drop in CMS-DRG Case Mix Index

As Maryland moved forward with the transition to APRs, many facilities experienced an increase in case mix from the base year under the APR-DRG classification system, but they noticed a decline under the CMS-DRG system. Two reasons for this decline are: (1) some cases were being coded to CMS-DRGs without CCs because the case was already assigned to an APR with a moderate or major severity level, and (2) different principal diagnoses were being selected when two conditions equally met the definition for principal diagnosis.

With the transition to APR-DRGs, queries for secondary diagnosis impacting SOI increased and became the primary focus. As the process increased for secondary diagnosis impacting SOI, coders could eliminate the process of querying for additional diagnoses that impacted CMS-DRG but had no impact on SOI. A patient who is admitted for a Left hemicolectomy (45.75) for Diverticulitis (562.11) and has Morbid obesity (278.01) will be assigned to APR-DRG 221 (Major small and large bowel procedures) with a SOI level of 2 (moderate). The CMS-DRG for this same situation will be 149 (Major small and large bowel procedures w/o CC). The patient's medical record indicates that he has a history of stable angina and appears to be receiving medication for angina. The

addition of Angina (413.9) will have no impact on changing the SOI subclass, so the coder might choose not to query for the additional diagnosis, even though this will impact the CMS-DRG by moving it into DRG 570 (Major small and large bowel procedures with CC without major gastrointestinal diagnosis).

Selection of principal diagnosis when two conditions equally met the criteria for principal diagnosis could have contributed to the decline in case-mix index with the transition. Coders might have optimized the principal condition for the APR-DRG classification, declining the case mix under the CMS-DRG classification. For example, the medical record of a patient who is admitted with shortness of breath due to an acute exacerbation of COPD and pneumonia and also has malnutrition will show that if both COPD and pneumonia were present on admission and both were equally treated, there is a difference with optimization.

Principal Diagnosis of COPD: CMS-DRG 088 (Chronic obstructive pulmonary disease) (RW 0.8878) APR-DRG 140/3 (Chronic obstructive pulmonary disease–level 3) (RW 1.1208)

Principal Diagnosis of Pneumonia: CMS-DRG 089 (Simple pneumonia) (RW 1.03) APR-DRG 139/2 (Other pneumonia–level 2) (RW 0.7200)

Under the APR-DRG system, the optimized reimbursement would be COPD. Under the CMS-DRG system, the optimized reimbursement would be pneumonia.

Strategies in Changing SOI for Specific Circumstances

Get the Principal Diagnosis Right

Assigning the correct principal diagnosis is more crucial under the APR-DRG system than under the CMS-DRG system. Often, the specificity of the ICD-9-CM code assigned as the principal diagnosis will impact the APR-DRG and/or the SOI assigned to the case.

The following example of a patient admitted with a myocardial infarction demonstrates the SOI subclass change. A patient assigned to code 410.91 (Acute myocardial infarction, unspecified site) will be assigned to APR-DRG 190 (Acute myocardial infarction), and the SOI subclass will be level 1. With improved documentation of the specific site of the myocardial infarction, such as ICD-9-CM codes 410.01, 410.11, 410.21, 410.31, 410.41, or 410.51 (Myocardial infarction, specified sites such as anterolateral, anterior, inferolateral, etc.), the SOI subclass will change to level 2. The CMS-DRG assigned to a myocardial infarction is not dependent on the specific site of the myocardial infarction.

Another example that demonstrates this same scenario is a patient admitted with major depression, recurrent episode, severe. The presence or absence of psychotic behavior impacts the SOI subclass by changing the patient from an APR-DRG 751 with an SOI subclass of 1 to an SOI subclass of 2. The CMS-DRG remains 430 (Psychosis). Again, these scenarios show the importance of thorough record review, complete and accurate coding, and the need for improved documentation.

The specificity of the principal diagnosis can impact the final APR-DRG assignment and help increase the case mix. A patient admitted with Dehydration (276.51) will be assigned a CMS-DRG 297 (Nutritional and miscellaneous metabolic disorders >17 with CC), whereas the APR-DRG will be 422 (Hypovolemia/electrolyte disorder) with an SOI subclass of 1, for an RW of 0.2877. If a complete review of the medical record determines that the patient also had Hyponatremia (276.1) on admission, the coding rules stipulate that 276.1 should be assigned as the principal diagnosis, thus changing the APR-DRG to 425 (Electrolyte disorder except hypovolemia) with an SOI subclass of 1, for an RW 0.4298. The CMS-DRG is not impacted by this change of principal diagnosis.

Effect of Multiple Conditions that Qualify as Principal Diagnosis

The effect of multiple conditions that qualify as principal diagnoses becomes a significant challenge for coders under a severity-based system. Under the CMS-DRG system, the effect of multiple conditions is only dependent on one element—the final DRG. Under the APR-DRG system, the effect of multiple conditions is dependent not only on the DRG but also on the SOI subclass. Many coders are able to memorize which CMS-DRGs carry the higher RW, and this makes it relatively easy for them to optimize their principal diagnosis. In the APR-DRG system, the process becomes much more time consuming and is dependent on the SOI subclass of each individual APR. It is impossible for coders to memorize the best way to optimize for APRs, and each case must be reviewed independently depending on all the secondary codes and procedures assigned to the case.

The following scenarios demonstrate this difference.

Example 1   Patient is a 2-year-old child admitted with acute asthma with Status asthmaticus (493.91) and Pneumonia (486). Both conditions were present on admission and were treated equally. The patient also developed Tachycardia (785.0) during admission due to Albuterol (E945.7).

Principal Diagnosis of Asthma with Status Asthmaticus: CMS-DRG—098 APR-DRG—141 SOI 2 (RW 0.5536) Principal Diagnosis of Pneumonia: CMS-DRG—091 APR-DRG—139 SOI 2 (RW 0.7200)

Optimized Reimbursement—Pneumonia (APR-DRG 139 SOI 2)

Now using this same scenario, the coder identifies that the patient appears to have hypokalemia, which was treated with potassium supplements, during the stay. If the coder queries the physician for this additional code, the optimized principal diagnosis will change because of the impact of the additional condition.

Principal Diagnosis of Status Asthmaticus: CMS-DRG—098 APR-DRG—141 SOI 3 (RW 0.9330)

Principal Diagnosis of Pneumonia: CMS-DRG—091 APR-DRG—139 SOI 2 (RW 0.7200)

Optimized Reimbursement—Status Asthmaticus (APR-DRG 141 SOI 3) The addition of 276.8 (Hypokalemia) impacted the SOI subclass for the asthma with status asthmaticus but did not impact the subclass for the pneumonia.

Example 2   A patient was admitted with congestive heart failre (CHF) and acute exacerbation of COPD and developed acute respiratory failure during the stay.

Principal Diagnosis of CHF: CMS-DRG—127 APR-DRG—194 SOI 3 (RW 1.3262)

Principal Diagnosis of COPD: CMS-DRG—088 APR-DRG—140 SOI 3 (RW 1.1208)

Optimized Reimbursement—CHF (APR-DRG 194 SOI 3)

Now using the same scenario, it is identified that the patient also received Mechanical ventilation therapy (96.71) during the hospital stay.

Principal Diagnosis of CHF: CMS-DRG—127 APR-DRG—194 SOI 3 (RW 1.3262)

Principal Diagnosis of COPD: CMS-DRG—088 APR-DRG—140 SOI 4 (RW 2.3228)

Optimized Reimbursement—COPD (APR-DRG 140 SOI 4)

The addition of the mechanical ventilation therapy had an impact on the SOI subclass for the principal diagnosis of COPD, but had no impact on the principal diagnosis of CHF.

Identifying Level 3 and Level 4 CCs

As previously stated, the CMS-DRG and APR-DRG classification systems differ. CMS-DRGs generally look for one complication or comorbidity as a secondary diagnosis to change the DRG, whereas APR-DRGs rely on all secondary diagnoses and numerous other factors to change the SOI subclass between four distinct levels. Understanding how the SOI subclass is assigned and adjusted based on these numerous factors is an important component of analyzing and moving the SOI subclass. How easily a classification can move from one SOI level to another depends on the APR-DRG assigned to the case. When analyzing the data, coders need to be aware of these situations and be aware that grouping different APRs together and analyzing the average SOI from these groupings will not be an effective classification method. Each APR and each SOI subclass within that APR-DRG must be analyzed independently. SOI subclasses are not the same between APR-DRGs. They do not represent similar patients.

The four SOI subclasses help to clinically group similar resource-intensive cases better than the CMS-DRG system. Following is an example of how the interaction of all secondary diagnoses and procedures helps group a patient admitted with the same principal diagnosis from one SOI subclass to another and better defines the different resources needed to treat each instance. A patient admitted with congestive heart failure with no other secondary conditions is grouped to APR-DRG 194, SOI subclass 1, with an RW of 0.6201. The same patient admitted with congestive heart failure and a urinary tract infection will be grouped to APR-DRG 194, SOI subclass 2, with an RW of 0.8304. If this patient develops acute respiratory failure during the stay, she will then be classified to APR-DRG 194, SOI subclass 3, with an RW of 1.3262. Additionally, if during the stay, the patient is placed on mechanical ventilation for >96 hours, she would be classified to APR-DRG 194, SOI subclass 4, with an RW of 3.2508. Notice the extreme difference in RW between subclass 3 (RW 1.3262) and subclass 4 (RW 3.2508). Because these cases would require different resources, each was grouped separately. Under the CMS-DRG system, all of these cases would be grouped to CMS-DRG 127 with no differentiation between the intensity of each case.

Changing from Level 1 to Level 2—Easy

In the APR-DRG system, moving from SOI subclass 1 (minor) to SOI subclass 2 (moderate) is considered the easiest. Just like in the CMS-DRG system (with or without CC), the SOI subclass can change to a 2" by adding one more secondary code. In general, common secondary codes such as electrolyte imbalances, morbid obesity, dysphagia, COPD, CHF, late effects of strokes, and specific infectious organisms (for example, *Proteus* and *Staphylococcus*) will change the SOI. Some principal diagnoses without the presence of any secondary diagnoses will automatically assign a patient to a level 2 because of the severity (complexity of treatment) associated with the single diagnosis. Examples of these principal diagnoses are diabetic ketoacidosis (type I) and uncontrolled and ruptured abdominal aneurysm. Other patients will be assigned to an SOI 2 based solely on the principal diagnosis and the procedure performed. An example of this is a patient admitted with osteoarthritis of the hip and a total hip replacement. There are also specific combinations of three or more secondary diagnoses, all having a base severity level of 1, that will move the final SOI subclass to a 2.

Changing from Level 2 to Level 3—Difficult but Possible

The movement from SOI subclass 2 to SOI subclass 3 becomes more challenging. Many combinations of secondary diagnoses and procedures will help with the movement between these levels. In some instances just the combination of multiple level 2 secondary diagnoses will move a patient to subclass 3. Combinations of secondary diagnoses and procedures will also help with the movement from level 2 to 3. For the most part, these patients have multiple secondary diagnoses. There are some instances in which the severity of the principal diagnosis will move a patient to a level 3, as seen with the principal diagnosis of Intractable epilepsy (345.91). Some common level 3 secondary diagnoses are decubitus ulcer, pulmonary hypertension, acidosis, coma, malnutrition, and ventricular tachycardia. Some of these diagnoses are commonly documented only in the nursing notes. Therefore, coding professionals must thoroughly review all nursing notes and must query the physician for the clinical significance of these diagnoses. It is also important for coders to review laboratory results and radiologic examinations because common diagnoses such as acidosis and pulmonary hypertension can be identified from these reports. Even though these reports may not be documented by the physicians, they will provide information to the coding professional about when to query the physician.

Level 3 to Level 4—Must Have Organ Failure, MI, SIRS, or Multiple Level 3 Diagnoses

Level 4 patients are those who are severely ill and require extensive resources. Most of these patients have some type of organ failure assigned as a secondary diagnosis. Common conditions associated with subclass 4 patients are acute respiratory failure, acute renal failure, septicemia, acute pulmonary embolism, acute myocardial infarction, and acute stroke. It is possible, based on different combinations of APRs, procedures, and secondary diagnoses, to move a case to subclass 4 without the presence of organ failure as shown in the following example. A patient is admitted with a urinary tract infection, metabolic acidosis (base severity level 3), decubitus sacral ulcer (base severity level 3) pulmonary hypertension (base severity level 3), and thrombocytopenia (base severity level 3). This patient will be assigned to APR 463 (Kidney, urinary tract infection) with an SOI subclass of 4 (extreme). The combination of the multiple secondary diagnoses with base severity levels of 3 moved the patient's final subclass to 4.

In the APR-DRG classification system, movement between the SOI levels will affect the case mix. Because a case can move easily between SOI level 1 and SOI level 2, there will only be minimal case mix growth. The movement between SOI level 2 and SOI level 3 represents a slightly higher impact on case mix. However, the movement from SOI level 3 to SOI level 4 represents a significant change in case mix, generally doubling the RW.

It is important to understand the APR-DRG and the SOI subclass associated with that specific APR-DRG. Certain groups of patients and/or certain APR-DRGs will be more difficult to move than others. Analyzing the data becomes important to effectively select potential records for audits and secondary reviews. Reviewing length of stay and charges will help to identify areas of opportunity for case mix growth. But coding professionals need to understand the data and which groups of patients have potential for movement. Generally, obstetric patients will remain in subclasses 1 and 2. These patients will only obtain a subclass of 4 if they have an extremely poor outcome, such as stroke or pulmonary embolism following delivery. Psychiatric APR-DRGs generally will not be classified to subclass 4 unless ECT therapy is performed. Coding professionals should analyze reports to determine their facility's distribution between the SOI subclass within each APR against other similar facilities to identify areas of opportunity.

Unique Implementation Strategies

Implementation strategies became a significant component to achieving success under the APR-DRG system.

Complete, accurate documentation and complete, accurate coding are the two components that must be present to achieve success under this classification system. The days of documenting just one CC are gone. Now, all significant conditions impacting a patient's stay must be completely and accurately documented by a physician.

Clinical Documentation Improvement (CDI) Implementation

Clinical documentation improvement programs were established in most facilities in Maryland to help achieve the economic success of the new severity-based classification system. Facilities quickly realized the value that these programs have on improving the accuracy and completeness of documentation, which provides the facility with the information that is required to capture patient acuity, severity, and outcome data. This was a necessary process to ensure that all conditions are accounted for—those for which the patient is being treated and/or impacting the patient stay. Many hospitals now have clinical documentation specialists with a clinical background performing concurrent reviews on the medical records to obtain this additional documentation. The focus of the CDI program is to work with physicians to bridge the gap between clinical terminology and the ICD-9-CM language. These documentation specialists also participate in nursing rounds to help better understand the conditions impacting the length of stay or that require special treatment plans. They also are able to help with the specificity of the individual ICD-9-CM codes that impact the SOI and to ask multiple questions of the physicians. As stated earlier, the SOI is impacted by the interaction of multiple secondary conditions; therefore, all secondary conditions need to be documented. There can be times when the CDI employee will ask multiple questions on one record. If the facility does not have a solid documentation improvement program in place, the number of retrospective queries could become uncontrollable.

Forms

Evaluation and redesign of forms was also a significant factor in the implementation of APR-DRGs. Forms such as nutritional notes contain significant diagnoses that impact the SOI, but a licensed treating physician did not generally document the information written on these forms in the medical record. Therefore, these forms were redesigned to include the physician signature and a statement that the physician agreed with the assessment of the licensed nutritionist. This allowed coders to add the diagnosis of malnutrition to the medical record, and often, the specific type of malnutrition was included in the nutritional documentation. The specificity of the malnutrition does impact SOI. For example, the diagnoses of kwashiorkor has a standard SOI level of "4", whereas protein-calorie malnutrition NOS has a standard SOI level of "3".

The other important item on the nutritional note was the documentation of the BMI. The addition of the V-codes for BMI can impact SOI.

Redesign of other forms, such as the anesthesia evaluation form, has made them more valuable tools. Common chronic conditions and common general conditions affecting patient care were listed under specific body systems, making them easily available for the physician to list as additional secondary diagnoses. Redesign of history and physical forms and standard doctor order sheets to include common conditions impacting SOI also was implemented. Standard physician order sheets for insulin therapy now include the reminder prompt for Uncontrolled diabetes and Other manifestations associated with diabetes.

As was also done under the CMS-DRG system, specific doctor tips cards/sheets were developed to identify common conditions that impact specific specialties within the APR-DRG system. These tips include common diagnoses that impact the APR-DRGs but were frequently not documented by the physician.

Retrospective Queries

Retrospective queries are still a significant component for the accurate assignment of the APR and SOI level. The query process is extremely important to the success of the hospital's case mix. The documentation improvement program at the facility helps eliminate some of the retrospective queries but will never completely eliminate the retrospective process. Because of the detailed level of coding that is required for the accurate assignment of the APR and SOI, the retrospective query process has expanded. Many hospitals developed electronic query databases to manage this process. These databases help to make the queries more compliant by standardizing some of the information and help to monitor the response rate of the process. Reports of outstanding queries can be generated for follow-up, and reports can be generated to help track where additional physician education is needed.

Physician Advisors

With the implementation of APR-DRG or any severity-based DRG system, the hospitals need to develop strategies for improving physician documentation in the hospital records and to obtain physician buy-in. The hospital's reimbursement and patient care practices hinge on accurate and appropriate physician documentation. Documentation issues often occur when physicians lack a sufficient understanding of the methodology behind coding and how documentation, or the lack of it, affects proper coding. Coding guidelines prohibit the coding professional from making clinical judgments in the absence of proper documentation, and some coders are hesitant to approach physicians when information is ambiguous or needs clarification. An effective way to promote better documentation is through the use of a physician advisor. The physician advisor can assist with communication between the coder and the physician. The physician advisor can be responsible for contacting the attending physician regarding documentation issues, as well as providing education to the physicians on specific coding challenges and documentation issues. The physician advisor can help provide the communication link needed between the coders and physicians. The physician advisor can also provide coder training on disease processes and help communicate proper documentation strategies to the physicians through newsletters.

Policy Changes

Policy changes for the implementation of APR-DRGs included the requirement of indications for all medications ordered. This was an effective way to improve patient quality care and to assist the coders with coding all secondary diagnoses that were being treated during the hospital stay. It provided coders with the necessary link between the diagnosis and treatment.

Another policy change that occurred involved revisiting the productivity and quality standards for the coders. As complete coding became more essential and coders began querying the physicians more frequently for additional documentation, productivity standards needed to be adjusted. Coder quality and accuracy rates needed to be adjusted to include the possibility of APR-DRG and SOI changes.

Other policy changes included the extension of hospital-specific bill holds and the need for additional reviews. Because all secondary diagnoses can have an impact on the SOI level, which in turn impacts case mix, hospitals had to evaluate the need for additional audits and/or second-level reviews. These second-level reviews provided an opportunity to reevaluate the documentation in the medical record to accurately assign APR-DRGs and SOIs. Sometimes additional information was obtained from reports that were not available to the coder during the initial coding process. Hospitals developed internal audit databases to help monitor and trend retrospective changes to records and used the information obtained from database reports to help streamline coder education and physician education.

Policies regarding the extent of procedure coding also needed to be adjusted. Non-OR procedures that had no impact on CMS-DRGs do have an impact on APR-DRGs and/or SOI levels. Therefore, facilities needed to include these in the policies of non-OR procedures to be coded by the health information management (HIM) department.

Summary

The implementation of APR-DRGs for Maryland hospitals proved to be challenging, as is any major change, but it also brought about many positive changes. Developing a transition team consisting of members from HIM, finance, IS, and physician support was an initial and important step to a successful implementation. This transition team helped to provide teamwork and support for the new classification system.

Maryland hospitals are now approaching their third year of using the APR-DRG classification system to measure case mix growth. The positive changes from this transition include better quality coding, improved documentation, and coding professionals who are better educated about disease processes and pharmacology. Maryland hospitals have seen an increase in their case mix and are reviewing the reasons for the increase. The hospitals continue to analyze their data to track root APR-DRG case mix growth changes versus SOI case mix growth to help determine real case mix growth versus case mix growth due to coding changes. Maryland hospitals will continue to monitor the changes in case mix and coding practices to eliminate case mix changes due to overcoding and/or undercoding. A severity-based APR-DRG classification system does classify patients more accurately, but it also will challenge coding staff and physicians to continue accurate coding practices and to provide complete documentation.

References

Averill, Richard F., Norbert Goldfield, M.D., Jack S. Hughes, M.D., et al. 2003. *All Patient Refined Diagnosis Related Groups, Definitions Manual, Version 20.0*, Volume 1, 2, and 3. Wallingford, CT: 3M Health Information Systems.

Centers for Medicare and Medicaid Services (CMS) and the National Center for Health Statistics (NCHS). 2006. *ICD-9-CM Official Guidelines for Coding and Reporting*. Available online from www.cdc.gov/nchs/datawh/ftpserv/ftpicd9/ftpicd9.htm

American Hospital Association. 2005. *Coding Clinic for ICD-9-CM* 96–98(4).

Chapter 5

Ready, Set, Implement!

Before Moving Forward, Learn From the Past

The migration to the MS-DRG is the most significant change to the Inpatient Prospective Payment System (IPPS) since the implementation of DRGs in 1983. HIM professionals who were practicing at that time probably recall the challenges and opportunities for improved documentation that were realized when DRGs were implemented. Although much time and many resources have been invested to improve processes in the acute care setting, some facilities continue to struggle to get the level of documentation needed for coding specificity. As a result, clinical documentation improvement (CDI) programs have emerged in an effort to help educate clinicians and form partnerships with the coding staff.

Apart from the IPPS methodology, healthcare has undergone other prospective payment systems that were developed to help control the costs associated with the care of the Medicare population. These prospective payment systems were adopted in many cases by other payers, such as Medicaid, Champus, and commercial payers, such as Blue Cross and Blue Shield.

Some of the payment methodologies developed in previous years include:

- Ambulatory Payment Groups (APGs)
- Ambulatory Payment Classifications (APCs) (This included the use of modifiers and the application of National Correct Coding Initiative (NCCI) edits for hospital outpatients.)
- PPS for skilled nursing facilities
- Inpatient rehabilitation
- Long-term care hospitals
- Inpatient psychiatric facilities
- Home care

Each facility has experienced its own challenges in implementing each of these payment methodologies, depending on many factors, including urban versus rural settings, profit versus nonprofit status, the medical staff, hospital administration, and governing boards. A good look at that history may provide insight into what made the transition easy or difficult at the time. Moving forward to the implementation to the MS-DRG, facilities must use these experiences to apply what worked and learn from what did not work. This won't guarantee a smooth transition, but it certainly can't hurt!

Starting Over: It's a New Methodology With New Guidelines

Before rolling out MS-DRG education programs, facilities must thoroughly understand the new regulations. To win, a coach must be able to lead the team to the finish line. Facilities must be prepared to answer difficult questions and to support their recommendations with facts and data; anecdotal information is not credible when presenting changes of this magnitude. The information regarding MS-DRGs is readily available on the CMS Web site and in the *Federal Register*.

Once a facility understands the MS-DRG system, its methodology, and its impact on the organization, the rollout within the organization can get underway. The first step in that process is to gain administrative support. Administrative endorsement is critical to the success of a facility's educational efforts. The first meeting will likely be with the person leading the rollout and the hospital administrator or chief financial officer. At this initial meeting, the person leading the rollout should provide a high-level presentation outlining the key elements of the IPPS and the operational and financial impact to the organization.

Because this is such a major change to the IPPS, additional presentations (again at a high level) should be made to the Chief Medical Officer (CMO) and the governing board. In the meeting with the CMO, the rollout leader should focus on issues that will relate to physician documentation, the impact on the organization, and the need for a physician champion or advisor in the organization. Buy-in from the medical staff will be smoother if an individual who is well respected by the medical staff works as a liaison to the physicians.

A very brief overview of the changes should also be made to the governing board. They need to understand the changes in methodology, the potential financial impact, and operational issues associated with this change.

Training for Key Groups

Various groups within the organization need training, and in most cases, that training should be customized to each group's specific needs in terms of its operational issues.

Health Information Management Leadership and Coding Professionals

This group has a comprehensive understanding of the Medicare or CMS-DRG; therefore, training for this group needs to emphasize the structure of the MS-DRG, its format, and logic, including the revision of the complication and comorbidity (CC) structure. These changes to the CC list completely overhaul the list as well as the methodology behind it. The CMS-DRG had groups of DRG pairs, which were DRGs with and without CC (for example, DRG 90 [Simple pneumonia without CC] and DRG 89 [Simple pneumonia with CC]). Some DRGs did not have a CC pair, such as DRG 143 (Chest pain).

The MS-DRG contains DRGs with or without CCs, major complications and comorbidities (MCC), no CC, or a combination of these. Coding professionals need to understand this methodology and to be able to identify when a significant CC may be present and when to query the physician for clarification. Use of queries should always follow AHIMA's Practice Brief policies and procedures on the use of a query in Appendix C.

Another area to address is the reference the RAND Corporation[3] report made in the difference between "efficient" coding and "complete" coding. That report indicated that some coding professionals have been coding efficiently, which was defined as coding until a CC condition was found and then ending the coding session for that encounter. However, complete coding requires the coding professional to code all applicable

diagnoses and procedures according to official coding guidelines. If coding professionals have not been coding "completely" this should be addressed, not only for the benefit of having a higher MS-DRG, but also so the quality of the data best reflects the care and treatment of the patient. Reimbursement is not the only incentive for accurate coding. ICD-9-CM diagnosis and procedure codes are used to ensure data validity for research, quality initiatives, financial planning, and clinical program best practice development, just to name a few. If coding professionals have been following official coding guidelines, they have been coding completely all along.

Medicare believes that all hospitals will experience potential case mix growth due to improved coding and documentation and coding changes. As a result, CMS will reduce the standardized payment amounts over a 3-year period. For FY2008, the adjustment will be 1.2 percent. Then the adjustment will be 1.8 percent for the next 2 years. The total standardized payment reduction over the 3-year period will be 4.8 percent. This payment reduction is meant to offset any improvement in documentation and/or coding.

Contract Coding Professionals

If a facility hires contract coding professionals for backlogs or during vacations for coding staff, this issue must be addressed with the coding vendor to ensure that the temporary coding professionals code completely. In some cases, contract coding professionals are paid by production, which may become an incentive for efficient coding. Contracting for a per hour rate may circumvent that incentive.

Present on Admission and Query Process

Although the present on admission (POA) indicator is not part of the MS-DRG, it does affect coding and is being implemented at the same time as the new IPPS. Coding professionals should be trained on the appropriate use of the POA indicator and should query the physician when necessary. The query process is typically retrospective, but it can be a concurrent process when the facility has either concurrent coding professionals or a clinical documentation improvement program using either coding professionals or nurses who communicate with the physician during the patient's stay. Having a concurrent process in place will help to lower the discharge not final billed (DNFB) days and avoid having to wait for a response after the patient has been discharged. The query process is the same for both the POA indicator and for clarification regarding diagnoses or procedures. Incorporating the query for the POA indicator on existing query forms will ensure that the physician only has to respond to one form.

Finance Department

The finance department will need fewer details than the coding staff; they need to understand the *basic* methodology of the MS-DRG and the influence it will have on the case mix index (CMI). The finance department uses the CMI for financial planning and forecasting, which will be more difficult in the first few years of migration to the MS-DRG. Because the CMS-DRG and the MS-DRG are structured differently and have different relative weights, a comparison of the two is almost impossible. Various vendors offer the service of regrouping historical CMS-DRG data files into MS-DRG data files to help facilitate a more meaningful comparison; facilities should consider this as an option. Many facilities have used APR-DRGs in concert with the CMS-DRG, using the APR-DRG as a measure of severity of illness (SOI). Facilities may want to consider keeping the APR-DRG grouper as a point of comparison.

It is critical for the finance department to understand that the DNFB will likely be affected by increased queries for specificity in diagnoses and by the POA indicator. The CFO must understand the need for coding professionals to query and support that process even when it increases the DNFB. Past experience with DRGs and attempts to educate physicians indicates that it will be a long and sometimes uphill battle to accomplish effective training. Having the support of finance and administration will be helpful.

Payer Contracting

Another issue that must be addressed is in the area of payer contracting. Many non-Medicare payers contract with hospitals to provide payment based on the CMS-DRG, and some facilities are planning on retaining the CMS-DRG for the purpose of continued support in that payment methodology. However, this is not an option if the facility and payer want to have a DRG that is updated annually. Currently, CMS reviews and recalibrates DRGs annually based on an analysis of submitted claims. CMS will not continue to do that after the implementation of the MS-DRG. Therefore, if a vendor would continue to support the CMS-DRG grouper, it would be supporting the grouper as it currently exists without any annual changes. This would not support any new technology, new codes and DRGs, or recalibration due to costs. It is critical that the finance department and third-party payers understand this as

they move forward and make decisions on how to contract for payment to the healthcare facility. Options could be to migrate to the MS-DRG, APR-DRG, or payment based on a percentage of billed charges. Past experience with third-party payers (including Medicaid and other federal payments) indicates that other payers often adopt payment methodologies used by CMS. Therefore, it is likely that third-party payers also will want to adjust payments based on the POA indicator. HIM professionals should take this opportunity to educate third-party payers contracting with their facility to help in the transition to the new IPPS.

Replacement of Implanted Devices

Finally, as part of the proposed rule, CMS is changing the method by which hospitals are reimbursed for implants that are provided to them at low or no cost. Although this change is not part of the MS-DRG, it is part of the proposed rule, and it will both affect reimbursement and be a cumbersome manual process. Hospitals will be required to submit an invoice with the claim, which will need to state the amount the hospital paid for the device along with documentation of the usual cost of the device. The claim will then be suspended by the fiscal intermediary for calculation of a reduced payment.

Physician Education

This will be one of the most challenging aspects of the implementation process because physicians are inundated with regulations and paperwork and just want to care for their patients. They often do not see why a query is necessary and question why the coding professional can't make a determination himself or herself. For example, an obstetrical patient's chart had documentation of a second-degree perineal laceration. The coding professional did not see documentation in the record of a repair of the laceration and generated a query for the physician asking if this was repaired. The physician responded verbally (in the middle of the department), shouting, "Of course it was repaired. Do you think I would not repair a second-degree laceration?" This behavior from physicians discourages coding professionals from using the query process, which results in incomplete diagnoses or coding of procedures by the coding professional and poor data collection.

Improving Communication Between the Physician and the Coding Professional

What can be done to improve the communication between the physician and coding professional? The use of physician advisors or champions, which has been discussed in previous chapters, may help. A physician will be more likely to listen to and discuss coding issues with another physician than a coding professional because the physician "knows what he or she is talking about." Hospitals may want to consider hiring a physician to work with the coding supervisor or manager as a liaison to the medical staff.

Another method of physician education would be to form a partnership between quality management or care management and the coding or HIM manager. HIM certainly has the background to address technical issues, but the physician is more likely to respond in a positive way to another clinician. These are not the only methods of physician education. What works for one organization may not work for another, so any viable option would be worth trying. Key members of the organization should do some brainstorming to develop a plan for physician education. Physicians who are employed by an organization may be more accessible and

more likely to listen and work together in an educational process. A physician education program should have three main objectives: (1) to provide the physicians with the information, (2) to determine the information to provide to them, and (3) to show the physicians that an educational program will provide some benefit to them.

Benefits for the Physicians

Physicians are sometimes reluctant to spend the time or energy on initiatives that they believe have no direct impact on or benefit for them. Figure 5.1 provides brainstorming ideas that may help start the educational process. One additional option for convincing physicians to participate in an educational program is to suggest that they support this initiative because it is critical to the organization and then explain why.

When implementing a physician education program, the information should be presented as concisely

Figure 5.1   Brainstorming Ideas to start the Educational Process

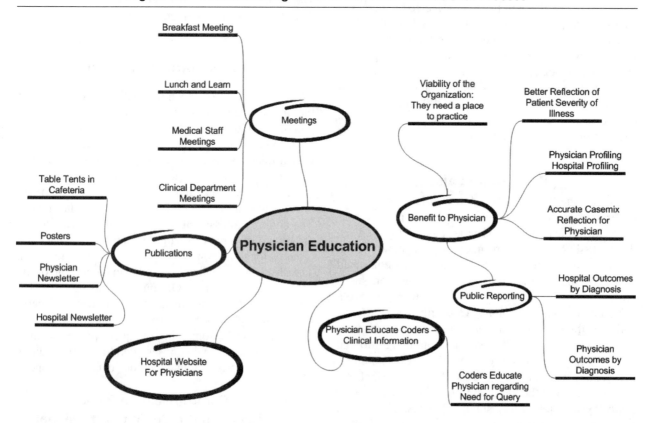

as possible. Only the information that is absolutely necessary to communicate what the expectations are for acceptable documentation should be presented. To clarify such significant changes as the MS-DRG and POA indicators, information should be presented in segments in different formats and media. Organizations may want conduct physician education programs quarterly or monthly, focusing on one or two topics. For example, the first quarterly update could focus on the POA indicator and the new IPPS and how that will generate more queries. And the next quarterly update could focus on the importance of documenting the patient's stage in chronic renal failure. Whichever schedule and method are used, all elements of each educational program should focus on the same issue. For example, education on the types of congestive heart failure that are specified in ICD-9-CM might be prepsented on posters, table tents in the physician's dining room, newsletters, and the hospital Web site for physicians. The educational objective is that less is more. Presenting less information in small increments is more effective than presenting a massive amount of coding and documentation information all at once.

Physicians need to understand that it is critical that they follow approved documentation practices and that following these practices will lead to an increase in queries. Often, physicians do not realize that ICD-9-CM codes exist to specify the stages. Physicians are familiar with CPT codes because that is the classification by which they are reimbursed. Because ICD-9-CM really has not affected their payment, they have not considered it an important area of focus.

Clinical Programs

If an organization has protocols for specific clinical programs, applicable information regarding MS-DRGs that relate to the clinical program could be presented at those meetings. Most clinical programs use APR-DRGs or CMS-DRGs as benchmarks for data analysis, and movement to the MS-DRG will impact that process and the outcome of analysis. A high-level overview comparing the MS-DRG grouper to the previous DRG method will be critical, along with a detailed explanation of the CC and MCC schematic approach. Figure 5.2 illustrates how movement to the revised CC methodology relates to the APR-DRG severity rating. Figure 5.3 denotes the structure of the base MS-DRG and the subsequent split to CC and MCC groupings.

Each clinical program or clinical department meeting could emphasize diagnoses and/or procedures

Figure 5.2   CC Severity Levels

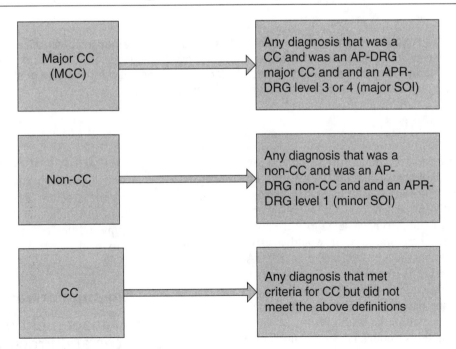

Figure 5.3   Structure of MS-DRG

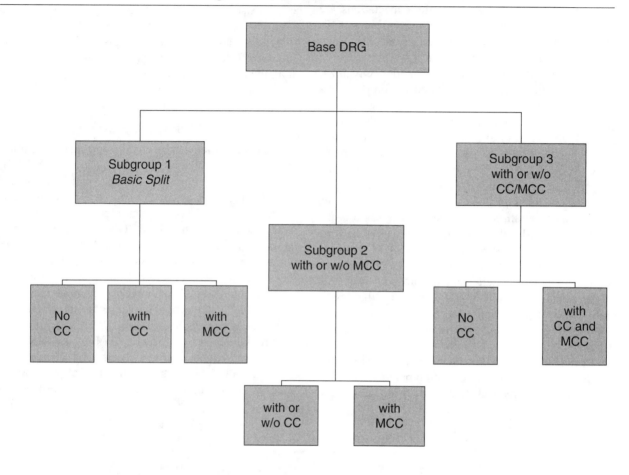

Medicare's revised CC list includes significant acute disease, acute exacerbations of significant chronic diseases, advanced or end-stage chronic diseases, and chronic diseases associated with extensive debility. (Significant acute disease includes acute myocardial infarction, cerebrovascular accident or stroke, acute respiratory failure, acute renal failure, pneumonic, septicemia, etc.)

that are relevant to that program. For example, a presentation to pulmonologists could describe respiratory MS-DRGs and the need to document any chronic respiratory conditions (such as COPD or chronic respiratory failure) that also have acute exacerbations or other systemic symptomology. It would also be important to document the acute exacerbation as POA, or not POA. It is essential for physicians to understand that complete and accurate documentation is critical in ensuring that the patient's condition and treatment are adequately reflected in the health record.

These presentations should be short—no longer than 15 minutes each—as there are other critical issues on the meeting agendas.

Other Critical Groups

Other groups and/or departments will also need some education regarding the structure of MS-DRGs and the requirement for the POA indicator. Table 5.1 outlines some of those groups and the information that needs to be communicated to them.

Moving Forward

Effective Management of Coding Services and Processes

Effective management of coding department processes includes analyzing those processes and improving them so

Table 5.1 Key Areas for Training		
Department or Group	**Information to Be Presented**	**Key Points**
Infection Control	• **Conditions that are POA:** – High cost or high volume or both – Results in the assignment of a case to a DRG that has a higher payment when present as a secondary diagnosis – Could reasonably have been prevented through application of evidence-based guidelines • **High-level overview of the MS-DRG**	Those conditions in the Final Rule of the *Federal Register* determined to have been hospital-acquired conditions may affect payment reduction
Case Management	• **High-level overview of MS-DRG** • **Compare/contrast the CMS-DRG and MS-DRG** • **Postacute care transfer** • **Deficit Reduction Act**	• Differentiate between CMS-DRG complications and comorbidities and MS-DRG CC and MCC structure • Transfer policy applies to each MS-DRG that shares a base MS DRG if one of the MS-DRGs within the base MS-DRG qualifies for a postacute care transfer payment – Critical to have disposition of patient documented in a consistent place in the health record • Hospital-acquired conditions on POA policy
Case Mix Users	• **Detailed overview of MS-DRG** • **POA Indicator**	• Comprehensive review of MS DRG format and logic • Description of CC and MCC methodology • Discussion of effect on case mix and analysis of data (retrospectively and prospectively) • Inclusion of the POA indicator and internal uses for that information
Compliance Department	• **High-level overview of MS-DRG** • **Compare/contrast the CMS-DRG and MS-DRG** • **Postacute care transfers** • **Deficit Reduction Act and POA requirement**	• Forecasting Quality Improvement Organization's (QIO) activities – PEPPER Reports (CC/MCC conditions) – Transfer policy – Quality of care reviews

they are efficient and adaptable. The changes to the IPPS and collection of POA indicators present a challenge to the coding department because it will need more time to determine whether conditions are POA and will increase the need for physician queries.

Even when HIM coding functions have been evaluated and refined through process change, organizations should reevaluate those functions and perform a staffing analysis to ensure the HIM department has adequate staff to meet the additional coding functions, which include increased communications with the physician.

Process Management in HIM

Organizations should conduct a process analysis to gain a thorough understanding of the current coding process, asking the following questions:

1. Can improvements be made to better use the existing staff?
2. What noncoding functions does the coding staff complete?
3. Is there a way to simplify the process and work "smarter" by eliminating and/or reassigning noncoding functions?

Published estimates predict that coding productivity will increase by up to 20 percent and may increase even more in facilities in which coding professionals are and have always coded "completely." However, even in these cases, productivity will decrease somewhat because of the need to query more often for the POA and specificity in chronic conditions. Productivity is affected not only by the time it takes to write the query (which in some cases can be a macro in word-processing or encoder software) but also by the time it takes to re-review the record and make any necessary adjustments to the coding for an encounter once the physician responds to the query.

Analysis of the impact of the IPPS and POA coding requirements should be conducted and productivity standards should be refined to reflect those changes. For example, a study could be completed in which the coding professional completes a query form for additional specificity and/or for POA clarification for a 2-week period. At the same time, the coding professional could collect their coding productivity. Then these analyses could be compared with those over a 2-week period prior to the changes. Once this comparison is completed, the HIM coding manager should ask this question: How many coding professionals does the HIM department need? When calculating the number of coding professionals needed to meet the required

coding hours per day, the coding manager should use the number of annual budgeted hours per coding professional minus the number of hours per year that each coding professional accrues for vacation, sick leave, and other activities that take the coding professional away from work, such as training and meetings.

Cross Training

If the change in productivity is significant, there are options other than hiring more coding professionals. If the coding department is large, are all coding professionals cross trained? If not, cross training would give the facility optimal resources. For example, outpatient coding professionals could be cross trained to help cover the inpatient workload and inpatient coding professionals who specialize in areas such as OB, newborn, or non-Medicare accounts, could be cross trained to code all types and payers.

Coding professionals do not always see cross training as beneficial to them. But it can be when it expands their career path opportunity so they can gain expertise coding multiple patient types, which will enable them to progress to higher job classifications, salaries, and leadership roles within their organizations. For organizations, these opportunities for career expansion provide incentives that help them retain their current coding professionals and recruit new ones in a competitive market. Depending on the model developed, career path expansion also can increase productivity promoting cross training.

An alternative to career path expansion may be an incentive program, which can be monetary or nonmonetary (such as movie tickets, free lunch coupons, candy bars, or an extra hour off). Every option for recognition should be considered when looking at an incentive program, and an organization's human resources department should be consulted before implementing any such incentive or career path expansion program.

Other Process Improvement

What else can be done to increase productivity or improve existing processes? The IPPS changes and POA requirement will increase the query process, and facilities should have a concurrent query process or clinical documentation improvement (CDI) program. If coding professionals have the opportunity to query physicians concurrently, it will help to elicit a response prior to discharge, which will eliminate the need for querying after discharge and will allow the record to be coded and billed in a timely manner. This benefits the organization by keeping DNFB down, prevents physicians from being inundated with retrospective queries, and encourages better and more timely communication between physicians and the coding professionals.

Organizations that do not have CDI programs may want to evaluate the need for one. A CDI program may use either coding professionals or nurses or may be a hybrid program that uses both to communicate with and query physicians on a concurrent basis. In some cases, using a clinical professional such as a nurse is more successful than using a coding professional for the same reason having a physician advisor works so well—it involves one clinical professional speaking with another.

What about the query itself? Most facilities have standard query forms, and many have forms for specific questions regarding such as topics as diabetes mellitus and its related complications. If such a query is needed, along with a POA for the same patient (such as, Was the diabetes mellitus out of control at the time of admission?), facilities should consider creating forms that will incorporate both questions. This will save time for both coding professionals and physicians.

Beyond Coding

Monitoring Coding and the Case Mix

How do facilities monitor coding in the new IPPS to ensure that coding professionals are not underutilizing or overutilizing MS-DRGs? In the past, most organizations have used MedPar as a benchmark for their case mix. Variances are then identified and records reviewed proactively to ensure quality of coded data. Those reports look at the CMS-DRG pairs (with and without CC) or may compare one DRG to another, such as transient ischemic attack (TIA) versus cerebrovascular accident (CVA).

Until MedPar has comparison data (which may be anywhere from 2 to 3 years from the implementation of the MS-DRG), organizations should develop internal monitoring mechanisms of their own by comparing their data to a predetermined threshold. For instance, does the organization have greater than 11 percent of a particular MS-DRG falling into a MS-DRG with MCCs? If so, that may be an indication to review those cases to ensure that the coding is accurate. In large organizations with multiple acute care facilities, this may include benchmarking with other like-size facilities as well. If an organization uses MedPar as a benchmark, it could look at a variance in CMS-DRGs based on a percentage (such as 10 percent or more).

Another area that has a large volume of historical data is in the CMI, which is used as a benchmark for SOI and financial planning. Relative weights will be very different in the MS-DRG, which will make historical comparison difficult at best. So facilities should develop a way to trend SOI comparing the MS-DRG or APR-DRG to the previous CMS-DRG.

Coding validation reviews are one characteristic of a good coding compliance plan. Proactive coding reviews should be completed at least once a year on all patient types, but more than one review is recommended. Proactive reviews are coding reviews in which there is no suspected coding error. Such reviews are completed as a monitoring tool. But when an error or problem is suspected or known, that review is no longer a proactive review but rather a compliance review. Compliance reviews should be conducted when identified, regardless of the number of times in a given year.

Because the MS-DRG and POA indicators are new to coding professionals, facilities should increase their proactive coding reviews to ensure quality of coding and to identify any potential problems in either coding or documentation. Facilities can use the previously described monitoring method to determine which MS-DRGs should be reviewed. For example, if base MS-DRGs (with or without CC or MCC) have a significant variance, they should be reviewed to determine that certain groups are not overcoded or undercoded. The review may not show any coding errors, but it is still needed to validate that coding is accurate and that the HIM compliance plan is being followed. The review may show opportunities for improved documentation, and that information should be communicated to the appropriate medical staff for follow-up.

Query Rates

Keeping track of query results can be tremendously beneficial because it allows facilities to identify what types of queries have been generated. For example, do particular physicians tend to have more queries than others? Does one or more clinical departments query more than others? If that is the case, the HIM coding manager or director should address these situations by speaking with the medical staff director or physician advisor/champion. It is the responsibility of the HIM department to identify the deficiencies and the need for documentation improvement, but ultimately it is a responsibility of the medical staff to address those needs and make improvements.

Development of an IPPS Team

This chapter began with a discussion of previous inpatient and outpatient prospective payment systems and what had or had not worked in organizations when they were implemented. Teams that have implemented such systems have been referred to by many names, such as the IPPS team, the DRG team, or the APC team. But whatever their name, their goals and objectives were the same: to ensure that the coding and grouping of the DRG or APC was complete and accurate.

Although the MS-DRG isn't completely different from the CMS-DRG, there are enough differences that it does require an implementation team to ensure a smooth transition. As with any other team, there needs to be a reporting structure. What person or committee is ultimately responsible for the success of the IPPS team? Who has the executive responsibility to make sure there is a smooth migration from the CMS-DRG to MS-DRG? The group charged with this responsibility may differ from one organization to another. It could be finance, case mix, patient accounting, or clinical programs. Each organization must make that determination. Once the reporting structure is determined, the team members should be selected. Membership should include staff from the following areas:

- Team lead (HIM coding manager)
- Physician advisor or liaison
- Finance
- Quality/case management
- Case mix staff (decision support)
- Clinical programs representative (ad hoc)
- Others (ad hoc)

Once the team has been assembled it is important to determine and state the purpose of the team and the reporting structure. Once that has been discussed, the following steps should be taken:

- Determine the mission statement and objectives
- Determine the frequency of meetings
- Determine the ground rules
- Identify customers (internal and external) and
- their requirements

The agenda for meetings will vary depending on the organization's objectives. Each member should be responsible for monitoring and/or reporting some area of variance to the team. For example, the coding manager may report on coding validation review outcomes, the quality management representative may report on conditions not POA and efforts to reduce those incidents, or the case mix representative may report on the CMI for discussion on variances.

When applicable, team members should be assigned to follow-up. Such assignments may include inviting ad hoc members to the next meeting to discuss variances and possible solutions (for example, inviting a member

of cardiac clinical programs to discuss documentation of congestive heart failure with acute manifestations). Finally, the team lead should report the team's findings to the individual or committee responsible for the IPPS team. This is a continual process that remains in place until it is determined that additional meetings will only be required on an as-needed basis.

A Look to the Future: Forecasting

What does the future hold for HIM and coding? Every day offers unique challenges presented by regulatory and technological changes, and HIM and healthcare organizations must remain ready to take on those challenges. As healthcare organizations develop electronic health records (EHR), it is imperative that they consider the importance of capturing specificity in the documentation at the time of entry. This will help to reduce the need for physician queries. Enhancements to electronic documentation may include prompts to the physician. For example, if "anemia" is documented, a program may ask the physician to specify the type of anemia.

The following other issues may or may not be implemented at this time, but they are being considered by regulatory entities:

Future changes to the IPPS. As this book has discussed, the CMS proposed rule is to implement the MS-DRG for FY2008. However, the final RAND Corporation report will not be published until after the MS-DRG is implemented. Depending on the final recommendation, CMS may decide to select another methodology for the severity refined grouping and may implement an alternative methodology for the following year. This will impact healthcare operations as dramatically as the implementation of the MS-DRG and will require retraining in all areas affected and discussed in this chapter.

The final rule included eight conditions that will be subject to the rule effective October 1, 2007, and will impact payment if not POA October 8, 2008. In addition, CMS has identified three additional conditions to be added to the list for FY2009. CMS has indicated that additional conditions will be added as they meet the criteria set by CMS, including having a unique code.

Healthcare organizations are experiencing pay-for-performance initiatives, such as Hospital Reporting of Quality Data. Those elements required for submission continue to grow and healthcare organizations will need additional resources to abstract and submit these elements to CMS.

What about pay-for-performance for physicians? Will CMS also require physicians to meet certain quality measures to be reimbursed for their services? Currently physicians are reimbursed by submission of CPT codes describing services rendered. Will this practice continue? Will quality measures and ICD-9-CM codes also be added to the equation?

The financial impact will be felt in FY2008 and will need to be considered by healthcare organizations' financial departments. Process improvement initiatives should be ongoing to ensure the best use of resources.

Finally, is the HIM department staffed for these challenges? Should resources be reallocated? What can organizations do to prepare for future challenges and change? These are significant issues and it is critical that healthcare organizations keep current with proposed legislation and comment to CMS on proposed rules. The HIM professional can play an important role in any organization regarding changes to coding, documentation, and IPPS methodologies.

References

CMS Web site. Accessed at: http://cms.hhs.gov/AcuteInpatientPPS/

Federal Register. Accessed at: http://www.access.gpo.gov/su_docs/fedreg/a070503c.html

Interim RAND Corporation Report on the Evaluation of Severity-Adjusted DRGs. Accessed at: http://cms.hhs.gov/Reports/downloads/Wynn0307.pdf

Additional Resources

Orenstein, A. *Effective Management of Coding Services: Performance Management and Process Improvement* (3rd ed). Chicago: AHIMA.

Orenstein A., Clemens B., Dalton C.: 2007. A coding career path. *Journal of AHIMA,* July/August.

Appendix A

MS-DRG Tables

The following links will provide lists of DRGs with their relative weights for short-term and long-term care hospitals. These links will also provide the Crosswalks and MS-DRG Summary Table.

Short-Term

http://www.cms.hhs.gov/AcuteInpatientPPS/01_overview.asp

Select Acute Inpatient Files for Download. Sort by Year 2008. Select Table 5-List of MS-DRG, Relative Weighting Factors, and Geometric and Arithmetic Mean Length of Stay.

Long-Term

http://www.cms.hhs.gov/AcuteInpatientPPS/IPPS/list.asp#TopOfPage

Sort by year 2008. Select CMS-1533-FC. Go to Table 11 FY 2008 MS-LTC-DRGs, Relative Weights, Geometric Average Length of Stay, Short Stay Outlier Threshold and IPPS Comparable Threshold.

Appendix B

2007 CMS DRG CC and 2008 MS-DRG CC/MCC Table

2008 ICD-9-CM	CMS DRG	MS-DRG	Short Title
0010		MS-DRG CC	CHOLERA D/T VIB CHOLERAE
0011		MS-DRG CC	CHOLERA D/T VIB EL TOR
0019		MS-DRG CC	CHOLERA NOS
0020		MS-DRG CC	TYPHOID FEVER
0021		MS-DRG CC	PARATYPHOID FEVER A
0022		MS-DRG CC	PARATYPHOID FEVER B
0023		MS-DRG CC	PARATYPHOID FEVER C
0029		MS-DRG CC	PARATYPHOID FEVER NOS
0030		MS-DRG CC	SALMONELLA ENTERITIS
0031		MS-DRG MCC	SALMONELLA SEPTICEMIA
00321		MS-DRG MCC	SALMONELLA MENINGITIS
00322		MS-DRG MCC	SALMONELLA PNEUMONIA
00323		MS-DRG CC	SALMONELLA ARTHRITIS
00324		MS-DRG CC	SALMONELLA OSTEOMYELITIS
00329		MS-DRG CC	LOCAL SALMONELLA INF NEC
0038		MS-DRG CC	SALMONELLA INFECTION NEC
0039		MS-DRG CC	SALMONELLA INFECTION NOS
0040		MS-DRG CC	SHIGELLA DYSENTERIAE
0050		MS-DRG CC	STAPH FOOD POISONING
0051		MS-DRG CC	BOTULISM FOOD POISONING
0052		MS-DRG CC	FOOD POIS D/T C. PERFRIN
0053		MS-DRG CC	FOOD POIS: CLOSTRID NEC
0054		MS-DRG CC	FOOD POIS: V. PARAHAEM

(Continued)

2008 ICD-9-CM	CMS DRG	MS-DRG	Short Title
00581		MS-DRG CC	FOOD POISN D/T V. VULNIF
00589		MS-DRG CC	BACT FOOD POISONING NEC
0060		MS-DRG CC	AC AMEBIASIS W/O ABSCESS
0061		MS-DRG CC	CHR AMEBIASIS W/O ABSCESS
0062		MS-DRG CC	AMEBIC NONDYSENT COLITIS
0063		MS-DRG MCC	AMEBIC LIVER ABSCESS
0064		MS-DRG MCC	AMEBIC LUNG ABSCESS
0065		MS-DRG MCC	AMEBIC BRAIN ABSCESS
0068		MS-DRG CC	AMEBIC INFECTION NEC
0071		MS-DRG CC	GIARDIASIS
0072		MS-DRG CC	COCCIDIOSIS
0074		MS-DRG CC	CRYPTOSPORIDIOSIS
0075		MS-DRG CC	CYCLOSPORIASIS
0078		MS-DRG CC	PROTOZOAL INTEST DIS NEC
0079		MS-DRG CC	PROTOZOAL INTEST DIS NOS
00800		MS-DRG CC	INTEST INFEC E COLI NOS
00801		MS-DRG CC	INT INF E COLI ENTRPATH
00802		MS-DRG CC	INT INF E COLI ENTRTOXGN
00803		MS-DRG CC	INT INF E COLI ENTRNVSV
00804		MS-DRG CC	INT INF E COLI ENTRHMRG
00809		MS-DRG CC	INT INF E COLI SPCF NEC
0081		MS-DRG CC	ARIZONA ENTERITIS
0082		MS-DRG CC	AEROBACTER ENTERITIS
0083		MS-DRG CC	PROTEUS ENTERITIS
00841	CMS CC	MS-DRG CC	STAPHYLOCOCC ENTERITIS
00842	CMS CC	MS-DRG CC	PSEUDOMONAS ENTERITIS
00843	CMS CC	MS-DRG CC	INT INFEC CAMPYLOBACTER
00844	CMS CC	MS-DRG CC	INT INF YRSNIA ENTRCLTCA
00845	CMS CC	MS-DRG CC	INT INF CLSTRDIUM DFCILE
00846	CMS CC	MS-DRG CC	INTES INFEC OTH ANAEROBES
00847	CMS CC	MS-DRG CC	INT INF OTH GRM NEG BCTR
00849	CMS CC	MS-DRG CC	BACTERIAL ENTERITIS NEC
0085		MS-DRG CC	BACTERIAL ENTERITIS NOS
00861		MS-DRG CC	INTES INFEC ROTAVIRUS
00862		MS-DRG CC	INTES INFEC ADENOVIRUS
00863		MS-DRG CC	INT INF NORWALK VIRUS
00864		MS-DRG CC	INT INF OTH SML RND VRUS
00865		MS-DRG CC	INTES INFEC CALCIVIRUS
00866		MS-DRG CC	INTES INFEC ASTROVIRUS

2008 ICD-9-CM	CMS DRG	MS-DRG	Short Title
00867		MS-DRG CC	INT INF ENTEROVIRUS NEC
00869		MS-DRG CC	OTHER VIRAL INTES INFEC
0090		MS-DRG CC	INFECTIOUS ENTERITIS NOS
0091		MS-DRG CC	ENTERITIS OF INFECT ORIG
0092		MS-DRG CC	INFECTIOUS DIARRHEA NOS
0093		MS-DRG CC	DIARRHEA OF INFECT ORIG
01000		MS-DRG CC	PRIM TB COMPLEX-UNSPEC
01001		MS-DRG CC	PRIM TB COMPLEX-NO EXAM
01002		MS-DRG CC	PRIM TB COMPLEX-EXM UNKN
01003		MS-DRG CC	PRIM TB COMPLEX-MICRO DX
01004		MS-DRG CC	PRIM TB COMPLEX-CULT DX
01005		MS-DRG CC	PRIM TB COMPLEX-HISTO DX
01006		MS-DRG CC	PRIM TB COMPLEX-OTH TEST
01010		MS-DRG CC	PRIM TB PLEURISY-UNSPEC
01011		MS-DRG CC	PRIM TB PLEURISY-NO EXAM
01012		MS-DRG CC	PRIM TB PLEUR-EXAM UNKN
01013		MS-DRG CC	PRIM TB PLEURIS-MICRO DX
01014		MS-DRG CC	PRIM TB PLEURISY-CULT DX
01015		MS-DRG CC	PRIM TB PLEURIS-HISTO DX
01016		MS-DRG CC	PRIM TB PLEURIS-OTH TEST
01080		MS-DRG CC	PRIM PROG TB NEC-UNSPEC
01081		MS-DRG CC	PRIM PROG TB NEC-NO EXAM
01082		MS-DRG CC	PRIM PROG TB NEC-EXAM UNKN
01083		MS-DRG CC	PRIM PROG TB NEC-MICRO DX
01084		MS-DRG CC	PRIM PROG TB NEC-CULT DX
01085		MS-DRG CC	PRIM PROG TB NEC-HISTO DX
01086		MS-DRG CC	PRIM PROG TB NEC-OTH TEST
01090		MS-DRG CC	PRIMARY TB NOS-UNSPEC
01091		MS-DRG CC	PRIMARY TB NOS-NO EXAM
01092		MS-DRG CC	PRIMARY TB NOS-EXAM UNKN
01093		MS-DRG CC	PRIMARY TB NOS-MICRO DX
01094		MS-DRG CC	PRIMARY TB NOS-CULT DX
01095		MS-DRG CC	PRIMARY TB NOS-HISTO DX
01096		MS-DRG CC	PRIMARY TB NOS-OTH TEST
01100	CMS CC	MS-DRG CC	TB LUNG INFILTR-UNSPEC
01101	CMS CC	MS-DRG CC	TB LUNG INFILTR-NO EXAM
01102	CMS CC	MS-DRG CC	TB LUNG INFILTR-EXM UNKN
01103	CMS CC	MS-DRG CC	TB LUNG INFILTR-MICRO DX
01104	CMS CC	MS-DRG CC	TB LUNG INFILTR-CULT DX

2008 ICD-9-CM	CMS DRG	MS-DRG	Short Title
01105	CMS CC	MS-DRG CC	TB LUNG INFILTR-HISTO DX
01106	CMS CC	MS-DRG CC	TB LUNG INFILTR-OTH TEST
01110	CMS CC	MS-DRG CC	TB LUNG NODULAR-UNSPEC
01111	CMS CC	MS-DRG CC	TB LUNG NODULAR-NO EXAM
01112	CMS CC	MS-DRG CC	TB LUNG NODULAR-EXAM UNKN
01113	CMS CC	MS-DRG CC	TB LUNG NODULAR-MICRO DX
01114	CMS CC	MS-DRG CC	TB LUNG NODULAR-CULT DX
01115	CMS CC	MS-DRG CC	TB LUNG NODULAR-HISTO DX
01116	CMS CC	MS-DRG CC	TB LUNG NODULAR-OTH TEST
01120	CMS CC	MS-DRG CC	TB LUNG W CAVITY-UNSPEC
01121	CMS CC	MS-DRG CC	TB LUNG W CAVITY-NO EXAM
01122	CMS CC	MS-DRG CC	TB LUNG CAVITY-EXAM UNKN
01123	CMS CC	MS-DRG CC	TB LUNG W CAVIT-MICRO DX
01124	CMS CC	MS-DRG CC	TB LUNG W CAVITY-CULT DX
01125	CMS CC	MS-DRG CC	TB LUNG W CAVIT-HISTO DX
01126	CMS CC	MS-DRG CC	TB LUNG W CAVIT-OTH TEST
01130	CMS CC	MS-DRG CC	TB OF BRONCHUS-UNSPEC
01131	CMS CC	MS-DRG CC	TB OF BRONCHUS-NO EXAM
01132	CMS CC	MS-DRG CC	TB OF BRONCHUS-EXAM UNKN
01133	CMS CC	MS-DRG CC	TB OF BRONCHUS-MICRO DX
01134	CMS CC	MS-DRG CC	TB OF BRONCHUS-CULT DX
01135	CMS CC	MS-DRG CC	TB OF BRONCHUS-HISTO DX
01136	CMS CC	MS-DRG CC	TB OF BRONCHUS-OTH TEST
01140	CMS CC	MS-DRG CC	TB LUNG FIBROSIS-UNSPEC
01141	CMS CC	MS-DRG CC	TB LUNG FIBROSIS-NO EXAM
01142	CMS CC	MS-DRG CC	TB LUNG FIBROSIS-EXAM UNKN
01143	CMS CC	MS-DRG CC	TB LUNG FIBROSIS-MICRO DX
01144	CMS CC	MS-DRG CC	TB LUNG FIBROSIS-CULT DX
01145	CMS CC	MS-DRG CC	TB LUNG FIBROSIS-HISTO DX
01146	CMS CC	MS-DRG CC	TB LUNG FIBROSIS-OTH TEST
01150	CMS CC	MS-DRG CC	TB BRONCHIECTASIS-UNSPEC
01151	CMS CC	MS-DRG CC	TB BRONCHIECT-NO EXAM
01152	CMS CC	MS-DRG CC	TB BRONCHIECT-EXAM UNKN
01153	CMS CC	MS-DRG CC	TB BRONCHIECT-MICRO DX
01154	CMS CC	MS-DRG CC	TB BRONCHIECT-CULT DX
01155	CMS CC	MS-DRG CC	TB BRONCHIECT-HISTO DX
01156	CMS CC	MS-DRG CC	TB BRONCHIECT-OTH TEST
01160	CMS CC	MS-DRG MCC	TB PNEUMONIA-UNSPEC
01161	CMS CC	MS-DRG MCC	TB PNEUMONIA-NO EXAM

2008 ICD-9-CM	CMS DRG	MS-DRG	Short Title
01162	CMS CC	MS-DRG MCC	TB PNEUMONIA-EXAM UNKN
01163	CMS CC	MS-DRG MCC	TB PNEUMONIA-MICRO DX
01164	CMS CC	MS-DRG MCC	TB PNEUMONIA-CULT DX
01165	CMS CC	MS-DRG MCC	TB PNEUMONIA-HISTO DX
01166	CMS CC	MS-DRG MCC	TB PNEUMONIA-OTH TEST
01170	CMS CC	MS-DRG CC	TB PNEUMOTHORAX-UNSPEC
01171	CMS CC	MS-DRG CC	TB PNEUMOTHORAX-NO EXAM
01172	CMS CC	MS-DRG CC	TB PNEUMOTHORAX-EXAM UNKN
01173	CMS CC	MS-DRG CC	TB PNEUMOTHORAX-MICRO DX
01174	CMS CC	MS-DRG CC	TB PNEUMOTHORAX-CULT DX
01175	CMS CC	MS-DRG CC	TB PNEUMOTHORAX-HISTO DX
01176	CMS CC	MS-DRG CC	TB PNEUMOTHORAX-OTH TEST
01180	CMS CC	MS-DRG CC	PULMONARY TB NEC-UNSPEC
01181	CMS CC	MS-DRG CC	PULMONARY TB NEC-NO EXAM
01182	CMS CC	MS-DRG CC	PULMONARY TB NEC-EXAM UNKN
01183	CMS CC	MS-DRG CC	PULMONARY TB NEC-MICRO DX
01184	CMS CC	MS-DRG CC	PULMONARY TB NEC-CULT DX
01185	CMS CC	MS-DRG CC	PULMONARY TB NEC-HISTO DX
01186	CMS CC	MS-DRG CC	PULMONARY TB NEC-OTH TEST
01190	CMS CC	MS-DRG CC	PULMONARY TB NOS-UNSPEC
01191	CMS CC	MS-DRG CC	PULMONARY TB NOS-NO EXAM
01192	CMS CC	MS-DRG CC	PULMONARY TB NOS-EXAM UNKN
01193	CMS CC	MS-DRG CC	PULMONARY TB NOS-MICRO DX
01194	CMS CC	MS-DRG CC	PULMONARY TB NOS-CULT DX
01195	CMS CC	MS-DRG CC	PULMONARY TB NOS-HISTO DX
01196	CMS CC	MS-DRG CC	PULMONARY TB NOS-OTH TEST
01200	CMS CC	MS-DRG CC	TB PLEURISY-UNSPEC
01201	CMS CC	MS-DRG CC	TB PLEURISY-NO EXAM
01202	CMS CC	MS-DRG CC	TB PLEURISY-EXAM UNKN
01203	CMS CC	MS-DRG CC	TB PLEURISY-MICRO DX
01204	CMS CC	MS-DRG CC	TB PLEURISY-CULT DX
01205	CMS CC	MS-DRG CC	TB PLEURISY-HISTOLOG DX
01206	CMS CC	MS-DRG CC	TB PLEURISY-OTH TEST
01210	CMS CC	MS-DRG CC	TB THORACIC NODES-UNSPEC
01211	CMS CC	MS-DRG CC	TB THORAX NODE-NO EXAM
01212	CMS CC	MS-DRG CC	TB THORAX NODE-EXAM UNKN
01213	CMS CC	MS-DRG CC	TB THORAX NODE-MICRO DX
01214	CMS CC	MS-DRG CC	TB THORAX NODE-CULT DX
01215	CMS CC	MS-DRG CC	TB THORAX NODE-HISTO DX

(Continued)

2008 ICD-9-CM	CMS DRG	MS-DRG	Short Title
01216	CMS CC	MS-DRG CC	TB THORAX NODE-OTH TEST
01220		MS-DRG CC	ISOL TRACHEAL TB-UNSPEC
01221		MS-DRG CC	ISOL TRACHEAL TB-NO EXAM
01222		MS-DRG CC	ISOL TRACHEAL TB-EXAM UNKN
01223		MS-DRG CC	ISOLAT TRACHEAL TB-MICRO DX
01224		MS-DRG CC	ISOL TRACHEAL TB-CULT DX
01225		MS-DRG CC	ISOLAT TRACHEAL TB-HISTO DX
01226		MS-DRG CC	ISOLAT TRACHEAL TB-OTH TEST
01230		MS-DRG CC	TB LARYNGITIS-UNSPEC
01231		MS-DRG CC	TB LARYNGITIS-NO EXAM
01232		MS-DRG CC	TB LARYNGITIS-EXAM UNKN
01233		MS-DRG CC	TB LARYNGITIS-MICRO DX
01234		MS-DRG CC	TB LARYNGITIS-CULT DX
01235		MS-DRG CC	TB LARYNGITIS-HISTO DX
01236		MS-DRG CC	TB LARYNGITIS-OTH TEST
01280		MS-DRG CC	RESP TB NEC-UNSPEC
01281		MS-DRG CC	RESP TB NEC-NO EXAM
01282		MS-DRG CC	RESP TB NEC-EXAM UNKN
01283		MS-DRG CC	RESP TB NEC-MICRO DX
01284		MS-DRG CC	RESP TB NEC-CULT DX
01285		MS-DRG CC	RESP TB NEC-HISTO DX
01286		MS-DRG CC	RESP TB NEC-OTH TEST
01300	CMS CC	MS-DRG MCC	TB MENINGITIS-UNSPEC
01301	CMS CC	MS-DRG MCC	TB MENINGITIS-NO EXAM
01302	CMS CC	MS-DRG MCC	TB MENINGITIS-EXAM UNKN
01303	CMS CC	MS-DRG MCC	TB MENINGITIS-MICRO DX
01304	CMS CC	MS-DRG MCC	TB MENINGITIS-CULT DX
01305	CMS CC	MS-DRG MCC	TB MENINGITIS-HISTO DX
01306	CMS CC	MS-DRG MCC	TB MENINGITIS-OTH TEST
01310	CMS CC	MS-DRG MCC	TUBRCLMA MENINGES-UNSPEC
01311	CMS CC	MS-DRG MCC	TUBRCLMA MENING-NO EXAM
01312	CMS CC	MS-DRG MCC	TUBRCLMA MENING-EXAM UNKN
01313	CMS CC	MS-DRG MCC	TUBRCLMA MENING-MICRO DX
01314	CMS CC	MS-DRG MCC	TUBRCLMA MENING-CULT DX
01315	CMS CC	MS-DRG MCC	TUBRCLMA MENING-HISTO DX
01316	CMS CC	MS-DRG MCC	TUBRCLMA MENING-OTH TEST
01320	CMS CC	MS-DRG MCC	TUBRCLMA BRAIN-UNSPEC
01321	CMS CC	MS-DRG MCC	TUBRCLMA BRAIN-NO EXAM
01322	CMS CC	MS-DRG MCC	TUBRCLMA BRAIN-EXAM UNKN

2008 ICD-9-CM	CMS DRG	MS-DRG	Short Title
01323	CMS CC	MS-DRG MCC	TUBRCLMA BRAIN-MICRO DX
01324	CMS CC	MS-DRG MCC	TUBRCLMA BRAIN-CULT DX
01325	CMS CC	MS-DRG MCC	TUBRCLMA BRAIN-HISTO DX
01326	CMS CC	MS-DRG MCC	TUBRCLMA BRAIN-OTH TEST
01330	CMS CC	MS-DRG MCC	TB BRAIN ABSCESS-UNSPEC
01331	CMS CC	MS-DRG MCC	TB BRAIN ABSCESS-NO EXAM
01332	CMS CC	MS-DRG MCC	TB BRAIN ABSCESS-EXAM UNKN
01333	CMS CC	MS-DRG MCC	TB BRAIN ABSCESS-MICRO DX
01334	CMS CC	MS-DRG MCC	TB BRAIN ABSCESS-CULT DX
01335	CMS CC	MS-DRG MCC	TB BRAIN ABSCESS-HISTO DX
01336	CMS CC	MS-DRG MCC	TB BRAIN ABSCESS-OTH TEST
01340	CMS CC	MS-DRG MCC	TUBRCLMA SP CORD-UNSPEC
01341	CMS CC	MS-DRG MCC	TUBRCLMA SP CORD-NO EXAM
01342	CMS CC	MS-DRG MCC	TUBRCLMA SP CD-EXAM UNKN
01343	CMS CC	MS-DRG MCC	TUBRCLMA SP CRD-MICRO DX
01344	CMS CC	MS-DRG MCC	TUBRCLMA SP CORD-CULT DX
01345	CMS CC	MS-DRG MCC	TUBRCLMA SP CRD-HISTO DX
01346	CMS CC	MS-DRG MCC	TUBRCLMA SP CRD-OTH TEST
01350	CMS CC	MS-DRG MCC	TB SP CRD ABSCESS-UNSPEC
01351	CMS CC	MS-DRG MCC	TB SP CRD ABSCESS-NO EXAM
01352	CMS CC	MS-DRG MCC	TB SP CRD ABSCESS-EXAM UNKN
01353	CMS CC	MS-DRG MCC	TB SP CRD ABSCESS-MICRO DX
01354	CMS CC	MS-DRG MCC	TB SP CRD ABSCESS-CULT DX
01355	CMS CC	MS-DRG MCC	TB SP CRD ABSCESS-HISTO DX
01356	CMS CC	MS-DRG MCC	TB SP CRD ABSCESS-OTH TEST
01360	CMS CC	MS-DRG MCC	TB ENCEPHALITIS-UNSPEC
01361	CMS CC	MS-DRG MCC	TB ENCEPHALITIS-NO EXAM
01362	CMS CC	MS-DRG MCC	TB ENCEPHALITIS-EXAM UNKN
01363	CMS CC	MS-DRG MCC	TB ENCEPHALITIS-MICRO DX
01364	CMS CC	MS-DRG MCC	TB ENCEPHALITIS-CULT DX
01365	CMS CC	MS-DRG MCC	TB ENCEPHALITIS-HISTO DX
01366	CMS CC	MS-DRG MCC	TB ENCEPHALITIS-OTH TEST
01380	CMS CC	MS-DRG MCC	CNS TB NEC-UNSPEC
01381	CMS CC	MS-DRG MCC	CNS TB NEC-NO EXAM
01382	CMS CC	MS-DRG MCC	CNS TB NEC-EXAM UNKN
01383	CMS CC	MS-DRG MCC	CNS TB NEC-MICRO DX
01384	CMS CC	MS-DRG MCC	CNS TB NEC-CULT DX
01385	CMS CC	MS-DRG MCC	CNS TB NEC-HISTO DX
01386	CMS CC	MS-DRG MCC	CNS TB NEC-OTH TEST

2008 ICD-9-CM	CMS DRG	MS-DRG	Short Title
01390	CMS CC	MS-DRG MCC	CNS TB NOS-UNSPEC
01391	CMS CC	MS-DRG MCC	CNS TB NOS-NO EXAM
01392	CMS CC	MS-DRG MCC	CNS TB NOS-EXAM UNKN
01393	CMS CC	MS-DRG MCC	CNS TB NOS-MICRO DX
01394	CMS CC	MS-DRG MCC	CNS TB NOS-CULT DX
01395	CMS CC	MS-DRG MCC	CNS TB NOS-HISTO DX
01396	CMS CC	MS-DRG MCC	CNS TB NOS-OTH TEST
01400	CMS CC	MS-DRG MCC	TB PERITONITIS-UNSPEC
01401	CMS CC	MS-DRG MCC	TB PERITONITIS-NO EXAM
01402	CMS CC	MS-DRG MCC	TB PERITONITIS-EXAM UNKN
01403	CMS CC	MS-DRG MCC	TB PERITONITIS-MICRO DX
01404	CMS CC	MS-DRG MCC	TB PERITONITIS-CULT DX
01405	CMS CC	MS-DRG MCC	TB PERITONITIS-HISTO DX
01406	CMS CC	MS-DRG MCC	TB PERITONITIS-OTH TEST
01480	CMS CC	MS-DRG CC	INTESTINAL TB NEC-UNSPEC
01481	CMS CC	MS-DRG CC	INTESTINAL TB NEC-NO EXAM
01482	CMS CC	MS-DRG CC	INTESTINAL TB NEC-EXAM UNKN
01483	CMS CC	MS-DRG CC	INTESTINAL TB NEC-MICRO DX
01484	CMS CC	MS-DRG CC	INTESTINAL TB NEC-CULT DX
01485	CMS CC	MS-DRG CC	INTESTINAL TB NEC-HISTO DX
01486	CMS CC	MS-DRG CC	INTESTINAL TB NEC-OTH TEST
01500		MS-DRG CC	TB OF VERTEBRA-UNSPEC
01501		MS-DRG CC	TB OF VERTEBRA-NO EXAM
01502		MS-DRG CC	TB OF VERTEBRA-EXAM UNKN
01503		MS-DRG CC	TB OF VERTEBRA-MICRO DX
01504		MS-DRG CC	TB OF VERTEBRA-CULT DX
01505		MS-DRG CC	TB OF VERTEBRA-HISTO DX
01506		MS-DRG CC	TB OF VERTEBRA-OTH TEST
01510		MS-DRG CC	TB OF HIP-UNSPEC
01511		MS-DRG CC	TB OF HIP-NO EXAM
01512		MS-DRG CC	TB OF HIP-EXAM UNKN
01513		MS-DRG CC	TB OF HIP-MICRO DX
01514		MS-DRG CC	TB OF HIP-CULT DX
01515		MS-DRG CC	TB OF HIP-HISTO DX
01516		MS-DRG CC	TB OF HIP-OTH TEST
01520		MS-DRG CC	TB OF KNEE-UNSPEC
01521		MS-DRG CC	TB OF KNEE-NO EXAM
01522		MS-DRG CC	TB OF KNEE-EXAM UNKN
01523		MS-DRG CC	TB OF KNEE-MICRO DX

2008 ICD-9-CM	CMS DRG	MS-DRG	Short Title
01524		MS-DRG CC	TB OF KNEE-CULT DX
01525		MS-DRG CC	TB OF KNEE-HISTO DX
01526		MS-DRG CC	TB OF KNEE-OTH TEST
01550		MS-DRG CC	TB OF LIMB BONES-UNSPEC
01551		MS-DRG CC	TB LIMB BONES-NO EXAM
01552		MS-DRG CC	TB LIMB BONES-EXAM UNKN
01553		MS-DRG CC	TB LIMB BONES-MICRO DX
01554		MS-DRG CC	TB LIMB BONES-CULT DX
01555		MS-DRG CC	TB LIMB BONES-HISTO DX
01556		MS-DRG CC	TB LIMB BONES-OTH TEST
01560		MS-DRG CC	TB OF MASTOID-UNSPEC
01561		MS-DRG CC	TB OF MASTOID-NO EXAM
01562		MS-DRG CC	TB OF MASTOID-EXAM UNKN
01563		MS-DRG CC	TB OF MASTOID-MICRO DX
01564		MS-DRG CC	TB OF MASTOID-CULT DX
01565		MS-DRG CC	TB OF MASTOID-HISTO DX
01566		MS-DRG CC	TB OF MASTOID-OTH TEST
01570		MS-DRG CC	TB OF BONE NEC-UNSPEC
01571		MS-DRG CC	TB OF BONE NEC-NO EXAM
01572		MS-DRG CC	TB OF BONE NEC-EXAM UNKN
01573		MS-DRG CC	TB OF BONE NEC-MICRO DX
01574		MS-DRG CC	TB OF BONE NEC-CULT DX
01575		MS-DRG CC	TB OF BONE NEC-HISTO DX
01576		MS-DRG CC	TB OF BONE NEC-OTH TEST
01580		MS-DRG CC	TB OF JOINT NEC-UNSPEC
01581		MS-DRG CC	TB OF JOINT NEC-NO EXAM
01582		MS-DRG CC	TB JOINT NEC-EXAM UNKN
01583		MS-DRG CC	TB OF JOINT NEC-MICRO DX
01584		MS-DRG CC	TB OF JOINT NEC-CULT DX
01585		MS-DRG CC	TB OF JOINT NEC-HISTO DX
01586		MS-DRG CC	TB OF JOINT NEC-OTH TEST
01590		MS-DRG CC	TB BONE/JOINT NOS-UNSPEC
01591		MS-DRG CC	TB BONE/JOINT NOS-NO EXAM
01592		MS-DRG CC	TB BONE/JOINT NOS-EXAM UNKN
01593		MS-DRG CC	TB BONE/JOINT NOS-MICRO DX
01594		MS-DRG CC	TB BONE/JOINT NOS-CULT DX
01595		MS-DRG CC	TB BONE/JOINT NOS-HISTO DX
01596		MS-DRG CC	TB BONE/JOINT NOS-OTH TEST
01600		MS-DRG CC	TB OF KIDNEY-UNSPEC

(Continued)

2008 ICD-9-CM	CMS DRG	MS-DRG	Short Title
01601		MS-DRG CC	TB OF KIDNEY-NO EXAM
01602		MS-DRG CC	TB OF KIDNEY-EXAM UNKN
01603		MS-DRG CC	TB OF KIDNEY-MICRO DX
01604		MS-DRG CC	TB OF KIDNEY-CULT DX
01605		MS-DRG CC	TB OF KIDNEY-HISTO DX
01606		MS-DRG CC	TB OF KIDNEY-OTH TEST
01610		MS-DRG CC	TB OF BLADDER-UNSPEC
01611		MS-DRG CC	TB OF BLADDER-NO EXAM
01612		MS-DRG CC	TB OF BLADDER-EXAM UNKN
01613		MS-DRG CC	TB OF BLADDER-MICRO DX
01614		MS-DRG CC	TB OF BLADDER-CULT DX
01615		MS-DRG CC	TB OF BLADDER-HISTO DX
01616		MS-DRG CC	TB OF BLADDER-OTH TEST
01620		MS-DRG CC	TB OF URETER-UNSPEC
01621		MS-DRG CC	TB OF URETER-NO EXAM
01622		MS-DRG CC	TB OF URETER-EXAM UNKN
01623		MS-DRG CC	TB OF URETER-MICRO DX
01624		MS-DRG CC	TB OF URETER-CULT DX
01625		MS-DRG CC	TB OF URETER-HISTO DX
01626		MS-DRG CC	TB OF URETER-OTH TEST
01630		MS-DRG CC	TB URINARY NEC-UNSPEC
01631		MS-DRG CC	TB URINARY NEC-NO EXAM
01632		MS-DRG CC	TB URINARY NEC-EXAM UNKN
01633		MS-DRG CC	TB URINARY NEC-MICRO DX
01634		MS-DRG CC	TB URINARY NEC-CULT DX
01635		MS-DRG CC	TB URINARY NEC-HISTO DX
01636		MS-DRG CC	TB URINARY NEC-OTH TEST
01640		MS-DRG CC	TB EPIDIDYMIS-UNSPEC
01641		MS-DRG CC	TB EPIDIDYMIS-NO EXAM
01642		MS-DRG CC	TB EPIDIDYMIS-EXAM UNKN
01643		MS-DRG CC	TB EPIDIDYMIS-MICRO DX
01644		MS-DRG CC	TB EPIDIDYMIS-CULT DX
01645		MS-DRG CC	TB EPIDIDYMIS-HISTO DX
01646		MS-DRG CC	TB EPIDIDYMIS-OTH TEST
01650		MS-DRG CC	TB MALE GENIT NEC-UNSPEC
01651		MS-DRG CC	TB MALE GENIT NEC-NO EXAM
01652		MS-DRG CC	TB MALE GENIT NEC-EX UNKN
01653		MS-DRG CC	TB MALE GENIT NEC-MICRO DX
01654		MS-DRG CC	TB MALE GENIT NEC-CULT DX

2008 ICD-9-CM	CMS DRG	MS-DRG	Short Title
01655		MS-DRG CC	TB MALE GENIT NEC-HISTO DX
01656		MS-DRG CC	TB MALE GENIT NEC-OTH TEST
01660		MS-DRG CC	TB OVARY & TUBE-UNSPEC
01661		MS-DRG CC	TB OVARY & TUBE-NO EXAM
01662		MS-DRG CC	TB OVARY & TUBE-EXAM UNKN
01663		MS-DRG CC	TB OVARY & TUBE-MICRO DX
01664		MS-DRG CC	TB OVARY & TUBE-CULT DX
01665		MS-DRG CC	TB OVARY & TUBE-HISTO DX
01666		MS-DRG CC	TB OVARY & TUBE-OTH TEST
01670		MS-DRG CC	TB FEMALE GEN NEC-UNSPEC
01671		MS-DRG CC	TB FEM GEN NEC-NO EXAM
01672		MS-DRG CC	TB FEM GEN NEC-EXAM UNKN
01673		MS-DRG CC	TB FEM GEN NEC-MICRO DX
01674		MS-DRG CC	TB FEM GEN NEC-CULT DX
01675		MS-DRG CC	TB FEM GEN NEC-HISTO DX
01676		MS-DRG CC	TB FEM GEN NEC-OTH TEST
01690		MS-DRG CC	GU TB NOS-UNSPEC
01691		MS-DRG CC	GU TB NOS-NO EXAM
01692		MS-DRG CC	GU TB NOS-EXAM UNKN
01693		MS-DRG CC	GU TB NOS-MICRO DX
01694		MS-DRG CC	GU TB NOS-CULT DX
01695		MS-DRG CC	GU TB NOS-HISTO DX
01696		MS-DRG CC	GU TB NOS-OTH TEST
01700		MS-DRG CC	TB SKIN/SUBCUTAN-UNSPEC
01701		MS-DRG CC	TB SKIN/SUBCUTAN-NO EXAM
01702		MS-DRG CC	TB SKIN/SUBCUTAN-EXAM UNKN
01703		MS-DRG CC	TB SKIN/SUBCUTAN-MICRO DX
01704		MS-DRG CC	TB SKIN/SUBCUTAN-CULT DX
01705		MS-DRG CC	TB SKIN/SUBCUTAN-HISTO DX
01706		MS-DRG CC	TB SKIN/SUBCUTAN-OTH TEST
01720	CMS CC	MS-DRG CC	TB PERIPH LYMPH-UNSPEC
01721	CMS CC	MS-DRG CC	TB PERIPH LYMPH-NO EXAM
01722	CMS CC	MS-DRG CC	TB PERIPH LYMPH-EXAM UNK
01723	CMS CC	MS-DRG CC	TB PERIPH LYMPH-MICRO DX
01724	CMS CC	MS-DRG CC	TB PERIPH LYMPH-CULT DX
01725	CMS CC	MS-DRG CC	TB PERIPH LYMPH-HISTO DX
01726	CMS CC	MS-DRG CC	TB PERIPH LYMPH-OTH TEST
01730	CMS CC	MS-DRG CC	TB OF EYE-UNSPEC
01731	CMS CC	MS-DRG CC	TB OF EYE-NO EXAM

2008 ICD-9-CM	CMS DRG	MS-DRG	Short Title
01732	CMS CC	MS-DRG CC	TB OF EYE-EXAM UNKN
01733	CMS CC	MS-DRG CC	TB OF EYE-MICRO DX
01734	CMS CC	MS-DRG CC	TB OF EYE-CULT DX
01735	CMS CC	MS-DRG CC	TB OF EYE-HISTO DX
01736	CMS CC	MS-DRG CC	TB OF EYE-OTH TEST
01740	CMS CC	MS-DRG CC	TB OF EAR-UNSPEC
01741	CMS CC	MS-DRG CC	TB OF EAR-NO EXAM
01742	CMS CC	MS-DRG CC	TB OF EAR-EXAM UNKN
01743	CMS CC	MS-DRG CC	TB OF EAR-MICRO DX
01744	CMS CC	MS-DRG CC	TB OF EAR-CULT DX
01745	CMS CC	MS-DRG CC	TB OF EAR-HISTO DX
01746	CMS CC	MS-DRG CC	TB OF EAR-OTH TEST
01750	CMS CC	MS-DRG CC	TB OF THYROID-UNSPEC
01751	CMS CC	MS-DRG CC	TB OF THYROID-NO EXAM
01752	CMS CC	MS-DRG CC	TB OF THYROID-EXAM UNKN
01753	CMS CC	MS-DRG CC	TB OF THYROID-MICRO DX
01754	CMS CC	MS-DRG CC	TB OF THYROID-CULT DX
01755	CMS CC	MS-DRG CC	TB OF THYROID-HISTO DX
01756	CMS CC	MS-DRG CC	TB OF THYROID-OTH TEST
01760	CMS CC	MS-DRG CC	TB OF ADRENAL-UNSPEC
01761	CMS CC	MS-DRG CC	TB OF ADRENAL-NO EXAM
01762	CMS CC	MS-DRG CC	TB OF ADRENAL-EXAM UNKN
01763	CMS CC	MS-DRG CC	TB OF ADRENAL-MICRO DX
01764	CMS CC	MS-DRG CC	TB OF ADRENAL-CULT DX
01765	CMS CC	MS-DRG CC	TB OF ADRENAL-HISTO DX
01766	CMS CC	MS-DRG CC	TB OF ADRENAL-OTH TEST
01770	CMS CC	MS-DRG CC	TB OF SPLEEN-UNSPEC
01771	CMS CC	MS-DRG CC	TB OF SPLEEN-NO EXAM
01772	CMS CC	MS-DRG CC	TB OF SPLEEN-EXAM UNKN
01773	CMS CC	MS-DRG CC	TB OF SPLEEN-MICRO DX
01774	CMS CC	MS-DRG CC	TB OF SPLEEN-CULT DX
01775	CMS CC	MS-DRG CC	TB OF SPLEEN-HISTO DX
01776	CMS CC	MS-DRG CC	TB OF SPLEEN-OTH TEST
01780	CMS CC	MS-DRG CC	TB ESOPHAGUS-UNSPEC
01781	CMS CC	MS-DRG CC	TB ESOPHAGUS-NO EXAM
01782	CMS CC	MS-DRG CC	TB ESOPHAGUS-EXAM UNKN
01783	CMS CC	MS-DRG CC	TB ESOPHAGUS-MICRO DX
01784	CMS CC	MS-DRG CC	TB ESOPHAGUS-CULT DX
01785	CMS CC	MS-DRG CC	TB ESOPHAGUS-HISTO DX

2008 ICD-9-CM	CMS DRG	MS-DRG	Short Title
01786	CMS CC	MS-DRG CC	TB ESOPHAGUS-OTH TEST
01790	CMS CC	MS-DRG CC	TB OF ORGAN NEC-UNSPEC
01791	CMS CC	MS-DRG CC	TB OF ORGAN NEC-NO EXAM
01792	CMS CC	MS-DRG CC	TB OF ORGAN NEC-EXAM UNKN
01793	CMS CC	MS-DRG CC	TB OF ORGAN NEC-MICRO DX
01794	CMS CC	MS-DRG CC	TB OF ORGAN NEC-CULT DX
01795	CMS CC	MS-DRG CC	TB OF ORGAN NEC-HISTO DX
01796	CMS CC	MS-DRG CC	TB OF ORGAN NEC-OTH TEST
01800	CMS CC	MS-DRG MCC	ACUTE MILIARY TB-UNSPEC
01801	CMS CC	MS-DRG MCC	ACUTE MILIARY TB-NO EXAM
01802	CMS CC	MS-DRG MCC	ACUTE MILIARY TB-EXAM UNKN
01803	CMS CC	MS-DRG MCC	ACUTE MILIARY TB-MICRO DX
01804	CMS CC	MS-DRG MCC	ACUTE MILIARY TB-CULT DX
01805	CMS CC	MS-DRG MCC	ACUTE MILIARY TB-HISTO DX
01806	CMS CC	MS-DRG MCC	ACUTE MILIARY TB-OTH TEST
01880	CMS CC	MS-DRG MCC	MILIARY TB NEC-UNSPEC
01881	CMS CC	MS-DRG MCC	MILIARY TB NEC-NO EXAM
01882	CMS CC	MS-DRG MCC	MILIARY TB NEC-EXAM UNKN
01883	CMS CC	MS-DRG MCC	MILIARY TB NEC-MICRO DX
01884	CMS CC	MS-DRG MCC	MILIARY TB NEC-CULT DX
01885	CMS CC	MS-DRG MCC	MILIARY TB NEC-HISTO DX
01886	CMS CC	MS-DRG MCC	MILIARY TB NEC-OTH TEST
01890	CMS CC	MS-DRG MCC	MILIARY TB NOS-UNSPEC
01891	CMS CC	MS-DRG MCC	MILIARY TB NOS-NO EXAM
01892	CMS CC	MS-DRG MCC	MILIARY TB NOS-EXAM UNKN
01893	CMS CC	MS-DRG MCC	MILIARY TB NOS-MICRO DX
01894	CMS CC	MS-DRG MCC	MILIARY TB NOS-CULT DX
01895	CMS CC	MS-DRG MCC	MILIARY TB NOS-HISTO DX
01896	CMS CC	MS-DRG MCC	MILIARY TB NOS-OTH TEST
0200		MS-DRG MCC	BUBONIC PLAGUE
0201		MS-DRG MCC	CELLULOCUTANEOUS PLAGUE
0202		MS-DRG MCC	SEPTICEMIC PLAGUE
0203		MS-DRG MCC	PRIMARY PNEUMONIC PLAGUE
0204		MS-DRG MCC	SECONDARY PNEUMONIC PLAGUE
0205		MS-DRG MCC	PNEUMONIC PLAGUE NOS
0208		MS-DRG MCC	OTHER TYPES OF PLAGUE
0209		MS-DRG MCC	PLAGUE NOS
0210		MS-DRG CC	ULCEROGLANDUL TULAREMIA
0211		MS-DRG CC	ENTERIC TULAREMIA

(Continued)

2008 ICD-9-CM	CMS DRG	MS-DRG	Short Title
0212		MS-DRG CC	PULMONARY TULAREMIA
0213		MS-DRG CC	OCULOGLANDULAR TULAREMIA
0218		MS-DRG CC	TULAREMIA NEC
0219		MS-DRG CC	TULAREMIA NOS
0220		MS-DRG CC	CUTANEOUS ANTHRAX
0221		MS-DRG MCC	PULMONARY ANTHRAX
0222		MS-DRG CC	GASTROINTESTINAL ANTHRAX
0223		MS-DRG MCC	ANTHRAX SEPTICEMIA
0228		MS-DRG CC	OTHER ANTHRAX MANIFEST
0229		MS-DRG CC	ANTHRAX NOS
0238		MS-DRG CC	BRUCELLOSIS NEC
0239		MS-DRG CC	BRUCELLOSIS NOS
024		MS-DRG CC	GLANDERS
025		MS-DRG CC	MELIOIDOSIS
0260		MS-DRG CC	SPIRILLARY FEVER
0261		MS-DRG CC	STREPTOBACILLARY FEVER
0269		MS-DRG CC	RAT-BITE FEVER NOS
0270		MS-DRG CC	LISTERIOSIS
0272		MS-DRG CC	PASTEURELLOSIS
0278		MS-DRG CC	ZOONOTIC BACT DIS NEC
0279		MS-DRG CC	ZOONOTIC BACT DIS NOS
0300		MS-DRG CC	LEPROMATOUS LEPROSY
0301		MS-DRG CC	TUBERCULOID LEPROSY
0302		MS-DRG CC	INDETERMINATE LEPROSY
0303		MS-DRG CC	BORDERLINE LEPROSY
0308		MS-DRG CC	LEPROSY NEC
0309		MS-DRG CC	LEPROSY NOS
0310	CMS CC	MS-DRG CC	PULMONARY MYCOBACTERIA
0311		MS-DRG CC	CUTANEOUS MYCOBACTERIA
0312		MS-DRG CC	DMAC BACTEREMIA
0318		MS-DRG CC	MYCOBACTERIAL DIS NEC
0319		MS-DRG CC	MYCOBACTERIAL DIS NOS
0320		MS-DRG CC	FAUCIAL DIPHTHERIA
0321		MS-DRG CC	NASOPHARYNX DIPHTHERIA
0322		MS-DRG CC	ANT NASAL DIPHTHERIA
0323		MS-DRG CC	LARYNGEAL DIPHTHERIA
03281		MS-DRG CC	CONJUNCTIVAL DIPHTHERIA
03282		MS-DRG CC	DIPHTHERITIC MYOCARDITIS
03283		MS-DRG CC	DIPHTHERITIC PERITONITIS

2008 ICD-9-CM	CMS DRG	MS-DRG	Short Title
03284		MS-DRG CC	DIPHTHERITIC CYSTITIS
03285		MS-DRG CC	CUTANEOUS DIPHTHERIA
03289		MS-DRG CC	DIPHTHERIA NEC
0329		MS-DRG CC	DIPHTHERIA NOS
0330		MS-DRG CC	BORDETELLA PERTUSSIS
0331		MS-DRG CC	BORDETELLA PARAPERTUSSIS
0338		MS-DRG CC	WHOOPING COUGH NEC
0339		MS-DRG CC	WHOOPING COUGH NOS
0341		MS-DRG CC	SCARLET FEVER
0360	CMS CC	MS-DRG MCC	MENINGOCOCCAL MENINGITIS
0361	CMS CC	MS-DRG MCC	MENINGOCOCCAL ENCEPHALITIS
0362	CMS CC	MS-DRG MCC	MENINGOCOCCEMIA
0363	CMS CC	MS-DRG MCC	MENINGOCOCCAL ADRENAL SYND
03640	CMS CC	MS-DRG MCC	MENINGOCOCCAL CARDITIS NOS
03641	CMS CC	MS-DRG MCC	MENINGOCOCCAL PERICARDITIS
03642	CMS CC	MS-DRG MCC	MENINGOCOCCAL ENDOCARDITIS
03643	CMS CC	MS-DRG MCC	MENINGOCOCCAL MYOCARDITIS
03681	CMS CC	MS-DRG CC	MENINGOCOCCAL OPTIC NEURIT
03682	CMS CC	MS-DRG CC	MENINGOCOCCAL ARTHROPATHY
03689	CMS CC	MS-DRG CC	MENINGOCOCCAL INFECT NEC
0369	CMS CC	MS-DRG CC	MENINGOCOCCAL INFECT NOS
037	CMS CC	MS-DRG MCC	TETANUS
0380	CMS CC	MS-DRG MCC	STREPTOCOCCAL SEPTICEMIA
03810	CMS CC	MS-DRG MCC	STAPHYLCOCC SEPTICEM NOS
03811	CMS CC	MS-DRG MCC	STAPH AUREUS SEPTICEMIA
03819	CMS CC	MS-DRG MCC	STAPHYLCOCC SEPTICEM NEC
0382	CMS CC	MS-DRG MCC	PNEUMOCOCCAL SEPTICEMIA
0383	CMS CC	MS-DRG MCC	ANAEROBIC SEPTICEMIA
03840	CMS CC	MS-DRG MCC	GRAM-NEG SEPTICEMIA NOS
03841	CMS CC	MS-DRG MCC	H. INFLUENZAE SEPTICEMIA
03842	CMS CC	MS-DRG MCC	E COLI SEPTICEMIA
03843	CMS CC	MS-DRG MCC	PSEUDOMONAS SEPTICEMIA
03844	CMS CC	MS-DRG MCC	SERRATIA SEPTICEMIA
03849	CMS CC	MS-DRG MCC	GRAM-NEG SEPTICEMIA NEC
0388	CMS CC	MS-DRG MCC	SEPTICEMIA NEC
0389	CMS CC	MS-DRG MCC	SEPTICEMIA NOS
0390		MS-DRG CC	CUTANEOUS ACTINOMYCOSIS
0391		MS-DRG CC	PULMONARY ACTINOMYCOSIS
0392		MS-DRG CC	ABDOMINAL ACTINOMYCOSIS

(Continued)

2008 ICD-9-CM	CMS DRG	MS-DRG	Short Title
0393		MS-DRG CC	CERVICOFAC ACTINOMYCOSIS
0394		MS-DRG CC	MADURA FOOT
0398		MS-DRG CC	ACTINOMYCOSIS NEC
0399		MS-DRG CC	ACTINOMYCOSIS NOS
0400	CMS CC	MS-DRG MCC	GAS GANGRENE
0402		MS-DRG CC	WHIPPLE'S DISEASE
0403		MS-DRG CC	NECROBACILLOSIS
04041		MS-DRG CC	INFANT BOTULISM
04042		MS-DRG CC	WOUND BOTULISM
04081		MS-DRG CC	TROPICAL PYOMYOSITIS
04082	CMS CC	MS-DRG MCC	TOXIC SHOCK SYNDROME
042	CMS CC	MS-DRG MCC	HUMAN IMMUNO VIRUS DIS
04500		MS-DRG MCC	AC BULBAR POLIO-TYPE NOS
04501		MS-DRG MCC	AC BULBAR POLIO-TYPE 1
04502		MS-DRG MCC	AC BULBAR POLIO-TYPE 2
04503		MS-DRG MCC	AC BULBAR POLIO-TYPE 3
04510		MS-DRG MCC	PARAL POLIO NEC-TYPE NOS
04511		MS-DRG MCC	PARAL POLIO NEC-TYPE 1
04512		MS-DRG MCC	PARAL POLIO NEC-TYPE 2
04513		MS-DRG MCC	PARAL POLIO NEC-TYPE 3
0460		MS-DRG CC	KURU
0461		MS-DRG CC	JAKOB-CREUTZFELDT DIS
0462	CMS CC	MS-DRG CC	SUBAC SCLEROS PANENCEPH
0463		MS-DRG CC	PROG MULTIFOC LEUKOENCEP
0468		MS-DRG CC	CNS SLOW VIRUS INFEC NEC
0469		MS-DRG CC	CNS SLOW VIRUS INFEC NOS
0470		MS-DRG CC	COXSACKIE VIRUS MENING
0471		MS-DRG CC	ECHO VIRUS MENINGITIS
0478		MS-DRG CC	VIRAL MENINGITIS NEC
0479		MS-DRG CC	VIRAL MENINGITIS NOS
048		MS-DRG CC	OTH ENTEROVIRAL CNS DIS
0490		MS-DRG CC	LYMPHOCYTIC CHORIOMENING
0491		MS-DRG CC	ADENOVIRAL MENINGITIS
0498		MS-DRG CC	VIRAL ENCEPHALITIS NEC
0499		MS-DRG CC	VIRAL ENCEPHALITIS NOS
0500		MS-DRG CC	VARIOLA MAJOR
0501		MS-DRG CC	ALASTRIM
0502		MS-DRG CC	MODIFIED SMALLPOX
0509		MS-DRG CC	SMALLPOX NOS

2008 ICD-9-CM	CMS DRG	MS-DRG	Short Title
0520	CMS CC	MS-DRG MCC	POSTVARICELLA ENCEPHALIT
0521	CMS CC	MS-DRG MCC	VARICELLA PNEUMONITIS
0522	CMS CC	MS-DRG MCC	POSTVARICELLA MYELITIS
0527	CMS CC	MS-DRG CC	VARICELLA COMPLICAT NEC
0528	CMS CC	MS-DRG CC	VARICELLA COMPLICAT NOS
0529	CMS CC	MS-DRG CC	VARICELLA UNCOMPLICATED
0530	CMS CC	MS-DRG MCC	HERPES ZOSTER MENINGITIS
05310	CMS CC	MS-DRG CC	HERPES ZOSTER NERV SYST NOS
05311	CMS CC	MS-DRG CC	GENICULATE HERPES ZOSTER
05312	CMS CC	MS-DRG CC	POSTHERPES TRIGEM NEURAL
05313	CMS CC	MS-DRG CC	POSTHERPES POLYNEUROPATH
05314	CMS CC	MS-DRG MCC	HERPES ZOSTER MYELITIS
05319	CMS CC	MS-DRG CC	HERPES ZOSTER NERV SYST NEC
05320		MS-DRG CC	HERPES ZOSTER OF EYELID
05321		MS-DRG CC	HERPES ZOSTER KERATOCONJUNCT
05322		MS-DRG CC	HERPES ZOSTER IRIDOCYCLITIS
05329		MS-DRG CC	HERPES ZOSTER OF EYE NEC
05371		MS-DRG CC	HERPES ZOSTER OTITIS EXTERNA
05379	CMS CC	MS-DRG CC	HERPES ZOSTER COMPLICATED NEC
0538	CMS CC	MS-DRG CC	HERPES ZOSTER COMPLICATED NOS
0542		MS-DRG CC	HERPETIC GINGIVOSTOMAT
0543	CMS CC	MS-DRG MCC	HERPETIC ENCEPHALITIS
05440		MS-DRG CC	HERPES SIMPLEX EYE NOS
05441		MS-DRG CC	HERPES SIMPLEX OF EYELID
05442		MS-DRG CC	DENDRITIC KERATITIS
05443		MS-DRG CC	HERPES SIMPLEX KERATITIS
05444		MS-DRG CC	HERPES SIMPLEX IRIDOCYCLITIS
05449		MS-DRG CC	HERPES SIMPLEX EYE NEC
0545	CMS CC	MS-DRG MCC	HERPETIC SEPTICEMIA
05471	CMS CC	MS-DRG CC	VISCERAL HERPES SIMPLEX
05472	CMS CC	MS-DRG MCC	HERPES SIMPLEX MENINGITIS
05474	CMS CC	MS-DRG MCC	HERPES SIMPLEX MYELITIS
05479	CMS CC	MS-DRG CC	HERPES SIMPLEX COMPLICAT NEC
0548	CMS CC		HERPES SIMPLEX COMPLICAT NOS
0550	CMS CC	MS-DRG MCC	POSTMEASLES ENCEPHALITIS
0551	CMS CC	MS-DRG MCC	POSTMEASLES PNEUMONIA
0552	CMS CC		POSTMEASLES OTITIS MEDIA
05571	CMS CC	MS-DRG CC	MEASLES KERATITIS
05579	CMS CC	MS-DRG CC	MEASLES COMPLICATION NEC

(Continued)

2008 ICD-9-CM	CMS DRG	MS-DRG	Short Title
0558	CMS CC		MEASLES COMPLICATION NOS
0559	CMS CC		MEASLES UNCOMPLICATED
05600	CMS CC	MS-DRG CC	RUBELLA NERVE COMPL NOS
05601	CMS CC	MS-DRG MCC	RUBELLA ENCEPHALITIS
05609	CMS CC	MS-DRG CC	RUBELLA NERVE COMPL NEC
05671	CMS CC	MS-DRG CC	ARTHRITIS DUE TO RUBELLA
05679	CMS CC	MS-DRG CC	RUBELLA COMPLICATION NEC
0568	CMS CC		RUBELLA COMPLICATION NOS
0569	CMS CC		RUBELLA UNCOMPLICATED
0570		MS-DRG CC	ERYTHEMA INFECTIOSUM
05821		MS-DRG MCC	HUMAN HERPESVIR 6 ENCEPH
05829		MS-DRG MCC	HUMAN HERPESVR ENCPH NEC
0600		MS-DRG CC	SYLVATIC YELLOW FEVER
0601		MS-DRG CC	URBAN YELLOW FEVER
0609		MS-DRG CC	YELLOW FEVER NOS
061		MS-DRG CC	DENGUE
0620		MS-DRG MCC	JAPANESE ENCEPHALITIS
0621		MS-DRG MCC	WEST EQUINE ENCEPHALITIS
0622		MS-DRG MCC	EAST EQUINE ENCEPHALITIS
0623		MS-DRG MCC	ST LOUIS ENCEPHALITIS
0624		MS-DRG MCC	AUSTRALIAN ENCEPHALITIS
0625		MS-DRG MCC	CALIFORNIA ENCEPHALITIS
0628		MS-DRG MCC	MOSQUIT-BORNE ENCEPHALITIS NEC
0629		MS-DRG MCC	MOSQUIT-BORNE ENCEPHALITIS NOS
0630		MS-DRG MCC	RUSSIA SPR-SUMMER ENCEPHALITIS
0631		MS-DRG MCC	LOUPING ILL
0632		MS-DRG MCC	CENT EUROPE ENCEPHALITIS
0638		MS-DRG MCC	TICK-BORNE ENCEPHALITIS NEC
0639		MS-DRG MCC	TICK-BORNE ENCEPHALITIS NOS
064		MS-DRG MCC	VIR ENCEPHALITIS ARTHROPOD NEC
0650		MS-DRG CC	CRIMEAN HEMORRHAGIC FEV
0651		MS-DRG CC	OMSK HEMORRHAGIC FEVER
0652		MS-DRG CC	KYASANUR FOREST DISEASE
0653		MS-DRG CC	TICK-BORNE HEM FEVER NEC
0654		MS-DRG CC	MOSQUITO-BORNE HEM FEVER
0658		MS-DRG CC	ARTHROPOD HEM FEVER NEC
0659		MS-DRG CC	ARTHROPOD HEM FEVER NOS
0660		MS-DRG CC	PHLEBOTOMUS FEVER
0661		MS-DRG CC	TICK-BORNE FEVER

2008 ICD-9-CM	CMS DRG	MS-DRG	Short Title
0662		MS-DRG CC	VENEZUELAN EQUINE FEVER
0663		MS-DRG CC	MOSQUITO-BORNE FEVER NEC
06640		MS-DRG MCC	WEST NILE FEVER NOS
06641		MS-DRG MCC	WEST NILE FEVER W/ENCEPH
06642		MS-DRG MCC	WEST NILE NEURO MAN NEC
06649		MS-DRG MCC	WEST NILE W COMPLIC NEC
0668		MS-DRG CC	ARTHROPOD VIRUS NEC
0669		MS-DRG CC	ARTHROPOD VIRUS NOS
0700		MS-DRG MCC	HEPATITIS A WITH COMA
0701		MS-DRG CC	HEPATITIS A W/O COMA
07020	CMS CC	MS-DRG MCC	HPT B ACTE COMA WO DLTA
07021	CMS CC	MS-DRG MCC	HPT B ACTE COMA W DLTA
07022	CMS CC	MS-DRG MCC	HPT B CHRN COMA WO DLTA
07023	CMS CC	MS-DRG MCC	HPT B CHRN COMA W DLTA
07030	CMS CC	MS-DRG CC	HPT B ACTE WO CM WO DLTA
07031	CMS CC	MS-DRG CC	HPT B ACTE WO CM W DLTA
07032	CMS CC	MS-DRG CC	HPT B CHRN WO CM WO DLTA
07033	CMS CC	MS-DRG CC	HPT B CHRN WO CM W DLTA
07041	CMS CC	MS-DRG MCC	HPT C ACUTE W HEPAT COMA
07042	CMS CC	MS-DRG MCC	HPT DLT WO B W HPT COMA
07043	CMS CC	MS-DRG MCC	HPT E W HEPAT COMA
07044	CMS CC	MS-DRG MCC	CHRNC HPT C W HEPAT COMA
07049	CMS CC	MS-DRG MCC	OTH VRL HEPAT W HPT COMA
07051	CMS CC	MS-DRG CC	HPT C ACUTE WO HPAT COMA
07052	CMS CC	MS-DRG CC	HPT DLT WO B WO HPT COMA
07053	CMS CC	MS-DRG CC	HPT E WO HEPAT COMA
07054	CMS CC		CHRNC HPT C WO HPAT COMA
07059	CMS CC	MS-DRG CC	OTH VRL HPAT WO HPT COMA
0706	CMS CC	MS-DRG MCC	VIRAL HEPAT NOS W COMA
07070	CMS CC		HPT C W/O HEPAT COMA NOS
07071	CMS CC	MS-DRG MCC	HPT C W HEPATIC COMA NOS
0709	CMS CC	MS-DRG CC	VIRAL HEPAT NOS W/O COMA
071		MS-DRG CC	RABIES
0720	CMS CC	MS-DRG CC	MUMPS ORCHITIS
0721	CMS CC	MS-DRG MCC	MUMPS MENINGITIS
0722	CMS CC	MS-DRG MCC	MUMPS ENCEPHALITIS
0723	CMS CC	MS-DRG CC	MUMPS PANCREATITIS
07271	CMS CC	MS-DRG CC	MUMPS HEPATITIS
07272	CMS CC	MS-DRG CC	MUMPS POLYNEUROPATHY

(Continued)

2008 ICD-9-CM	CMS DRG	MS-DRG	Short Title
07279	CMS CC	MS-DRG CC	MUMPS COMPLICATION NEC
0728	CMS CC	MS-DRG CC	MUMPS COMPLICATION NOS
0729	CMS CC		MUMPS UNCOMPLICATED
0730		MS-DRG MCC	ORNITHOSIS PNEUMONIA
0737		MS-DRG CC	ORNITHOSIS COMPLICAT NEC
0738		MS-DRG CC	ORNITHOSIS COMPLICAT NOS
0739		MS-DRG CC	ORNITHOSIS NOS
07420		MS-DRG CC	COXSACKIE CARDITIS NOS
07421		MS-DRG CC	COXSACKIE PERICARDITIS
07422		MS-DRG CC	COXSACKIE ENDOCARDITIS
07423		MS-DRG CC	COXSACKIE MYOCARDITIS
0783		MS-DRG CC	CAT-SCRATCH DISEASE
0785		MS-DRG CC	CYTOMEGALOVIRAL DISEASE
0786		MS-DRG CC	HEM NEPHROSONEPHRITIS
0787		MS-DRG CC	ARENAVIRAL HEM FEVER
07951		MS-DRG CC	HTLV-1 INFECTION OTH DIS
07952		MS-DRG CC	HTLV-II INFECTN OTH DIS
07953		MS-DRG CC	HIV-2 INFECTION OTH DIS
07981		MS-DRG CC	HANTAVIRUS INFECTION
07982	CMS CC	MS-DRG CC	SARS ASSOC CORONAVIRUS
07983		MS-DRG CC	PARVOVIRUS B19
080		MS-DRG CC	LOUSE-BORNE TYPHUS
0810		MS-DRG CC	MURINE TYPHUS
0811		MS-DRG CC	BRILL'S DISEASE
0812		MS-DRG CC	SCRUB TYPHUS
0819		MS-DRG CC	TYPHUS NOS
0820		MS-DRG CC	SPOTTED FEVERS
0821		MS-DRG CC	BOUTONNEUSE FEVER
0822		MS-DRG CC	NORTH ASIAN TICK FEVER
0823		MS-DRG CC	QUEENSLAND TICK TYPHUS
08240		MS-DRG CC	EHRLICHIOSIS NOS
08241		MS-DRG CC	EHRLICHIOSIS CHAFEENSIS
08249		MS-DRG CC	EHRLICHIOSIS NEC
0828		MS-DRG CC	TICK-BORNE RICKETTS NEC
0829		MS-DRG CC	TICK-BORNE RICKETTS NOS
0830		MS-DRG CC	Q FEVER
0831		MS-DRG CC	TRENCH FEVER
0832		MS-DRG CC	RICKETTSIALPOX
0838		MS-DRG CC	RICKETTSIOSES NEC

2008 ICD-9-CM	CMS DRG	MS-DRG	Short Title
0839		MS-DRG CC	RICKETTSIOSIS NOS
0840		MS-DRG MCC	FALCIPARUM MALARIA
0841		MS-DRG CC	VIVAX MALARIA
0842		MS-DRG CC	QUARTAN MALARIA
0843	.	MS-DRG CC	OVALE MALARIA
0844		MS-DRG CC	MALARIA NEC
0845		MS-DRG CC	MIXED MALARIA
0846		MS-DRG CC	MALARIA NOS
0847		MS-DRG CC	INDUCED MALARIA
0848		MS-DRG CC	BLACKWATER FEVER
0849		MS-DRG CC	MALARIA COMPLICATED NEC
0850		MS-DRG CC	VISCERAL LEISHMANIASIS
0851		MS-DRG CC	CUTAN LEISHMANIAS URBAN
0852		MS-DRG CC	CUTAN LEISHMANIAS ASIAN
0853		MS-DRG CC	CUTAN LEISHMANIAS ETHIOP
0854		MS-DRG CC	CUTAN LEISHMANIAS AMER
0855		MS-DRG CC	MUCOCUTAN LEISHMANIASIS
0859		MS-DRG CC	LEISHMANIASIS NOS
0860	CMS CC	MS-DRG CC	CHAGAS DISEASE OF HEART
0861		MS-DRG CC	CHAGAS DIS OF OTH ORGAN
0862		MS-DRG CC	CHAGAS DISEASE NOS
0863		MS-DRG CC	GAMBIAN TRYPANOSOMIASIS
0864		MS-DRG CC	RHODESIAN TRYPANOSOMIAS
0865		MS-DRG CC	AFRICAN TRYPANOSOMA NOS
0869		MS-DRG CC	TRYPANOSOMIASIS NOS
0870		MS-DRG CC	LOUSE-BORNE RELAPS FEVER
0871		MS-DRG CC	TICK-BORNE RELAPS FEVER
0879		MS-DRG CC	RELAPSING FEVER NOS
0880		MS-DRG CC	BARTONELLOSIS
08881		MS-DRG CC	LYME DISEASE
08882		MS-DRG CC	BABESIOSIS
0900		MS-DRG CC	EARLY CONG SYPH SYMPTOM
0902		MS-DRG CC	EARLY CONGEN SYPH NOS
0903		MS-DRG CC	SYPHILITIC KERATITIS
09040	CMS CC	MS-DRG CC	JUVENILE NEUROSYPH NOS
09041	CMS CC	MS-DRG MCC	CONGEN SYPH ENCEPHALITIS
09042	CMS CC	MS-DRG MCC	CONGEN SYPH MENINGITIS
09049	CMS CC	MS-DRG CC	JUVENILE NEUROSYPH NEC
0905		MS-DRG CC	LATE CONGEN SYPH SYMPTOM

(Continued)

2008 ICD-9-CM	CMS DRG	MS-DRG	Short Title
0913		MS-DRG CC	SECONDARY SYPH SKIN
0914		MS-DRG CC	SYPHILITIC ADENOPATHY
09150		MS-DRG CC	SYPHILITIC UVEITIS NOS
09151		MS-DRG CC	SYPHILITIC CHORIORETINITIS
09152		MS-DRG CC	SYPHILITIC IRIDOCYCLITIS
09161		MS-DRG CC	SYPHILITIC PERIOSTITIS
09162		MS-DRG CC	SYPHILITIC HEPATITIS
09169		MS-DRG CC	SECOND SYPHILIS VISCERA NEC
0917		MS-DRG CC	SECOND SYPHILIS RELAPSE
09181		MS-DRG MCC	ACUTE SYPHILIS MENINGITIS
09182		MS-DRG CC	SYPHILITIC ALOPECIA
09189		MS-DRG CC	SECONDARY SYPHILIS NEC
0919		MS-DRG CC	SECONDARY SYPHILIS NOS
0930	CMS CC	MS-DRG CC	AORTIC ANEURYSM, SYPHIL
0931	CMS CC	MS-DRG CC	SYPHILITIC AORTITIS
09320	CMS CC	MS-DRG CC	SYPHILITIC ENDOCARDITIS NOS
09321	CMS CC	MS-DRG CC	SYPHILITIC MITRAL VALVE
09322	CMS CC	MS-DRG CC	SYPHILITIC AORTIC VALVE
09323	CMS CC	MS-DRG CC	SYPHILITIC TRICUSPID VALVE
09324	CMS CC	MS-DRG CC	SYPHILITIC PULMONARY VALVE
09381	CMS CC	MS-DRG CC	SYPHILITIC PERICARDITIS
09382	CMS CC	MS-DRG CC	SYPHILITIC MYOCARDITIS
09389	CMS CC	MS-DRG CC	CARDIOVASCULAR SYPH NEC
0939	CMS CC	MS-DRG CC	CARDIOVASCULAR SYPH NOS
0940	CMS CC	MS-DRG CC	TABES DORSALIS
0941	CMS CC	MS-DRG CC	GENERAL PARESIS
0942	CMS CC	MS-DRG MCC	SYPHILITIC MENINGITIS
0943	CMS CC	MS-DRG CC	ASYMPTOMAT NEUROSYPHILIS
09481	CMS CC	MS-DRG MCC	SYPHILITIC ENCEPHALITIS
09482		MS-DRG CC	SYPHILITIC PARKINSONISM
09483		MS-DRG CC	SYPHILITIC DISSEM RETINITIS
09484		MS-DRG CC	SYPHILITIC OPTIC ATROPHY
09485		MS-DRG CC	SYPHILITIC RETROBULB NEURITIS
09486		MS-DRG CC	SYPHILITIC ACOUSTIC NEURITIS
09487	CMS CC	MS-DRG MCC	SYPHILITIC RUPT CEREB ANEURYSM
09489	CMS CC	MS-DRG CC	NEUROSYPHILIS NEC
0949	CMS CC	MS-DRG CC	NEUROSYPHILIS NOS
0950		MS-DRG CC	SYPHILITIC EPISCLERITIS
0951		MS-DRG CC	SYPHILIS OF LUNG

2008 ICD-9-CM	CMS DRG	MS-DRG	Short Title
0952		MS-DRG CC	SYPHILITIC PERITONITIS
0953		MS-DRG CC	SYPHILIS OF LIVER
0954		MS-DRG CC	SYPHILIS OF KIDNEY
0955		MS-DRG CC	SYPHILIS OF BONE
0956		MS-DRG CC	SYPHILIS OF MUSCLE
0957		MS-DRG CC	SYPHILIS OF TENDON/BURSA
0958		MS-DRG CC	LATE SYMPT SYPHILIS NEC
0959		MS-DRG CC	LATE SYMPT SYPHILIS NOS
0980	CMS CC	MS-DRG CC	ACUTE GC INFECT LOWER GU
09810	CMS CC	MS-DRG CC	GC (ACUTE) UPPER GU NOS
09811	CMS CC	MS-DRG CC	GC CYSTITIS (ACUTE)
09812	CMS CC	MS-DRG CC	GC PROSTATITIS (ACUTE)
09813	CMS CC	MS-DRG CC	GC ORCHITIS (ACUTE)
09814	CMS CC	MS-DRG CC	GC SEM VESICULIT (ACUTE)
09815	CMS CC	MS-DRG CC	GC CERVICITIS (ACUTE)
09816	CMS CC	MS-DRG CC	GC ENDOMETRITIS (ACUTE)
09817	CMS CC	MS-DRG CC	ACUTE GC SALPINGITIS
09819	CMS CC	MS-DRG CC	GC (ACUTE) UPPER GU NEC
09840		MS-DRG CC	GONOCOCCAL CONJUNCTIVIT
09841		MS-DRG CC	GONOCOCCAL IRIDOCYCLITIS
09842		MS-DRG CC	GONOCOCCAL ENDOPHTHALMIA
09843		MS-DRG CC	GONOCOCCAL KERATITIS
09849		MS-DRG CC	GONOCOCCAL EYE NEC
09850		MS-DRG CC	GONOCOCCAL ARTHRITIS
09851		MS-DRG CC	GONOCOCCAL SYNOVITIS
09852		MS-DRG CC	GONOCOCCAL BURSITIS
09853		MS-DRG CC	GONOCOCCAL SPONDYLITIS
09859		MS-DRG CC	GC INFECT JOINT NEC
09881		MS-DRG CC	GONOCOCCAL KERATOSIS
09882		MS-DRG MCC	GONOCOCCAL MENINGITIS
09883		MS-DRG MCC	GONOCOCCAL PERICARDITIS
09884		MS-DRG MCC	GONOCOCCAL ENDOCARDITIS
09885		MS-DRG CC	GONOCOCCAL HEART DIS NEC
09886		MS-DRG CC	GONOCOCCAL PERITONITIS
09889		MS-DRG CC	GONOCOCCAL INF SITE NEC
09956		MS-DRG CC	OT VD CHLM TRCH PRTONEUM
1000		MS-DRG CC	LEPTOSPIROS ICTEROHEM
10081		MS-DRG MCC	LEPTOSPIRAL MENINGITIS
10089		MS-DRG CC	LEPTOSPIRAL INFECT NEC

(Continued)

2008 ICD-9-CM	CMS DRG	MS-DRG	Short Title
1009		MS-DRG CC	LEPTOSPIROSIS NOS
101		MS-DRG CC	VINCENT'S ANGINA
1120	CMS CC	MS-DRG CC	THRUSH
1122		MS-DRG CC	CANDIDIASIS UROGENITAL NEC
1124	CMS CC	MS-DRG MCC	CANDIDIASIS OF LUNG
1125	CMS CC	MS-DRG MCC	DISSEMINATED CANDIDIASIS
11281	CMS CC	MS-DRG MCC	CANDIDAL ENDOCARDITIS
11282	CMS CC	MS-DRG CC	CANDIDAL OTITIS EXTERNA
11283	CMS CC	MS-DRG MCC	CANDIDAL MENINGITIS
11284	CMS CC	MS-DRG CC	CANDIDAL ESOPHAGITIS
11285	CMS CC	MS-DRG CC	CANDIDAL ENTERITIS
11289		MS-DRG CC	CANDIDIASIS SITE NEC
1140	CMS CC	MS-DRG CC	PRIMARY COCCIDIOIDOMYCOS
1141		MS-DRG CC	PRIM CUTAN COCCIDIOID
1142	CMS CC	MS-DRG MCC	COCCIDIOIDAL MENINGITIS
1143	CMS CC	MS-DRG CC	PROGRESS COCCIDIOID NEC
1144		MS-DRG CC	CH PL COCCIDIOIDOMYCOSIS
1145		MS-DRG CC	PL COCCIDIOIDOMYCOSIS NOS
1149	CMS CC	MS-DRG CC	COCCIDIOIDOMYCOSIS NOS
11500	CMS CC		HISTOPLASMA CAPSULAT NOS
11501	CMS CC	MS-DRG MCC	HISTOPLASM CAPSUL MENING
11502	CMS CC	MS-DRG CC	HISTOPLASM CAPSUL RETINA
11503	CMS CC	MS-DRG MCC	HISTOPLASM CAPS PERICARD
11504	CMS CC	MS-DRG MCC	HISTOPLASM CAPS ENDOCARD
11505	CMS CC	MS-DRG MCC	HISTOPLASM CAPS PNEUMON
11509		MS-DRG CC	HISTOPLASMA CAPSULAT NEC
11510	CMS CC		HISTOPLASMA DUBOISII NOS
11511	CMS CC	MS-DRG MCC	HISTOPLASM DUBOIS MENING
11512	CMS CC	MS-DRG CC	HISTOPLASM DUBOIS RETINA
11513	CMS CC	MS-DRG MCC	HISTOPLASM DUB PERICARD
11514	CMS CC	MS-DRG MCC	HISTOPLASM DUB ENDOCARD
11515	CMS CC	MS-DRG MCC	HISTOPLASM DUB PNEUMONIA
11519	CMS CC	MS-DRG CC	HISTOPLASMA DUBOISII NEC
11590	CMS CC		HISTOPLASMOSIS NOS
11591	CMS CC	MS-DRG MCC	HISTOPLASMOSIS MENINGIT
11592	CMS CC	MS-DRG CC	HISTOPLASMOSIS RETINITIS
11593	CMS CC	MS-DRG MCC	HISTOPLASMOSIS PERICARD
11594	CMS CC	MS-DRG MCC	HISTOPLASMOSIS ENDOCARD
11595	CMS CC	MS-DRG MCC	HISTOPLASMOSIS PNEUMONIA

2008 ICD-9-CM	CMS DRG	MS-DRG	Short Title
11599	CMS CC		HISTOPLASMOSIS NEC
1160	CMS CC	MS-DRG CC	BLASTOMYCOSIS
1161	CMS CC	MS-DRG CC	PARACOCCIDIOIDOMYCOSIS
1173	CMS CC	MS-DRG CC	ASPERGILLOSIS
1174	CMS CC	MS-DRG CC	MYCOTIC MYCETOMAS
1175	CMS CC	MS-DRG CC	CRYPTOCOCCOSIS
1176	CMS CC	MS-DRG CC	ALLESCHERIOSIS
1177	CMS CC	MS-DRG MCC	ZYGOMYCOSIS
1178		MS-DRG CC	DEMATIACIOUS FUNGI INF
1179		MS-DRG CC	MYCOSES NEC & NOS
118	CMS CC	MS-DRG CC	OPPORTUNISTIC MYCOSES
1200		MS-DRG CC	SCHISTOSOMA HAEMATOBIUM
1201		MS-DRG CC	SCHISTOSOMA MANSONI
1202		MS-DRG CC	SCHISTOSOMA JAPONICUM
1203		MS-DRG CC	CUTANEOUS SCHISTOSOMA
1208		MS-DRG CC	SCHISTOSOMIASIS NEC
1209		MS-DRG CC	SCHISTOSOMIASIS NOS
1210		MS-DRG CC	OPISTHORCHIASIS
1211		MS-DRG CC	CLONORCHIASIS
1212		MS-DRG CC	PARAGONIMIASIS
1213		MS-DRG CC	FASCIOLIASIS
1214		MS-DRG CC	FASCIOLOPSIASIS
1215		MS-DRG CC	METAGONIMIASIS
1216		MS-DRG CC	HETEROPHYIASIS
1218		MS-DRG CC	TREMATODE INFECTION NEC
1220		MS-DRG CC	ECHINOCOCC GRANUL LIVER
1221		MS-DRG CC	ECHINOCOCC GRANUL LUNG
1222		MS-DRG CC	ECHINOCOCC GRAN THYROID
1223		MS-DRG CC	ECHINOCOCC GRANUL NEC
1224		MS-DRG CC	ECHINOCOCC GRANUL NOS
1225		MS-DRG CC	ECHINOCOC MULTILOC LIVER
1226		MS-DRG CC	ECHINOCOCC MULTILOC NEC
1227		MS-DRG CC	ECHINOCOCC MULTILOC NOS
1228		MS-DRG CC	ECHINOCOCCOSIS NOS LIVER
1229		MS-DRG CC	ECHINOCOCCOSIS NEC/NOS
1230		MS-DRG CC	TAENIASIS SOLIUM INTESTINE
1231		MS-DRG CC	CYSTICERCOSIS
1232		MS-DRG CC	TAENIASIS SAGINATA INFECT
1233		MS-DRG CC	TAENIASIS NOS

(Continued)

2008 ICD-9-CM	CMS DRG	MS-DRG	Short Title
1234		MS-DRG CC	DIPHYLLOBOTHRIAS INTEST
1235		MS-DRG CC	SPARGANOSIS
1236		MS-DRG CC	HYMENOLEPIASIS
1238		MS-DRG CC	CESTODE INFECTION NEC
124		MS-DRG CC	TRICHINOSIS
1250		MS-DRG CC	BANCROFTIAN FILARIASIS
1251		MS-DRG CC	MALAYAN FILARIASIS
1252		MS-DRG CC	LOIASIS
1253		MS-DRG CC	ONCHOCERCIASIS
1254		MS-DRG CC	DIPETALONEMIASIS
1255		MS-DRG CC	MANSONELLA OZZARDI INFEC
1256		MS-DRG CC	FILARIASIS NEC
1257		MS-DRG CC	DRACONTIASIS
1259		MS-DRG CC	FILARIASIS NOS
1260		MS-DRG CC	ANCYLOSTOMA DUODENALE
1261		MS-DRG CC	NECATOR AMERICANUS
1262		MS-DRG CC	ANCYLOSTOMA BRAZILIENSE
1263		MS-DRG CC	ANCYLOSTOMA CEYLANICUM
1268		MS-DRG CC	ANCYLOSTOMA NEC
1269		MS-DRG CC	ANCYLOSTOMIASIS NOS
1270		MS-DRG CC	ASCARIASIS
1271		MS-DRG CC	ANISAKIASIS
1272		MS-DRG CC	STRONGYLOIDIASIS
1273		MS-DRG CC	TRICHURIASIS
1274		MS-DRG CC	ENTEROBIASIS
1275		MS-DRG CC	CAPILLARIASIS
1276		MS-DRG CC	TRICHOSTRONGYLIASIS
1277		MS-DRG CC	INTEST HELMINTHIASIS NEC
1278		MS-DRG CC	MIXED INTESTINE HELMINTHIASIS
1279		MS-DRG CC	INTEST HELMINTHIASIS NOS
1300	CMS CC	MS-DRG MCC	TOXOPLASM MENINGOENCEPH
1301	CMS CC	MS-DRG CC	TOXOPLASM CONJUNCTIVITIS
1302	CMS CC	MS-DRG CC	TOXOPLASMA CHORIORETINIT
1303	CMS CC	MS-DRG MCC	TOXOPLASMA MYOCARDITIS
1304	CMS CC	MS-DRG MCC	TOXOPLASMA PNEUMONITIS
1305	CMS CC	MS-DRG CC	TOXOPLASMA HEPATITIS
1307	CMS CC	MS-DRG CC	TOXOPLASMOSIS SITE NEC
1308	CMS CC	MS-DRG MCC	MULTISYSTEM TOXOPLASMOSIS
1309		MS-DRG CC	TOXOPLASMOSIS NOS

2008 ICD-9-CM	CMS DRG	MS-DRG	Short Title
135	CMS CC		SARCOIDOSIS
1362		MS-DRG MCC	FREE-LIVING AMEBA INFECT
1363	CMS CC	MS-DRG MCC	PNEUMOCYSTOSIS
1364		MS-DRG CC	PSOROSPERMIASIS
1365		MS-DRG CC	SARCOSPORIDIOSIS
1370	CMS CC		LATE EFFECT TB, RESP/NOS
1371	CMS CC		LATE EFFECT CNS TB
1372	CMS CC		LATE EFFECT GU TB
138	CMS CC		LATE EFFECT ACUTE POLIO
1500	CMS CC	MS-DRG CC	MALIG NEO CERVICAL ESOPHAG
1501	CMS CC	MS-DRG CC	MALIG NEO THORACIC ESOPHAG
1502	CMS CC	MS-DRG CC	MALIG NEO ABDOMIN ESOPHAG
1503	CMS CC	MS-DRG CC	MALIG NEO UPPER 3RD ESOPH
1504	CMS CC	MS-DRG CC	MALIG NEO MIDDLE 3RD ESOPH
1505	CMS CC	MS-DRG CC	MALIG NEO LOWER 3RD ESOPH
1508	CMS CC	MS-DRG CC	MALIG NEO ESOPHAGUS NEC
1509	CMS CC	MS-DRG CC	MALIG NEO ESOPHAGUS NOS
1510	CMS CC	MS-DRG CC	MALIG NEO STOMACH CARDIA
1511	CMS CC	MS-DRG CC	MALIGNANT NEO PYLORUS
1512	CMS CC	MS-DRG CC	MALIG NEO PYLORIC ANTRUM
1513	CMS CC	MS-DRG CC	MALIG NEO STOMACH FUNDUS
1514	CMS CC	MS-DRG CC	MALIG NEO STOMACH BODY
1515	CMS CC	MS-DRG CC	MALIG NEO STOM LESSER CURV
1516	CMS CC	MS-DRG CC	MALIG NEO STOM GREAT CURV
1518	CMS CC	MS-DRG CC	MALIG NEOPL STOMACH NEC
1519	CMS CC	MS-DRG CC	MALIG NEOPL STOMACH NOS
1520	CMS CC	MS-DRG CC	MALIGNANT NEOPL DUODENUM
1521	CMS CC	MS-DRG CC	MALIGNANT NEOPL JEJUNUM
1522	CMS CC	MS-DRG CC	MALIGNANT NEOPLASM ILEUM
1523	CMS CC	MS-DRG CC	MALIG NEO MECKEL'S DIVERT
1528	CMS CC	MS-DRG CC	MALIG NEO SMALL BOWEL NEC
1529	CMS CC	MS-DRG CC	MALIG NEO SMALL BOWEL NOS
1530	CMS CC	MS-DRG CC	MALIG NEO HEPATIC FLEXURE
1531	CMS CC	MS-DRG CC	MALIG NEO TRANSVERSE COLON
1532	CMS CC	MS-DRG CC	MALIG NEO DESCEND COLON
1533	CMS CC	MS-DRG CC	MALIG NEO SIGMOID COLON
1534	CMS CC	MS-DRG CC	MALIGNANT NEOPLASM CECUM
1535	CMS CC	MS-DRG CC	MALIGNANT NEO APPENDIX
1536	CMS CC	MS-DRG CC	MALIG NEO ASCEND COLON

(Continued)

2008 ICD-9-CM	CMS DRG	MS-DRG	Short Title
1537	CMS CC	MS-DRG CC	MALIG NEO SPLENIC FLEXURE
1538	CMS CC	MS-DRG CC	MALIGNANT NEO COLON NEC
1539	CMS CC	MS-DRG CC	MALIGNANT NEO COLON NOS
1540	CMS CC	MS-DRG CC	MALIG NEO RECTOSIGMOID JCT
1541	CMS CC	MS-DRG CC	MALIGNANT NEOPL RECTUM
1542	CMS CC	MS-DRG CC	MALIG NEOPL ANAL CANAL
1543	CMS CC	MS-DRG CC	MALIGNANT NEO ANUS NOS
1548	CMS CC	MS-DRG CC	MALIG NEO RECTUM/ANUS NEC
1550	CMS CC	MS-DRG CC	MALIG NEO LIVER, PRIMARY
1551	CMS CC	MS-DRG CC	MALIG NEO INTRAHEPAT DUCTS
1552	CMS CC	MS-DRG CC	MALIGNANT NEO LIVER NOS
1560	CMS CC	MS-DRG CC	MALIG NEO GALLBLADDER
1561	CMS CC	MS-DRG CC	MALIG NEO EXTRAHEPAT DUCTS
1562	CMS CC	MS-DRG CC	MALIG NEO AMPULLA OF VATER
1568	CMS CC	MS-DRG CC	MALIG NEO BILIARY NEC
1569	CMS CC	MS-DRG CC	MALIG NEO BILIARY NOS
1570	CMS CC	MS-DRG CC	MALIG NEO PANCREAS HEAD
1571	CMS CC	MS-DRG CC	MALIG NEO PANCREAS BODY
1572	CMS CC	MS-DRG CC	MALIG NEO PANCREAS TAIL
1573	CMS CC	MS-DRG CC	MALIG NEO PANCREATIC DUCT
1574	CMS CC	MS-DRG CC	MALIG NEO ISLET LANGERHANS
1578	CMS CC	MS-DRG CC	MALIG NEO PANCREAS NEC
1579	CMS CC	MS-DRG CC	MALIG NEO PANCREAS NOS
1580		MS-DRG CC	MALIG NEO RETROPERITONEUM
1588		MS-DRG CC	MALIG NEO PERITONEUM NEC
1589		MS-DRG CC	MALIG NEO PERITONEUM NOS
1620		MS-DRG CC	MALIGNANT NEO TRACHEA
1622	CMS CC	MS-DRG CC	MALIG NEO MAIN BRONCHUS
1623	CMS CC	MS-DRG CC	MALIG NEO UPPER LOBE LUNG
1624	CMS CC	MS-DRG CC	MALIG NEO MIDDLE LOBE LUNG
1625	CMS CC	MS-DRG CC	MALIG NEO LOWER LOBE LUNG
1628	CMS CC	MS-DRG CC	MALIG NEO BRONCH/LUNG NEC
1629	CMS CC	MS-DRG CC	MALIG NEO BRONCH/LUNG NOS
1630	CMS CC	MS-DRG CC	MALIG NEO PARIETAL PLEURA
1631	CMS CC	MS-DRG CC	MALIG NEO VISCERAL PLEURA
1638	CMS CC	MS-DRG CC	MALIG NEOPL PLEURA NEC
1639	CMS CC	MS-DRG CC	MALIG NEOPL PLEURA NOS
1640	CMS CC	MS-DRG CC	MALIGNANT NEOPL THYMUS
1641	CMS CC	MS-DRG CC	MALIGNANT NEOPL HEART

2008 ICD-9-CM	CMS DRG	MS-DRG	Short Title
1642	CMS CC	MS-DRG CC	MALIG NEO ANT MEDIASTINUM
1643	CMS CC	MS-DRG CC	MALIG NEO POST MEDIASTINUM
1648	CMS CC	MS-DRG CC	MALIG NEO MEDIASTINUM NEC
1649	CMS CC	MS-DRG CC	MALIG NEO MEDIASTINUM NOS
1700		MS-DRG CC	MALIG NEO SKULL/FACE BONE
1701		MS-DRG CC	MALIGNANT NEO MANDIBLE
1702		MS-DRG CC	MALIG NEO VERTEBRAE
1703		MS-DRG CC	MALIG NEO RIBS/STERN/CLAV
1704		MS-DRG CC	MALIG NEO LONG BONES ARM
1705		MS-DRG CC	MALIG NEO BONES WRIST/HAND
1706		MS-DRG CC	MALIG NEO PELVIC GIRDLE
1707		MS-DRG CC	MALIG NEO LONG BONES LEG
1708		MS-DRG CC	MALIG NEO BONES ANKLE/FOOT
1709		MS-DRG CC	MALIG NEOPL BONE NOS
1710		MS-DRG CC	MALIG NEO SOFT TISSUE HEAD
1712		MS-DRG CC	MALIG NEO SOFT TISSUE ARM
1713		MS-DRG CC	MALIG NEO SOFT TISSUE LEG
1714		MS-DRG CC	MALIG NEO SOFT TIS THORAX
1715		MS-DRG CC	MALIG NEO SOFT TIS ABDOMEN
1716		MS-DRG CC	MALIG NEO SOFT TIS PELVIS
1717		MS-DRG CC	MALIG NEOPL TRUNK NOS
1718		MS-DRG CC	MALIG NEO SOFT TISSUE NEC
1719		MS-DRG CC	MALIG NEO SOFT TISSUE NOS
1760		MS-DRG CC	SKIN - KAPOSI'S SARCOMA
1761		MS-DRG CC	SFT TISUE - KAPOSI'S SRCMA
1762		MS-DRG CC	PALATE - KAPOSI'S SARCOMA
1763		MS-DRG CC	GI SITES - KAPOSI'S SRCOMA
1764	CMS CC	MS-DRG CC	LUNG - KAPOSI'S SARCOMA
1765	CMS CC	MS-DRG CC	LYM NDS - KAPOSI'S SARCOMA
1768		MS-DRG CC	SPF STS - KAPOSI'S SARCOMA
1769		MS-DRG CC	KAPOSI'S SARCOMA NOS
1830		MS-DRG CC	MALIGN NEOPL OVARY
1890	CMS CC	MS-DRG CC	MALIG NEOPL KIDNEY
1891	CMS CC	MS-DRG CC	MALIG NEO RENAL PELVIS
1892	CMS CC	MS-DRG CC	MALIGN NEOPL URETER
1893		MS-DRG CC	MALIGN NEOPL URETHRA
1894		MS-DRG CC	MALIG NEO PARAURETHRAL
1898		MS-DRG CC	MALIG NEO URINARY NEC
1899		MS-DRG CC	MALIG NEO URINARY NOS

(Continued)

2008 ICD-9-CM	CMS DRG	MS-DRG	Short Title
1910	CMS CC	MS-DRG CC	MALIGN NEOPL CEREBRUM
1911	CMS CC	MS-DRG CC	MALIG NEO FRONTAL LOBE
1912	CMS CC	MS-DRG CC	MAL NEO TEMPORAL LOBE
1913	CMS CC	MS-DRG CC	MAL NEO PARIETAL LOBE
1914	CMS CC	MS-DRG CC	MAL NEO OCCIPITAL LOBE
1915	CMS CC	MS-DRG CC	MAL NEO CEREB VENTRICLE
1916	CMS CC	MS-DRG CC	MAL NEO CEREBELLUM NOS
1917	CMS CC	MS-DRG CC	MAL NEO BRAINSTEM
1918	CMS CC	MS-DRG CC	MALIG NEO BRAIN NEC
1919	CMS CC	MS-DRG CC	MALIG NEO BRAIN NOS
1920	CMS CC	MS-DRG CC	MAL NEO CRANIAL NERVES
1921	CMS CC	MS-DRG CC	MAL NEO CEREBRAL MENING
1922	CMS CC	MS-DRG CC	MAL NEO SPINAL CORD
1923	CMS CC	MS-DRG CC	MAL NEO SPINAL MENINGES
1928	CMS CC	MS-DRG CC	MAL NEO NERVOUS SYST NEC
1929		MS-DRG CC	MAL NEO NERVOUS SYST NOS
1940		MS-DRG CC	MALIGN NEOPL ADRENAL
1941		MS-DRG CC	MALIG NEO PARATHYROID
1943		MS-DRG CC	MALIG NEO PITUITARY
1944		MS-DRG CC	MALIGN NEO PINEAL GLAND
1945		MS-DRG CC	MAL NEO CAROTID BODY
1946		MS-DRG CC	MAL NEO PARAGANGLIA NEC
1948		MS-DRG CC	MAL NEO ENDOCRINE NEC
1949		MS-DRG CC	MAL NEO ENDOCRINE NOS
1960	CMS CC	MS-DRG CC	MAL NEO LYMPH-HEAD/NECK
1961	CMS CC	MS-DRG CC	MAL NEO LYMPH-INTRATHOR
1962	CMS CC	MS-DRG CC	MAL NEO LYMPH INTRA-ABD
1963	CMS CC	MS-DRG CC	MAL NEO LYMPH-AXILLA/ARM
1965	CMS CC	MS-DRG CC	MAL NEO LYMPH-INGUIN/LEG
1966	CMS CC	MS-DRG CC	MAL NEO LYMPH-INTRAPELV
1968	CMS CC	MS-DRG CC	MAL NEO LYMPH NODE-MULT
1969	CMS CC	MS-DRG CC	MAL NEO LYMPH NODE NOS
1970	CMS CC	MS-DRG CC	SECONDARY MALIG NEO LUNG
1971	CMS CC	MS-DRG CC	SEC MAL NEO MEDIASTINUM
1972	CMS CC	MS-DRG CC	SECOND MALIG NEO PLEURA
1973	CMS CC	MS-DRG CC	SEC MALIG NEO RESP NEC
1974	CMS CC	MS-DRG CC	SEC MALIG NEO SM BOWEL
1975	CMS CC	MS-DRG CC	SEC MALIG NEO LG BOWEL
1976	CMS CC	MS-DRG CC	SEC MAL NEO PERITONEUM

2008 ICD-9-CM	CMS DRG	MS-DRG	Short Title
1977	CMS CC	MS-DRG CC	SECONDARY MALIG NEO LIVER
1978	CMS CC	MS-DRG CC	SECONDARY MAL NEO GI NEC
1980	CMS CC	MS-DRG CC	SECONDARY MALIG NEO KIDNEY
1981	CMS CC	MS-DRG CC	SECONDARY MALIG NEO URIN NEC
1982	CMS CC	MS-DRG CC	SECONDARY MALIG NEO SKIN
1983	CMS CC	MS-DRG CC	SECONDARY MAL NEO BRAIN/SPINE
1984	CMS CC	MS-DRG CC	SECONDARY MALIG NEO NERVE NEC
1985	CMS CC	MS-DRG CC	SECONDARY MALIG NEO BONE
1986	CMS CC	MS-DRG CC	SECONDARY MALIG NEO OVARY
1987	CMS CC	MS-DRG CC	SECONDARY MALIG NEO ADRENAL
19881	CMS CC	MS-DRG CC	SECONDARY MALIG NEO BREAST
19882	CMS CC	MS-DRG CC	SECONDARY MALIG NEO GENITAL
19889	CMS CC	MS-DRG CC	SECONDARY MALIG NEO NEC
1990	CMS CC	MS-DRG CC	MALIG NEO DISSEMINATED
20000	CMS CC	MS-DRG CC	RETCLSRC UNSP XTRNDL ORG
20001	CMS CC	MS-DRG CC	RETICULOSARCOMA HEAD
20002	CMS CC	MS-DRG CC	RETICULOSARCOMA THORAX
20003	CMS CC	MS-DRG CC	RETICULOSARCOMA ABDOM
20004	CMS CC	MS-DRG CC	RETICULOSARCOMA AXILLA
20005	CMS CC	MS-DRG CC	RETICULOSARCOMA INGUIN
20006	CMS CC	MS-DRG CC	RETICULOSARCOMA PELVIC
20007	CMS CC	MS-DRG CC	RETICULOSARCOMA SPLEEN
20008	CMS CC	MS-DRG CC	RETICULOSARCOMA MULT
20010	CMS CC	MS-DRG CC	LYMPHOSARCOMA UNSP XTRNDL ORG
20011	CMS CC	MS-DRG CC	LYMPHOSARCOMA HEAD
20012	CMS CC	MS-DRG CC	LYMPHOSARCOMA THORAX
20013	CMS CC	MS-DRG CC	LYMPHOSARCOMA ABDOM
20014	CMS CC	MS-DRG CC	LYMPHOSARCOMA AXILLA
20015	CMS CC	MS-DRG CC	LYMPHOSARCOMA INGUIN
20016	CMS CC	MS-DRG CC	LYMPHOSARCOMA PELVIC
20017	CMS CC	MS-DRG CC	LYMPHOSARCOMA SPLEEN
20018	CMS CC	MS-DRG CC	LYMPHOSARCOMA MULT
20020	CMS CC	MS-DRG CC	BURKITT'S TMR UNSP XTRNDL ORG
20021	CMS CC	MS-DRG CC	BURKITT'S TUMOR HEAD
20022	CMS CC	MS-DRG CC	BURKITT'S TUMOR THORAX
20023	CMS CC	MS-DRG CC	BURKITT'S TUMOR ABDOM
20024	CMS CC	MS-DRG CC	BURKITT'S TUMOR AXILLA
20025	CMS CC	MS-DRG CC	BURKITT'S TUMOR INGUIN
20026	CMS CC	MS-DRG CC	BURKITT'S TUMOR PELVIC

(Continued)

2008 ICD-9-CM	CMS DRG	MS-DRG	Short Title
20027	CMS CC	MS-DRG CC	BURKITT'S TUMOR SPLEEN
20028	CMS CC	MS-DRG CC	BURKITT'S TUMOR MULT
20030	CMS CC	MS-DRG CC	MARGIN ZONE LYM XTRNDL
20031	CMS CC	MS-DRG CC	MARGIN ZONE LYM HEAD
20032	CMS CC	MS-DRG CC	MARGIN ZONE LYM THORAX
20033	CMS CC	MS-DRG CC	MARGIN ZONE LYM ABDOM
20034	CMS CC	MS-DRG CC	MARGIN ZONE LYM AXILLA
20035	CMS CC	MS-DRG CC	MARGIN ZONE LYM INGUIN
20036	CMS CC	MS-DRG CC	MARGIN ZONE LYM PELVIC
20037	CMS CC	MS-DRG CC	MARGIN ZONE LYMPH SPLEEN
20038	CMS CC	MS-DRG CC	MARGIN ZONE LYMPH MULTIP
20040	CMS CC	MS-DRG CC	MANTLE CELL LYM XTRRNDL
20041	CMS CC	MS-DRG CC	MANTLE CELL LYMPH HEAD
20042	CMS CC	MS-DRG CC	MANTLE CELL LYMPH THORAX
20043	CMS CC	MS-DRG CC	MANTLE CELL LYMPH ABDOM
20044	CMS CC	MS-DRG CC	MANTLE CELL LYMPH AXILLA
20045	CMS CC	MS-DRG CC	MANTLE CELL LYMPH INGUIN
20046	CMS CC	MS-DRG CC	MANTLE CELL LYMPH PELVIC
20047	CMS CC	MS-DRG CC	MANTLE CELL LYMPH SPLEEN
20048	CMS CC	MS-DRG CC	MANTLE CELL LYMPH MULTIP
20050	CMS CC	MS-DRG CC	PRIMARY CNS LYMPH XTRNDL
20051	CMS CC	MS-DRG CC	PRIMARY CNS LYMPH HEAD
20052	CMS CC	MS-DRG CC	PRIMARY CNS LYMPH THORAX
20053	CMS CC	MS-DRG CC	PRIMARY CNS LYMPH ABDOM
20054	CMS CC	MS-DRG CC	PRIMARY CNS LYMPH AXILLA
20055	CMS CC	MS-DRG CC	PRIMARY CNS LYM INGUIN
20056	CMS CC	MS-DRG CC	PRIMARY CNS LYMPH PELVIC
20057	CMS CC	MS-DRG CC	PRIMARY CNS LYMPH SPLEEN
20058	CMS CC	MS-DRG CC	PRIMARY CNS LYMPH MULTIP
20060	CMS CC	MS-DRG CC	ANAPLASTIC LYMPH XTRNDL
20061	CMS CC	MS-DRG CC	ANAPLASTIC LYMPH HEAD
20062	CMS CC	MS-DRG CC	ANAPLASTIC LYMPH THORAX
20063	CMS CC	MS-DRG CC	ANAPLASTIC LYMPH ABDOM
20064	CMS CC	MS-DRG CC	ANAPLASTIC LYMPH AXILLA
20065	CMS CC	MS-DRG CC	ANAPLASTIC LYMPH INGUIN
20066	CMS CC	MS-DRG CC	ANAPLASTIC LYMPH PELVIC
20067	CMS CC	MS-DRG CC	ANAPLASTIC LYMPH SPLEEN
20068	CMS CC	MS-DRG CC	ANAPLASTIC LYMPH MULTIP
20070	CMS CC	MS-DRG CC	LARGE CELL LYMPH XTRNDL

2008 ICD-9-CM	CMS DRG	MS-DRG	Short Title
20071	CMS CC	MS-DRG CC	LARGE CELL LYMPHOMA HEAD
20072	CMS CC	MS-DRG CC	LARGE CELL LYMPH THORAX
20073	CMS CC	MS-DRG CC	LARGE CELL LYMPH ABDOM
20074	CMS CC	MS-DRG CC	LARGE CELL LYMPH AXILLA
20075	CMS CC	MS-DRG CC	LARGE CELL LYMPH INGUIN
20076	CMS CC	MS-DRG CC	LARGE CELL LYMPH PELVIC
20077	CMS CC	MS-DRG CC	LARGE CELL LYMPH SPLEEN
20078	CMS CC	MS-DRG CC	LARGE CELL LYMPH MULTIP
20080	CMS CC	MS-DRG CC	OTH VARN UNSP XTRNDL ORG
20081	CMS CC	MS-DRG CC	MIXED LYMPHOSARC HEAD
20082	CMS CC	MS-DRG CC	MIXED LYMPHOSARC THORAX
20083	CMS CC	MS-DRG CC	MIXED LYMPHOSARC ABDOM
20084	CMS CC	MS-DRG CC	MIXED LYMPHOSARC AXILLA
20085	CMS CC	MS-DRG CC	MIXED LYMPHOSARC INGUIN
20086	CMS CC	MS-DRG CC	MIXED LYMPHOSARC PELVIC
20087	CMS CC	MS-DRG CC	MIXED LYMPHOSARC SPLEEN
20088	CMS CC	MS-DRG CC	MIXED LYMPHOSARC MULT
20100	CMS CC	MS-DRG CC	HODGKINS PRG UNSP XTRNDL ORG
20101	CMS CC	MS-DRG CC	HODGKINS PARAGRAN HEAD
20102	CMS CC	MS-DRG CC	HODGKINS PARAGRAN THORAX
20103	CMS CC	MS-DRG CC	HODGKINS PARAGRAN ABDOM
20104	CMS CC	MS-DRG CC	HODGKINS PARAGRAN AXILLA
20105	CMS CC	MS-DRG CC	HODGKINS PARAGRAN INGUIN
20106	CMS CC	MS-DRG CC	HODGKINS PARAGRAN PELVIC
20107	CMS CC	MS-DRG CC	HODGKINS PARAGRAN SPLEEN
20108	CMS CC	MS-DRG CC	HODGKINS PARAGRAN MULT
20110	CMS CC	MS-DRG CC	HODGKINS GRN UNSP XTRNDL ORG
20111	CMS CC	MS-DRG CC	HODGKINS GRANULOM HEAD
20112	CMS CC	MS-DRG CC	HODGKINS GRANULOM THORAX
20113	CMS CC	MS-DRG CC	HODGKINS GRANULOM ABDOM
20114	CMS CC	MS-DRG CC	HODGKINS GRANULOM AXILLA
20115	CMS CC	MS-DRG CC	HODGKINS GRANULOM INGUIN
20116	CMS CC	MS-DRG CC	HODGKINS GRANULOM PELVIC
20117	CMS CC	MS-DRG CC	HODGKINS GRANULOM SPLEEN
20118	CMS CC	MS-DRG CC	HODGKINS GRANULOM MULT
20120	CMS CC	MS-DRG CC	HODGKINS SRC UNSP XTRNDL ORG
20121	CMS CC	MS-DRG CC	HODGKINS SARCOMA HEAD
20122	CMS CC	MS-DRG CC	HODGKINS SARCOMA THORAX
20123	CMS CC	MS-DRG CC	HODGKINS SARCOMA ABDOM

(Continued)

2008 ICD-9-CM	CMS DRG	MS-DRG	Short Title
20124	CMS CC	MS-DRG CC	HODGKINS SARCOMA AXILLA
20125	CMS CC	MS-DRG CC	HODGKINS SARCOMA INGUIN
20126	CMS CC	MS-DRG CC	HODGKINS SARCOMA PELVIC
20127	CMS CC	MS-DRG CC	HODGKINS SARCOMA SPLEEN
20128	CMS CC	MS-DRG CC	HODGKINS SARCOMA MULT
20140	CMS CC	MS-DRG CC	LYM-HST UNSP XTRNDL ORGN
20141	CMS CC	MS-DRG CC	HODGKINS LYMPH-HISTIO HEAD
20142	CMS CC	MS-DRG CC	HODGKINS LYMPH-HISTIO THORAX
20143	CMS CC	MS-DRG CC	HODGKINS LYMPH-HISTIO ABDOM
20144	CMS CC	MS-DRG CC	HODGKINS LYMPH-HISTIO AXILLA
20145	CMS CC	MS-DRG CC	HODGKINS LYMPH-HISTIO INGUIN
20146	CMS CC	MS-DRG CC	HODGKINS LYMPH-HISTIO PELVIC
20147	CMS CC	MS-DRG CC	HODGKINS LYMPH-HISTIO SPLEEN
20148	CMS CC	MS-DRG CC	HODGKINS LYMPH-HISTIO MULT
20150	CMS CC	MS-DRG CC	NDR SCLR UNSP XTRNDL ORG
20151	CMS CC	MS-DRG CC	HODGKINS NODUL SCLERO HEAD
20152	CMS CC	MS-DRG CC	HODGKINS NODUL SCLERO THORAX
20153	CMS CC	MS-DRG CC	HODGKINS NODUL SCLERO ABDOM
20154	CMS CC	MS-DRG CC	HODGKINS NODUL SCLERO AXILLA
20155	CMS CC	MS-DRG CC	HODGKINS NODUL SCLERO INGUIN
20156	CMS CC	MS-DRG CC	HODGKINS NODUL SCLERO PELVIC
20157	CMS CC	MS-DRG CC	HODGKINS NODUL SCLERO SPLEEN
20158	CMS CC	MS-DRG CC	HODGKINS NODUL SCLERO MULT
20160	CMS CC	MS-DRG CC	MXD CELR UNSP XTRNDL ORG
20161	CMS CC	MS-DRG CC	HODGKINS MIX CELL HEAD
20162	CMS CC	MS-DRG CC	HODGKINS MIX CELL THORAX
20163	CMS CC	MS-DRG CC	HODGKINS MIX CELL ABDOM
20164	CMS CC	MS-DRG CC	HODGKINS MIX CELL AXILLA
20165	CMS CC	MS-DRG CC	HODGKINS MIX CELL INGUIN
20166	CMS CC	MS-DRG CC	HODGKINS MIX CELL PELVIC
20167	CMS CC	MS-DRG CC	HODGKINS MIX CELL SPLEEN
20168	CMS CC	MS-DRG CC	HODGKINS MIX CELL MULT
20170	CMS CC	MS-DRG CC	LYM DPLT UNSP XTRNDL ORG
20171	CMS CC	MS-DRG CC	HODGKINS LYMPH DEPLET HEAD
20172	CMS CC	MS-DRG CC	HODGKINS LYMPH DEPLET THORAX
20173	CMS CC	MS-DRG CC	HODGKINS LYMPH DEPLET ABDOM
20174	CMS CC	MS-DRG CC	HODGKINS LYMPH DEPLET AXILLA
20175	CMS CC	MS-DRG CC	HODGKINS LYMPH DEPLET INGUIN
20176	CMS CC	MS-DRG CC	HODGKINS LYMPH DEPLET PELVIC

2008 ICD-9-CM	CMS DRG	MS-DRG	Short Title
20177	CMS CC	MS-DRG CC	HODGKINS LYMPH DEPLET SPLEEN
20178	CMS CC	MS-DRG CC	HODGKINS LYMPH DEPLET MULT
20190	CMS CC	MS-DRG CC	HODGKINS DIS UNSP XTRNDL ORG
20191	CMS CC	MS-DRG CC	HODGKINS DIS NOS HEAD
20192	CMS CC	MS-DRG CC	HODGKINS DIS NOS THORAX
20193	CMS CC	MS-DRG CC	HODGKINS DIS NOS ABDOM
20194	CMS CC	MS-DRG CC	HODGKINS DIS NOS AXILLA
20195	CMS CC	MS-DRG CC	HODGKINS DIS NOS INGUIN
20196	CMS CC	MS-DRG CC	HODGKINS DIS NOS PELVIC
20197	CMS CC	MS-DRG CC	HODGKINS DIS NOS SPLEEN
20198	CMS CC	MS-DRG CC	HODGKINS DIS NOS MULT
20200	CMS CC	MS-DRG CC	NODULAR LYM UNSP XTRNDL ORG
20201	CMS CC	MS-DRG CC	NODULAR LYMPHOMA HEAD
20202	CMS CC	MS-DRG CC	NODULAR LYMPHOMA THORAX
20203	CMS CC	MS-DRG CC	NODULAR LYMPHOMA ABDOM
20204	CMS CC	MS-DRG CC	NODULAR LYMPHOMA AXILLA
20205	CMS CC	MS-DRG CC	NODULAR LYMPHOMA INGUIN
20206	CMS CC	MS-DRG CC	NODULAR LYMPHOMA PELVIC
20207	CMS CC	MS-DRG CC	NODULAR LYMPHOMA SPLEEN
20208	CMS CC	MS-DRG CC	NODULAR LYMPHOMA MULT
20210	CMS CC	MS-DRG CC	MYCOSIS FNG UNSP XTRNDL ORG
20211	CMS CC	MS-DRG CC	MYCOSIS FUNGOIDES HEAD
20212	CMS CC	MS-DRG CC	MYCOSIS FUNGOIDES THORAX
20213	CMS CC	MS-DRG CC	MYCOSIS FUNGOIDES ABDOM
20214	CMS CC	MS-DRG CC	MYCOSIS FUNGOIDES AXILLA
20215	CMS CC	MS-DRG CC	MYCOSIS FUNGOIDES INGUIN
20216	CMS CC	MS-DRG CC	MYCOSIS FUNGOIDES PELVIC
20217	CMS CC	MS-DRG CC	MYCOSIS FUNGOIDES SPLEEN
20218	CMS CC	MS-DRG CC	MYCOSIS FUNGOIDES MULT
20220	CMS CC	MS-DRG CC	SEZARY'S DIS UNSP XTRNDL ORG
20221	CMS CC	MS-DRG CC	SEZARY'S DISEASE HEAD
20222	CMS CC	MS-DRG CC	SEZARY'S DISEASE THORAX
20223	CMS CC	MS-DRG CC	SEZARY'S DISEASE ABDOM
20224	CMS CC	MS-DRG CC	SEZARY'S DISEASE AXILLA
20225	CMS CC	MS-DRG CC	SEZARY'S DISEASE INGUIN
20226	CMS CC	MS-DRG CC	SEZARY'S DISEASE PELVIC
20227	CMS CC	MS-DRG CC	SEZARY'S DISEASE SPLEEN
20228	CMS CC	MS-DRG CC	SEZARY'S DISEASE MULT
20230	CMS CC	MS-DRG CC	MLG HIST UNSP XTRNDL ORG

(Continued)

2008 ICD-9-CM	CMS DRG	MS-DRG	Short Title
20231	CMS CC	MS-DRG CC	MAL HISTIOCYTOSIS HEAD
20232	CMS CC	MS-DRG CC	MAL HISTIOCYTOSIS THORAX
20233	CMS CC	MS-DRG CC	MAL HISTIOCYTOSIS ABDOM
20234	CMS CC	MS-DRG CC	MAL HISTIOCYTOSIS AXILLA
20235	CMS CC	MS-DRG CC	MAL HISTIOCYTOSIS INGUIN
20236	CMS CC	MS-DRG CC	MAL HISTIOCYTOSIS PELVIC
20237	CMS CC	MS-DRG CC	MAL HISTIOCYTOSIS SPLEEN
20238	CMS CC	MS-DRG CC	MAL HISTIOCYTOSIS MULT
20240	CMS CC	MS-DRG CC	LK RTCTL UNSP XTRNDL ORG
20241	CMS CC	MS-DRG CC	HAIRY-CELL LEUKEM HEAD
20242	CMS CC	MS-DRG CC	HAIRY-CELL LEUKEM THORAX
20243	CMS CC	MS-DRG CC	HAIRY-CELL LEUKEM ABDOM
20244	CMS CC	MS-DRG CC	HAIRY-CELL LEUKEM AXILLA
20245	CMS CC	MS-DRG CC	HAIRY-CELL LEUKEM INGUIN
20246	CMS CC	MS-DRG CC	HAIRY-CELL LEUKEM PELVIC
20247	CMS CC	MS-DRG CC	HAIRY-CELL LEUKEM SPLEEN
20248	CMS CC	MS-DRG CC	HAIRY-CELL LEUKEM MULT
20250	CMS CC	MS-DRG CC	LETTERER-SIWE UNSP XTRNDL ORG
20251	CMS CC	MS-DRG CC	LETTERER-SIWE DIS HEAD
20252	CMS CC	MS-DRG CC	LETTERER-SIWE DIS THORAX
20253	CMS CC	MS-DRG CC	LETTERER-SIWE DIS ABDOM
20254	CMS CC	MS-DRG CC	LETTERER-SIWE DIS AXILLA
20255	CMS CC	MS-DRG CC	LETTERER-SIWE DIS INGUIN
20256	CMS CC	MS-DRG CC	LETTERER-SIWE DIS PELVIC
20257	CMS CC	MS-DRG CC	LETTERER-SIWE DIS SPLEEN
20258	CMS CC	MS-DRG CC	LETTERER-SIWE DIS MULT
20260	CMS CC	MS-DRG CC	MLG MAST UNSP XTRNDL ORG
20261	CMS CC	MS-DRG CC	MAL MASTOCYTOSIS HEAD
20262	CMS CC	MS-DRG CC	MAL MASTOCYTOSIS THORAX
20263	CMS CC	MS-DRG CC	MAL MASTOCYTOSIS ABDOM
20264	CMS CC	MS-DRG CC	MAL MASTOCYTOSIS AXILLA
20265	CMS CC	MS-DRG CC	MAL MASTOCYTOSIS INGUIN
20266	CMS CC	MS-DRG CC	MAL MASTOCYTOSIS PELVIC
20267	CMS CC	MS-DRG CC	MAL MASTOCYTOSIS SPLEEN
20268	CMS CC	MS-DRG CC	MAL MASTOCYTOSIS MULT
20270	CMS CC	MS-DRG CC	PERIPH T CELL LYM XTRNDL
20271	CMS CC	MS-DRG CC	PERIPH T CELL LYMPH HEAD
20272	CMS CC	MS-DRG CC	PERIPH T CELL LYM THORAX
20273	CMS CC	MS-DRG CC	PERIPH T CELL LYM ABDOM

2008 ICD-9-CM	CMS DRG	MS-DRG	Short Title
20274	CMS CC	MS-DRG CC	PERIPH T CELL LYM AXILLA
20275	CMS CC	MS-DRG CC	PERIPH T CELL LYM INGUIN
20276	CMS CC	MS-DRG CC	PERIPH T CELL LYM PELVIC
20277	CMS CC	MS-DRG CC	PERIPH T CELL LYM SPLEEN
20278	CMS CC	MS-DRG CC	PERIPH T CELL LYM MULTIP
20280	CMS CC	MS-DRG CC	OTH LYMP UNSP XTRNDL ORG
20281	CMS CC	MS-DRG CC	LYMPHOMAS NEC HEAD
20282	CMS CC	MS-DRG CC	LYMPHOMAS NEC THORAX
20283	CMS CC	MS-DRG CC	LYMPHOMAS NEC ABDOM
20284	CMS CC	MS-DRG CC	LYMPHOMAS NEC AXILLA
20285	CMS CC	MS-DRG CC	LYMPHOMAS NEC INGUIN
20286	CMS CC	MS-DRG CC	LYMPHOMAS NEC PELVIC
20287	CMS CC	MS-DRG CC	LYMPHOMAS NEC SPLEEN
20288	CMS CC	MS-DRG CC	LYMPHOMAS NEC MULT
20290	CMS CC	MS-DRG CC	UNSP LYM UNSP XTRNDL ORG
20291	CMS CC	MS-DRG CC	LYMPHOID MAL NEC HEAD
20292	CMS CC	MS-DRG CC	LYMPHOID MAL NEC THORAX
20293	CMS CC	MS-DRG CC	LYMPHOID MAL NEC ABDOM
20294	CMS CC	MS-DRG CC	LYMPHOID MAL NEC AXILLA
20295	CMS CC	MS-DRG CC	LYMPHOID MAL NEC INGUIN
20296	CMS CC	MS-DRG CC	LYMPHOID MAL NEC PELVIC
20297	CMS CC	MS-DRG CC	LYMPHOID MAL NEC SPLEEN
20298	CMS CC	MS-DRG CC	LYMPHOID MAL NEC MULT
20300	CMS CC	MS-DRG CC	MULT MYELM W/O REMISSION
20301	CMS CC	MS-DRG CC	MULT MYELM W REMISSION
20310	CMS CC	MS-DRG CC	PLSM CELL LEUK W/O REMISSION
20311	CMS CC	MS-DRG CC	PLSM CELL LEUK W REMISSION
20380	CMS CC	MS-DRG CC	OTH IMNPRFL NPL W/O REMISSION
20381	CMS CC	MS-DRG CC	OTH IMNPRFL NPL W REMISSION
20400	CMS CC	MS-DRG CC	ACT LYM LEUK W/O REMISSION
20401	CMS CC	MS-DRG CC	ACT LYM LEUK W REMISSION
20410	CMS CC	MS-DRG CC	CHR LYM LEUK W/O REMISSION
20411	CMS CC	MS-DRG CC	CHR LYM LEUK W REMISSION
20420	CMS CC	MS-DRG CC	SBAC LYM LEUK W/O REMISSION
20421	CMS CC	MS-DRG CC	SBAC LYM LEUK W REMISSION
20480	CMS CC	MS-DRG CC	OTH LYM LEUK W/O REMISSION
20481	CMS CC	MS-DRG CC	OTH LYM LEUK W REMISSION
20490	CMS CC	MS-DRG CC	UNS LYM LEUK W/O REMISSION
20491	CMS CC	MS-DRG CC	UNS LYM LEUK W REMISSION

(Continued)

2008 ICD-9-CM	CMS DRG	MS-DRG	Short Title
20500	CMS CC	MS-DRG CC	ACT MYL LEUK W/O REMISSION
20501	CMS CC	MS-DRG CC	ACT MYL LEUK W REMISSION
20510	CMS CC	MS-DRG CC	CHR MYL LEUK W/O REMISSION
20511	CMS CC	MS-DRG CC	CHR MYL LEUK W REMISSION
20520	CMS CC	MS-DRG CC	SBAC MYL LEUK W/O REMISSION
20521	CMS CC	MS-DRG CC	SBAC MYL LEUK W REMISSION
20530	CMS CC	MS-DRG CC	MYL SRCOMA W/O REMISSION
20531	CMS CC	MS-DRG CC	MYL SRCOMA W REMISSION
20580	CMS CC	MS-DRG CC	OTH MYL LEUK W/O REMISSION
20581	CMS CC	MS-DRG CC	OTH MYL LEUK W REMISSION
20590	CMS CC	MS-DRG CC	UNS MYL LEUK W/O REMISSION
20591	CMS CC	MS-DRG CC	UNS MYL LEUK W REMISSION
20600	CMS CC	MS-DRG CC	ACT MONO LEUK W/O REMISSION
20601	CMS CC	MS-DRG CC	ACT MONO LEUK W REMISSION
20610	CMS CC	MS-DRG CC	CHR MONO LEUK W/O REMISSION
20611	CMS CC	MS-DRG CC	CHR MONO LEUK W REMISSION
20620	CMS CC	MS-DRG CC	SBAC MONO LEUK W/O REMISSION
20621	CMS CC	MS-DRG CC	SBAC MONO LEUK W REMISSION
20680	CMS CC	MS-DRG CC	OTH MONO LEUK W/O REMISSION
20681	CMS CC	MS-DRG CC	OTH MONO LEUK W REMISSION
20690	CMS CC	MS-DRG CC	UNS MONO LEUK W/O REMISSION
20691	CMS CC	MS-DRG CC	UNS MONO LEUK W REMISSION
20700	CMS CC	MS-DRG CC	ACT ERTH/ERYLK W/O REMISSION
20701	CMS CC	MS-DRG CC	ACT ERTH/ERYLK W REMISSION
20710	CMS CC	MS-DRG CC	CHR ERYTHRM W/O REMISSION
20711	CMS CC	MS-DRG CC	CHR ERYTHRM W REMISSION
20720	CMS CC	MS-DRG CC	MGKRYCYT LEUK W/O REMISSION
20721	CMS CC	MS-DRG CC	MGKRYCYT LEUK W REMISSION
20780	CMS CC	MS-DRG CC	OTH SPF LEUK W/O REMISSION
20781	CMS CC	MS-DRG CC	OTH SPF LEUK W REMISSION
20800	CMS CC	MS-DRG CC	ACT LEUK UNS CL W/O REMISSION
20801	CMS CC	MS-DRG CC	ACT LEUK UNS CL W REMISSION
20810	CMS CC	MS-DRG CC	CHR LEUK UNS CL W/O REMISSION
20811	CMS CC	MS-DRG CC	CHR LEUK UNS CL W REMISSION
20820	CMS CC	MS-DRG CC	SBAC LEUK UNS CL W/O REMISSION
20821	CMS CC	MS-DRG CC	SBAC LEUK UNS CL W REMISSION
20880	CMS CC	MS-DRG CC	OTH LEUK UNS CL W/O REMISSION
20881	CMS CC	MS-DRG CC	OTH LEUK UNS CL W REMISSION
20890	CMS CC	MS-DRG CC	LEUKEMIA NOS W/O REMISSION

2008 ICD-9-CM	CMS DRG	MS-DRG	Short Title
20891	CMS CC	MS-DRG CC	LEUKEMIA NOS W REMISSION
2385		MS-DRG CC	MASTOCYTOMA NOS
2386		MS-DRG CC	PLASMACYTOMA NOS
23873		MS-DRG CC	HI GRDE MYELODYS SYN LES
23874		MS-DRG CC	MYELODYSPLS SYN W 5Q DEL
23876		MS-DRG CC	MYELOFI W MYELO METAPLAS
23879		MS-DRG CC	LYMPH/HEMATPOITC TIS NEC
24200	CMS CC		TOX DIF GOITER NO CRISIS
24201	CMS CC	MS-DRG MCC	TOX DIF GOITER W CRISIS
24210	CMS CC		TOX UNINOD GOIT NO CRIS
24211	CMS CC	MS-DRG MCC	TOX UNINOD GOIT W CRISIS
24220	CMS CC		TOX MULTNOD GOIT NO CRIS
24221	CMS CC	MS-DRG MCC	TOX MULTNOD GOIT W CRIS
24230	CMS CC		TOX NOD GOITER NO CRISIS
24231	CMS CC	MS-DRG MCC	TOX NOD GOITER W CRISIS
24240	CMS CC		THYROTOX-ECT NOD NO CRIS
24241	CMS CC	MS-DRG MCC	THYROTOX-ECT NOD W CRIS
24280	CMS CC		THYROTOX ORIG NEC NO CRIS
24281	CMS CC	MS-DRG MCC	THYROTOX ORIG NEC W CRIS
24290	CMS CC		THYROTOX NOS NO CRISIS
24291	CMS CC	MS-DRG MCC	THYROTOX NOS W CRISIS
2450		MS-DRG CC	ACUTE THYROIDITIS
2463		MS-DRG CC	HEMORR/INFARC THYROID
25001	CMS CC		DMI WO CMP NT ST UNCNTRL
25002	CMS CC		DMII WO CMP UNCNTRLD
25003	CMS CC		DMI WO CMP UNCNTRLD
25010		MS-DRG MCC	DMII KETO NT ST UNCNTRLD
25011	CMS CC	MS-DRG MCC	DMI KETO NT ST UNCNTRLD
25012	CMS CC	MS-DRG MCC	DMII KETOACD UNCONTROLD
25013	CMS CC	MS-DRG MCC	DMI KETOACD UNCONTROLD
25020		MS-DRG MCC	DMII HPRSM NT ST UNCNTRL
25021	CMS CC	MS-DRG MCC	DMI HPRSM NT ST UNCNTRLD
25022	CMS CC	MS-DRG MCC	DMII HPROSMLR UNCONTROLD
25023	CMS CC	MS-DRG MCC	DMI HPROSMLR UNCONTROLD
25030		MS-DRG MCC	DMII O CM NT ST UNCNTRLD
25031	CMS CC	MS-DRG MCC	DMI O CM NT ST UNCNTRLD
25032	CMS CC	MS-DRG MCC	DMII OTH COMA UNCONTROLD
25033	CMS CC	MS-DRG MCC	DMI OTH COMA UNCONTROLD
25041	CMS CC		DMI RENL NT ST UNCNTRLD

(Continued)

2008 ICD-9-CM	CMS DRG	MS-DRG	Short Title
25042	CMS CC		DMII RENAL UNCNTRLD
25043	CMS CC		DMI RENAL UNCNTRLD
25051	CMS CC		DMI OPHTH NT ST UNCNTRLD
25052	CMS CC		DMII OPHTH UNCNTRLD
25053	CMS CC		DMI OPHTH UNCNTRLD
25061	CMS CC		DMI NEURO NT ST UNCNTRLD
25062	CMS CC		DMII NEURO UNCNTRLD
25063	CMS CC		DMI NEURO UNCNTRLD
25071	CMS CC		DMI CIRC NT ST UNCNTRLD
25072	CMS CC		DMII CIRC UNCNTRLD
25073	CMS CC		DMI CIRC UNCNTRLD
25081	CMS CC		DMI OTH NT ST UNCNTRLD
25082	CMS CC		DMII OTH UNCNTRLD
25083	CMS CC		DMI OTH UNCNTRLD
25091	CMS CC		DMI UNSPF NT ST UNCNTRLD
25092	CMS CC		DMII UNSPF UNCNTRLD
25093	CMS CC		DMI UNSPF UNCNTRLD
2510	CMS CC	MS-DRG CC	HYPOGLYCEMIC COMA
2513	CMS CC	MS-DRG CC	POSTSURG HYPOINSULINEMIA
2521	CMS CC		HYPOPARATHYROIDISM
2531		MS-DRG CC	ANT PITUIT HYPERFUNC NEC
2532	CMS CC	MS-DRG CC	PANHYPOPITUITARISM
2535	CMS CC	MS-DRG CC	DIABETES INSIPIDUS
2536		MS-DRG CC	NEUROHYPOPHYSIS DIS NEC
2541	CMS CC	MS-DRG CC	ABSCESS OF THYMUS
2550	CMS CC	MS-DRG CC	CUSHING'S SYNDROME
2553	CMS CC	MS-DRG CC	CORTICOADREN OVERACT NEC
25541	CMS CC	MS-DRG CC	GLUCOCORTICOID DEFICIENT
25542	CMS CC	MS-DRG CC	MINERALCORTICOID DEFCNT
2555	CMS CC	MS-DRG CC	ADRENAL HYPOFUNCTION NEC
2556	CMS CC	MS-DRG CC	MEDULLOADRENAL HYPERFUNC
25801	CMS CC		MULT ENDO NEOPLAS TYPE I
25802	CMS CC		MULT ENDO NEOP TYPE IIA
25803	CMS CC		MULT ENDO NEOP TYPE IIB
2581	CMS CC		COMB ENDOCR DYSFUNCT NEC
2588	CMS CC		POLYGLANDUL DYSFUNC NEC
2589	CMS CC		POLYGLANDUL DYSFUNC NOS
2592	CMS CC	MS-DRG CC	CARCINOID SYNDROME
260	CMS CC	MS-DRG MCC	KWASHIORKOR

2008 ICD-9-CM	CMS DRG	MS-DRG	Short Title
261	CMS CC	MS-DRG MCC	NUTRITIONAL MARASMUS
262	CMS CC	MS-DRG MCC	OTH SEVERE MALNUTRITION
2630	CMS CC		MALNUTRITION MOD DEGREE
2631	CMS CC		MALNUTRITION MILD DEGREE
2632	CMS CC	MS-DRG CC	ARREST DEVEL D/T MALNUTR
2638	CMS CC	MS-DRG CC	PROTEIN-CAL MALNUTR NEC
2639	CMS CC	MS-DRG CC	PROTEIN-CAL MALNUTR NOS
2650		MS-DRG CC	BERIBERI
2651		MS-DRG CC	THIAMINE DEFIC NEC/NOS
2660		MS-DRG CC	ARIBOFLAVINOSIS
2680		MS-DRG CC	RICKETS, ACTIVE
2700		MS-DRG CC	AMINO-ACID TRANSPORT DIS
2701		MS-DRG CC	PHENYLKETONURIA - PKU
2702		MS-DRG CC	AROM AMIN-ACID METAB NEC
2703		MS-DRG CC	BRAN-CHAIN AMIN-ACID DIS
2704		MS-DRG CC	SULPH AMINO-ACID MET DIS
2705		MS-DRG CC	DIS HISTIDINE METABOLISM
2706		MS-DRG CC	DIS UREA CYCLE METABOL
2707		MS-DRG CC	STRAIG AMIN-ACID MET NEC
2708		MS-DRG CC	DIS AMINO-ACID METAB NEC
2709		MS-DRG CC	DIS AMINO-ACID METAB NOS
2710		MS-DRG CC	GLYCOGENOSIS
2711		MS-DRG CC	GALACTOSEMIA
2718		MS-DRG CC	DIS CARBOHYDR METAB NEC
2733	CMS CC		MACROGLOBULINEMIA
27411		MS-DRG CC	URIC ACID NEPHROLITHIAS
2760	CMS CC	MS-DRG CC	HYPEROSMOLALITY
2761	CMS CC	MS-DRG CC	HYPOSMOLALITY
2762	CMS CC	MS-DRG CC	ACIDOSIS
2763	CMS CC	MS-DRG CC	ALKALOSIS
2764	CMS CC	MS-DRG CC	MIXED ACID-BASE BAL DIS
27650	CMS CC		VOLUME DEPLETION NOS
27651	CMS CC		DEHYDRATION
27652	CMS CC		HYPOVOLEMIA
2766	CMS CC		FLUID OVERLOAD
2767	CMS CC		HYPERPOTASSEMIA
2769	CMS CC		ELECTROLYT/FLUID DIS NEC
27700	CMS CC	MS-DRG CC	CYSTIC FIBROSIS W/O ILEUS
27701	CMS CC	MS-DRG MCC	CYSTIC FIBROSIS W ILEUS

(Continued)

2008 ICD-9-CM	CMS DRG	MS-DRG	Short Title
27702	CMS CC	MS-DRG MCC	CYSTIC FIBROSIS W PUL MAN
27703	CMS CC	MS-DRG CC	CYSTIC FIBROSIS W GI MAN
27709	CMS CC	MS-DRG CC	CYSTIC FIBROSIS NEC
2771		MS-DRG CC	DIS PORPHYRIN METABOLISM
2772		MS-DRG CC	PURINE/PYRIMID DIS NEC
27730		MS-DRG CC	AMYLOIDOSIS NOS
27731		MS-DRG CC	FAM MEDITERRANEAN FEVER
27739		MS-DRG CC	AMYLOIDOSIS NEC
2775		MS-DRG CC	MUCOPOLYSACCHARIDOSIS
27785		MS-DRG CC	DISORDERS ACID OXIDATION
27786		MS-DRG CC	PEROXISOMAL DISORDERS
27787		MS-DRG CC	DIS MITOCHONDRIAL METAB
27789		MS-DRG CC	METABOLISM DISORDER NEC
27900		MS-DRG CC	HYPOGAMMAGLOBULINEM NOS
27901		MS-DRG CC	SELECTIVE IGA IMMUNODEF
27902	CMS CC	MS-DRG CC	SELECTIVE IGM IMMUNODEF
27903	CMS CC	MS-DRG CC	SELECTIVE IG DEFIC NEC
27904	CMS CC	MS-DRG CC	CONG HYPOGAMMAGLOBULINEM
27905	CMS CC	MS-DRG CC	IMMUNODEFIC W HYPER-IGM
27906	CMS CC	MS-DRG CC	COMMON VARIABL IMMUNODEF
27909	CMS CC	MS-DRG CC	HUMORAL IMMUNITY DEF NEC
27910	CMS CC	MS-DRG CC	IMMUNDEF T-CELL DEF NOS
27911	CMS CC	MS-DRG CC	DIGEORGE'S SYNDROME
27912	CMS CC	MS-DRG CC	WISKOTT-ALDRICH SYNDROME
27913	CMS CC	MS-DRG CC	NEZELOF'S SYNDROME
27919	CMS CC	MS-DRG CC	DEFIC CELL IMMUNITY NOS
2792	CMS CC	MS-DRG CC	COMBINED IMMUNITY DEFIC
2793	CMS CC	MS-DRG CC	IMMUNITY DEFICIENCY NOS
2794	CMS CC		AUTOIMMUNE DISEASE NEC
2798	CMS CC		IMMUNE MECHANISM DIS NEC
2799	CMS CC		IMMUNE MECHANISM DIS NOS
2800	CMS CC		CHR BLOOD LOSS ANEMIA
2814	CMS CC		PROTEIN DEFIC ANEMIA
2818	CMS CC		NUTRITIONAL ANEMIA NEC
28241	CMS CC		THALASEMA HB-S W/O CRISIS
28242	CMS CC	MS-DRG MCC	THALASSEMIA HB-S W CRISIS
28249	CMS CC		THALASSEMIA NEC
28260	CMS CC		SICKLE CELL DISEASE NOS
28261	CMS CC		HB-SS DISEASE W/O CRISIS

2008 ICD-9-CM	CMS DRG	MS-DRG	Short Title
28262	CMS CC	MS-DRG MCC	HB-SS DISEASE W CRISIS
28263	CMS CC		HB-SS/HB-C DIS W/O CRSIS
28264	CMS CC	MS-DRG MCC	HB-S/HB-C DIS W CRISIS
28268	CMS CC		HB-S DIS W/O CRISIS NEC
28269	CMS CC	MS-DRG MCC	HB-SS DIS NEC W CRISIS
2828		MS-DRG CC	HERED HEMOLYTIC ANEM NEC
2829		MS-DRG CC	HERED HEMOLYTIC ANEM NOS
2830	CMS CC	MS-DRG CC	AUTOIMMUN HEMOLYTIC ANEM
28310	CMS CC	MS-DRG CC	NONAUTO HEM ANEMIA NOS
28311	CMS CC	MS-DRG MCC	HEMOLYTIC UREMIC SYND
28319	CMS CC	MS-DRG CC	OTH NONAUTO HEM ANEMIA
2832	CMS CC		HEMOLYTIC HEMOGLOBINURIA
2839	CMS CC	MS-DRG CC	ACQ HEMOLYTIC ANEMIA NOS
28401		MS-DRG CC	CONSTITUTION RBC APLASIA
28409		MS-DRG CC	CONST APLASTC ANEMIA NEC
2841		MS-DRG CC	PANCYTOPENIA
2842		MS-DRG CC	MYELOPHTHISIS
28481	CMS CC	MS-DRG MCC	RED CELL APLASIA
28489	CMS CC	MS-DRG MCC	APLASTIC ANEMIA NEC
2849	CMS CC	MS-DRG CC	APLASTIC ANEMIA NOS
2850	CMS CC		SIDEROBLASTIC ANEMIA
2851	CMS CC	MS-DRG CC	AC POSTHEMORRHAG ANEMIA
2860	CMS CC	MS-DRG MCC	CONG FACTOR VIII DIORD
2861	CMS CC	MS-DRG MCC	CONG FACTOR IX DISORDER
2862	CMS CC	MS-DRG CC	CONG FACTOR XI DISORDER
2863	CMS CC	MS-DRG CC	CONG DEF CLOT FACTOR NEC
2864	CMS CC	MS-DRG CC	VON WILLEBRAND'S DISEASE
2865	CMS CC	MS-DRG CC	INTR CIRCUL ANTICOAG DIS
2866	CMS CC	MS-DRG MCC	DEFIBRINATION SYNDROME
2867	CMS CC	MS-DRG CC	ACQ COAGUL FACTOR DEFIC
2869	CMS CC	MS-DRG CC	COAGULAT DEFECT NEC/NOS
2870	CMS CC	MS-DRG CC	ALLERGIC PURPURA
2871	CMS CC		THROMBOCYTOPATHY
2872	CMS CC		PURPURA NOS
28730	CMS CC		PRIM THROMBOCYTOPEN NOS
28731	CMS CC	MS-DRG CC	IMMUNE THROMBOCYT PURPRA
28732	CMS CC	MS-DRG CC	EVANS' SYNDROME
28733	CMS CC	MS-DRG CC	CONG/HERID THROMB PURPRA
28739	CMS CC		PRIM THROMBOCYTOPEN NEC

2008 ICD-9-CM	CMS DRG	MS-DRG	Short Title
2874	CMS CC		SECOND THROMBOCYTOPENIA
2875	CMS CC		THROMBOCYTOPENIA NOS
2878	CMS CC		HEMORRHAGIC COND NEC
2879	CMS CC		HEMORRHAGIC COND NOS
2881	CMS CC		FUNCTION DIS NEUTROPHILS
2884		MS-DRG CC	HEMOPHAGOCYTIC SYNDROMES
2897		MS-DRG CC	METHEMOGLOBINEMIA
28981	CMS CC	MS-DRG CC	PRIM HYPERCOAGULABLE ST
28982	CMS CC	MS-DRG CC	SEC HYPERCOAGULABLE ST
28983		MS-DRG CC	MYELOFIBROSIS
29011		MS-DRG CC	PRESENILE DELIRIUM
29012		MS-DRG CC	PRESENILE DELUSION
29013		MS-DRG CC	PRESENILE DEPRESSION
29020		MS-DRG CC	SENILE DELUSION
29021		MS-DRG CC	SENILE DEPRESSIVE
2903		MS-DRG CC	SENILE DELIRIUM
29041		MS-DRG CC	VASC DEMENTIA W DELIRIUM
29042		MS-DRG CC	VASC DEMENTIA W DELUSION
29043		MS-DRG CC	VASC DEMENTIA W DEPRESSN
2908		MS-DRG CC	SENILE PSYCHOSIS NEC
2909		MS-DRG CC	SENILE PSYCHOT COND NOS
2910	CMS CC	MS-DRG CC	DELIRIUM TREMENS
2911	CMS CC		ALCOHOL AMNESTIC DISORDR
2912	CMS CC	MS-DRG CC	ALCOHOL PERSIST DEMENTIA
2913	CMS CC	MS-DRG CC	ALCOH PSY DIS W HALLUCIN
2914	CMS CC		PATHOLOGIC ALCOHOL INTOX
29181	CMS CC	MS-DRG CC	ALCOHOL WITHDRAWAL
29182	CMS CC		ALCOHOL INDUCE SLEEP DISOR
29189	CMS CC	MS-DRG CC	ALCOHOL MENTAL DISOR NEC
2919	CMS CC	MS-DRG CC	ALCOHOL MENTAL DISOR NOS
2920	CMS CC	MS-DRG CC	DRUG WITHDRAWAL
29211	CMS CC	MS-DRG CC	DRUG PSYCH DISOR W DELUS
29212	CMS CC	MS-DRG CC	DRUG PSYCH DIS W HALLUCIN
2922	CMS CC		PATHOLOGIC DRUG INTOX
29281	CMS CC	MS-DRG CC	DRUG-INDUCED DELIRIUM
29282	CMS CC	MS-DRG CC	DRUG PERSISTING DEMENTIA
29283	CMS CC		DRUG PERSIST AMNESTC DIS
29284	CMS CC		DRUG-INDUCED MOOD DISORD
29285	CMS CC		DRUG-INDUCED SLEEP DISOR

2008 ICD-9-CM	CMS DRG	MS-DRG	Short Title
29289	CMS CC		DRUG MENTAL DISORDER NEC
2929	CMS CC		DRUG MENTAL DISORDER NOS
2930		MS-DRG CC	DELIRIUM D/T OTHER COND
2931		MS-DRG CC	SUBACUTE DELIRIUM
29381	CMS CC	MS-DRG CC	PSY DIS W DELUS OTH DIS
29382	CMS CC	MS-DRG CC	PSY DIS W HALLUC OTH DIS
29383	CMS CC		MOOD DISORDER OTHER DIS
29384	CMS CC		ANXIETY DISORDER OTH DIS
2939		MS-DRG CC	TRANSIENT MENTAL DIS NOS
29411		MS-DRG CC	DEMENTIA W BEHAVIOR DIST
29500	CMS CC	MS-DRG CC	SIMPL SCHIZOPHREN-UNSPEC
29501	CMS CC	MS-DRG CC	SIMPL SCHIZOPHREN-SUBCHR
29502	CMS CC	MS-DRG CC	SIMPLE SCHIZOPHREN-CHR
29503	CMS CC	MS-DRG CC	SIMP SCHIZ-SUBCHR/EXACER
29504	CMS CC	MS-DRG CC	SIMPL SCHIZO-CHR/EXACERB
29510	CMS CC	MS-DRG CC	HEBEPHRENIA-UNSPEC
29511	CMS CC	MS-DRG CC	HEBEPHRENIA-SUBCHRONIC
29512	CMS CC	MS-DRG CC	HEBEPHRENIA-CHRONIC
29513	CMS CC	MS-DRG CC	HEBEPHREN-SUBCHR/EXACERB
29514	CMS CC	MS-DRG CC	HEBEPHRENIA-CHR/EXACERB
29520		MS-DRG CC	CATATONIA-UNSPEC
29521	CMS CC	MS-DRG CC	CATATONIA-SUBCHRONIC
29522	CMS CC	MS-DRG CC	CATATONIA-CHRONIC
29523	CMS CC	MS-DRG CC	CATATONIA-SUBCHR/EXACERB
29524	CMS CC	MS-DRG CC	CATATONIA-CHR/EXACERB
29530	CMS CC	MS-DRG CC	PARANOID SCHIZO-UNSPEC
29531	CMS CC	MS-DRG CC	PARANOID SCHIZO-SUBCHR
29532	CMS CC	MS-DRG CC	PARANOID SCHIZO-CHRONIC
29533	CMS CC	MS-DRG CC	PARANOID SCHIZO-SUBCHR/EXAC
29534	CMS CC	MS-DRG CC	PARANOID SCHIZO-CHR/EXACERB
29540	CMS CC	MS-DRG CC	SCHIZOPHRENIFORM DIS NOS
29541	CMS CC	MS-DRG CC	SCHIZOPHRENIC DIS-SUBCHR
29542	CMS CC	MS-DRG CC	SCHIZOPHRENIC DIS-CHRONIC
29543	CMS CC	MS-DRG CC	SCHIZOPHRENIC DIS-SUBCHR/EXACER
29544	CMS CC	MS-DRG CC	SCHIZOPHRENIC DIS-CHR/EXACER
29553		MS-DRG CC	LAT SCHIZOPHRENIC-SUBCHR/EXACER
29554		MS-DRG CC	LATENT SCHIZOPHRENIC-CHR/EXACER
29560	CMS CC	MS-DRG CC	SCHIZOPHRENIC DIS RESID NOS
29561	CMS CC	MS-DRG CC	SCHIZOPHRENIC DIS RESID-SUBCH

(Continued)

2008 ICD-9-CM	CMS DRG	MS-DRG	Short Title
29562	CMS CC	MS-DRG CC	SCHIZOPHRENIC DIS RESID-CHR
29563	CMS CC	MS-DRG CC	SCHIZOPHRENIC RESID SUBCHR/EXAC
29564	CMS CC	MS-DRG CC	SCHIZOPHRENIC RESID-CHRO/EXAC
29570	CMS CC		SCHIZOAFFECTIVE DIS NOS
29571	CMS CC	MS-DRG CC	SCHIZOAFFECTV DIS-SUBCHR
29572	CMS CC	MS-DRG CC	SCHIZOAFFECTIVE DIS-CHR
29573	CMS CC	MS-DRG CC	SCHIZOAFFECTIVE DIS-SUBCH/EXAC
29574	CMS CC	MS-DRG CC	SCHIZOAFFECTIVE DIS-CHR/EXAC
29580	CMS CC	MS-DRG CC	SCHIZOPHRENIA NEC-UNSPEC
29581	CMS CC	MS-DRG CC	SCHIZOPHRENIA NEC-SUBCHR
29582	CMS CC	MS-DRG CC	SCHIZOPHRENIA NEC-CHR
29583	CMS CC	MS-DRG CC	SCHIZOPHRENIA NEC-SUBCHR/EXACER
29584	CMS CC	MS-DRG CC	SCHIZOPHRENIA NEC-CHR/EXACERB
29590	CMS CC		SCHIZOPHRENIA NOS-UNSPEC
29591	CMS CC	MS-DRG CC	SCHIZOPHRENIA NOS-SUBCHR
29592	CMS CC	MS-DRG CC	SCHIZOPHRENIA NOS-CHR
29593	CMS CC	MS-DRG CC	SCHIZOPHRENIA NOS-SUBCHR/EXACER
29594	CMS CC	MS-DRG CC	SCHIZOPHRENIA NOS-CHR/EXACERB
29600		MS-DRG CC	BIPOL I SINGLE MANIC NOS
29601		MS-DRG CC	BIPOL I SINGLE MANC-MILD
29602		MS-DRG CC	BIPOL I SINGLE MANIC-MOD
29603		MS-DRG CC	BIPOL I SING-SEV W/O PSY
29604	CMS CC	MS-DRG CC	BIPOL I SIN MAN-SEV W PSY
29610		MS-DRG CC	RECUR MANIC DIS-UNSPEC
29611		MS-DRG CC	RECUR MANIC DIS-MILD
29612		MS-DRG CC	RECUR MANIC DIS-MOD
29613		MS-DRG CC	RECUR MANIC DIS-SEVERE
29614	CMS CC	MS-DRG CC	RECUR MANIC-SEV W PSYCHO
29620		MS-DRG CC	DEPRESSIVE PSYCHOSIS-UNSPEC
29621		MS-DRG CC	DEPRESSIVE PSYCHOSIS-MILD
29622		MS-DRG CC	DEPRESSIVE PSYCHOSIS-MOD
29623		MS-DRG CC	DEPRESSIVE PSYCHOSIS-SEVERE
29624		MS-DRG CC	DEPRESSIVE PSYCHOS-SEV W PSYCH
29630		MS-DRG CC	RECURR DEPR PSYCHOS-UNSP
29631		MS-DRG CC	RECURR DEPR PSYCHOS-MILD
29632		MS-DRG CC	RECURR DEPR PSYCHOS-MOD
29633		MS-DRG CC	RECURR DEPR PSYCH-SEVERE
29634	CMS CC	MS-DRG CC	RECURR DEPR PSYCH-PSYCHOTIC
29640		MS-DRG CC	BIPOL I CURRNT MANIC NOS

2008 ICD-9-CM	CMS DRG	MS-DRG	Short Title
29641		MS-DRG CC	BIPOL I CURRNT MANIC-MILD
29642		MS-DRG CC	BIPOL I CURRNT MANIC-MOD
29643		MS-DRG CC	BIPOL I MANC-SEV W/O PSY
29644	CMS CC	MS-DRG CC	BIPOL I MANIC-SEV W PSY
29650		MS-DRG CC	BIPOL I CURRNT DEPRES NOS
29651		MS-DRG CC	BIPOL I CURRNT DEPRESS-MILD
29652		MS-DRG CC	BIPOL I CURRNT DEPRESS-MOD
29653		MS-DRG CC	BIPOL I CURRNT DEP W/O PSY
29654	CMS CC	MS-DRG CC	BIPOL I CURRNT DEP W PSY
29660		MS-DRG CC	BIPOL I CURRNT MIXED NOS
29661		MS-DRG CC	BIPOL I CURRNT MIX-MILD
29662		MS-DRG CC	BIPOL I CURRNT MIXED-MOD
29663		MS-DRG CC	BIPOL I CURRNT MIX W/O PSY
29664	CMS CC	MS-DRG CC	BIPOL I CURRNT MIXED W PSY
29689		MS-DRG CC	BIPOLAR DISORDER NEC
29699		MS-DRG CC	EPISODIC MOOD DISORD NEC
2980	CMS CC	MS-DRG CC	REACT DEPRESS PSYCHOSIS
2981		MS-DRG CC	EXCITATIV TYPE PSYCHOSIS
2983	CMS CC	MS-DRG CC	ACUTE PARANOID REACTION
2984	CMS CC	MS-DRG CC	PSYCHOGEN PARANOID PSYCH
29900	CMS CC	MS-DRG CC	AUTISTIC DISORD-CURRENT
29901		MS-DRG CC	AUTISTIC DISORD-RESIDUAL
29910	CMS CC	MS-DRG CC	CHILDHD DISINTEGR-ACTIVE
29911		MS-DRG CC	CHILDHD DISINTEGR-RESID
29980	CMS CC	MS-DRG CC	PERVASV DEV DIS-CUR NEC
29981		MS-DRG CC	PERVASV DEV DIS-RES NEC
29990	CMS CC	MS-DRG CC	PERVASV DEV DIS-CUR NOS
29991		MS-DRG CC	PERVASV DEV DIS-RES NOS
30151		MS-DRG CC	CHR FACTITIOUS ILLNESS
30300	CMS CC		AC ALCOHOL INTOX-UNSPEC
30301	CMS CC		AC ALCOHOL INTOX-CONTIN
30302	CMS CC		AC ALCOHOL INTOX-EPISOD
30390	CMS CC		ALCOHOL DEP NEC/NOS-UNSPEC
30391	CMS CC		ALCOHOL DEP NEC/NOS-CONTIN
30392	CMS CC		ALCOHOL DEP NEC/NOS-EPISOD
30400	CMS CC		OPIOID DEPENDENCE-UNSPEC
30401	CMS CC	MS-DRG CC	OPIOID DEPENDENCE-CONTIN
30402	CMS CC		OPIOID DEPENDENCE-EPISOD
30410	CMS CC		SED,HYP,ANXIOLYT DEP-NOS

(Continued)

2008 ICD-9-CM	CMS DRG	MS-DRG	Short Title
30411	CMS CC	MS-DRG CC	SED,HYP,ANXIOLYT DEP-CON
30412	CMS CC		SED,HYP,ANXIOLYT DEP-EPI
30420	CMS CC		COCAINE DEPEND-UNSPEC
30421	CMS CC	MS-DRG CC	COCAINE DEPEND-CONTIN
30422	CMS CC		COCAINE DEPEND-EPISODIC
30440	CMS CC		AMPHETAMIN DEPEND-UNSPEC
30441	CMS CC	MS-DRG CC	AMPHETAMIN DEPEND-CONTIN
30442	CMS CC		AMPHETAMIN DEPEND-EPISOD
30450	CMS CC		HALLUCINOGEN DEP-UNSPEC
30451	CMS CC	MS-DRG CC	HALLUCINOGEN DEP-CONTIN
30452	CMS CC		HALLUCINOGEN DEP-EPISOD
30460	CMS CC		DRUG DEPEND NEC-UNSPEC
30461	CMS CC	MS-DRG CC	DRUG DEPEND NEC-CONTIN
30462	CMS CC		DRUG DEPEND NEC-EPISODIC
30470	CMS CC		OPIOID/OTHER DEP-UNSPEC
30471	CMS CC	MS-DRG CC	OPIOID/OTHER DEP-CONTIN
30472	CMS CC		OPIOID/OTHER DEP-EPISOD
30480	CMS CC		COMB DRUG DEP NEC-UNSPEC
30481	CMS CC	MS-DRG CC	COMB DRUG DEP NEC-CONTIN
30482	CMS CC		COMB DRUG DEP NEC-EPISOD
30490	CMS CC		DRUG DEPEND NOS-UNSPEC
30491	CMS CC	MS-DRG CC	DRUG DEPEND NOS-CONTIN
30492	CMS CC		DRUG DEPEND NOS-EPISODIC
30500	CMS CC		ALCOHOL ABUSE-UNSPEC
30501	CMS CC		ALCOHOL ABUSE-CONTINUOUS
30502	CMS CC		ALCOHOL ABUSE-EPISODIC
30530	CMS CC		HALLUCINOG ABUSE-UNSPEC
30531	CMS CC		HALLUCINOG ABUSE-CONTIN
30532	CMS CC		HALLUCINOG ABUSE-EPISOD
30540	CMS CC		SED,HYP,ANXIOLYTC AB-NOS
30541	CMS CC		SED,HYP,ANXIOLYTC AB-CON
30542	CMS CC		SED,HYP,ANXIOLYTC AB-EPI
30550	CMS CC		OPIOID ABUSE-UNSPEC
30551	CMS CC		OPIOID ABUSE-CONTINUOUS
30552	CMS CC		OPIOID ABUSE-EPISODIC
30560	CMS CC		COCAINE ABUSE-UNSPEC
30561	CMS CC		COCAINE ABUSE-CONTINUOUS
30562	CMS CC		COCAINE ABUSE-EPISODIC
30570	CMS CC		AMPHETAMINE ABUSE-UNSPEC

2008 ICD-9-CM	CMS DRG	MS-DRG	Short Title
30571	CMS CC		AMPHETAMINE ABUSE-CONTIN
30572	CMS CC		AMPHETAMINE ABUSE-EPISOD
30590	CMS CC		DRUG ABUSE NEC-UNSPEC
30591	CMS CC		DRUG ABUSE NEC-CONTIN
30592	CMS CC		DRUG ABUSE NEC-EPISODIC
3071	CMS CC	MS-DRG CC	ANOREXIA NERVOSA
30751		MS-DRG CC	BULIMIA NERVOSA
3181		MS-DRG CC	SEVERE MENTAL RETARDAT
3182		MS-DRG CC	PROFOUND MENTAL RETARDAT
3200	CMS CC	MS-DRG MCC	HEMOPHILUS MENINGITIS
3201	CMS CC	MS-DRG MCC	PNEUMOCOCCAL MENINGITIS
3202	CMS CC	MS-DRG MCC	STREPTOCOCCAL MENINGITIS
3203	CMS CC	MS-DRG MCC	STAPHYLOCOCC MENINGITIS
3207	CMS CC	MS-DRG MCC	MENINGITIS IN OTH BACT DIS
32081	CMS CC	MS-DRG MCC	ANAEROBIC MENINGITIS
32082	CMS CC	MS-DRG MCC	MENINGITIS GRAM-NEG BCT NEC
32089	CMS CC	MS-DRG MCC	MENINGITIS OTH SPCF BACT
3209	CMS CC	MS-DRG MCC	BACTERIAL MENINGITIS NOS
3210	CMS CC	MS-DRG MCC	CRYPTOCOCCAL MENINGITIS
3211	CMS CC	MS-DRG MCC	MENINGITIS IN OTH FUNGAL DIS
3212	CMS CC	MS-DRG MCC	MENINGITIS IN OTH VIRAL DIS
3213	CMS CC	MS-DRG MCC	TRYPANOSOMIASIS MENINGIT
3214	CMS CC	MS-DRG MCC	MENINGITIS D/T SARCOIDOSIS
3218	CMS CC	MS-DRG MCC	MENINGITIS IN OTH NONBAC DIS
3220	CMS CC	MS-DRG MCC	NONPYOGENIC MENINGITIS
3221	CMS CC	MS-DRG MCC	EOSINOPHILIC MENINGITIS
3222	CMS CC	MS-DRG CC	CHRONIC MENINGITIS
3229	CMS CC	MS-DRG MCC	MENINGITIS NOS
32301	CMS CC	MS-DRG MCC	ENCEPH/ENCEPHMYE OTH DIS
32302	CMS CC	MS-DRG MCC	MYELITIS-OTH VIRAL DIS
3231	CMS CC	MS-DRG MCC	RICKETTSIAL ENCEPHALITIS
3232	CMS CC	MS-DRG MCC	PROTOZOAL ENCEPHALITIS
32341	CMS CC	MS-DRG MCC	ENCEPH/MYELITIS-OTH INF
32342	CMS CC	MS-DRG MCC	MYELITIS D/T OTH INFECT
32351	CMS CC	MS-DRG MCC	ENCEPH/MYEL FOLWG IMMUNE
32352	CMS CC	MS-DRG MCC	MYELITIS FOLLWG IMMUNE
32361	CMS CC	MS-DRG MCC	INF AC DIS ENCEPHALOMYEL
32362	CMS CC	MS-DRG MCC	POSTINF ENCEPHALITIS NEC
32363	CMS CC	MS-DRG MCC	POSTINFECTIOUS MYELITIS

(Continued)

2008 ICD-9-CM	CMS DRG	MS-DRG	Short Title
32371	CMS CC	MS-DRG MCC	TOXIC ENCEPHALITIS & ENCEPHLOMY
32372	CMS CC	MS-DRG MCC	TOXIC MYELITIS
32381	CMS CC	MS-DRG MCC	ENCEPHALITIS & ENCEPHLALO NEC
32382	CMS CC	MS-DRG MCC	MYELITIS CAUSE NEC
3239	CMS CC	MS-DRG MCC	ENCEPHALITIS NOS
3240	CMS CC	MS-DRG MCC	INTRACRANIAL ABSCESS
3241	CMS CC	MS-DRG MCC	INTRASPINAL ABSCESS
3249	CMS CC	MS-DRG MCC	CNS ABSCESS NOS
325	CMS CC	MS-DRG MCC	PHLEBITIS INTRCRAN SINUS
3300		MS-DRG CC	LEUKODYSTROPHY
3301		MS-DRG CC	CEREBRAL LIPIDOSES
3302		MS-DRG CC	CEREB DEGEN IN LIPIDOSIS
3303		MS-DRG CC	CEREB DEG CHLD IN OTH DIS
3308		MS-DRG CC	CEREB DEGEN IN CHILD NEC
3309		MS-DRG CC	CEREB DEGEN IN CHILD NOS
3313		MS-DRG CC	COMMUNICAT HYDROCEPHALUS
3314	CMS CC	MS-DRG CC	OBSTRUCTIV HYDROCEPHALUS
3315		MS-DRG CC	NORML PRESSURE HYDROCEPH
33181		MS-DRG MCC	REYE'S SYNDROME
3321		MS-DRG CC	SECONDARY PARKINSONISM
3330		MS-DRG CC	DEGEN BASAL GANGLIA NEC
3334		MS-DRG CC	HUNTINGTON'S CHOREA
33371		MS-DRG CC	ATHETOID CEREBRAL PALSY
33372		MS-DRG CC	ACUTE DYSTONIA D/T DRUGS
33379		MS-DRG CC	ACQ TORSION DYSTONIA NEC
33390		MS-DRG CC	EXTRAPYRAMIDAL DIS NOS
33391		MS-DRG CC	STIFF-MAN SYNDROME
33392		MS-DRG MCC	NEUROLEPTIC MALGNT SYND
3340		MS-DRG CC	FRIEDREICH'S ATAXIA
3341		MS-DRG CC	HERED SPASTIC PARAPLEGIA
3342		MS-DRG CC	PRIMARY CEREBELLAR DEGEN
3343		MS-DRG CC	CEREBELLAR ATAXIA NEC
3344		MS-DRG CC	CEREBELLAR ATAX IN OTH DIS
3348		MS-DRG CC	SPINOCEREBELLAR DIS NEC
3349		MS-DRG CC	SPINOCEREBELLAR DIS NOS
3350	CMS CC	MS-DRG CC	WERDNIG-HOFFMANN DISEASE
33510	CMS CC	MS-DRG CC	SPINAL MUSCL ATROPHY NOS
33511	CMS CC	MS-DRG CC	KUGELBERG-WELANDER DIS
33519	CMS CC	MS-DRG CC	SPINAL MUSCL ATROPHY NEC

2008 ICD-9-CM	CMS DRG	MS-DRG	Short Title
33520	CMS CC	MS-DRG CC	AMYOTROPHIC SCLEROSIS
33521	CMS CC	MS-DRG CC	PROGRESSIVE MUSCULAR ATROPHY
33522	CMS CC	MS-DRG CC	PROGRESSIVE BULBAR PALSY
33523	CMS CC	MS-DRG CC	PSEUDOBULBAR PALSY
33524	CMS CC	MS-DRG CC	PRIM LATERAL SCLEROSIS
33529	CMS CC	MS-DRG CC	MOTOR NEURON DISEASE NEC
3358	CMS CC	MS-DRG CC	ANT HORN CELL DIS NEC
3359	CMS CC	MS-DRG CC	ANT HORN CELL DIS NOS
3360		MS-DRG CC	SYRINGOMYELIA
3361		MS-DRG MCC	VASCULAR MYELOPATHIES
3362		MS-DRG CC	COMB DEG CORD IN OTH DIS
3363		MS-DRG CC	MYELOPATHY IN OTH DIS
3368		MS-DRG CC	MYELOPATHY NEC
3369		MS-DRG CC	SPINAL CORD DISEASE NOS
3370		MS-DRG CC	IDIOPATH AUTO NEUROPATHY
3371		MS-DRG CC	AUT NEUROPTHY IN OTH DIS
33720		MS-DRG CC	UNSP RFLX SYMPTH DYSTRPH
33721		MS-DRG CC	RFLX SYM DYSTRPH UP LIMB
33722		MS-DRG CC	RFLX SYM DYSTRPH LWR LMB
33729		MS-DRG CC	RFLX SYM DYSTRPH OTH ST
340	CMS CC		MULTIPLE SCLEROSIS
3410		MS-DRG CC	NEUROMYELITIS OPTICA
3411		MS-DRG CC	SCHILDER'S DISEASE
34120		MS-DRG CC	ACUTE MYELITIS NOS
34121		MS-DRG CC	ACUTE MYELITIS OTH COND
34122		MS-DRG CC	IDIOPATHC TRANS MYELITIS
3418		MS-DRG CC	CNS DEMYELINATION NEC
3419		MS-DRG CC	CNS DEMYELINATION NOS
34200		MS-DRG CC	FLCCD HMIPLGA UNSPF SIDE
34201		MS-DRG CC	FLCCD HMIPLGA DOMNT SIDE
34202		MS-DRG CC	FLCCD HMIPLGA NONDMNT SDE
34210		MS-DRG CC	SPSTC HMIPLGA UNSPF SIDE
34211		MS-DRG CC	SPSTC HMIPLGA DOMNT SIDE
34212		MS-DRG CC	SPSTC HMIPLGA NONDMNT SDE
34280		MS-DRG CC	OT SP HMIPLGA UNSPF SIDE
34281		MS-DRG CC	OT SP HMIPLGA DOMNT SIDE
34282		MS-DRG CC	OT SP HMIPLGA NONDMNT SDE
34290		MS-DRG CC	UNSP HEMIPLGA UNSPF SIDE
34291		MS-DRG CC	UNSP HEMIPLGA DOMNT SIDE

(Continued)

2008 ICD-9-CM	CMS DRG	MS-DRG	Short Title
34292		MS-DRG CC	UNSP HMIPLGA NONDMNT SDE
3430		MS-DRG CC	CONGENITAL DIPLEGIA
3431		MS-DRG CC	CONGENITAL HEMIPLEGIA
3432	CMS CC	MS-DRG MCC	CONGENITAL QUADRIPLEGIA
3434		MS-DRG CC	INFANTILE HEMIPLEGIA
34400	CMS CC	MS-DRG MCC	QUADRIPLEGIA, UNSPECIFD
34401	CMS CC	MS-DRG MCC	QUADRIPLEGIA C1-C4, COMPLETE
34402	CMS CC	MS-DRG MCC	QUADRIPLEGIA C1-C4, INCOMPLT
34403	CMS CC	MS-DRG MCC	QUADRIPLEGIA C5-C7, COMPLETE
34404	CMS CC	MS-DRG MCC	QUADRIPLEGIA C5-C7, INCOMPLT
34409	CMS CC	MS-DRG MCC	OTHER QUADRIPLEGIA
3441		MS-DRG CC	PARAPLEGIA NOS
3442		MS-DRG CC	DIPLEGIA OF UPPER LIMBS
34460		MS-DRG CC	CAUDA EQUINA SYND NOS
34461		MS-DRG CC	NEUROGENIC BLADDER
34481		MS-DRG MCC	LOCKED-IN STATE
34501	CMS CC	MS-DRG CC	GEN NONCONV EP W INTR EP
34510	CMS CC		GEN CNV EPIL W/O INTR EP
34511	CMS CC	MS-DRG CC	GEN CNV EPIL W INTR EPIL
3452	CMS CC	MS-DRG MCC	PETIT MAL STATUS
3453	CMS CC	MS-DRG MCC	GRAND MAL STATUS
34540		MS-DRG CC	PSYMOTR EPIL W/O INT EPI
34541	CMS CC	MS-DRG CC	PSYMOTR EPIL W INTR EPIL
34550		MS-DRG CC	PART EPIL WO INTR EPIL
34551	CMS CC	MS-DRG CC	PART EPIL W INTR EPIL
34560		MS-DRG CC	INF SPASM W/O INTR EPIL
34561	CMS CC	MS-DRG CC	INF SPASM W INTRACT EPIL
34570		MS-DRG CC	EPIL PAR CONT W/O INT EP
34571	CMS CC	MS-DRG MCC	EPIL PAR CONT W INTR EPI
34580		MS-DRG CC	EPILEP NEC W/O INTR EPIL
34581	CMS CC	MS-DRG CC	EPILEPSY NEC W INTR EPIL
34591	CMS CC	MS-DRG CC	EPILEPSY NOS W INTR EPIL
3481	CMS CC	MS-DRG CC	ANOXIC BRAIN DAMAGE
34830		MS-DRG MCC	ENCEPHALOPATHY NOS
34831		MS-DRG MCC	METABOLIC ENCEPHALOPATHY
34839		MS-DRG MCC	ENCEPHALOPATHY NEC
3484		MS-DRG MCC	COMPRESSION OF BRAIN
3485		MS-DRG MCC	CEREBRAL EDEMA
3491	CMS CC	MS-DRG CC	COMPLICATION CNS DEVICE

2008 ICD-9-CM	CMS DRG	MS-DRG	Short Title
34981	CMS CC	MS-DRG CC	CEREBROSPINAL RHINORRHEA
34982	CMS CC	MS-DRG MCC	TOXIC ENCEPHALOPATHY
3563		MS-DRG CC	REFSUM'S DISEASE
3570	CMS CC	MS-DRG CC	AC INFECT POLYNEURITIS
35781		MS-DRG CC	CHR INFLAM POLYNEURITIS
35782		MS-DRG CC	CRIT ILLNESS NEUROPATHY
35800	CMS CC		MYASTHENIA GRAVS W/O AC EXAC
35801	CMS CC	MS-DRG MCC	MYASTHENIA GRAVS W AC EXAC
3581	CMS CC	MS-DRG CC	MYASTHENIA IN OTH DIS
3590	CMS CC	MS-DRG CC	CONG HERED MUSC DYSTRPHY
3591	CMS CC	MS-DRG CC	HERED PROG MUSC DYSTRPHY
3594		MS-DRG CC	TOXIC MYOPATHY
3596		MS-DRG CC	INFL MYOPATHY IN OTH DIS
35981		MS-DRG CC	CRITICAL ILLNESS MYOPTHY
36000		MS-DRG CC	PURULENT ENDOPHTHALM NOS
36001		MS-DRG CC	ACUTE ENDOPHTHALMITIS
36002		MS-DRG CC	PANOPHTHALMITIS
36004		MS-DRG CC	VITREOUS ABSCESS
36011		MS-DRG CC	SYMPATHETIC UVEITIS
36012		MS-DRG CC	PANUVEITIS
36013		MS-DRG CC	PARASITIC ENDOPHTHAL NOS
36019		MS-DRG CC	ENDOPHTHALMITIS NEC
3612		MS-DRG CC	SEROUS RETINA DETACHMENT
36181		MS-DRG CC	RETINAL TRACTION DETACH
36189		MS-DRG CC	RETINAL DETACHMENT NEC
3619		MS-DRG CC	RETINAL DETACHMENT NOS
36230		MS-DRG CC	RETINAL VASC OCCLUS NOS
36231		MS-DRG CC	CENT RETINA ARTERY OCCLU
36232		MS-DRG CC	ARTERIAL BRANCH OCCLUS
36233		MS-DRG CC	PART ARTERIAL OCCLUSION
36234		MS-DRG CC	TRANSIENT ARTERIAL OCCLU
36235		MS-DRG CC	CENT RETINAL VEIN OCCLUS
36240		MS-DRG CC	RETINA LAYER SEPARAT NOS
36242		MS-DRG CC	SEROUS DETACH PIGM EPITH
36243		MS-DRG CC	HEM DETACH PIGMNT EPITH
36284		MS-DRG CC	RETINAL ISCHEMIA
36310		MS-DRG CC	DISSEM CHORIORETINIT NOS
36311		MS-DRG CC	DISSEM CHOROIDITIS, POST
36312		MS-DRG CC	PERIPH DISEM CHOROIDITIS

(Continued)

2008 ICD-9-CM	CMS DRG	MS-DRG	Short Title
36313		MS-DRG CC	GEN DISSEM CHOROIDITIS
36314		MS-DRG CC	METASTAT DISSEM RETINIT
36315		MS-DRG CC	PIGMENT EPITHELIOPATHY
36320		MS-DRG CC	CHORIORETINITIS NOS
36363		MS-DRG CC	CHOROIDAL RUPTURE
36370		MS-DRG CC	CHOROIDAL DETACHMENT NOS
36371		MS-DRG CC	SEROUS CHOROID DETACHMNT
36372		MS-DRG CC	HEMORR CHOROID DETACHMNT
36400		MS-DRG CC	ACUTE IRIDOCYCLITIS NOS
36401		MS-DRG CC	PRIMARY IRIDOCYCLITIS
36402		MS-DRG CC	RECURRENT IRIDOCYCLITIS
36403		MS-DRG CC	SECONDRY IRITIS, INFECT
36422		MS-DRG CC	GLAUCOMATOCYCLIT CRISES
3643		MS-DRG CC	IRIDOCYCLITIS NOS
36522		MS-DRG CC	ACUTE ANGL-CLOS GLAUCOMA
36811		MS-DRG CC	SUDDEN VISUAL LOSS
36812		MS-DRG CC	TRANSIENT VISUAL LOSS
37601		MS-DRG CC	ORBITAL CELLULITIS
37602		MS-DRG CC	ORBITAL PERIOSTITIS
37603		MS-DRG CC	ORBITAL OSTEOMYELITIS
37700	CMS CC	MS-DRG CC	PAPILLEDEMA NOS
37701	CMS CC	MS-DRG CC	PAPILLEDEMA W INCR PRESS
37702	CMS CC		PAPILLEDEMA W DECR PRESS
37730		MS-DRG CC	OPTIC NEURITIS NOS
37731		MS-DRG CC	OPTIC PAPILLITIS
37732		MS-DRG CC	RETROBULBAR NEURITIS
37739		MS-DRG CC	OPTIC NEURITIS NEC
37751		MS-DRG CC	OPT CHIASM W PITUIT DIS
37752		MS-DRG CC	OPT CHIASM DIS/NEOPL NEC
37753		MS-DRG CC	OPT CHIASM W VASCUL DIS
37754		MS-DRG CC	OP CHIASM DIS W INFL DIS
37761		MS-DRG CC	VIS PATH DIS W NEOPLASMS
37762		MS-DRG CC	VIS PATH DIS W VASC DIS
37763		MS-DRG CC	VIS PATH DIS W INFL DIS
37771		MS-DRG CC	VIS CORTX DIS W NEOPLASM
37772		MS-DRG CC	VIS CORTX DIS W VASC DIS
37773		MS-DRG CC	VIS CORTEX DIS W INFLAM
38014		MS-DRG CC	MALIGNANT OTITIS EXTERNA
38300		MS-DRG CC	AC MASTOIDITIS W/O COMPL

2008 ICD-9-CM	CMS DRG	MS-DRG	Short Title
38301	CMS CC	MS-DRG CC	SUBPERI MASTOID ABSCESS
38302		MS-DRG CC	AC MASTOIDITIS-COMPL NEC
38330	CMS CC		POSTMASTOID COMPL NOS
38381	CMS CC		POSTAURICULAR FISTULA
38861		MS-DRG CC	CEREBROSP FLUID OTORRHEA
3910		MS-DRG CC	ACUTE RHEUMATIC PERICARD
3911		MS-DRG CC	ACUTE RHEUMATIC ENDOCARD
3912		MS-DRG CC	AC RHEUMATIC MYOCARDITIS
3918		MS-DRG CC	AC RHEUMATIC HRT DIS NEC
3919		MS-DRG CC	AC RHEUMATIC HRT DIS NOS
3920		MS-DRG CC	RHEUMATIC CHOREA W HRT INVOL
3929		MS-DRG CC	RHEUMATIC CHOREA NOS
393		MS-DRG CC	CHR RHEUMATIC PERICARD
3940	CMS CC		MITRAL STENOSIS
3941	CMS CC		RHEUMATIC MITRAL INSUFF
3942	CMS CC		MITRAL STENOSIS W INSUFF
3949	CMS CC		MITRAL VALVE DIS NEC/NOS
3950	CMS CC		RHEUMATIC AORTIC STENOSIS
3951	CMS CC		RHEUMATIC AORTIC INSUFF
3952	CMS CC		RHEUMATIC AORTIC STEN/INSUFF
3959	CMS CC		RHEUMATIC AORTIC DIS NEC/NOS
3960	CMS CC		MITRAL/AORTIC STENOSIS
3961	CMS CC		MITRAL STENOS/AORT INSUF
3962	CMS CC		MITRAL INSUF/AORT STENOS
3963	CMS CC		MITRAL/AORTIC VAL INSUFF
3968	CMS CC		MITRAL/AORTIC MULT INVOLV
3969	CMS CC		MITRAL/AORTIC V DIS NOS
3970	CMS CC		TRICUSPID VALVE DISEASE
3971	CMS CC		RHEUMATIC PULMON VALVE DIS
3979	CMS CC		RHEUMATIC ENDOCARDITIS NOS
3980	CMS CC	MS-DRG CC	RHEUMATIC MYOCARDITIS
39891	CMS CC	MS-DRG CC	RHEUMATIC HEART FAILURE
4010	CMS CC	MS-DRG CC	MALIGNANT HYPERTENSION
40200	CMS CC	MS-DRG CC	MAL HYP HT DIS W/O HF
40201	CMS CC	MS-DRG CC	MAL HYPERT HRT DIS W HF
40211	CMS CC	MS-DRG CC	BENIGN HYP HT DIS W HF
40291	CMS CC	MS-DRG CC	HYP HT DIS NOS W HT FAIL
40300	CMS CC	MS-DRG CC	MAL HYP KID W CR KID I-IV
40301	CMS CC	MS-DRG CC	MAL HYP KID W CR KID V

(Continued)

2008 ICD-9-CM	CMS DRG	MS-DRG	Short Title
40311	CMS CC	MS-DRG CC	BEN HYP KID W CR KID V
40391	CMS CC		HYP KID NOS W CR KID V
40400	CMS CC	MS-DRG CC	MAL HY HT/KD I-IV W/O HF
40401	CMS CC	MS-DRG CC	MAL HYP HT/KD I-IV W HF
40402	CMS CC	MS-DRG CC	MAL HY HT/KD ST V W/O HF
40403	CMS CC	MS-DRG CC	MAL HYP HT/KD STG V W HF
40411	CMS CC	MS-DRG CC	BEN HYP HT/KD I-IV W HF
40412	CMS CC	MS-DRG CC	BEN HY HT/KD ST V W/O HF
40413	CMS CC	MS-DRG CC	BEN HYP HT/KD STG V W HF
40491	CMS CC	MS-DRG CC	HYP HT/KD NOS I-IV W HF
40492	CMS CC	MS-DRG CC	HYP HT/KD NOS ST V W/O HF
40493	CMS CC	MS-DRG CC	HYP HT/KD NOS ST V W HF
40501	CMS CC	MS-DRG CC	MAL RENOVASC HYPERTENS
40509	CMS CC	MS-DRG CC	MAL SECOND HYPERTEN NEC
41001	CMS CC	MS-DRG MCC	AMI ANTEROLATERAL, INIT
41011	CMS CC	MS-DRG MCC	AMI ANTERIOR WALL, INIT
41021	CMS CC	MS-DRG MCC	AMI INFEROLATERAL, INIT
41031	CMS CC	MS-DRG MCC	AMI INFEROPOST, INITIAL
41041	CMS CC	MS-DRG MCC	AMI INFERIOR WALL, INIT
41051	CMS CC	MS-DRG MCC	AMI LATERAL NEC, INITIAL
41061	CMS CC	MS-DRG MCC	TRUE POST INFARCT, INIT
41071	CMS CC	MS-DRG MCC	SUBENDO INFARCT, INITIAL
41081	CMS CC	MS-DRG MCC	AMI NEC, INITIAL
41091	CMS CC	MS-DRG MCC	AMI NOS, INITIAL
4110		MS-DRG CC	POST MI SYNDROME
4111	CMS CC	MS-DRG CC	INTERMED CORONARY SYND
41181	CMS CC	MS-DRG CC	ACUTE COR OCCLSN W/O MI
41189	CMS CC	MS-DRG CC	ACUTE ISCHEMIC HRT DIS NEC
4130	CMS CC	MS-DRG CC	ANGINA DECUBITUS
4131	CMS CC	MS-DRG CC	PRINZMETAL ANGINA
4139	CMS CC		ANGINA PECTORIS NEC/NOS
41402		MS-DRG CC	CRN ATH ATLG VN BPS GRFT
41403		MS-DRG CC	CRN ATH NONATLG BLG GRFT
41404		MS-DRG CC	COR ATH ARTRY BYPAS GRFT
41406		MS-DRG CC	COR ATH NATV ART TP HRT
41407		MS-DRG CC	COR ATH BPS GRAFT TP HRT
41410		MS-DRG CC	ANEURYSM OF HEART
41412		MS-DRG MCC	DISSECTION COR ARTERY
41419		MS-DRG CC	ANEURYSM OF HEART NEC

2008 ICD-9-CM	CMS DRG	MS-DRG	Short Title
4150	CMS CC	MS-DRG MCC	ACUTE COR PULMONALE
41511	CMS CC	MS-DRG MCC	IATROGEN PULM EMB/INFARC
41512	CMS CC	MS-DRG MCC	SEPTIC PULMONARY EMBOLSM
41519	CMS CC	MS-DRG MCC	PULM EMBOL/INFARCT NEC
4160	CMS CC	MS-DRG CC	PRIM PULM HYPERTENSION
4161		MS-DRG CC	KYPHOSCOLIOTIC HEART DIS
4170		MS-DRG CC	ARTERIOVEN FISTU PUL VES
4171		MS-DRG CC	PULMON ARTERY ANEURYSM
4200	CMS CC	MS-DRG CC	ACUTE PERICARDIT IN OTH DIS
42090	CMS CC	MS-DRG CC	ACUTE PERICARDITIS NOS
42091	CMS CC	MS-DRG CC	ACUTE IDIOPATH PERICARDITIS
42099	CMS CC	MS-DRG CC	ACUTE PERICARDITIS NEC
4210	CMS CC	MS-DRG MCC	ACUTE/SUBAC BACT ENDOCARD
4211	CMS CC	MS-DRG MCC	ACUTE ENDOCARDIT IN OTH DIS
4219	CMS CC	MS-DRG MCC	ACUTE/SUBAC ENDOCARDIT NOS
4220	CMS CC	MS-DRG MCC	ACUTE MYOCARDIT IN OTH DIS
42290	CMS CC	MS-DRG MCC	ACUTE MYOCARDITIS NOS
42291	CMS CC	MS-DRG MCC	IDIOPATHIC MYOCARDITIS
42292	CMS CC	MS-DRG MCC	SEPTIC MYOCARDITIS
42293	CMS CC	MS-DRG MCC	TOXIC MYOCARDITIS
42299	CMS CC	MS-DRG MCC	ACUTE MYOCARDITIS NEC
4230	CMS CC	MS-DRG CC	HEMOPERICARDIUM
4231	CMS CC	MS-DRG CC	ADHESIVE PERICARDITIS
4232	CMS CC	MS-DRG CC	CONSTRICTIV PERICARDITIS
4233		MS-DRG CC	CARDIAC TAMPONADE
4238		MS-DRG CC	PERICARDIAL DISEASE NEC
4239		MS-DRG CC	PERICARDIAL DISEASE NOS
4240	CMS CC		MITRAL VALVE DISORDER
4241	CMS CC		AORTIC VALVE DISORDER
4242	CMS CC		NONRHEUM TRICUSP VAL DIS
4243	CMS CC		PULMONARY VALVE DISORDER
42490	CMS CC	MS-DRG CC	ENDOCARDITIS NOS
42491	CMS CC	MS-DRG CC	ENDOCARDITIS IN OTH DIS
42499	CMS CC	MS-DRG CC	ENDOCARDITIS NEC
4250	CMS CC	MS-DRG CC	ENDOMYOCARDIAL FIBROSIS
4251	CMS CC	MS-DRG CC	HYPERTR OBSTR CARDIOMYOP
4252	CMS CC	MS-DRG CC	OBSC AFRIC CARDIOMYOPATH
4253	CMS CC	MS-DRG CC	ENDOCARD FIBROELASTOSIS
4254	CMS CC	MS-DRG CC	PRIM CARDIOMYOPATHY NEC

(Continued)

2008 ICD-9-CM	CMS DRG	MS-DRG	Short Title
4255	CMS CC	MS-DRG CC	ALCOHOLIC CARDIOMYOPATHY
4257	CMS CC	MS-DRG CC	METABOLIC CARDIOMYOPATHY
4258	CMS CC	MS-DRG CC	CARDIOMYOPATH IN OTH DIS
4259	CMS CC	MS-DRG CC	SECOND CARDIOMYOPATH NOS
4260	CMS CC	MS-DRG CC	ATRIOVENT BLOCK COMPLETE
42612	CMS CC	MS-DRG CC	ATRIOVENT BLOCK-MOBITZ II
42613	CMS CC		AV BLOCK-2ND DEGREE NEC
42653	CMS CC	MS-DRG CC	BILAT BB BLOCK NEC
42654	CMS CC	MS-DRG CC	TRIFASCICULAR BLOCK
4266	CMS CC		OTHER HEART BLOCK
4267	CMS CC		ANOMALOUS AV EXCITATION
42681	CMS CC		LOWN-GANONG-LEVINE SYND
42689	CMS CC	MS-DRG CC	CONDUCTION DISORDER NEC
4269	CMS CC		CONDUCTION DISORDER NOS
4270	CMS CC	MS-DRG CC	PAROX ATRIAL TACHYCARDIA
4271	CMS CC	MS-DRG CC	PAROX VENTRIC TACHYCARD
4272	CMS CC		PAROX TACHYCARDIA NOS
42731	CMS CC		ATRIAL FIBRILLATION
42732	CMS CC	MS-DRG CC	ATRIAL FLUTTER
42741	CMS CC	MS-DRG MCC	VENTRICULAR FIBRILLATION
42742	CMS CC	MS-DRG MCC	VENTRICULAR FLUTTER
4275	CMS CC	MS-DRG MCC	CARDIAC ARREST
4280	CMS CC		CHF NOS
4281	CMS CC	MS-DRG CC	LEFT HEART FAILURE
42820	CMS CC	MS-DRG CC	SYSTOLIC HRT FAILURE NOS
42821	CMS CC	MS-DRG MCC	AC SYSTOLIC HRT FAILURE
42822	CMS CC	MS-DRG CC	CHR SYSTOLIC HRT FAILURE
42823	CMS CC	MS-DRG MCC	AC ON CHR SYST HRT FAIL
42830	CMS CC	MS-DRG CC	DIASTOLC HRT FAILURE NOS
42831	CMS CC	MS-DRG MCC	AC DIASTOLIC HRT FAILURE
42832	CMS CC	MS-DRG CC	CHR DIASTOLIC HRT FAIL
42833	CMS CC	MS-DRG MCC	AC ON CHR DIAST HRT FAIL
42840	CMS CC	MS-DRG CC	SYST/DIAST HRT FAIL NOS
42841	CMS CC	MS-DRG MCC	AC SYST/DIASTOL HRT FAIL
42842	CMS CC	MS-DRG CC	CHR SYST/DIASTL HRT FAIL
42843	CMS CC	MS-DRG MCC	AC/CHR SYST/DIA HRT FAIL
4289	CMS CC		HEART FAILURE NOS
4294	CMS CC		HRT DIS POSTCARDIAC SURG
4295	CMS CC	MS-DRG MCC	CHORDAE TENDINAE RUPTURE

2008 ICD-9-CM	CMS DRG	MS-DRG	Short Title
4296	CMS CC	MS-DRG MCC	PAPILLARY MUSCLE RUPTURE
42971	CMS CC	MS-DRG CC	ACQ CARDIAC SEPTL DEFECT
42979	CMS CC	MS-DRG CC	OTHER SEQUELAE OF MI NEC
42981	CMS CC	MS-DRG CC	PAPILLARY MUSCLE DIS NEC
42982	CMS CC	MS-DRG CC	HYPERKINETIC HEART DIS
42983		MS-DRG CC	TAKOTSUBO SYNDROME
430	CMS CC	MS-DRG MCC	SUBARACHNOID HEMORRHAGE
431	CMS CC	MS-DRG MCC	INTRACEREBRAL HEMORRHAGE
4320	CMS CC	MS-DRG MCC	NONTRAUM EXTRADURAL HEM
4321	CMS CC	MS-DRG MCC	SUBDURAL HEMORRHAGE
4329		MS-DRG CC	INTRACRANIAL HEMORR NOS
43301	CMS CC	MS-DRG MCC	OCL BSLR ART W INFRCT
43311	CMS CC	MS-DRG MCC	OCL CRTD ART W INFRCT
43321	CMS CC	MS-DRG MCC	OCL VRTB ART W INFRCT
43331	CMS CC	MS-DRG MCC	OCL MLT BI ART W INFRCT
43381	CMS CC	MS-DRG MCC	OCL SPCF ART W INFRCT
43391	CMS CC	MS-DRG MCC	OCL ART NOS W INFRCT
43401	CMS CC	MS-DRG MCC	CRBL THRMBS W INFRCT
43411	CMS CC	MS-DRG MCC	CRBL EMBLSM W INFRCT
43491	CMS CC	MS-DRG MCC	CRBL ART OCL NOS W INFRC
4350		MS-DRG CC	BASILAR ARTERY SYNDROME
4351		MS-DRG CC	VERTEBRAL ARTERY SYNDROM
4352		MS-DRG CC	SUBCLAVIAN STEAL SYNDROM
4353		MS-DRG CC	VERTBROBASLR ARTERY SYND
4358		MS-DRG CC	TRANS CEREB ISCHEMIA NEC
4359		MS-DRG CC	TRANS CEREB ISCHEMIA NOS
436	CMS CC	MS-DRG CC	CVA
4371		MS-DRG CC	AC CEREBROVASC INSUF NOS
4372	CMS CC	MS-DRG CC	HYPERTENS ENCEPHALOPATHY
4374	CMS CC	MS-DRG CC	CEREBRAL ARTERITIS
4375	CMS CC	MS-DRG CC	MOYAMOYA DISEASE
4376	CMS CC	MS-DRG CC	NONPYOGEN THROMBOS SINUS
43820		MS-DRG CC	LATE EF-HEMPLGA SIDE NOS
43821		MS-DRG CC	LATE EF-HEMPLGA DOM SIDE
43822		MS-DRG CC	LATE EF-HEMIPLGA NON-DOM
44024	CMS CC	MS-DRG CC	ATH EXT NTV ART GNGRENE
44100	CMS CC	MS-DRG MCC	DSCT OF AORTA UNSP SITE
44101	CMS CC	MS-DRG MCC	DSCT OF THORACIC AORTA
44102	CMS CC	MS-DRG MCC	DSCT OF ABDOMINAL AORTA

(Continued)

2008 ICD-9-CM	CMS DRG	MS-DRG	Short Title
44103	CMS CC	MS-DRG MCC	DSCT OF THORACOABD AORTA
4411	CMS CC	MS-DRG MCC	RUPTUR THORACIC ANEURYSM
4413	CMS CC	MS-DRG MCC	RUPTUR ABD AORTIC ANEURYSM
4415	CMS CC	MS-DRG MCC	RUPTUR AORTIC ANEURYSM NOS
4416	CMS CC	MS-DRG MCC	THORACOABD ANEURYSM RUPT
44321		MS-DRG MCC	DISSECTION CAROTID ARTERY
44322		MS-DRG MCC	DISSECTION ILIAC ARTERY
44323		MS-DRG MCC	DISSECTION RENAL ARTERY
44324		MS-DRG MCC	DISSECTION VERTEBRAL ARTERY
44329		MS-DRG MCC	DISSECTION ARTERY NEC
4440	CMS CC	MS-DRG CC	ABD AORTIC EMBOLISM
4441	CMS CC	MS-DRG CC	THORACIC AORTIC EMBOLISM
44421	CMS CC	MS-DRG CC	UPPER EXTREMITY EMBOLISM
44422	CMS CC	MS-DRG CC	LOWER EXTREMITY EMBOLISM
44481	CMS CC	MS-DRG CC	ILIAC ARTERY EMBOLISM
44489	CMS CC	MS-DRG CC	ARTERIAL EMBOLISM NEC
4449	CMS CC	MS-DRG CC	ARTERIAL EMBOLISM NOS
44501	CMS CC	MS-DRG CC	ATHEROEMBOLISM,UPPER EXT
44502	CMS CC	MS-DRG CC	ATHEROEMBOLISM,LOWER EXT
44581	CMS CC	MS-DRG CC	ATHEROEMBOLISM, KIDNEY
44589	CMS CC	MS-DRG CC	ATHEROEMBOLISM, SITE NEC
4460	CMS CC	MS-DRG CC	POLYARTERITIS NODOSA
4461		MS-DRG CC	MUCOCUTAN LYMPH NODE SYN
44620	CMS CC	MS-DRG CC	HYPERSENSIT ANGIITIS NOS
44621	CMS CC	MS-DRG CC	GOODPASTURE'S SYNDROME
44629	CMS CC	MS-DRG CC	HYPERSENSIT ANGIITIS NEC
4463	CMS CC	MS-DRG CC	LETHAL MIDLINE GRANULOMA
4464	CMS CC	MS-DRG CC	WEGENER'S GRANULOMATOSIS
4465	CMS CC		GIANT CELL ARTERITIS
4466	CMS CC	MS-DRG MCC	THROMBOT MICROANGIOPATHY
4467	CMS CC	MS-DRG CC	TAKAYASU'S DISEASE
4472		MS-DRG CC	RUPTURE OF ARTERY
4474		MS-DRG CC	CELIAC ART COMPRESS SYN
4475		MS-DRG CC	NECROSIS OF ARTERY
449		MS-DRG CC	SEPTIC ARTERIAL EMBOLISM
4510	CMS CC		SUPERFIC PHLEBITIS-LEG
45111	CMS CC	MS-DRG CC	FEMORAL VEIN PHLEBITIS
45119	CMS CC	MS-DRG CC	DEEP PHLEBITIS-LEG NEC
4512	CMS CC		THROMBOPHLEBITIS LEG NOS

2008 ICD-9-CM	CMS DRG	MS-DRG	Short Title
45181	CMS CC	MS-DRG CC	ILIAC THROMBOPHLEBITIS
45183		MS-DRG CC	PHLBTS DEEP VN UP EXTRM
45189		MS-DRG CC	THROMBOPHLEBITIS NEC
452	CMS CC	MS-DRG MCC	PORTAL VEIN THROMBOSIS
4530	CMS CC	MS-DRG MCC	BUDD-CHIARI SYNDROME
4531	CMS CC	MS-DRG CC	THROMBOPHLEBITIS MIGRANS
4532	CMS CC	MS-DRG MCC	VENA CAVA THROMBOSIS
4533	CMS CC	MS-DRG CC	RENAL VEIN THROMBOSIS
45340	CMS CC	MS-DRG CC	DVT/EMBLSM LOWER EXT NOS
45341	CMS CC	MS-DRG CC	DVT/EMB PROX LOWER EXT
45342	CMS CC	MS-DRG CC	DVT/EMB DISTAL LOWER EXT
4538	CMS CC	MS-DRG CC	VENOUS THROMBOSIS NEC
4539	CMS CC	MS-DRG CC	VENOUS THROMBOSIS NOS
4542		MS-DRG CC	VARICOS LEG ULCER/INFLAM
4560	CMS CC	MS-DRG MCC	ESOPHAG VARICES W BLEED
4561		MS-DRG CC	ESOPHAG VARICES W/O BLEED
45620	CMS CC	MS-DRG MCC	BLEED ESOPHAG VAR OTH DIS
45621		MS-DRG CC	ESOPHAG VARICE OTH DIS NOS
4590	CMS CC		HEMORRHAGE NOS
45911		MS-DRG CC	POSTPHLEBTC SYND W ULCER
45913		MS-DRG CC	POSTPHL SYN W ULC&INFLAM
4592		MS-DRG CC	COMPRESSION OF VEIN
45931		MS-DRG CC	CHR VENOUS HYPER W ULCER
45933		MS-DRG CC	CHR VEN HYP W ULC&INFLAM
46401		MS-DRG MCC	AC LARYNGITIS W OBSTRUCT
46411	CMS CC	MS-DRG MCC	AC TRACHEITIS W OBSTRUCT
46421	CMS CC	MS-DRG MCC	AC LARYNGOTRACH W OBSTR
46430		MS-DRG CC	AC EPIGLOTTITIS NO OBSTR
46431	CMS CC	MS-DRG MCC	AC EPIGLOTTITIS W OBSTR
46451		MS-DRG MCC	SUPRAGLOTTIS W OBSTR NOS
46611		MS-DRG CC	ACU BRONCHOLITIS D/T RSV
46619		MS-DRG CC	ACU BRNCHLTS D/T OTH ORG
475	CMS CC	MS-DRG CC	PERITONSILLAR ABSCESS
47821	CMS CC	MS-DRG CC	CELLULITIS OF PHARYNX
47822	CMS CC	MS-DRG CC	PARAPHARYNGEAL ABSCESS
47824	CMS CC	MS-DRG CC	RETROPHARYNGEAL ABSCESS
47830	CMS CC		VOCAL CORD PARALYSIS NOS
47831	CMS CC		VOCAL PARAL UNILAT PART
47832	CMS CC		VOCAL PARAL UNILAT TOTAL

(Continued)

2008 ICD-9-CM	CMS DRG	MS-DRG	Short Title
47833	CMS CC		VOCAL PARAL BILAT PART
47834	CMS CC	MS-DRG CC	VOCAL PARAL BILAT TOTAL
47871		MS-DRG CC	LARYNGEAL CELLULITIS
4800		MS-DRG MCC	ADENOVIRAL PNEUMONIA
4801		MS-DRG MCC	RESP SYNCYT VIRAL PNEUM
4802		MS-DRG MCC	PARINFLUENZA VIRAL PNEUM
4803	CMS CC	MS-DRG MCC	PNEUMONIA DUE TO SARS
4808		MS-DRG MCC	VIRAL PNEUMONIA NEC
4809		MS-DRG MCC	VIRAL PNEUMONIA NOS
481	CMS CC	MS-DRG MCC	PNEUMOCOCCAL PNEUMONIA
4820	CMS CC	MS-DRG MCC	K. PNEUMONIAE PNEUMONIA
4821	CMS CC	MS-DRG MCC	PSEUDOMONAL PNEUMONIA
4822	CMS CC	MS-DRG MCC	H. INFLUENZAE PNEUMONIA
48230	CMS CC	MS-DRG MCC	STREPTOCOCCAL PNEUMN NOS
48231	CMS CC	MS-DRG MCC	PNEUMONIA STRPTOCOCCUS A
48232	CMS CC	MS-DRG MCC	PNEUMONIA STRPTOCOCCUS B
48239	CMS CC	MS-DRG MCC	PNEUMONIA OTH STREP
48240	CMS CC	MS-DRG MCC	STAPHYLOCOCCAL PNEU NOS
48241	CMS CC	MS-DRG MCC	STAPH AUREUS PNEUMONIA
48249	CMS CC	MS-DRG MCC	STAPH PNEUMONIA NEC
48281	CMS CC	MS-DRG MCC	PNEUMONIA ANAEROBES
48282	CMS CC	MS-DRG MCC	PNEUMONIA E COLI
48283	CMS CC	MS-DRG MCC	PNEUMO OTH GRM-NEG BACT
48284	CMS CC	MS-DRG MCC	LEGIONNAIRES' DISEASE
48289	CMS CC	MS-DRG MCC	PNEUMONIA OTH SPCF BACT
4829	CMS CC	MS-DRG MCC	BACTERIAL PNEUMONIA NOS
4830	CMS CC	MS-DRG MCC	PNEU MYCPLSM PNEUMONIAE
4831	CMS CC	MS-DRG MCC	PNEUMONIA D/T CHLAMYDIA
4838	CMS CC	MS-DRG MCC	PNEUMON OTH SPEC ORGNSM
4841	CMS CC	MS-DRG MCC	PNEUM W CYTOMEG INCL DIS
4843	CMS CC	MS-DRG MCC	PNEUMONIA IN WHOOP COUGH
4845	CMS CC	MS-DRG MCC	PNEUMONIA IN ANTHRAX
4846	CMS CC	MS-DRG MCC	PNEUM IN ASPERGILLOSIS
4847	CMS CC	MS-DRG MCC	PNEUM IN OTH SYS MYCOSES
4848	CMS CC	MS-DRG MCC	PNEUM IN INFECT DIS NEC
485	CMS CC	MS-DRG MCC	BRONCHOPNEUMONIA ORG NOS
486	CMS CC	MS-DRG MCC	PNEUMONIA, ORGANISM NOS
4870	CMS CC	MS-DRG MCC	INFLUENZA WITH PNEUMONIA
4911	CMS CC		MUCOPURUL CHR BRONCHITIS

2008 ICD-9-CM	CMS DRG	MS-DRG	Short Title
49120	CMS CC		OBST CHR BRONC W/O EXAC
49121	CMS CC	MS-DRG CC	OBST CHR BRONC W(AC) EXAC
49122	CMS CC	MS-DRG CC	OBST CHR BRONC W AC BRONC
4918	CMS CC		CHRONIC BRONCHITIS NEC
4919	CMS CC		CHRONIC BRONCHITIS NOS
4928	CMS CC		EMPHYSEMA NEC
49301	CMS CC	MS-DRG CC	EXT ASTHMA W STATUS ASTH
49302	CMS CC	MS-DRG CC	EXT ASTHMA W(ACUTE) EXAC
49311	CMS CC	MS-DRG CC	INT ASTHMA W STATUS ASTH
49312	CMS CC	MS-DRG CC	INT ASTHMA W (AC) EXAC
49320	CMS CC		CHRONIC OBST ASTHMA NOS
49321	CMS CC	MS-DRG CC	CH OB ASTHMA W STAT ASTH
49322	CMS CC	MS-DRG CC	CH OBST ASTH W (AC) EXAC
49391	CMS CC	MS-DRG CC	ASTHMA W STATUS ASTHMAT
49392	CMS CC	MS-DRG CC	ASTHMA NOS W (AC) EXAC
4941	CMS CC	MS-DRG CC	BRONCHIECTASIS W AC EXAC
4950	CMS CC		FARMERS' LUNG
4951	CMS CC		BAGASSOSIS
4952	CMS CC		BIRD-FANCIERS' LUNG
4953	CMS CC		SUBEROSIS
4954	CMS CC		MALT WORKERS' LUNG
4955	CMS CC		MUSHROOM WORKERS' LUNG
4956	CMS CC		MAPL BARK-STRIPPRS' LUNG
4957	CMS CC	MS-DRG CC	"VENTILATION" PNEUMONIT
4958	CMS CC	MS-DRG CC	ALLERG ALVEOL/PNEUM NEC
4959	CMS CC	MS-DRG CC	ALLERG ALVEOL/PNEUM NOS
496	CMS CC		CHR AIRWAY OBSTRUCT NEC
5060	CMS CC	MS-DRG CC	FUM/VAPOR BRONC/PNEUMON
5061	CMS CC	MS-DRG MCC	FUM/VAPOR AC PULM EDEMA
5070	CMS CC	MS-DRG MCC	FOOD/VOMIT PNEUMONITIS
5071	CMS CC	MS-DRG MCC	OIL/ESSENCE PNEUMONITIS
5078	CMS CC	MS-DRG MCC	SOLID/LIQ PNEUMONIT NEC
5080	CMS CC	MS-DRG CC	AC PUL MANIF D/T RADIAT
5081	CMS CC	MS-DRG CC	CHR PUL MANIF D/T RADIAT
5100	CMS CC	MS-DRG MCC	EMPYEMA WITH FISTULA
5109	CMS CC	MS-DRG MCC	EMPYEMA W/O FISTULA
5111	CMS CC	MS-DRG MCC	BACT PLEUR/EFFUS NOT TB
5118	CMS CC	MS-DRG MCC	PLEURAL EFFUS NEC NOT TB
5119	CMS CC	MS-DRG CC	PLEURAL EFFUSION NOS

(Continued)

2008 ICD-9-CM	CMS DRG	MS-DRG	Short Title
5120	CMS CC	MS-DRG MCC	SPONT TENS PNEUMOTHORAX
5121	CMS CC	MS-DRG CC	IATROGENIC PNEUMOTHORAX
5128	CMS CC	MS-DRG CC	SPONT PNEUMOTHORAX NEC
5130	CMS CC	MS-DRG MCC	ABSCESS OF LUNG
5131	CMS CC	MS-DRG MCC	ABSCESS OF MEDIASTINUM
514		MS-DRG CC	PULM CONGEST/HYPOSTASIS
515	CMS CC		POSTINFLAM PULM FIBROSIS
5160	CMS CC	MS-DRG CC	PULM ALVEOLAR PROTEINOSIS
5161	CMS CC	MS-DRG CC	IDIO PULM HEMOSIDEROSIS
5162	CMS CC	MS-DRG CC	PULM ALVEOLAR MICROLITH
5163	CMS CC	MS-DRG CC	IDIO FIBROS ALVEOLITIS
5168	CMS CC	MS-DRG CC	ALVEOL PNEUMONOPATHY NEC
5169	CMS CC	MS-DRG CC	ALVEOL PNEUMONOPATHY NOS
5171	CMS CC	MS-DRG CC	RHEUMATIC PNEUMONIA
5172	CMS CC	MS-DRG CC	SYST SCLEROSIS LUNG DIS
5173	CMS CC	MS-DRG CC	ACUTE CHEST SYNDROME
5178	CMS CC		LUNG INVOLV IN OTH DIS
5180	CMS CC	MS-DRG CC	PULMONARY COLLAPSE
5181	CMS CC		INTERSTITIAL EMPHYSEMA
5183		MS-DRG CC	PULMONARY EOSINOPHILIA
5184	CMS CC	MS-DRG MCC	ACUTE LUNG EDEMA NOS
5185	CMS CC	MS-DRG MCC	POST TRAUM PULM INSUFFIC
5186	CMS CC	MS-DRG CC	ALRGC BRNCPUL ASPRGLOSIS
5187	CMS CC	MS-DRG CC	TRANSFSN REL AC LUNG INJ
51881	CMS CC	MS-DRG MCC	ACUTE RESPIRATRY FAILURE
51882	CMS CC	MS-DRG CC	OTHER PULMONARY INSUFF
51883	CMS CC	MS-DRG CC	CHRONIC RESPIRATORY FAIL
51884	CMS CC	MS-DRG MCC	ACUTE & CHRONC RESP FAIL
51900	CMS CC	MS-DRG CC	TRACHEOSTOMY COMP NOS
51901	CMS CC	MS-DRG CC	TRACHEOSTOMY INFECTION
51902	CMS CC	MS-DRG CC	TRACHEOSTOMY - MECH COMP
51909	CMS CC	MS-DRG CC	TRACHEOSTOMY COMP NEC
5192	CMS CC	MS-DRG MCC	MEDIASTINITIS
5220		MS-DRG CC	PULPITIS
5224		MS-DRG CC	AC APICAL PERIODONTITIS
5273	CMS CC	MS-DRG CC	SALIVARY GLAND ABSCESS
5274	CMS CC	MS-DRG CC	SALIVARY GLAND FISTULA
5283	CMS CC	MS-DRG CC	CELLULITIS/ABSCESS MOUTH
53012		MS-DRG CC	ACUTE ESOPHAGITIS

2008 ICD-9-CM	CMS DRG	MS-DRG	Short Title
53020		MS-DRG CC	ULCER ESOPHAGUS W/O BLEED
53021	CMS CC	MS-DRG MCC	ULCER ESOPHAGUS W BLEED
5304	CMS CC	MS-DRG MCC	PERFORATION OF ESOPHAGUS
5307	CMS CC	MS-DRG MCC	MALLORY-WEISS SYNDROME
53082	CMS CC	MS-DRG MCC	ESOPHAGEAL HEMORRHAGE
53084	CMS CC	MS-DRG MCC	TRACHEOESOPHAGEAL FSTULA
53086	CMS CC	MS-DRG CC	ESOPHAGOSTOMY INFECTION
53087	CMS CC	MS-DRG CC	MECH COMP ESOPHAGOSTOMY
53100	CMS CC	MS-DRG MCC	ACUTE STOMACH ULCER W HEM
53101	CMS CC	MS-DRG MCC	ACUTE STOMAC ULC W HEM-OBST
53110	CMS CC	MS-DRG MCC	ACUTE STOMACH ULCER W PERF
53111	CMS CC	MS-DRG MCC	ACUTE STOM ULC W PERF-OBST
53120	CMS CC	MS-DRG MCC	ACUTE STOMAC ULC W HEM/PERF
53121	CMS CC	MS-DRG MCC	ACUTE STOM ULC HEM/PERF-OBS
53130		MS-DRG CC	ACUTE STOMACH ULCER NOS
53131	CMS CC	MS-DRG MCC	ACUTE STOMACH ULC NOS-OBSTR
53140	CMS CC	MS-DRG MCC	CHR STOMACH ULC W HEM
53141	CMS CC	MS-DRG MCC	CHR STOM ULC W HEM-OBSTR
53150	CMS CC	MS-DRG MCC	CHR STOMACH ULCER W PERF
53151	CMS CC	MS-DRG MCC	CHR STOM ULC W PERF-OBST
53160	CMS CC	MS-DRG MCC	CHR STOMACH ULC HEM/PERF
53161	CMS CC	MS-DRG MCC	CHR STOM ULC HEM/PERF-OB
53171	CMS CC	MS-DRG MCC	CHR STOMACH ULC NOS-OBST
53191	CMS CC	MS-DRG MCC	STOMACH ULCER NOS-OBSTR
53200	CMS CC	MS-DRG MCC	AC DUODENAL ULCER W HEM
53201	CMS CC	MS-DRG MCC	AC DUODENAL ULC W HEM-OBST
53210	CMS CC	MS-DRG MCC	AC DUODENAL ULCER W PERF
53211	CMS CC	MS-DRG MCC	AC DUODENAL ULC PERF-OBSTR
53220	CMS CC	MS-DRG MCC	AC DUODENAL ULC W HEM/PERF
53221	CMS CC	MS-DRG MCC	AC DUODENAL ULC HEM/PERF-OBS
53230		MS-DRG CC	ACUTE DUODENAL ULCER NOS
53231	CMS CC	MS-DRG MCC	AC DUODENAL ULC NOS-OBST
53240		MS-DRG MCC	CHR DUODENAL ULCER W HEM
53241	CMS CC	MS-DRG MCC	CHR DUODENAL ULC HEM-OBSTR
53250	CMS CC	MS-DRG MCC	CHR DUODENAL ULCER W PERF
53251	CMS CC	MS-DRG MCC	CHR DUODENAL ULC PERF-OBST
53260	CMS CC	MS-DRG MCC	CHR DUODENAL ULC HEM/PERF
53261	CMS CC	MS-DRG MCC	CHR DUODENAL ULC HEM/PERF-OB
53271	CMS CC	MS-DRG MCC	CHR DUODENAL ULC NOS-OBSTR

2008 ICD-9-CM	CMS DRG	MS-DRG	Short Title
53291	CMS CC	MS-DRG MCC	DUODENAL ULCER NOS-OBSTR
53300	CMS CC	MS-DRG MCC	AC PEPTIC ULCER W HEMORR
53301	CMS CC	MS-DRG MCC	AC PEPTIC ULC W HEM-OBST
53310	CMS CC	MS-DRG MCC	AC PEPTIC ULCER W PERFOR
53311	CMS CC	MS-DRG MCC	AC PEPTIC ULC W PERF-OBS
53320	CMS CC	MS-DRG MCC	AC PEPTIC ULC W HEM/PERF
53321	CMS CC	MS-DRG MCC	AC PEPT ULC HEM/PERF-OBS
53330		MS-DRG CC	ACUTE PEPTIC ULCER NOS
53331	CMS CC	MS-DRG MCC	AC PEPTIC ULCER NOS-OBST
53340	CMS CC	MS-DRG MCC	CHR PEPTIC ULCER W HEM
53341	CMS CC	MS-DRG MCC	CHR PEPTIC ULC W HEM-OBS
53350	CMS CC	MS-DRG MCC	CHR PEPTIC ULCER W PERF
53351	CMS CC	MS-DRG MCC	CHR PEPTIC ULC PERF-OBST
53360	CMS CC	MS-DRG MCC	CHR PEPT ULC W HEM/PERF
53361	CMS CC	MS-DRG MCC	CHR PEPT ULC HEM/PERF-OB
53371	CMS CC	MS-DRG MCC	CHR PEPTIC ULCER NOS-OBS
53391	CMS CC	MS-DRG MCC	PEPTIC ULCER NOS-OBSTRUC
53400	CMS CC	MS-DRG MCC	AC MARGINAL ULCER W HEM
53401	CMS CC	MS-DRG MCC	AC MARGINAL ULC W HEM-OBST
53410	CMS CC	MS-DRG MCC	AC MARGINAL ULCER W PERF
53411	CMS CC	MS-DRG MCC	AC MARGINAL ULC W PERF-OBS
53420	CMS CC	MS-DRG MCC	AC MARGINAL ULC W HEM/PERF
53421	CMS CC	MS-DRG MCC	AC MARGINAL ULC HEM/PERF-OBS
53430		MS-DRG CC	AC MARGINAL ULCER NOS
53431	CMS CC	MS-DRG MCC	AC MARGINAL ULC NOS-OBST
53440	CMS CC	MS-DRG MCC	CHR MARGINAL ULCER W HEM
53441	CMS CC	MS-DRG MCC	CHR MARGINAL ULC W HEM-OBS
53450	CMS CC	MS-DRG MCC	CHR MARGINAL ULC W PERF
53451	CMS CC	MS-DRG MCC	CHR MARGINAL ULC PERF-OBST
53460	CMS CC	MS-DRG MCC	CHR MARGINAL ULC HEM/PERF
53461	CMS CC	MS-DRG MCC	CHR MARGINAL ULC HEM/PERF-OB
53471	CMS CC	MS-DRG MCC	CHR MARGINAL ULC NOS-OBS
53491	CMS CC	MS-DRG MCC	GASTROJEJUN ULC NOS-OBST
53501	CMS CC	MS-DRG MCC	ACUTE GASTRITIS W HMRHG
53511	CMS CC	MS-DRG MCC	ATRPH GASTRITIS W HMRHG
53521	CMS CC	MS-DRG MCC	GSTR MCSL HYPRT W HMRG
53531	CMS CC	MS-DRG MCC	ALCHL GSTRITIS W HMRHG
53541	CMS CC	MS-DRG MCC	OTH SPF GASTRT W HMRHG
53551	CMS CC	MS-DRG MCC	GSTR/DDNTS NOS W HMRHG

2008 ICD-9-CM	CMS DRG	MS-DRG	Short Title
53561	CMS CC	MS-DRG MCC	DUODENITIS W HMRHG
5361	CMS CC	MS-DRG CC	AC DILATION OF STOMACH
53640	CMS CC		GASTROSTOMY COMP NOS
53641	CMS CC	MS-DRG CC	GASTROSTOMY INFECTION
53642	CMS CC	MS-DRG CC	GASTROSTOMY COMP - MECH
53649	CMS CC		GASTROSTOMY COMP NEC
5370	CMS CC	MS-DRG CC	ACQ PYLORIC STENOSIS
5373	CMS CC	MS-DRG CC	DUODENAL OBSTRUCTION NEC
5374	CMS CC	MS-DRG CC	GASTRIC/DUODENAL FISTULA
53783	CMS CC	MS-DRG MCC	ANGIO STM/DUDN W HMRHG
53784	CMS CC	MS-DRG MCC	DIEULAFOY LES, STOM & DUOD
538		MS-DRG CC	GI MUCOSITIS (ULCERATVE)
5400	CMS CC	MS-DRG MCC	AC APPEND W PERITONITIS
5401	CMS CC	MS-DRG MCC	ABSCESS OF APPENDIX
5409	CMS CC	MS-DRG CC	ACUTE APPENDICITIS NOS
55000	CMS CC	MS-DRG MCC	UNILAT ING HERNIA W GANG
55001	CMS CC	MS-DRG MCC	RECUR UNIL ING HERN-GANG
55002	CMS CC	MS-DRG MCC	BILAT ING HERNIA W GANG
55003	CMS CC	MS-DRG MCC	RECUR BIL ING HERN-GANG
55010		MS-DRG CC	UNILAT ING HERNIA W OBST
55011		MS-DRG CC	RECUR UNIL ING HERN-OBST
55012		MS-DRG CC	BILAT ING HERNIA W OBST
55013		MS-DRG CC	RECUR BIL ING HERN-OBSTR
55100	CMS CC	MS-DRG MCC	UNIL FEMORAL HERN W GANG
55101	CMS CC	MS-DRG MCC	REC UNIL FEM HERN W GANG
55102	CMS CC	MS-DRG MCC	BILAT FEM HERN W GANG
55103	CMS CC	MS-DRG MCC	RECUR BIL FEM HERN-GANG
5511	CMS CC	MS-DRG MCC	UMBILICAL HERNIA W GANGR
55120	CMS CC	MS-DRG MCC	GANGR VENTRAL HERNIA NOS
55121	CMS CC	MS-DRG MCC	GANGR INCISIONAL HERNIA
55129	CMS CC	MS-DRG MCC	GANGR VENTRAL HERNIA NEC
5513	CMS CC	MS-DRG MCC	DIAPHRAGM HERNIA W GANGR
5518	CMS CC	MS-DRG MCC	HERNIA, SITE NEC W GANGR
5519	CMS CC	MS-DRG MCC	HERNIA, SITE NOS W GANGR
55200	CMS CC	MS-DRG CC	UNIL FEMORAL HERN W OBST
55201	CMS CC	MS-DRG CC	REC UNIL FEM HERN W OBST
55202	CMS CC	MS-DRG CC	BIL FEMORAL HERN W OBSTR
55203	CMS CC	MS-DRG CC	REC BIL FEM HERN W OBSTR
5521	CMS CC	MS-DRG CC	UMBILICAL HERNIA W OBSTR

(Continued)

2008 ICD-9-CM	CMS DRG	MS-DRG	Short Title
55220	CMS CC	MS-DRG CC	OBSTR VENTRAL HERNIA NOS
55221	CMS CC	MS-DRG CC	OBSTR INCISIONAL HERNIA
55229	CMS CC	MS-DRG CC	OBSTR VENTRAL HERNIA NEC
5523	CMS CC	MS-DRG CC	DIAPHRAGM HERNIA W OBSTR
5528	CMS CC	MS-DRG CC	HERNIA, SITE NEC W OBSTR
5529	CMS CC	MS-DRG CC	HERNIA, SITE NOS W OBSTR
5550		MS-DRG CC	REG ENTERITIS, SM INTEST
5551		MS-DRG CC	REG ENTERITIS, LG INTEST
5552		MS-DRG CC	REG ENTERIT SM/LG INTEST
5559		MS-DRG CC	REGIONAL ENTERITIS NOS
5560		MS-DRG CC	ULCERATIVE ENTEROCOLITIS
5561		MS-DRG CC	ULCERATIVE ILEOCOLITIS
5562		MS-DRG CC	ULCERATIVE PROCTITIS
5563		MS-DRG CC	ULCERTVE PRCTOSIGMOIDTIS
5564		MS-DRG CC	PSEUDOPOLYPOSIS COLON
5565		MS-DRG CC	LFTSDED ULCERTVE COLITIS
5566		MS-DRG CC	UNIVRSL ULCERTVE COLITIS
5568		MS-DRG CC	OTHER ULCERATIVE COLITIS
5569		MS-DRG CC	ULCERATVE COLITIS UNSPCF
5570	CMS CC	MS-DRG MCC	AC VASC INSUFF INTESTINE
5571		MS-DRG CC	CHR VASC INSUFF INTEST
5579		MS-DRG CC	VASC INSUFF INTEST NOS
5581	CMS CC	MS-DRG CC	RADIATION GASTROENTERIT
5582	CMS CC	MS-DRG CC	TOXIC GASTROENTERITIS
5600	CMS CC	MS-DRG CC	INTUSSUSCEPTION
5601	CMS CC	MS-DRG CC	PARALYTIC ILEUS
5602	CMS CC	MS-DRG MCC	VOLVULUS OF INTESTINE
56030	CMS CC	MS-DRG CC	IMPACTION INTESTINE NOS
56031	CMS CC	MS-DRG CC	GALLSTONE ILEUS
56039	CMS CC	MS-DRG CC	IMPACTION INTESTINE NEC
56081	CMS CC	MS-DRG CC	INTESTINAL ADHES W OBSTR
56089	CMS CC	MS-DRG CC	INTESTINAL OBSTRUCT NEC
5609	CMS CC	MS-DRG CC	INTESTINAL OBSTRUCT NOS
56201		MS-DRG CC	DVRTCLI SML INT W/O HMRG
56202	CMS CC	MS-DRG MCC	DVRTCLO SML INT W HMRHG
56203	CMS CC	MS-DRG MCC	DVRTCLI SML INT W HMRHG
56211		MS-DRG CC	DVRTCLI COLON W/O HMRHG
56212	CMS CC	MS-DRG MCC	DVRTCLO COLON W HMRHG
56213	CMS CC	MS-DRG MCC	DVRTCLI COLON W HMRHG

2008 ICD-9-CM	CMS DRG	MS-DRG	Short Title
5647		MS-DRG CC	MEGACOLON NEC
56481		MS-DRG CC	NEUROGENIC BOWEL
566	CMS CC	MS-DRG CC	ANAL & RECTAL ABSCESS
5670	CMS CC	MS-DRG MCC	PERITONITIS IN INFEC DIS
5671	CMS CC	MS-DRG MCC	PNEUMOCOCCAL PERITONITIS
56721	CMS CC	MS-DRG MCC	PERITONITIS (ACUTE) GEN
56722	CMS CC	MS-DRG MCC	PERITONEAL ABSCESS
56723	CMS CC	MS-DRG MCC	SPONTAN BACT PERITONITIS
56729	CMS CC	MS-DRG MCC	SUPPURAT PERITONITIS NEC
56731	CMS CC	MS-DRG MCC	PSOAS MUSCLE ABSCESS
56738	CMS CC	MS-DRG MCC	RETROPERITON ABSCESS NEC
56739	CMS CC	MS-DRG MCC	RETROPERITON INFECT NEC
56781	CMS CC	MS-DRG MCC	CHOLEPERITONITIS
56782	CMS CC	MS-DRG CC	SCLEROSING MESENTERITIS
56789	CMS CC	MS-DRG MCC	PERITONITIS NEC
5679	CMS CC	MS-DRG MCC	PERITONITIS NOS
56881	CMS CC	MS-DRG MCC	HEMOPERITONEUM
56882		MS-DRG CC	PERITONEAL EFFUSION
5693	CMS CC	MS-DRG CC	RECTAL & ANAL HEMORRHAGE
56941		MS-DRG CC	RECTAL & ANAL ULCER
5695	CMS CC	MS-DRG CC	INTESTINAL ABSCESS
56960	CMS CC		COLOSTOMY/ENTER COMP NOS
56961	CMS CC	MS-DRG CC	COLOSTOMY/ENTEROST INFECTN
56962	CMS CC	MS-DRG CC	COLOSTOMY/ENTER COMP-MECH
56969	CMS CC	MS-DRG CC	COLOSTOMY/ENTEROS COMP NEC
56981		MS-DRG CC	INTESTINAL FISTULA
56982		MS-DRG CC	ULCERATION OF INTESTINE
56983	CMS CC	MS-DRG MCC	PERFORATION OF INTESTINE
56985	CMS CC	MS-DRG MCC	ANGIO INTES W HMRHG
56986	CMS CC	MS-DRG MCC	DIEULAFOY LES, INTESTINE
570	CMS CC	MS-DRG MCC	ACUTE NECROSIS OF LIVER
5712	CMS CC		ALCOHOL CIRRHOSIS LIVER
57149	CMS CC		CHRONIC HEPATITIS NEC
5715	CMS CC		CIRRHOSIS OF LIVER NOS
5716	CMS CC		BILIARY CIRRHOSIS
5720	CMS CC	MS-DRG MCC	ABSCESS OF LIVER
5721	CMS CC	MS-DRG MCC	PORTAL PYEMIA
5722	CMS CC	MS-DRG MCC	HEPATIC COMA
5723		MS-DRG CC	PORTAL HYPERTENSION

(Continued)

2008 ICD-9-CM	CMS DRG	MS-DRG	Short Title
5724	CMS CC	MS-DRG MCC	HEPATORENAL SYNDROME
5731	CMS CC	MS-DRG CC	HEPATITIS IN VIRAL DIS
5732	CMS CC	MS-DRG CC	HEPATITIS IN OTH INF DIS
5733	CMS CC		HEPATITIS NOS
5734	CMS CC	MS-DRG MCC	HEPATIC INFARCTION
57400	CMS CC	MS-DRG CC	CHOLELITH W AC CHOLECYST
57401	CMS CC	MS-DRG CC	CHOLELITH/AC GB INF-OBST
57410	CMS CC	MS-DRG CC	CHOLELITH W CHOLECYS NEC
57411	CMS CC	MS-DRG CC	CHOLELITH/GB INF NEC-OBS
57421	CMS CC	MS-DRG CC	CHOLELITHIAS NOS W OBSTR
57430	CMS CC	MS-DRG CC	CHOLEDOCHOLITH/AC GB INF
57431	CMS CC	MS-DRG CC	CHOLEDOCHLITH/AC GB-OBST
57440	CMS CC	MS-DRG CC	CHOLEDOCHLITH/GB INF NEC
57441	CMS CC	MS-DRG CC	CHOLEDOCHLITH/GB NEC-OBS
57450	CMS CC		CHOLEDOCHOLITHIASIS NOS
57451	CMS CC	MS-DRG CC	CHOLEDOCHLITH NOS W OBST
57460	CMS CC	MS-DRG CC	GALL&BIL CAL W/AC W/O OB
57461	CMS CC	MS-DRG CC	GALL&BIL CAL W/AC W OBS
57470	CMS CC	MS-DRG CC	GALL&BIL CAL W/OTH W/O OB
57471	CMS CC	MS-DRG CC	GALL&BIL CAL W/OTH W OBS
57480	CMS CC	MS-DRG CC	GALL&BIL CAL W/AC&CHR W/O
57481	CMS CC	MS-DRG MCC	GALL&BIL CAL W/AC&CH W OB
57490	CMS CC		GALL&BIL CAL W/O CHO W/O
57491	CMS CC	MS-DRG CC	GALL&BIL CAL W/O CH W OB
5750	CMS CC	MS-DRG CC	ACUTE CHOLECYSTITIS
57512	CMS CC	MS-DRG CC	ACUTE & CHR CHOLECYSTITIS
5752	CMS CC	MS-DRG CC	OBSTRUCTION GALLBLADDER
5753	CMS CC	MS-DRG CC	HYDROPS OF GALLBLADDER
5754	CMS CC	MS-DRG MCC	PERFORATION GALLBLADDER
5755	CMS CC	MS-DRG CC	FISTULA OF GALLBLADDER
5761	CMS CC	MS-DRG CC	CHOLANGITIS
5762		MS-DRG MCC	OBSTRUCTION OF BILE DUCT
5763	CMS CC	MS-DRG MCC	PERFORATION OF BILE DUCT
5764	CMS CC	MS-DRG CC	FISTULA OF BILE DUCT
5770	CMS CC	MS-DRG MCC	ACUTE PANCREATITIS
5771		MS-DRG CC	CHRONIC PANCREATITIS
5772	CMS CC	MS-DRG CC	PANCREAT CYST/PSEUDOCYST
5780	CMS CC	MS-DRG CC	HEMATEMESIS
5781	CMS CC	MS-DRG CC	BLOOD IN STOOL

2008 ICD-9-CM	CMS DRG	MS-DRG	Short Title
5789	CMS CC	MS-DRG CC	GASTROINTEST HEMORR NOS
5791		MS-DRG CC	TROPICAL SPRUE
5792		MS-DRG CC	BLIND LOOP SYNDROME
5793	CMS CC	MS-DRG CC	INTEST POSTOP NONABSORB
5794		MS-DRG CC	PANCREATIC STEATORRHEA
5798		MS-DRG CC	INTEST MALABSORPTION NEC
5799		MS-DRG CC	INTEST MALABSORPTION NOS
5800	CMS CC	MS-DRG MCC	AC PROLIFERAT NEPHRITIS
5804	CMS CC	MS-DRG MCC	AC RAPIDLY PROGR NEPHRITIS
58081	CMS CC	MS-DRG MCC	AC NEPHRITIS IN OTH DIS
58089	CMS CC	MS-DRG MCC	ACUTE NEPHRITIS NEC
5809		MS-DRG MCC	ACUTE NEPHRITIS NOS
5810	CMS CC	MS-DRG CC	NEPHROTIC SYN, PROLIFER
5811	CMS CC	MS-DRG CC	EPIMEMBRANOUS NEPHRITIS
5812	CMS CC	MS-DRG CC	MEMBRANOPROLIF NEPHROSIS
5813	CMS CC	MS-DRG CC	MINIMAL CHANGE NEPHROSIS
58181	CMS CC	MS-DRG CC	NEPHROTIC SYN IN OTH DIS
58189	CMS CC	MS-DRG CC	NEPHROTIC SYNDROME NEC
5819	CMS CC	MS-DRG CC	NEPHROTIC SYNDROME NOS
5820		MS-DRG CC	CHR PROLIFERAT NEPHRITIS
5821		MS-DRG CC	CHR MEMBRANOUS NEPHRITIS
5822		MS-DRG CC	CHR MEMBRANOPROLIF NEPHR
5824		MS-DRG CC	CHR RAPID PROGR NEPHRIT
58281		MS-DRG CC	CHR NEPHRITIS IN OTH DIS
58289		MS-DRG CC	CHRONIC NEPHRITIS NEC
5829		MS-DRG CC	CHRONIC NEPHRITIS NOS
5830		MS-DRG CC	PROLIFERAT NEPHRITIS NOS
5831		MS-DRG CC	MEMBRANOUS NEPHRITIS NOS
5832		MS-DRG CC	MEMBRANOPROLIF NEPHR NOS
5834	CMS CC	MS-DRG MCC	RAPIDLY PROG NEPHRIT NOS
5836		MS-DRG MCC	RENAL CORT NECROSIS NOS
5837		MS-DRG CC	NEPHR NOS/MEDULL NECROS
5845	CMS CC	MS-DRG MCC	LOWER NEPHRON NEPHROSIS
5846	CMS CC	MS-DRG MCC	AC RENAL FAIL, CORT NECR
5847	CMS CC	MS-DRG MCC	AC REN FAIL, MEDULL NECR
5848	CMS CC	MS-DRG MCC	AC RENAL FAILURE NEC
5849	CMS CC	MS-DRG MCC	ACUTE RENAL FAILURE NOS
5851	CMS CC		CHRO KIDNEY DIS STAGE I
5852	CMS CC		CHRO KIDNEY DIS STAGE II

2008 ICD-9-CM	CMS DRG	MS-DRG	Short Title
5853	CMS CC		CHR KIDNEY DIS STAGE III
5854	CMS CC	MS-DRG CC	CHR KIDNEY DIS STAGE IV
5855	CMS CC	MS-DRG CC	CHR KIDNEY DIS STAGE V
5856	CMS CC	MS-DRG MCC	END STAGE RENAL DISEASE
5859	CMS CC		CHRONIC KIDNEY DIS NOS
5881		MS-DRG CC	NEPHROGEN DIABETES INSIP
58881		MS-DRG CC	SEC HYPERPARATHYRD-RENAL
59001		MS-DRG CC	CHR PYELONEPH W MED NECR
59010	CMS CC	MS-DRG CC	AC PYELONEPHRITIS NOS
59011	CMS CC	MS-DRG MCC	AC PYELONEPHR W MED NECR
5902	CMS CC	MS-DRG MCC	RENAL/PERIRENAL ABSCESS
5903	CMS CC	MS-DRG CC	PYELOURETERITIS CYSTICA
59080	CMS CC	MS-DRG CC	PYELONEPHRITIS NOS
59081	CMS CC	MS-DRG CC	PYELONEPHRITIS IN OTH DIS
5909	CMS CC		INFECTION OF KIDNEY NOS
591	CMS CC	MS-DRG CC	HYDRONEPHROSIS
5921	CMS CC	MS-DRG CC	CALCULUS OF URETER
5934		MS-DRG CC	URETERIC OBSTRUCTION NEC
5935	CMS CC	MS-DRG CC	HYDROURETER
59381		MS-DRG CC	RENAL VASCULAR DISORDER
59382		MS-DRG CC	URETERAL FISTULA
5950	CMS CC	MS-DRG CC	ACUTE CYSTITIS
5951	CMS CC		CHR INTERSTIT CYSTITIS
5952	CMS CC		CHRONIC CYSTITIS NEC
5954	CMS CC		CYSTITIS IN OTH DIS
59581	CMS CC		CYSTITIS CYSTICA
59582	CMS CC	MS-DRG CC	IRRADIATION CYSTITIS
59589	CMS CC		CYSTITIS NEC
5959	CMS CC		CYSTITIS NOS
5960	CMS CC		BLADDER NECK OBSTRUCTION
5961	CMS CC	MS-DRG CC	INTESTINOVESICAL FISTULA
5962	CMS CC	MS-DRG CC	VESICAL FISTULA NEC
5964	CMS CC		ATONY OF BLADDER
5966	CMS CC	MS-DRG MCC	BLADDER RUPT, NONTRAUM
5967	CMS CC	MS-DRG CC	BLADDER WALL HEMORRHAGE
5970	CMS CC	MS-DRG CC	URETHRAL ABSCESS
5981	CMS CC		TRAUM URETHRAL STRICTURE
5982	CMS CC		POSTOP URETHRAL STRICTUR
5990	CMS CC	MS-DRG CC	URIN TRACT INFECTION NOS

2008 ICD-9-CM	CMS DRG	MS-DRG	Short Title
5991		MS-DRG CC	URETHRAL FISTULA
5994	CMS CC		URETHRAL FALSE PASSAGE
59960	CMS CC		URINARY OBSTRUCTION NOS
59969	CMS CC		URINARY OBSTRUCTION NEC
5997	CMS CC		HEMATURIA
6010	CMS CC	MS-DRG CC	ACUTE PROSTATITIS
6012	CMS CC	MS-DRG CC	ABSCESS OF PROSTATE
6013	CMS CC		PROSTATOCYSTITIS
6021	CMS CC		PROSTATIC CONGEST/HEMORR
6031	CMS CC	MS-DRG CC	INFECTED HYDROCELE
6040	CMS CC	MS-DRG CC	ORCHITIS WITH ABSCESS
6073		MS-DRG CC	PRIAPISM
60782		MS-DRG CC	VASCULAR DISORDER, PENIS
60820		MS-DRG CC	TORSION OF TESTIS NOS
60821		MS-DRG CC	EXTRAVAG TORS SPERM CORD
60822		MS-DRG CC	INTRAVAG TORS SPERM CORD
60823		MS-DRG CC	TORSION APPENDIX TESTIS
60824		MS-DRG CC	TORSION APPY EPIDIDYMIS
61172	CMS CC		LUMP OR MASS IN BREAST
6140	CMS CC	MS-DRG CC	AC SALPINGO-OOPHORITIS
6143	CMS CC	MS-DRG CC	ACUTE PARAMETRITIS
6145	CMS CC	MS-DRG MCC	AC PELV PERITONITIS-FEM
6147		MS-DRG CC	CHR PELV PERITON NEC-FEM
6150	CMS CC	MS-DRG CC	AC UTERINE INFLAMMATION
6163	CMS CC	MS-DRG CC	BARTHOLIN'S GLND ABSCESS
6164	CMS CC	MS-DRG CC	ABSCESS OF VULVA NEC
61681		MS-DRG CC	MUCOSITIS CERV,VAG,VULVA
6190		MS-DRG CC	URIN-GENITAL FISTUL, FEM
6191		MS-DRG CC	DIGEST-GENIT FISTUL, FEM
6192		MS-DRG CC	GENITAL-SKIN FISTUL, FEM
6198		MS-DRG CC	FEM GENITAL FISTULA NEC
6199		MS-DRG CC	FEM GENITAL FISTULA NOS
6205		MS-DRG CC	TORSION OF OVARY OR TUBE
6207	CMS CC		BROAD LIGAMENT HEMATOMA
63300		MS-DRG CC	ABD PREG W/O INTRAUT PREG
63301		MS-DRG CC	ABD PREG W INTRAUT PREG
63310		MS-DRG CC	TUBAL PREG W/O INTRAUT PRG
63311		MS-DRG CC	TUBAL PREG W INTRAUT PREG
63320		MS-DRG CC	OVARN PREG W/O INTRAUT PRG

(Continued)

2008 ICD-9-CM	CMS DRG	MS-DRG	Short Title
63321		MS-DRG CC	OVARIAN PREG W INTRA PRG
63380		MS-DRG CC	ECT PREG NEC W/O INTRA PRG
63381		MS-DRG CC	ECTPC PRG NEC W INTRA PREG
63390		MS-DRG CC	ECT PREG NOS W/O INTRA PRG
63391		MS-DRG CC	ECTP PREG NOS W INTRA PREG
63400	CMS CC	MS-DRG CC	SPON ABOR W PEL INF-UNSP
63401	CMS CC	MS-DRG CC	SPON ABOR W PELV INF-INC
63402	CMS CC	MS-DRG CC	SPON ABOR W PEL INF-COMP
63410	CMS CC		SPON ABORT W HEMORR-UNSP
63411	CMS CC		SPON ABORT W HEMORR-INC
63412	CMS CC		SPON ABORT W HEMORR-COMP
63420	CMS CC	MS-DRG CC	SPON AB W PELV DAMAG-UNSP
63421	CMS CC	MS-DRG CC	SPON AB W PELV DAMAG-INC
63422	CMS CC	MS-DRG CC	SPON AB W PELV DAMAG-COMP
63430	CMS CC	MS-DRG MCC	SPON AB W REN FAIL-UNSP
63431	CMS CC	MS-DRG MCC	SPON AB W REN FAIL-INC
63432	CMS CC	MS-DRG MCC	SPON AB W REN FAIL-COMP
63440	CMS CC	MS-DRG CC	SPON AB W METAB DIS-UNSP
63441	CMS CC	MS-DRG CC	SPON AB W METAB DIS-INC
63442	CMS CC	MS-DRG CC	SPON AB W METAB DIS-COMP
63450	CMS CC	MS-DRG MCC	SPON ABORT W SHOCK-UNSP
63451	CMS CC	MS-DRG MCC	SPON ABORT W SHOCK-INC
63452	CMS CC	MS-DRG MCC	SPON ABORT W SHOCK-COMP
63460	CMS CC	MS-DRG CC	SPON ABORT W EMBOL-UNSP
63461	CMS CC	MS-DRG MCC	SPON ABORT W EMBOL-INC
63462	CMS CC	MS-DRG MCC	SPON ABORT W EMBOL-COMP
63470	CMS CC	MS-DRG CC	SPON AB W COMPL NEC-UNSP
63471	CMS CC	MS-DRG CC	SPON AB W COMPL NEC-INC
63472	CMS CC	MS-DRG CC	SPON AB W COMPL NEC-COMP
63480	CMS CC	MS-DRG CC	SPON AB W COMPL NOS-UNSP
63481	CMS CC	MS-DRG CC	SPON AB W COMPL NOS-INC
63482	CMS CC	MS-DRG CC	SPON AB W COMPL NOS-COMP
63490	CMS CC		SPON ABORT UNCOMPL-UNSP
63491	CMS CC		SPON ABORT UNCOMPL-INC
63492	CMS CC		SPON ABORT UNCOMPL-COMP
63500		MS-DRG CC	LEG ABOR W PELV INF-UNSP
63501		MS-DRG CC	LEG ABOR W PELV INF-INC
63502		MS-DRG CC	LEG ABOR W PELV INF-COMP
63520		MS-DRG CC	LEG AB W PELV DAMAG-UNSP

2008 ICD-9-CM	CMS DRG	MS-DRG	Short Title
63521		MS-DRG CC	LEG AB W PELV DAMAG-INC
63522		MS-DRG CC	LEG AB W PELV DAMAG-COMP
63530		MS-DRG MCC	LEG ABOR W REN FAIL-UNSP
63531		MS-DRG MCC	LEG ABOR W REN FAIL-INC
63532		MS-DRG MCC	LEG ABOR W REN FAIL-COMP
63540		MS-DRG CC	LEG AB W METAB DIS-UNSP
63541		MS-DRG CC	LEG AB W METAB DIS-INC
63542		MS-DRG CC	LEG AB W METAB DIS-COMP
63550		MS-DRG MCC	LEGAL ABORT W SHOCK-UNSP
63551		MS-DRG MCC	LEGAL ABORT W SHOCK-INC
63552		MS-DRG MCC	LEGAL ABORT W SHOCK-COMP
63560		MS-DRG MCC	LEGAL ABORT W EMBOL-UNSP
63561		MS-DRG MCC	LEGAL ABORT W EMBOL-INC
63562		MS-DRG MCC	LEGAL ABORT W EMBOL-COMP
63570		MS-DRG CC	LEG AB W COMPL NEC-UNSP
63571		MS-DRG CC	LEG AB W COMPL NEC-INC
63572		MS-DRG CC	LEG AB W COMPL NEC-COMP
63580		MS-DRG CC	LEG AB W COMPL NOS-UNSP
63581		MS-DRG CC	LEG AB W COMPL NOS-INC
63582		MS-DRG CC	LEG AB W COMPL NOS-COMP
63600		MS-DRG CC	ILLEG AB W PELV INF-UNSP
63601		MS-DRG CC	ILLEG AB W PELV INF-INC
63602		MS-DRG CC	ILLEG AB W PELV INF-COMP
63620		MS-DRG CC	ILLEG AB W PEL DAMG-UNSP
63621		MS-DRG CC	ILLEG AB W PEL DAMAG-INC
63622		MS-DRG CC	ILLEG AB W PEL DAMG-COMP
63630		MS-DRG MCC	ILLEG AB W REN FAIL-UNSP
63631		MS-DRG MCC	ILLEG AB W REN FAIL-INC
63632		MS-DRG MCC	ILLEG AB W REN FAIL-COMP
63640		MS-DRG CC	ILLEG AB W MET DIS-UNSP
63641		MS-DRG CC	ILLEG AB W METAB DIS-INC
63642		MS-DRG CC	ILLEG AB W MET DIS-COMP
63650		MS-DRG MCC	ILLEG ABORT W SHOCK-UNSP
63651		MS-DRG MCC	ILLEG ABORT W SHOCK-INC
63652		MS-DRG MCC	ILLEG ABORT W SHOCK-COMP
63660		MS-DRG MCC	ILLEG AB W EMBOLISM-UNSP
63661		MS-DRG MCC	ILLEG AB W EMBOLISM-INC
63662		MS-DRG MCC	ILLEG AB W EMBOLISM-COMP
63670		MS-DRG CC	ILLG AB W COMPL NEC-UNSP

(Continued)

2008 ICD-9-CM	CMS DRG	MS-DRG	Short Title
63671		MS-DRG CC	ILLEG AB W COMPL NEC-INC
63672		MS-DRG CC	ILLG AB W COMPL NEC-COMP
63680		MS-DRG CC	ILLG AB W COMPL NOS-UNSP
63681		MS-DRG CC	ILLEG AB W COMPL NOS-INC
63682		MS-DRG CC	ILLG AB W COMPL NOS-COMP
63700		MS-DRG CC	ABORT NOS W PEL INF-UNSP
63701		MS-DRG CC	ABORT NOS W PEL INF-INC
63702		MS-DRG CC	ABORT NOS W PEL INF-COMP
63720		MS-DRG CC	AB NOS W PELV DAMAG-UNSP
63721		MS-DRG CC	AB NOS W PELV DAMAG-INC
63722		MS-DRG CC	AB NOS W PELV DAMAG-COMP
63730		MS-DRG MCC	AB NOS W RENAL FAIL-UNSP
63731		MS-DRG MCC	AB NOS W RENAL FAIL-INC
63732		MS-DRG MCC	AB NOS W RENAL FAIL-COMP
63740		MS-DRG CC	AB NOS W METAB DIS-UNSP
63741		MS-DRG CC	AB NOS W METAB DIS-INC
63742		MS-DRG CC	AB NOS W METAB DIS-COMP
63750		MS-DRG MCC	ABORT NOS W SHOCK-UNSP
63751		MS-DRG MCC	ABORT NOS W SHOCK-INC
63752		MS-DRG MCC	ABORT NOS W SHOCK-COMP
63760		MS-DRG MCC	AB NOS W EMBOLISM-UNSP
63761		MS-DRG MCC	AB NOS W EMBOLISM-INC
63762		MS-DRG MCC	AB NOS W EMBOLISM-COMP
63770		MS-DRG CC	AB NOS W COMPL NEC-UNSP
63771		MS-DRG CC	AB NOS W COMPL NEC-INC
63772		MS-DRG CC	AB NOS W COMPL NEC-COMP
63780		MS-DRG CC	AB NOS W COMPL NOS-UNSP
63781		MS-DRG CC	AB NOS W COMPL NOS-INC
63782		MS-DRG CC	AB NOS W COMPL NOS-COMP
6380		MS-DRG CC	ATTEM ABORT W PELVIC INF
6381		MS-DRG CC	ATTEM ABORT W HEMORRHAGE
6382		MS-DRG CC	ATTEM ABORT W PELV DAMAG
6383		MS-DRG MCC	ATTEM ABORT W RENAL FAIL
6384		MS-DRG CC	ATTEM ABOR W METABOL DIS
6385		MS-DRG MCC	ATTEM ABORTION W SHOCK
6386		MS-DRG MCC	ATTEMP ABORT W EMBOLISM
6387		MS-DRG CC	ATTEMP ABORT W COMPL NEC
6388		MS-DRG CC	ATTEMP ABORT W COMPL NOS
6390	CMS CC	MS-DRG CC	POSTABORTION GU INFECT

2008 ICD-9-CM	CMS DRG	MS-DRG	Short Title
6391	CMS CC	MS-DRG CC	POSTABORTION HEMORRHAGE
6392	CMS CC	MS-DRG CC	POSTABORT PELVIC DAMAGE
6393	CMS CC	MS-DRG MCC	POSTABORTION RENAL FAILURE
6394	CMS CC	MS-DRG CC	POSTABORTION METABOLIC DIS
6395	CMS CC	MS-DRG MCC	POSTABORTION SHOCK
6396	CMS CC	MS-DRG MCC	POSTABORTION EMBOLISM
6398	CMS CC	MS-DRG CC	POSTABORTION COMPL NEC
6399	CMS CC	MS-DRG CC	POSTABORTION COMPL NOS
64000	CMS CC		THREATENED ABORT-UNSPEC
64001	CMS CC	MS-DRG CC	THREATENED ABORT-DELIVER
64003	CMS CC	MS-DRG CC	THREATEN ABORT-ANTEPART
64080	CMS CC		HEM EARLY PREG NEC-UNSP
64081	CMS CC		HEM EARLY PREG NEC-DELIV
64083	CMS CC		HEM EARLY PG NEC-ANTEPAR
64090	CMS CC		HEMORR EARLY PREG-UNSPEC
64091	CMS CC		HEM EARLY PREG-DELIVERED
64093	CMS CC	MS-DRG CC	HEM EARLY PREG-ANTEPART
64100	CMS CC		PLACENTA PREVIA-UNSPEC
64101	CMS CC	MS-DRG CC	PLACENTA PREVIA-DELIVER
64103	CMS CC	MS-DRG CC	PLACENTA PREVIA-ANTEPART
64110	CMS CC		PLACENTA PREV HEM-UNSPEC
64111	CMS CC	MS-DRG MCC	PLACENTA PREV HEM-DELIV
64113	CMS CC	MS-DRG MCC	PLACEN PREV HEM-ANTEPART
64121		MS-DRG MCC	PREM SEPAR PLACEN-DELIV
64123		MS-DRG CC	PREM SEPAR PLAC-ANTEPART
64130	CMS CC		COAG DEF HEMORR-UNSPEC
64131	CMS CC	MS-DRG MCC	COAG DEF HEMORR-DELIVER
64133	CMS CC	MS-DRG MCC	COAG DEF HEMORR-ANTEPART
64180	CMS CC		ANTEPARTUM HEM NEC-UNSPEC
64181	CMS CC		ANTEPARTUM HEM NEC-DELIV
64183	CMS CC		ANTEPART HEM NEC-ANTEPAR
64190	CMS CC		ANTEPARTUM HEM NOS-UNSPEC
64191	CMS CC		ANTEPARTUM HEM NOS-DELIV
64193	CMS CC		ANTEPARTUM HEM NOS-ANTEPAR
64201		MS-DRG CC	ESSEN HYPERTEN-DELIVERED
64202		MS-DRG CC	ESSEN HYPERTEN-DEL W P/P
64203		MS-DRG CC	ESSEN HYPERTEN-ANTEPART
64211		MS-DRG MCC	RENAL HYPERTEN PG-DELIV
64212		MS-DRG MCC	RENAL HYPERTEN-DEL P/P

(Continued)

2008 ICD-9-CM	CMS DRG	MS-DRG	Short Title
64213		MS-DRG CC	RENAL HYPERTEN-ANTEPART
64214		MS-DRG CC	RENAL HYPERTEN-POSTPART
64231		MS-DRG CC	TRANS HYPERTEN-DELIVERED
64232		MS-DRG CC	TRANS HYPERTEN-DEL W P/P
64240	CMS CC		MILD/NOS PREECLAMP-UNSP
64241	CMS CC	MS-DRG CC	MILD/NOS PREECLAMP-DELIV
64242	CMS CC	MS-DRG MCC	MILD PREECLAMP-DEL W P/P
64243	CMS CC	MS-DRG CC	MILD/NOS PREECLAMP-ANTEP
64244	CMS CC	MS-DRG CC	MILD/NOS PREECLAMP-P/P
64250	CMS CC		SEVERE PREECLAMP-UNSPEC
64251	CMS CC	MS-DRG MCC	SEVERE PREECLAMP-DELIVER
64252	CMS CC	MS-DRG MCC	SEV PREECLAMP-DEL W P/P
64253	CMS CC	MS-DRG MCC	SEV PREECLAMP-ANTEPARTUM
64254	CMS CC	MS-DRG MCC	SEV PREECLAMP-POSTPARTUM
64260	CMS CC		ECLAMPSIA-UNSPECIFIED
64261	CMS CC	MS-DRG MCC	ECLAMPSIA-DELIVERED
64262	CMS CC	MS-DRG MCC	ECLAMPSIA-DELIV W P/P
64263	CMS CC	MS-DRG MCC	ECLAMPSIA-ANTEPARTUM
64264	CMS CC	MS-DRG MCC	ECLAMPSIA-POSTPARTUM
64270	CMS CC		TOX W OLD HYPERTEN-UNSP
64271	CMS CC	MS-DRG MCC	TOX W OLD HYPERTEN-DELIV
64272	CMS CC	MS-DRG MCC	TOX W OLD HYP-DEL W P/P
64273	CMS CC	MS-DRG MCC	TOX W OLD HYPER-ANTEPART
64274	CMS CC	MS-DRG MCC	TOX W OLD HYPER-POSTPART
64291		MS-DRG CC	HYPERTENS NOS-DELIVERED
64292		MS-DRG CC	HYPERTENS NOS-DEL W P/P
64293		MS-DRG CC	HYPERTENS NOS-ANTEPARTUM
64294		MS-DRG CC	HYPERTENS NOS-POSTPARTUM
64400	CMS CC		THREAT PREM LABOR-UNSPEC
64403	CMS CC	MS-DRG MCC	THREAT PREM LABOR-ANTEPART
64410	CMS CC		THREAT LABOR NEC-UNSPEC
64413	CMS CC	MS-DRG CC	THREAT LABOR NEC-ANTEPAR
64420		MS-DRG CC	EARLY ONSET DELIV-UNSPEC
64421		MS-DRG MCC	EARLY ONSET DELIVERY-DEL
64621		MS-DRG CC	RENAL DIS NOS-DELIVERED
64622		MS-DRG CC	RENAL DIS NOS-DEL W P/P
64623		MS-DRG CC	RENAL DIS NOS-ANTEPARTUM
64624		MS-DRG CC	RENAL DIS NOS-POSTPARTUM
64631		MS-DRG CC	HABITUAL ABORTER-DELIVER

2008 ICD-9-CM	CMS DRG	MS-DRG	Short Title
64660	CMS CC		GU INFECT IN PREG-UNSPEC
64661	CMS CC	MS-DRG CC	GU INFECTION-DELIVERED
64662	CMS CC	MS-DRG CC	GU INFECTION-DELIV W P/P
64663	CMS CC	MS-DRG CC	GU INFECTION-ANTEPARTUM
64664	CMS CC	MS-DRG CC	GU INFECTION-POSTPARTUM
64670	CMS CC		LIVER DIS IN PREG-UNSPEC
64671	CMS CC	MS-DRG CC	LIVER DISORDER-DELIVERED
64673	CMS CC	MS-DRG CC	LIVER DISORDER-ANTEPART
64701		MS-DRG CC	SYPHILIS-DELIVERED
64702		MS-DRG CC	SYPHILIS-DELIVERED W P/P
64703		MS-DRG CC	SYPHILIS-ANTEPARTUM
64704		MS-DRG CC	SYPHILIS-POSTPARTUM
64711		MS-DRG CC	GONORRHEA-DELIVERED
64712		MS-DRG CC	GONORRHEA-DELIVER W P/P
64713		MS-DRG CC	GONORRHEA-ANTEPARTUM
64714		MS-DRG CC	GONORRHEA-POSTPARTUM
64721		MS-DRG CC	OTHER VD-DELIVERED
64722		MS-DRG CC	OTHER VD-DELIVERED W P/P
64723		MS-DRG CC	OTHER VD-ANTEPARTUM
64724		MS-DRG CC	OTHER VD-POSTPARTUM
64730	CMS CC		TB IN PREG-UNSPECIFIED
64731	CMS CC	MS-DRG CC	TUBERCULOSIS-DELIVERED
64732	CMS CC	MS-DRG CC	TUBERCULOSIS-DELIV W P/P
64733	CMS CC	MS-DRG CC	TUBERCULOSIS-ANTEPARTUM
64734	CMS CC	MS-DRG CC	TUBERCULOSIS-POSTPARTUM
64740	CMS CC		MALARIA IN PREG-UNSPEC
64741	CMS CC	MS-DRG CC	MALARIA-DELIVERED
64742	CMS CC	MS-DRG CC	MALARIA-DELIVERED W P/P
64743	CMS CC	MS-DRG CC	MALARIA-ANTEPARTUM
64744	CMS CC	MS-DRG CC	MALARIA-POSTPARTUM
64751		MS-DRG CC	RUBELLA-DELIVERED
64752		MS-DRG CC	RUBELLA-DELIVERED W P/P
64753		MS-DRG CC	RUBELLA-ANTEPARTUM
64754		MS-DRG CC	RUBELLA-POSTPARTUM
64761		MS-DRG CC	OTH VIRAL DIS-DELIVERED
64762		MS-DRG CC	OTH VIRAL DIS-DEL W P/P
64763		MS-DRG CC	OTH VIRAL DIS-ANTEPARTUM
64764		MS-DRG CC	OTH VIRAL DIS-POSTPARTUM
64781		MS-DRG CC	INFECT DIS NEC-DELIVERED

(Continued)

2008 ICD-9-CM	CMS DRG	MS-DRG	Short Title
64782		MS-DRG CC	INFECT DIS NEC-DEL W P/P
64783		MS-DRG CC	INFECT DIS NEC-ANTEPART
64784		MS-DRG CC	INFECT DIS NEC-POSTPART
64791		MS-DRG CC	INFECT NOS-DELIVERED
64792		MS-DRG CC	INFECT NOS-DELIVER W P/P
64793		MS-DRG CC	INFECT NOS-ANTEPARTUM
64794		MS-DRG CC	INFECT NOS-POSTPARTUM
64800	CMS CC	MS-DRG CC	DIABETES IN PREG-UNSPEC
64801	CMS CC	MS-DRG MCC	DIABETES-DELIVERED
64802	CMS CC	MS-DRG MCC	DIABETES-DELIVERED W P/P
64803	CMS CC	MS-DRG CC	DIABETES-ANTEPARTUM
64804	CMS CC	MS-DRG CC	DIABETES-POSTPARTUM
64820	CMS CC		ANEMIA IN PREG-UNSPEC
64821	CMS CC		ANEMIA-DELIVERED
64822	CMS CC		ANEMIA-DELIVERED W P/P
64823	CMS CC		ANEMIA-ANTEPARTUM
64824	CMS CC		ANEMIA-POSTPARTUM
64830	CMS CC		DRUG DEPEND PREG-UNSPEC
64831	CMS CC	MS-DRG CC	DRUG DEPENDENCE-DELIVER
64832	CMS CC	MS-DRG CC	DRUG DEPENDEN-DEL W P/P
64833	CMS CC	MS-DRG CC	DRUG DEPENDENCE-ANTEPART
64834	CMS CC	MS-DRG CC	DRUG DEPENDENCE-POSTPART
64850	CMS CC		CONGEN CV DIS PREG-UNSP
64851	CMS CC	MS-DRG CC	CONGEN CV DIS-DELIVERED
64852	CMS CC	MS-DRG CC	CONGEN CV DIS-DEL W P/P
64853	CMS CC	MS-DRG CC	CONGEN CV DIS-ANTEPARTUM
64854	CMS CC	MS-DRG CC	CONGEN CV DIS-POSTPARTUM
64860	CMS CC		CV DIS NEC PREG-UNSPEC
64861	CMS CC	MS-DRG CC	CV DIS NEC PREG-DELIVER
64862	CMS CC	MS-DRG CC	CV DIS NEC-DELIVER W P/P
64863	CMS CC	MS-DRG CC	CV DIS NEC-ANTEPARTUM
64864	CMS CC	MS-DRG CC	CV DIS NEC-POSTPARTUM
64871		MS-DRG CC	BONE DISORDER-DELIVERED
64872		MS-DRG CC	BONE DISORDER-DEL W P/P
64873		MS-DRG CC	BONE DISORDER-ANTEPARTUM
64874		MS-DRG CC	BONE DISORDER-POSTPARTUM
64930		MS-DRG CC	COAGULATION DEF-UNSPEC
64931		MS-DRG CC	COAGULATION DEF-DELIV
64932		MS-DRG CC	COAGULATN DEF-DEL W P/P

2008 ICD-9-CM	CMS DRG	MS-DRG	Short Title
64933		MS-DRG CC	COAGULATION DEF-ANTEPART
64934		MS-DRG CC	COAGULATION DEF-POSTPART
64941		MS-DRG CC	EPILEPSY-DELIVERED
64942		MS-DRG CC	EPILEPSY-DELIVERED W P/P
64943		MS-DRG CC	EPILEPSY-ANTEPARTUM
64944		MS-DRG CC	EPILEPSY-POSTPARTUM
65101		MS-DRG CC	TWIN PREGNANCY-DELIVERED
65111		MS-DRG CC	TRIPLET PREGNANCY-DELIV
65113		MS-DRG CC	TRIPLET PREG-ANTEPARTUM
65121		MS-DRG CC	QUADRUPLET PREG-DELIVER
65123		MS-DRG CC	QUADRUPLET PREG-ANTEPART
65141		MS-DRG CC	TRIPLETS W FET LOSS-DEL
65143		MS-DRG CC	TRIPLETS W FET LOSS-ANTEPART
65151		MS-DRG CC	QUADS W FETAL LOSS-DEL
65153		MS-DRG CC	QUADS W FETAL LOSS-ANTEPART
65181		MS-DRG CC	MULTI GESTAT NEC-DELIVER
65183		MS-DRG CC	MULTI GESTAT NEC-ANTEPART
65451		MS-DRG MCC	CERVICAL INCOMPET-DELIV
65452		MS-DRG MCC	CERV INCOMPET-DEL W P/P
65453		MS-DRG MCC	CERV INCOMPET-ANTEPARTUM
65454		MS-DRG MCC	CERV INCOMPET-POSTPARTUM
65613		MS-DRG CC	RH ISOIMMUNIZAT-ANTEPART
65631		MS-DRG CC	FETAL DISTRESS-DELIVERED
65641		MS-DRG CC	INTRAUTER DEATH-DELIVER
65643		MS-DRG CC	INTRAUTER DEATH-ANTEPART
65651		MS-DRG CC	POOR FETAL GROWTH-DELIV
65701		MS-DRG CC	POLYHYDRAMNIOS-DELIVERED
65801		MS-DRG CC	OLIGOHYDRAMNIOS-DELIVER
65803		MS-DRG CC	OLIGOHYDRAMNIOS-ANTEPAR
65841		MS-DRG MCC	AMNIOTIC INFECTION-DELIV
65843		MS-DRG MCC	AMNIOTIC INFECT-ANTEPART
65881		MS-DRG CC	AMNIOTIC PROB NEC-DELIV
65921		MS-DRG CC	PYREXIA IN LABOR-DELIVER
65930	CMS CC		SEPTICEMIA IN LABOR-UNSP
65931	CMS CC	MS-DRG MCC	SEPTICEM IN LABOR-DELIV
65933	CMS CC	MS-DRG MCC	SEPTICEM IN LABOR-ANTEPART
66003		MS-DRG CC	OBSTRUC/FET MALPOS-ANTEPART
66211		MS-DRG CC	PROLONG LABOR NOS-DELIV
66421		MS-DRG CC	DEL W 3 DEG LACERAT-DEL

(Continued)

2008 ICD-9-CM	CMS DRG	MS-DRG	Short Title
66431		MS-DRG CC	DEL W 4 DEG LACERAT-DEL
66461		MS-DRG CC	ANAL SPHINCTER TEAR-DEL
66464		MS-DRG CC	ANAL SPHINCTR TEAR W P/P
66500	CMS CC		PRELABOR RUPT UTERUS-UNSP
66501	CMS CC	MS-DRG MCC	PRELABOR RUPT UTERUS-DEL
66503	CMS CC	MS-DRG MCC	PRELAB RUPT UTER-ANTEPAR
66510	CMS CC		RUPTURE UTERUS NOS-UNSP
66511	CMS CC	MS-DRG MCC	RUPTURE UTERUS NOS-DELIV
66520	CMS CC		INVERSION OF UTERUS-UNSP
66522		MS-DRG CC	INVERS UTERUS-DEL W P/P
66531		MS-DRG CC	LACERAT OF CERVIX-DELIV
66541		MS-DRG CC	HIGH VAGINAL LACER-DELIV
66551		MS-DRG CC	OB INJ PELV ORG NEC-DEL
66561		MS-DRG CC	DAMAGE TO PELVIC JT-DEL
66571		MS-DRG CC	OB PELVIC HEMATOMA-DELIV
66572		MS-DRG CC	PELVIC HEMATOM-DEL W PP
66602		MS-DRG CC	THRD-STAGE HEM-DEL W P/P
66604		MS-DRG CC	THIRD-STAGE HEM-POSTPART
66612		MS-DRG CC	POSTPART HEM NEC-DEL W P/P
66614		MS-DRG CC	POSTPART HEM NEC-POSTPAR
66622		MS-DRG CC	DELAY P/P HEM-DEL W P/P
66624		MS-DRG CC	DELAY P/PART HEM-POSTPAR
66632	CMS CC	MS-DRG CC	P/P COAG DEF-DEL W P/P
66634	CMS CC		POSTPART COAG DEF-POSTPA
66800	CMS CC		PULM COMPL IN DEL-UNSPEC
66801	CMS CC		PULM COMPL IN DEL-DELIV
66802	CMS CC		PULM COMPL DEL W P/P
66803	CMS CC		PULM COMPL ANTEPART
66804	CMS CC		PULM COMPL POSTPART
66810	CMS CC		HEART COMPL IN DEL-UNSP
66811	CMS CC		HEART COMPL IN DEL-DELIV
66812	CMS CC		HEART COMPL DEL W P/P
66813	CMS CC		HEART COMPL ANTEPART
66814	CMS CC		HEART COMPL POSTPART
66820	CMS CC		CNS COMPL LABOR/DEL-UNSP
66821	CMS CC		CNS COMPL LAB/DEL-DELIV
66822	CMS CC		CNS COMPL DEL W P/P
66823	CMS CC		CNS COMPL IN DEL-ANTEPAR
66824	CMS CC		CNS COMPL IN DEL-POSTPAR

2008 ICD-9-CM	CMS DRG	MS-DRG	Short Title
66880	CMS CC		ANESTH COMPL DEL NEC-UNSP
66881	CMS CC		ANESTH COMPL NEC-DELIVER
66882	CMS CC		ANESTH COMPL NEC-DEL P/P
66883	CMS CC		ANESTH COMPL ANTEPARTUM
66884	CMS CC		ANESTH COMPL-POSTPARTUM
66890	CMS CC		ANESTH COMPL DEL NOS-UNSP
66891	CMS CC		ANESTH COMPL NOS-DELIVER
66892	CMS CC		ANESTH COMPL NOS-DEL P/P
66893	CMS CC		ANESTH COMPL-ANTEPARTUM
66894	CMS CC		ANESTH COMPL-POSTPARTUM
66911		MS-DRG MCC	OBSTETRIC SHOCK-DELIVER
66912		MS-DRG MCC	OBSTETRIC SHOCK-DELIV W P/P
66913		MS-DRG MCC	OBSTETRIC SHOCK-ANTEPAR
66914		MS-DRG MCC	OBSTETRIC SHOCK-POSTPART
66921		MS-DRG MCC	MATERN HYPOTEN SYN-DELIV
66922		MS-DRG MCC	MATERN HYPOTEN-DEL W P/P
66924		MS-DRG CC	MATERN HYPOTENS-POSTPART
66930	CMS CC		AC REN FAIL W DELIV-UNSP
66932	CMS CC	MS-DRG MCC	AC REN FAIL-DELIV W P/P
66934	CMS CC	MS-DRG MCC	AC RENAL FAILURE-POSTPAR
67000	CMS CC		MAJOR PUERP INFECT-UNSP
67002	CMS CC	MS-DRG MCC	MAJOR PUERP INF-DEL P/P
67004	CMS CC	MS-DRG MCC	MAJOR PUERP INF-POSTPART
67120	CMS CC	MS-DRG CC	THROMBOPHLEB PREG-UNSPEC
67121	CMS CC	MS-DRG CC	THROMBOPHLEBITIS-DELIVER
67122	CMS CC	MS-DRG CC	THROMBOPHLEB-DELIV W P/P
67123	CMS CC	MS-DRG CC	THROMBOPHLEBIT-ANTEPART
67124	CMS CC	MS-DRG CC	THROMBOPHLEBIT-POSTPART
67130	CMS CC	MS-DRG CC	DEEP THROMB ANTEPAR-UNSP
67131	CMS CC	MS-DRG MCC	DEEP THROMB ANTEPAR-DELIV
67133	CMS CC	MS-DRG MCC	DEEP VEIN THROMB-ANTEPAR
67140	CMS CC	MS-DRG CC	DEEP THROMB POSTPAR-UNSP
67142	CMS CC	MS-DRG MCC	THROMB POSTPAR-DEL W P/P
67144	CMS CC	MS-DRG MCC	DEEP VEIN THROMB-POSTPAR
67150		MS-DRG CC	THROMBOSIS NEC PREG-UNSP
67151		MS-DRG CC	THROMBOSIS NEC-DELIVERED
67152		MS-DRG CC	THROMB NEC-DELIV W P/P
67153		MS-DRG CC	THROMBOSIS NEC-ANTEPART
67154		MS-DRG CC	THROMBOSIS NEC-POSTPART

(Continued)

2008 ICD-9-CM	CMS DRG	MS-DRG	Short Title
67180		MS-DRG CC	VENOUS COMPL PREG NEC-UNSP
67181		MS-DRG CC	VENOUS COMPL NEC-DELIVER
67182		MS-DRG CC	VENOUS COMP NEC-DELIV W P/P
67183		MS-DRG CC	VENOUS COMPL NEC-ANTEPAR
67184		MS-DRG CC	VENOUS COMPL NEC-POSTPAR
67190		MS-DRG CC	VENOUS COMPL PREG NOS-UNSP
67191		MS-DRG CC	VENOUS COMPL NOS-DELIVER
67192		MS-DRG CC	VENOUS COMP NOS-DELIV W P/P
67202		MS-DRG CC	PUERP PYREXIA-DEL W P/P
67204		MS-DRG CC	PUERP PYREXIA-POSTPARTUM
67300	CMS CC		OB AIR EMBOLISM-UNSPEC
67301	CMS CC	MS-DRG MCC	OB AIR EMBOLISM-DELIVER
67302	CMS CC	MS-DRG MCC	OB AIR EMBOL-DELIV W P/P
67303	CMS CC	MS-DRG MCC	OB AIR EMBOLISM-ANTEPART
67304	CMS CC	MS-DRG MCC	OB AIR EMBOLISM-POSTPART
67310	CMS CC		AMNIOTIC EMBOLISM-UNSPEC
67311	CMS CC	MS-DRG MCC	AMNIOTIC EMBOLISM-DELIV
67312	CMS CC	MS-DRG MCC	AMNIOT EMBOL-DELIV W P/P
67313	CMS CC	MS-DRG MCC	AMNIOTIC EMBOL-ANTEPART
67314	CMS CC	MS-DRG MCC	AMNIOTIC EMBOL-POSTPART
67320	CMS CC		OB PULM EMBOL NOS-UNSPEC
67321	CMS CC	MS-DRG MCC	PULM EMBOL NOS-DELIVERED
67322	CMS CC	MS-DRG MCC	PULM EMBOL NOS-DEL W P/P
67323	CMS CC	MS-DRG MCC	PULM EMBOL NOS-ANTEPART
67324	CMS CC	MS-DRG MCC	PULM EMBOL NOS-POSTPART
67330	CMS CC	MS-DRG CC	OB PYEMIC EMBOL-UNSPEC
67331	CMS CC	MS-DRG MCC	OB PYEMIC EMBOL-DELIVER
67332	CMS CC	MS-DRG MCC	OB PYEM EMBOL-DEL W P/P
67333	CMS CC	MS-DRG MCC	OB PYEMIC EMBOL-ANTEPART
67334	CMS CC	MS-DRG MCC	OB PYEMIC EMBOL-POSTPART
67380	CMS CC		OB PULMON EMBOL NEC-UNSP
67381	CMS CC	MS-DRG MCC	PULMON EMBOL NEC-DELIVER
67382	CMS CC	MS-DRG MCC	PULM EMBOL NEC-DEL W P/P
67383	CMS CC	MS-DRG MCC	PULMON EMBOL NEC-ANTEPAR
67384	CMS CC	MS-DRG MCC	PULMON EMBOL NEC-POSTPAR
67400	CMS CC		PUERP CEREBVASC DIS-UNSP
67401	CMS CC	MS-DRG MCC	PUERP CEREBVASC DIS-DELIV
67402	CMS CC	MS-DRG CC	CEREBVASC DIS-DELIV W P/P
67403	CMS CC	MS-DRG CC	CEREBROVASC DIS-ANTEPART

2008 ICD-9-CM	CMS DRG	MS-DRG	Short Title
67404	CMS CC	MS-DRG CC	CEREBROVASC DIS-POSTPART
67410	CMS CC		DISRUPT C-SECT WND-UNSP
67412	CMS CC		DISRUPT C-SECT-DEL W P/P
67420	CMS CC		DISRUPT PERINEUM-UNSPEC
67422	CMS CC		DISRUPT PERIN-DEL W P/P
67424	CMS CC		DISRUPT PERINEUM-POSTPAR
67450	CMS CC	MS-DRG MCC	PERIPARTUM CARDIOMY-UNSPEC
67451	CMS CC	MS-DRG MCC	PERIPARTUM CARDIOMY-DEL
67452	CMS CC	MS-DRG MCC	PERIPARTUM CARD DEL W P/P
67453	CMS CC	MS-DRG MCC	PERIPARTUM CARD-ANTEPART
67454	CMS CC	MS-DRG MCC	PERIPARTUM CARD-POSTPART
67510	CMS CC		BREAST ABSCESS PREG-UNSP
67511	CMS CC	MS-DRG CC	BREAST ABSCESS-DELIVERED
67512	CMS CC	MS-DRG CC	BREAST ABSCESS-DEL W P/P
6800	CMS CC		CARBUNCLE OF FACE
6801	CMS CC		CARBUNCLE OF NECK
6802	CMS CC		CARBUNCLE OF TRUNK
6803	CMS CC		CARBUNCLE OF ARM
6804	CMS CC		CARBUNCLE OF HAND
6805	CMS CC		CARBUNCLE OF BUTTOCK
6806	CMS CC		CARBUNCLE OF LEG
6807	CMS CC		CARBUNCLE OF FOOT
6808	CMS CC		CARBUNCLE, SITE NEC
6809	CMS CC		CARBUNCLE NOS
6820	CMS CC	MS-DRG CC	CELLULITIS OF FACE
6821	CMS CC	MS-DRG CC	CELLULITIS OF NECK
6822	CMS CC	MS-DRG CC	CELLULITIS OF TRUNK
6823	CMS CC	MS-DRG CC	CELLULITIS OF ARM
6824		MS-DRG CC	CELLULITIS OF HAND
6825	CMS CC	MS-DRG CC	CELLULITIS OF BUTTOCK
6826	CMS CC	MS-DRG CC	CELLULITIS OF LEG
6827	CMS CC	MS-DRG CC	CELLULITIS OF FOOT
6828	CMS CC	MS-DRG CC	CELLULITIS, SITE NEC
6829	CMS CC	MS-DRG CC	CELLULITIS NOS
684	CMS CC		IMPETIGO
6850	CMS CC	MS-DRG CC	PILONIDAL CYST W ABSCESS
68601		MS-DRG CC	PYODERMA GANGRENOSUM
6944	CMS CC	MS-DRG CC	PEMPHIGUS
6945	CMS CC	MS-DRG CC	PEMPHIGOID

(Continued)

2008 ICD-9-CM	CMS DRG	MS-DRG	Short Title
6950	CMS CC	MS-DRG CC	TOXIC ERYTHEMA
6951		MS-DRG CC	ERYTHEMA MULTIFORME
6960	CMS CC		PSORIATIC ARTHROPATHY
70700	CMS CC	MS-DRG CC	DECUBITUS ULCER SITE NOS
70701	CMS CC	MS-DRG CC	DECUBITUS ULCER,ELBOW
70702	CMS CC	MS-DRG MCC	DECUBITUS ULCER,UP BACK
70703	CMS CC	MS-DRG MCC	DECUBITUS ULCER,LOW BACK
70704	CMS CC	MS-DRG MCC	DECUBITUS ULCER,HIP
70705	CMS CC	MS-DRG MCC	DECUBITUS ULCER,BUTTOCK
70706	CMS CC	MS-DRG MCC	DECUBITUS ULCER,ANKLE
70707	CMS CC	MS-DRG MCC	DECUBITUS ULCER,HEEL
70709	CMS CC	MS-DRG CC	DECUBITUS ULCER,SITE NEC
70710	CMS CC	MS-DRG CC	ULCER OF LOWER LIMB NOS
70711	CMS CC	MS-DRG CC	ULCER OF THIGH
70712	CMS CC	MS-DRG CC	ULCER OF CALF
70713	CMS CC	MS-DRG CC	ULCER OF ANKLE
70714	CMS CC	MS-DRG CC	ULCER OF HEEL & MIDFOOT
70715	CMS CC		ULCER OTHER PART OF FOOT
70719	CMS CC	MS-DRG CC	ULCER OTH PART LOW LIMB
7100	CMS CC		SYST LUPUS ERYTHEMATOSUS
7101	CMS CC		SYSTEMIC SCLEROSIS
7103	CMS CC	MS-DRG CC	DERMATOMYOSITIS
7104	CMS CC	MS-DRG CC	POLYMYOSITIS
7105	CMS CC	MS-DRG CC	EOSINOPHILIA MYALGIA SND
7108	CMS CC	MS-DRG CC	DIFF CONNECT TIS DIS NEC
71100	CMS CC	MS-DRG CC	PYOGEN ARTHRITIS-UNSPEC
71101	CMS CC	MS-DRG CC	PYOGEN ARTHRITIS-SHLDER
71102	CMS CC	MS-DRG CC	PYOGEN ARTHRITIS-UP/ARM
71103	CMS CC	MS-DRG CC	PYOGEN ARTHRITIS-FOREARM
71104	CMS CC	MS-DRG CC	PYOGEN ARTHRITIS-HAND
71105	CMS CC	MS-DRG CC	PYOGEN ARTHRITIS-PELVIS
71106	CMS CC	MS-DRG CC	PYOGEN ARTHRITIS-L/LEG
71107	CMS CC	MS-DRG CC	PYOGEN ARTHRITIS-ANKLE
71108	CMS CC	MS-DRG CC	PYOGEN ARTHRITIS NEC
71109	CMS CC	MS-DRG CC	PYOGEN ARTHRITIS-MULT
71110		MS-DRG CC	REITER ARTHRITIS-UNSPEC
71111		MS-DRG CC	REITER ARTHRITIS-SHLDER
71112		MS-DRG CC	REITER ARTHRITIS-UP/ARM
71113		MS-DRG CC	REITER ARTHRITIS-FOREARM

2008 ICD-9-CM	CMS DRG	MS-DRG	Short Title
71114		MS-DRG CC	REITER ARTHRITIS-HAND
71115		MS-DRG CC	REITER ARTHRITIS-PELVIS
71116		MS-DRG CC	REITER ARTHRITIS-L/LEG
71117		MS-DRG CC	REITER ARTHRITIS-ANKLE
71118		MS-DRG CC	REITER ARTHRITIS NEC
71119		MS-DRG CC	REITER ARTHRITIS-MULT
71120		MS-DRG CC	BEHCET ARTHRITIS-UNSPEC
71121		MS-DRG CC	BEHCET ARTHRITIS-SHLDER
71122		MS-DRG CC	BEHCET ARTHRITIS-UP/ARM
71123		MS-DRG CC	BEHCET ARTHRITIS-FOREARM
71124		MS-DRG CC	BEHCET ARTHRITIS-HAND
71125		MS-DRG CC	BEHCET ARTHRITIS-PELVIS
71126		MS-DRG CC	BEHCET ARTHRITIS-L/LEG
71127		MS-DRG CC	BEHCET ARTHRITIS-ANKLE
71128		MS-DRG CC	BEHCET ARTHRITIS NEC
71129		MS-DRG CC	BEHCET ARTHRITIS-MULT
71130		MS-DRG CC	DYSENTER ARTHRITIS-UNSPEC
71131		MS-DRG CC	DYSENTER ARTHRITIS-SHLDER
71132		MS-DRG CC	DYSENTER ARTHRITIS-UP/ARM
71133		MS-DRG CC	DYSENTER ARTHRITIS-FOREARM
71134		MS-DRG CC	DYSENTER ARTHRITIS-HAND
71135		MS-DRG CC	DYSENTER ARTHRITIS-PELVIS
71136		MS-DRG CC	DYSENTER ARTHRITIS-L/LEG
71137		MS-DRG CC	DYSENTER ARTHRITIS-ANKLE
71138		MS-DRG CC	DYSENTER ARTHRITIS NEC
71139		MS-DRG CC	DYSENTER ARTHRITIS-MULT
71140		MS-DRG CC	BACT ARTHRITIS-UNSPEC
71141		MS-DRG CC	BACT ARTHRITIS-SHLDER
71142		MS-DRG CC	BACT ARTHRITIS-UP/ARM
71143		MS-DRG CC	BACT ARTHRITIS-FOREARM
71144		MS-DRG CC	BACT ARTHRITIS-HAND
71145		MS-DRG CC	BACT ARTHRITIS-PELVIS
71146		MS-DRG CC	BACT ARTHRITIS-L/LEG
71147		MS-DRG CC	BACT ARTHRITIS-ANKLE
71148		MS-DRG CC	BACT ARTHRITIS NEC
71149		MS-DRG CC	BACT ARTHRITIS-MULT
71150		MS-DRG CC	VIRAL ARTHRITIS-UNSPEC
71151		MS-DRG CC	VIRAL ARTHRITIS-SHLDER
71152		MS-DRG CC	VIRAL ARTHRITIS-UP/ARM

(Continued)

2008 ICD-9-CM	CMS DRG	MS-DRG	Short Title
71153		MS-DRG CC	VIRAL ARTHRITIS-FOREARM
71154		MS-DRG CC	VIRAL ARTHRITIS-HAND
71155		MS-DRG CC	VIRAL ARTHRITIS-PELVIS
71156		MS-DRG CC	VIRAL ARTHRITIS-L/LEG
71157		MS-DRG CC	VIRAL ARTHRITIS-ANKLE
71158		MS-DRG CC	VIRAL ARTHRITIS NEC
71159		MS-DRG CC	VIRAL ARTHRITIS-MULT
71160	CMS CC	MS-DRG CC	MYCOTIC ARTHRITIS-UNSPEC
71161	CMS CC	MS-DRG CC	MYCOTIC ARTHRITIS-SHLDER
71162	CMS CC	MS-DRG CC	MYCOTIC ARTHRITIS-UP/ARM
71163	CMS CC	MS-DRG CC	MYCOTIC ARTHRIT-FOREARM
71164	CMS CC	MS-DRG CC	MYCOTIC ARTHRITIS-HAND
71165	CMS CC	MS-DRG CC	MYCOTIC ARTHRITIS-PELVIS
71166	CMS CC	MS-DRG CC	MYCOTIC ARTHRITIS-L/LEG
71167	CMS CC	MS-DRG CC	MYCOTIC ARTHRITIS-ANKLE
71168	CMS CC	MS-DRG CC	MYCOTIC ARTHRITIS NEC
71169	CMS CC	MS-DRG CC	MYCOTIC ARTHRITIS-MULT
71170		MS-DRG CC	HELMINTH ARTHRIT-UNSPEC
71171		MS-DRG CC	HELMINTH ARTHRIT-SHLDER
71172		MS-DRG CC	HELMINTH ARTHRIT-UP/ARM
71173		MS-DRG CC	HELMINTH ARTHRIT-FOREARM
71174		MS-DRG CC	HELMINTH ARTHRIT-HAND
71175		MS-DRG CC	HELMINTH ARTHRIT-PELVIS
71176		MS-DRG CC	HELMINTH ARTHRIT-L/LEG
71177		MS-DRG CC	HELMINTH ARTHRIT-ANKLE
71178		MS-DRG CC	HELMINTH ARTHRIT NEC
71179		MS-DRG CC	HELMINTH ARTHRIT-MULT
71180		MS-DRG CC	INF ARTHRITIS NEC-UNSPEC
71181		MS-DRG CC	INF ARTHRITIS NEC-SHLDER
71182		MS-DRG CC	INF ARTHRITIS NEC-UP/ARM
71183		MS-DRG CC	INF ARTHRIT NEC-FOREARM
71184		MS-DRG CC	INF ARTHRITIS NEC-HAND
71185		MS-DRG CC	INF ARTHRITIS NEC-PELVIS
71186		MS-DRG CC	INF ARTHRITIS NEC-L/LEG
71187		MS-DRG CC	INF ARTHRITIS NEC-ANKLE
71188		MS-DRG CC	INF ARTHRIT NEC-OTH SITE
71189		MS-DRG CC	INF ARTHRITIS NEC-MULT
71190		MS-DRG CC	INF ARTHRITIS NOS-UNSPEC
71191		MS-DRG CC	INF ARTHRITIS NOS-SHLDER

2008 ICD-9-CM	CMS DRG	MS-DRG	Short Title
71192		MS-DRG CC	INF ARTHRITIS NOS-UP/ARM
71193		MS-DRG CC	INF ARTHRIT NOS-FOREARM
71194		MS-DRG CC	INF ARTHRIT NOS-HAND
71195		MS-DRG CC	INF ARTHRIT NOS-PELVIS
71196		MS-DRG CC	INF ARTHRIT NOS-L/LEG
71197		MS-DRG CC	INF ARTHRIT NOS-ANKLE
71198		MS-DRG CC	INF ARTHRIT NOS-OTH SITE
71199		MS-DRG CC	INF ARTHRITIS NOS-MULT
7141	CMS CC		FELTY'S SYNDROME
7142	CMS CC		SYST RHEUM ARTHRITIS NEC
71430	CMS CC		JUV RHEUM ARTHRITIS NOS
71431	CMS CC	MS-DRG CC	POLYART JUV RHEUM ARTHR
71432	CMS CC		PAUCIART JUV RHEUM ARTHR
71433	CMS CC		MONOART JUV RHEUM ARTHR
71910		MS-DRG CC	HEMARTHROSIS-UNSPEC
71911		MS-DRG CC	HEMARTHROSIS-SHLDER
71912		MS-DRG CC	HEMARTHROSIS-UP/ARM
71913		MS-DRG CC	HEMARTHROSIS-FOREARM
71914		MS-DRG CC	HEMARTHROSIS-HAND
71915		MS-DRG CC	HEMARTHROSIS-PELVIS
71916		MS-DRG CC	HEMARTHROSIS-L/LEG
71917		MS-DRG CC	HEMARTHROSIS-ANKLE
71918		MS-DRG CC	HEMARTHROSIS-JT NEC
71919		MS-DRG CC	HEMARTHROSIS-MULT JTS
7211		MS-DRG CC	CERV SPONDYL W MYELOPATH
72141		MS-DRG CC	SPOND COMPR THOR SP CORD
72142		MS-DRG CC	SPOND COMPR LUMB SP CORD
7217		MS-DRG CC	TRAUMATIC SPONDYLOPATHY
72191		MS-DRG CC	SPONDYLOSIS NOS W MYELOP
72271		MS-DRG CC	CERV DISC DIS W MYELOPAT
72272		MS-DRG CC	THOR DISC DIS W MYELOPAT
72273		MS-DRG CC	LUMB DISC DIS W MYELOPAT
72280	CMS CC		POSTLAMINECTOMY SYND NOS
72281	CMS CC		POSTLAMINECTOMY SYND-CERV
72282	CMS CC		POSTLAMINECTOMY SYND-THORAC
72283	CMS CC		POSTLAMINECTOMY SYND-LUMBAR
7234	CMS CC		BRACHIAL NEURITIS NOS
7235	CMS CC		TORTICOLLIS NOS
7280	CMS CC	MS-DRG CC	INFECTIVE MYOSITIS

(Continued)

2008 ICD-9-CM	CMS DRG	MS-DRG	Short Title
72886	CMS CC	MS-DRG MCC	NECROTIZING FASCIITIS
72888	CMS CC	MS-DRG CC	RHABDOMYOLYSIS
72971		MS-DRG CC	NONTRAUM COMP SYN-UP EXT
72972		MS-DRG CC	NONTRAUM COMP SYN-LOW EX
72973		MS-DRG CC	NONTRAUMA COMP SYN-ABD
72979		MS-DRG CC	NONTRAUMA COMP SYN NEC
73000	CMS CC	MS-DRG CC	AC OSTEOMYELITIS-UNSPEC
73001	CMS CC	MS-DRG CC	AC OSTEOMYELITIS-SHLDER
73002	CMS CC	MS-DRG CC	AC OSTEOMYELITIS-UP/ARM
73003	CMS CC	MS-DRG CC	AC OSTEOMYELITIS-FOREARM
73004	CMS CC	MS-DRG CC	AC OSTEOMYELITIS-HAND
73005	CMS CC	MS-DRG CC	AC OSTEOMYELITIS-PELVIS
73006	CMS CC	MS-DRG CC	AC OSTEOMYELITIS-L/LEG
73007	CMS CC	MS-DRG CC	AC OSTEOMYELITIS-ANKLE
73008	CMS CC	MS-DRG CC	AC OSTEOMYELITIS NEC
73009	CMS CC	MS-DRG CC	AC OSTEOMYELITIS-MULT
73010		MS-DRG CC	CHR OSTEOMYELITIS-UNSP
73011		MS-DRG CC	CHR OSTEOMYELIT-SHLDER
73012		MS-DRG CC	CHR OSTEOMYELIT-UP/ARM
73013		MS-DRG CC	CHR OSTEOMYELIT-FOREARM
73014		MS-DRG CC	CHR OSTEOMYELIT-HAND
73015		MS-DRG CC	CHR OSTEOMYELIT-PELVIS
73016		MS-DRG CC	CHR OSTEOMYELIT-L/LEG
73017		MS-DRG CC	CHR OSTEOMYELIT-ANKLE
73018		MS-DRG CC	CHR OSTEOMYELIT NEC
73019		MS-DRG CC	CHR OSTEOMYELIT-MULT
73020		MS-DRG CC	OSTEOMYELITIS NOS-UNSPEC
73021		MS-DRG CC	OSTEOMYELITIS NOS-SHLDER
73022		MS-DRG CC	OSTEOMYELITIS NOS-UP/ARM
73023		MS-DRG CC	OSTEOMYELIT NOS-FOREARM
73024		MS-DRG CC	OSTEOMYELITIS NOS-HAND
73025		MS-DRG CC	OSTEOMYELITIS NOS-PELVIS
73026		MS-DRG CC	OSTEOMYELITIS NOS-L/LEG
73027		MS-DRG CC	OSTEOMYELITIS NOS-ANKLE
73028		MS-DRG CC	OSTEOMYELIT NOS-OTH SITE
73029		MS-DRG CC	OSTEOMYELITIS NOS-MULT
73080	CMS CC	MS-DRG CC	BONE INFECT NEC-UNSPEC
73081	CMS CC	MS-DRG CC	BONE INFECT NEC-SHLDER
73082	CMS CC	MS-DRG CC	BONE INFECT NEC-UP/ARM

2008 ICD-9-CM	CMS DRG	MS-DRG	Short Title
73083	CMS CC	MS-DRG CC	BONE INFECT NEC-FOREARM
73084	CMS CC	MS-DRG CC	BONE INFECT NEC-HAND
73085	CMS CC	MS-DRG CC	BONE INFECT NEC-PELVIS
73086	CMS CC	MS-DRG CC	BONE INFECT NEC-L/LEG
73087	CMS CC	MS-DRG CC	BONE INFECT NEC-ANKLE
73088	CMS CC	MS-DRG CC	BONE INFECT NEC-OTH SITE
73089	CMS CC	MS-DRG CC	BONE INFECT NEC-MULT
73090		MS-DRG CC	BONE INFEC NOS-UNSP SITE
73091		MS-DRG CC	BONE INFECT NOS-SHLDER
73092		MS-DRG CC	BONE INFECT NOS-UP/ARM
73093	CMS CC	MS-DRG CC	BONE INFECT NOS-FOREARM
73094	CMS CC	MS-DRG CC	BONE INFECT NOS-HAND
73095	CMS CC	MS-DRG CC	BONE INFECT NOS-PELVIS
73096		MS-DRG CC	BONE INFECT NOS-L/LEG
73097		MS-DRG CC	BONE INFECT NOS-ANKLE
73098		MS-DRG CC	BONE INFECT NOS-OTH SITE
73099		MS-DRG CC	BONE INFECT NOS-MULT
73310		MS-DRG CC	PATH FX UNSPECIFIED SITE
73311		MS-DRG CC	PATH FX HUMERUS
73312		MS-DRG CC	PATH FX DSTL RADIUS ULNA
73313		MS-DRG CC	PATH FX VERTEBRAE
73314		MS-DRG CC	PATH FX NECK OF FEMUR
73315		MS-DRG CC	PATH FX OTH SPCF PRT FMR
73316		MS-DRG CC	PATH FX TIBIA FIBULA
73319		MS-DRG CC	PATH FX OTH SPECIF SITE
73340		MS-DRG CC	ASEPT NECROSIS BONE NOS
73341		MS-DRG CC	ASEPTIC NECROSIS HUMERUS
73342		MS-DRG CC	ASEPTIC NECROSIS FEMUR
73343		MS-DRG CC	ASEPT NECRO FEMUR CONDYL
73344		MS-DRG CC	ASEPTIC NECROSIS TALUS
73345		MS-DRG CC	ASEPTIC NECROSIS OF JAW
73349		MS-DRG CC	ASEPT NECROSIS BONE NEC
73381		MS-DRG CC	MALUNION OF FRACTURE
73382		MS-DRG CC	NONUNION OF FRACTURE
7400		MS-DRG MCC	ANENCEPHALUS
7401		MS-DRG MCC	CRANIORACHISCHISIS
7402		MS-DRG MCC	INIENCEPHALY
74100	CMS CC	MS-DRG CC	SPIN BIF W HYDROCEPH NOS
74101	CMS CC	MS-DRG CC	SPIN BIF W HYDRCEPH-CERV

(Continued)

2008 ICD-9-CM	CMS DRG	MS-DRG	Short Title
74102	CMS CC	MS-DRG CC	SPIN BIF W HYDRCEPH-DORS
74103	CMS CC	MS-DRG CC	SPIN BIF W HYDRCEPH-LUMB
74190	CMS CC		SPINA BIFIDA
74191	CMS CC		SPINA BIFIDA-CERV
74192	CMS CC		SPINA BIFIDA-DORSAL
74193	CMS CC		SPINA BIFIDA-LUMBAR
7420		MS-DRG CC	ENCEPHALOCELE
7422		MS-DRG MCC	REDUCTION DEFORM, BRAIN
7424		MS-DRG CC	BRAIN ANOMALY NEC
7450	CMS CC	MS-DRG MCC	COMMON TRUNCUS
74510	CMS CC	MS-DRG MCC	COMPL TRANSPOS GREAT VES
74511	CMS CC	MS-DRG MCC	DOUBLE OUTLET RT VENTRIC
74512	CMS CC	MS-DRG CC	CORRECT TRANSPOS GRT VES
74519	CMS CC	MS-DRG MCC	TRANSPOS GREAT VESS NEC
7452	CMS CC	MS-DRG MCC	TETRALOGY OF FALLOT
7453	CMS CC	MS-DRG MCC	COMMON VENTRICLE
7454	CMS CC	MS-DRG CC	VENTRICULAR SEPT DEFECT
7455		MS-DRG CC	SECUNDUM ATRIAL SEPT DEF
74560	CMS CC	MS-DRG CC	ENDOCARD CUSHION DEF NOS
74561		MS-DRG CC	OSTIUM PRIMUM DEFECT
74569	CMS CC	MS-DRG CC	ENDOCARD CUSHION DEF NEC
7457	CMS CC	MS-DRG MCC	COR BILOCULARE
74600		MS-DRG CC	PULMONARY VALVE ANOM NOS
74601	CMS CC	MS-DRG MCC	CONG PULMON VALV ATRESIA
74602	CMS CC	MS-DRG CC	CONG PULMON VALVE STENOS
74609		MS-DRG CC	PULMONARY VALVE ANOM NEC
7461	CMS CC	MS-DRG MCC	CONG TRICUSP ATRES/STEN
7462	CMS CC	MS-DRG MCC	EBSTEIN'S ANOMALY
7463	CMS CC	MS-DRG CC	CONG AORTA VALV STENOSIS
7464	CMS CC	MS-DRG CC	CONG AORTA VALV INSUFFIC
7465	CMS CC	MS-DRG CC	CONGEN MITRAL STENOSIS
7466	CMS CC	MS-DRG CC	CONG MITRAL INSUFFICIENC
7467	CMS CC	MS-DRG MCC	HYPOPLAS LEFT HEART SYND
74681	CMS CC	MS-DRG MCC	CONG SUBAORTIC STENOSIS
74682	CMS CC	MS-DRG MCC	COR TRIATRIATUM
74683	CMS CC	MS-DRG CC	INFUNDIB PULMON STENOSIS
74684	CMS CC	MS-DRG MCC	OBSTRUCT HEART ANOM NEC
74685		MS-DRG CC	CORONARY ARTERY ANOMALY
74686	CMS CC	MS-DRG MCC	CONGENITAL HEART BLOCK

2008 ICD-9-CM	CMS DRG	MS-DRG	Short Title
74687		MS-DRG CC	MALPOSITION OF HEART
7470		MS-DRG CC	PATENT DUCTUS ARTERIOSUS
74710	CMS CC	MS-DRG CC	COARCTATION OF AORTA
74711	CMS CC	MS-DRG MCC	INTERRUPT OF AORTIC ARCH
74720		MS-DRG CC	CONG ANOM OF AORTA NOS
74721		MS-DRG CC	ANOMALIES OF AORTIC ARCH
74722	CMS CC	MS-DRG CC	AORTIC ATRESIA/STENOSIS
74729		MS-DRG CC	CONG ANOM OF AORTA NEC
7473		MS-DRG MCC	PULMONARY ARTERY ANOM
74740		MS-DRG CC	GREAT VEIN ANOMALY NOS
74741		MS-DRG CC	TOT ANOM PULM VEN CONNEC
74742		MS-DRG CC	PART ANOM PULM VEN CONN
74749		MS-DRG CC	GREAT VEIN ANOMALY NEC
74781		MS-DRG MCC	CEREBROVASCULAR ANOMALY
74782		MS-DRG CC	SPINAL VESSEL ANOMALY
74783		MS-DRG MCC	PERSISTENT FETAL CIRC
74789		MS-DRG CC	CIRCULATORY ANOMALY NEC
7479		MS-DRG CC	CIRCULATORY ANOMALY NOS
7483		MS-DRG CC	LARYNGOTRACH ANOMALY NEC
7484	CMS CC	MS-DRG CC	CONGENITAL CYSTIC LUNG
7485	CMS CC	MS-DRG MCC	AGENESIS OF LUNG
74861	CMS CC	MS-DRG CC	CONGEN BRONCHIECTASIS
7503		MS-DRG MCC	CONG ESOPH FISTULA/ATRES
7504		MS-DRG CC	ESOPHAGEAL ANOMALY NEC
7511		MS-DRG CC	ATRESIA SMALL INTESTINE
7512		MS-DRG CC	ATRESIA LARGE INTESTINE
7513		MS-DRG CC	HIRSCHSPRUNG'S DISEASE
7514		MS-DRG CC	INTESTINAL FIXATION ANOM
7515		MS-DRG CC	INTESTINAL ANOMALY NEC
75160		MS-DRG CC	BILIARY & LIVER ANOM NOS
75161		MS-DRG MCC	BILIARY ATRESIA
75162		MS-DRG CC	CONG CYSTIC LIVER DIS
75169		MS-DRG CC	BILIARY & LIVER ANOM NEC
7517		MS-DRG CC	PANCREAS ANOMALIES
7530		MS-DRG CC	RENAL AGENESIS
75310		MS-DRG CC	CYSTIC KIDNEY DISEAS NOS
75311		MS-DRG CC	CONGENITAL RENAL CYST
75312		MS-DRG CC	POLYCYSTIC KIDNEY NOS
75313		MS-DRG CC	POLYCYSTIC KID-AUTOSOM DOM

(Continued)

2008 ICD-9-CM	CMS DRG	MS-DRG	Short Title
75314		MS-DRG CC	POLYCYSTIC KID-AUTOSOM REC
75315		MS-DRG CC	RENAL DYSPLASIA
75316		MS-DRG CC	MEDULLARY CYSTIC KIDNEY
75317		MS-DRG CC	MEDULLARY SPONGE KIDNEY
75319		MS-DRG CC	CYSTIC KIDNEY DISEAS NEC
75320		MS-DRG CC	OBS DFCT REN PLV&URT NOS
75321		MS-DRG CC	CONGEN OBST URTROPLV JNC
75322		MS-DRG CC	CONG OBST URETEROVES JNC
75323		MS-DRG CC	CONGENITAL URETEROCELE
75329		MS-DRG CC	OBST DEF REN PLV&URT NEC
7535		MS-DRG CC	BLADDER EXSTROPHY
7536		MS-DRG CC	CONGEN URETHRAL STENOSIS
7542		MS-DRG CC	CONG POSTURAL DEFORMITY
75489		MS-DRG CC	NONTERATOGENIC ANOM NEC
75555		MS-DRG MCC	ACROCEPHALOSYNDACTYLY
75613		MS-DRG CC	CONG ABSENCE OF VERTEBRA
7563		MS-DRG CC	RIB & STERNUM ANOMAL NEC
75651		MS-DRG CC	OSTEOGENESIS IMPERFECTA
75652		MS-DRG CC	OSTEOPETROSIS
7566		MS-DRG MCC	ANOMALIES OF DIAPHRAGM
75670		MS-DRG MCC	CONGN ANOML ABD WALL NOS
75671		MS-DRG MCC	PRUNE BELLY SYNDROME
75679		MS-DRG MCC	CONGN ANOML ABD WALL NEC
75683		MS-DRG CC	EHLERS-DANLOS SYNDROME
7581		MS-DRG CC	PATAU'S SYNDROME
7582		MS-DRG CC	EDWARDS' SYNDROME
75831		MS-DRG CC	CRI-DU-CHAT SYNDROME
75832		MS-DRG MCC	VELO-CARDIO-FACIAL SYND
75833		MS-DRG CC	MICRODELETIONS NEC
75839		MS-DRG CC	AUTOSOMAL DELETIONS NEC
7590		MS-DRG CC	ANOMALIES OF SPLEEN
7593		MS-DRG CC	SITUS INVERSUS
7594		MS-DRG MCC	CONJOINED TWINS
7595		MS-DRG CC	TUBEROUS SCLEROSIS
7596		MS-DRG CC	HAMARTOSES NEC
7597		MS-DRG CC	MULT CONGEN ANOMAL NEC
75981		MS-DRG CC	PRADER-WILLI SYNDROME
75982		MS-DRG CC	MARFAN SYNDROME
75989		MS-DRG CC	SPECFIED CONG ANOMAL NEC

2008 ICD-9-CM	CMS DRG	MS-DRG	Short Title
76501	CMS CC		EXTREME IMMATUR < 500G
76502	CMS CC		EXTREME IMMATUR 500-749 G
76503	CMS CC		EXTREME IMMATUR 750-999 G
76504	CMS CC		EXTREME IMMAT 1000-1249 G
76505	CMS CC		EXTREME IMMAT 1250-1499 G
76506	CMS CC		EXTREME IMMAT 1500-1749 G
76507	CMS CC		EXTREME IMMAT 1750-1999 G
76508	CMS CC		EXTREME IMMAT 2000-2499 G
7670	CMS CC	MS-DRG MCC	CEREBRAL HEM AT BIRTH
76711	CMS CC	MS-DRG CC	EPICRANIAL SUBAPO HEMORR
7685	CMS CC	MS-DRG MCC	SEVERE BIRTH ASPHYXIA
7687		MS-DRG MCC	HYPOXIC-ISCHEMIC ENCEPH
769	CMS CC	MS-DRG MCC	RESPIRATORY DISTRESS SYN
7700	CMS CC	MS-DRG MCC	CONGENITAL PNEUMONIA
77012	CMS CC	MS-DRG MCC	MECONIUM ASP W RESP SYMP
77014	CMS CC	MS-DRG MCC	AMNIOTIC ASP W RESP SYM
77016	CMS CC	MS-DRG MCC	BLOOD ASP W RESP SYMPT
77018	CMS CC	MS-DRG MCC	NB ASP W RESP SYMP NEC
7702	CMS CC	MS-DRG MCC	NB INTERSTIT EMPHYSEMA
7703	CMS CC	MS-DRG MCC	NB PULMONARY HEMORRHAGE
7704	CMS CC	MS-DRG CC	PRIMARY ATELECTASIS
7705	CMS CC	MS-DRG CC	NB ATELECTASIS NEC/NOS
7707	CMS CC	MS-DRG MCC	PERINATAL CHR RESP DIS
77081		MS-DRG CC	PRIMARY APNEA OF NEWBORN
77082		MS-DRG CC	OTHER APNEA OF NEWBORN
77083		MS-DRG CC	CYANOTIC ATTACK, NEWBORN
77084	CMS CC	MS-DRG MCC	RESP FAILURE OF NEWBORN
77086	CMS CC	MS-DRG MCC	STOMACH CONT ASP W RESP
77087		MS-DRG MCC	NB RESPIRATORY ARREST
7710	CMS CC	MS-DRG CC	CONGENITAL RUBELLA
7711	CMS CC	MS-DRG MCC	CONG CYTOMEGALOVIRUS INF
7712		MS-DRG MCC	CONGENITAL INFEC NEC
7713	CMS CC	MS-DRG MCC	TETANUS NEONATORUM
7714		MS-DRG CC	OMPHALITIS OF NEWBORN
7715		MS-DRG CC	NEONATAL INFEC MASTITIS
77181	CMS CC	MS-DRG MCC	NB SEPTICEMIA [SEPSIS]
77182		MS-DRG CC	NB URINARY TRACT INFECTN
77183	CMS CC	MS-DRG CC	BACTEREMIA OF NEWBORN
77189		MS-DRG CC	PERINATAL INFECTION NEC

(Continued)

2008 ICD-9-CM	CMS DRG	MS-DRG	Short Title
77210	CMS CC	MS-DRG CC	NB INTRAVEN HEM NOS
77211	CMS CC	MS-DRG CC	NB INTRAVEN HEM,GRADE I
77212	CMS CC	MS-DRG CC	NB INTRAVEN HEM,GRADE II
77213	CMS CC	MS-DRG MCC	NB INTRAVN HEM,GRADE III
77214	CMS CC	MS-DRG MCC	NB INTRAVEN HEM,GRADE IV
7722	CMS CC	MS-DRG MCC	NB SUBARACHNOID HEMORR
7724	CMS CC	MS-DRG MCC	NB GI HEMORRHAGE
7725	CMS CC	MS-DRG CC	NB ADRENAL HEMORRHAGE
7730	CMS CC		NB HEMOLYT DIS:RH ISOIMM
7731	CMS CC		NB HEMOLYT DIS-ABO ISOIM
7732	CMS CC		NB HEMOLYT DIS-ISOIM NEC
7733	CMS CC	MS-DRG MCC	HYDROPS FETALIS:ISOIMM
7734	CMS CC	MS-DRG MCC	NB KERNICTERUS:ISOIMMUN
7740	CMS CC		PERINAT JAUND-HERED ANEM
7741	CMS CC		PERINAT JAUND:HEMOLYSIS
7742	CMS CC		NEONAT JAUND PRETERM DEL
77430	CMS CC		DELAY CONJUGAT JAUND NOS
77431	CMS CC		NEONAT JAUND IN OTH DIS
77439	CMS CC		DELAY CONJUGAT JAUND NEC
7744	CMS CC	MS-DRG MCC	FETAL/NEONATAL HEPATITIS
7745	CMS CC		PERINATAL JAUNDICE NEC
7747	CMS CC	MS-DRG MCC	NB KERNICTERUS
7751	CMS CC	MS-DRG CC	NEONAT DIABETES MELLITUS
7752	CMS CC	MS-DRG CC	NEONAT MYASTHENIA GRAVIS
7753	CMS CC	MS-DRG CC	NEONATAL THYROTOXICOSIS
7754	CMS CC	MS-DRG CC	HYPOCALCEM/HYPOMAGNES NB
7755	CMS CC		NEONATAL DEHYDRATION
7756	CMS CC		NEONATAL HYPOGLYCEMIA
7757	CMS CC	MS-DRG MCC	LATE METAB ACIDOSIS NB
77581		MS-DRG CC	NB ACIDOSIS NEC
77589		MS-DRG CC	NEONAT ENDO/MET DIS NEC
7760	CMS CC	MS-DRG CC	NB HEMORRHAGIC DISEASE
7761	CMS CC	MS-DRG MCC	NEONATAL THROMBOCYTOPEN
7762	CMS CC	MS-DRG MCC	DISSEM INTRAVASC COAG NB
7763	CMS CC	MS-DRG CC	OTH NEONATAL COAG DIS
7765		MS-DRG CC	CONGENITAL ANEMIA
7766		MS-DRG CC	ANEMIA OF PREMATURITY
7767		MS-DRG MCC	NEONATAL NEUTROPENIA
7771	CMS CC		MECONIUM OBSTRUCTION

2008 ICD-9-CM	CMS DRG	MS-DRG	Short Title
7772	CMS CC		INTEST OBST-INSPISS MILK
7774		MS-DRG CC	TRANSITORY ILEUS OF NB
7775	CMS CC	MS-DRG MCC	NECROT ENTEROCOLITIS NB
7776	CMS CC	MS-DRG MCC	PERINATAL INTEST PERFOR
7780	CMS CC	MS-DRG MCC	HYDROPS FETALIS NO ISOIM
7781		MS-DRG CC	SCLEREMA NEONATORUM
7785		MS-DRG CC	EDEMA OF NEWBORN NEC/NOS
7790	CMS CC	MS-DRG MCC	CONVULSIONS IN NEWBORN
7791	CMS CC		NB CEREB IRRIT NEC/NOS
7792		MS-DRG MCC	CNS DYSFUNCTION SYN NB
7793	CMS CC		NB FEEDING PROBLEMS
7794	CMS CC	MS-DRG CC	NB DRUG REACTION/INTOXIC
7795		MS-DRG CC	NB DRUG WITHDRAWAL SYNDR
7797	CMS CC	MS-DRG MCC	PERIVENT LEUKOMALACIA
77985	CMS CC	MS-DRG MCC	NB CARDIAC ARREST
78001	CMS CC	MS-DRG MCC	COMA
78003	CMS CC	MS-DRG CC	PERSISTENT VEGTV STATE
7801	CMS CC	MS-DRG CC	HALLUCINATIONS
78031	CMS CC	MS-DRG CC	FEBRILE CONVULSIONS NOS
78032	CMS CC	MS-DRG CC	COMPLX FEBRILE CONVULSNS
78039	CMS CC		CONVULSIONS NEC
7814		MS-DRG CC	TRANSIENT LIMB PARALYSIS
7816		MS-DRG CC	MENINGISMUS
7817	CMS CC	MS-DRG CC	TETANY
7818		MS-DRG CC	NEUROLOGIC NEGLECT SYNDR
7824		MS-DRG CC	JAUNDICE NOS
7843		MS-DRG CC	APHASIA
7854	CMS CC	MS-DRG CC	GANGRENE
78550	CMS CC	MS-DRG CC	SHOCK NOS
78551	CMS CC	MS-DRG MCC	CARDIOGENIC SHOCK
78552	CMS CC	MS-DRG MCC	SEPTIC SHOCK
78559	CMS CC	MS-DRG MCC	SHOCK W/O TRAUMA NEC
78603	CMS CC		APNEA
78604	CMS CC	MS-DRG CC	CHEYNE-STOKES RESPIRATN
7863	CMS CC	MS-DRG CC	HEMOPTYSIS
78820	CMS CC		RETENTION URINE NOS
78829	CMS CC		OTH SPCF RETENTION URINE
7888		MS-DRG CC	EXTRAVASATION OF URINE
78951	CMS CC	MS-DRG CC	MALIGNANT ASCITES

(Continued)

2008 ICD-9-CM	CMS DRG	MS-DRG	Short Title
78959	CMS CC	MS-DRG CC	ASCITES NEC
79001		MS-DRG CC	DROP, HEMATOCRIT, PRECIP
7907	CMS CC	MS-DRG CC	BACTEREMIA
7911	CMS CC	MS-DRG CC	CHYLURIA
7913	CMS CC	MS-DRG CC	MYOGLOBINURIA
79901	CMS CC	MS-DRG CC	ASPHYXIA
79902	CMS CC		HYPOXEMIA
7991	CMS CC	MS-DRG MCC	RESPIRATORY ARREST
7994	CMS CC	MS-DRG CC	CACHEXIA
80000	CMS CC	MS-DRG CC	CLOSED SKULL VAULT FX
80001	CMS CC	MS-DRG CC	CL SKULL VLT FX W/O COMA
80002	CMS CC	MS-DRG CC	CL SKULL VLT FX-BRF COMA
80003	CMS CC	MS-DRG MCC	CL SKULL VLT FX-MOD COMA
80004	CMS CC	MS-DRG MCC	CL SKL VLT FX-PROLN COMA
80005	CMS CC	MS-DRG MCC	CL SKUL VLT FX-DEEP COMA
80006	CMS CC	MS-DRG CC	CL SKULL VLT FX-COMA NOS
80009	CMS CC	MS-DRG CC	CL SKL VLT FX-CONCUS NOS
80010	CMS CC	MS-DRG MCC	CL SKL VLT FX/CEREBR LAC
80011	CMS CC	MS-DRG MCC	CL SKULL VLT FX W/O COMA
80012	CMS CC	MS-DRG MCC	CL SKULL VLT FX-BRF COMA
80013	CMS CC	MS-DRG MCC	CL SKULL VLT FX-MOD COMA
80014	CMS CC	MS-DRG MCC	CL SKL VLT FX-PROLN COMA
80015	CMS CC	MS-DRG MCC	CL SKUL VLT FX-DEEP COMA
80016	CMS CC	MS-DRG MCC	CL SKULL VLT FX-COMA NOS
80019	CMS CC	MS-DRG MCC	CL SKL VLT FX-CONCUS NOS
80020	CMS CC	MS-DRG MCC	CL SKL VLT FX/MENING HEM
80021	CMS CC	MS-DRG MCC	CL SKULL VLT FX W/O COMA
80022	CMS CC	MS-DRG MCC	CL SKULL VLT FX-BRF COMA
80023	CMS CC	MS-DRG MCC	CL SKULL VLT FX-MOD COMA
80024	CMS CC	MS-DRG MCC	CL SKL VLT FX-PROLN COMA
80025	CMS CC	MS-DRG MCC	CL SKUL VLT FX-DEEP COMA
80026	CMS CC	MS-DRG MCC	CL SKULL VLT FX-COMA NOS
80029	CMS CC	MS-DRG MCC	CL SKL VLT FX-CONCUS NOS
80030	CMS CC	MS-DRG MCC	CL SKULL VLT FX/HEM NEC
80031	CMS CC	MS-DRG MCC	CL SKULL VLT FX W/O COMA
80032	CMS CC	MS-DRG MCC	CL SKULL VLT FX-BRF COMA
80033	CMS CC	MS-DRG MCC	CL SKULL VLT FX-MOD COMA
80034	CMS CC	MS-DRG MCC	CL SKL VLT FX-PROLN COMA
80035	CMS CC	MS-DRG MCC	CL SKUL VLT FX-DEEP COMA

2008 ICD-9-CM	CMS DRG	MS-DRG	Short Title
80036	CMS CC	MS-DRG MCC	CL SKULL VLT FX-COMA NOS
80039	CMS CC	MS-DRG MCC	CL SKL VLT FX-CONCUS NOS
80040	CMS CC	MS-DRG CC	CL SKL VLT FX/BR INJ NEC
80041	CMS CC	MS-DRG CC	CL SKULL VLT FX W/O COMA
80042	CMS CC	MS-DRG CC	CL SKULL VLT FX-BRF COMA
80043	CMS CC	MS-DRG MCC	CL SKULL VLT FX-MOD COMA
80044	CMS CC	MS-DRG MCC	CL SKL VLT FX-PROLN COMA
80045	CMS CC	MS-DRG MCC	CL SKUL VLT FX-DEEP COMA
80046	CMS CC	MS-DRG CC	CL SKULL VLT FX-COMA NOS
80049	CMS CC	MS-DRG CC	CL SKL VLT FX-CONCUS NOS
80050	CMS CC	MS-DRG MCC	OPN SKULL VAULT FRACTURE
80051	CMS CC	MS-DRG MCC	OPN SKUL VLT FX W/O COMA
80052	CMS CC	MS-DRG MCC	OPN SKUL VLT FX-BRF COMA
80053	CMS CC	MS-DRG MCC	OPN SKUL VLT FX-MOD COMA
80054	CMS CC	MS-DRG MCC	OPN SKL VLT FX-PROLN COM
80055	CMS CC	MS-DRG MCC	OPN SKL VLT FX-DEEP COMA
80056	CMS CC	MS-DRG MCC	OPN SKUL VLT FX-COMA NOS
80059	CMS CC	MS-DRG MCC	OP SKL VLT FX-CONCUS NOS
80060	CMS CC	MS-DRG MCC	OPN SKL VLT FX/CEREB LAC
80061	CMS CC	MS-DRG MCC	OPN SKUL VLT FX W/O COMA
80062	CMS CC	MS-DRG MCC	OPN SKUL VLT FX-BRF COMA
80063	CMS CC	MS-DRG MCC	OPN SKUL VLT FX-MOD COMA
80064	CMS CC	MS-DRG MCC	OPN SKL VLT FX-PROLN COM
80065	CMS CC	MS-DRG MCC	OPN SKL VLT FX-DEEP COMA
80066	CMS CC	MS-DRG MCC	OPN SKUL VLT FX-COMA NOS
80069	CMS CC	MS-DRG MCC	OP SKL VLT FX-CONCUS NOS
80070	CMS CC	MS-DRG MCC	OPN SKL VLT FX/MENIN HEM
80071	CMS CC	MS-DRG MCC	OPN SKUL VLT FX W/O COMA
80072	CMS CC	MS-DRG MCC	OPN SKUL VLT FX-BRF COMA
80073	CMS CC	MS-DRG MCC	OPN SKUL VLT FX-MOD COMA
80074	CMS CC	MS-DRG MCC	OPN SKL VLT FX-PROLN COM
80075	CMS CC	MS-DRG MCC	OPN SKL VLT FX-DEEP COMA
80076	CMS CC	MS-DRG MCC	OPN SKUL VLT FX-COMA NOS
80079	CMS CC	MS-DRG MCC	OP SKL VLT FX-CONCUS NOS
80080	CMS CC	MS-DRG MCC	OPN SKULL VLT FX/HEM NEC
80081	CMS CC	MS-DRG MCC	OPN SKUL VLT FX W/O COMA
80082	CMS CC	MS-DRG MCC	OPN SKUL VLT FX-BRF COMA
80083	CMS CC	MS-DRG MCC	OPN SKUL VLT FX-MOD COMA
80084	CMS CC	MS-DRG MCC	OPN SKL VLT FX-PROLN COM

(Continued)

2008 ICD-9-CM	CMS DRG	MS-DRG	Short Title
80085	CMS CC	MS-DRG MCC	OPN SKL VLT FX-DEEP COMA
80086	CMS CC	MS-DRG MCC	OPN SKUL VLT FX-COMA NOS
80089	CMS CC	MS-DRG MCC	OP SKL VLT FX-CONCUS NOS
80090	CMS CC	MS-DRG MCC	OP SKL VLT FX/BR INJ NEC
80091	CMS CC	MS-DRG MCC	OPN SKUL VLT FX W/O COMA
80092	CMS CC	MS-DRG MCC	OPN SKUL VLT FX-BRF COMA
80093	CMS CC	MS-DRG MCC	OPN SKUL VLT FX-MOD COMA
80094	CMS CC	MS-DRG MCC	OPN SKL VLT FX-PROLN COM
80095	CMS CC	MS-DRG MCC	OP SKUL VLT FX-DEEP COMA
80096	CMS CC	MS-DRG MCC	OPN SKUL VLT FX-COMA NOS
80099	CMS CC	MS-DRG MCC	OP SKL VLT FX-CONCUS NOS
80100	CMS CC	MS-DRG CC	CLOS SKULL BASE FRACTURE
80101	CMS CC	MS-DRG CC	CL SKUL BASE FX W/O COMA
80102	CMS CC	MS-DRG CC	CL SKUL BASE FX-BRF COMA
80103	CMS CC	MS-DRG MCC	CL SKUL BASE FX-MOD COMA
80104	CMS CC	MS-DRG MCC	CL SKL BASE FX-PROL COMA
80105	CMS CC	MS-DRG MCC	CL SKL BASE FX-DEEP COMA
80106	CMS CC	MS-DRG CC	CL SKUL BASE FX-COMA NOS
80109	CMS CC	MS-DRG CC	CL SKULL BASE FX-CONCUSS
80110	CMS CC	MS-DRG MCC	CL SKL BASE FX/CEREB LAC
80111	CMS CC	MS-DRG MCC	CL SKUL BASE FX W/O COMA
80112	CMS CC	MS-DRG MCC	CL SKUL BASE FX-BRF COMA
80113	CMS CC	MS-DRG MCC	CL SKUL BASE FX-MOD COMA
80114	CMS CC	MS-DRG MCC	CL SKL BASE FX-PROL COMA
80115	CMS CC	MS-DRG MCC	CL SKL BASE FX-DEEP COMA
80116	CMS CC	MS-DRG MCC	CL SKUL BASE FX-COMA NOS
80119	CMS CC	MS-DRG MCC	CL SKULL BASE FX-CONCUSS
80120	CMS CC	MS-DRG MCC	CL SKL BASE FX/MENIN HEM
80121	CMS CC	MS-DRG MCC	CL SKUL BASE FX W/O COMA
80122	CMS CC	MS-DRG MCC	CL SKUL BASE FX/BRF COMA
80123	CMS CC	MS-DRG MCC	CL SKUL BASE FX-MOD COMA
80124	CMS CC	MS-DRG MCC	CL SKL BASE FX-PROL COMA
80125	CMS CC	MS-DRG MCC	CL SKL BASE FX-DEEP COMA
80126	CMS CC	MS-DRG MCC	CL SKUL BASE FX-COMA NOS
80129	CMS CC	MS-DRG MCC	CL SKULL BASE FX-CONCUSS
80130	CMS CC	MS-DRG MCC	CL SKULL BASE FX/HEM NEC
80131	CMS CC	MS-DRG MCC	CL SKUL BASE FX W/O COMA
80132	CMS CC	MS-DRG MCC	CL SKUL BASE FX-BRF COMA
80133	CMS CC	MS-DRG MCC	CL SKUL BASE FX-MOD COMA

2008 ICD-9-CM	CMS DRG	MS-DRG	Short Title
80134	CMS CC	MS-DRG MCC	CL SKL BASE FX-PROL COMA
80135	CMS CC	MS-DRG MCC	CL SKL BASE FX-DEEP COMA
80136	CMS CC	MS-DRG MCC	CL SKUL BASE FX-COMA NOS
80139	CMS CC	MS-DRG MCC	CL SKULL BASE FX-CONCUSS
80140	CMS CC	MS-DRG CC	CL SK BASE FX/BR INJ NEC
80141	CMS CC	MS-DRG CC	CL SKUL BASE FX W/O COMA
80142	CMS CC	MS-DRG CC	CL SKUL BASE FX-BRF COMA
80143	CMS CC	MS-DRG MCC	CL SKUL BASE FX-MOD COMA
80144	CMS CC	MS-DRG MCC	CL SKL BASE FX-PROL COMA
80145	CMS CC	MS-DRG MCC	CL SKL BASE FX-DEEP COMA
80146	CMS CC	MS-DRG CC	CL SKUL BASE FX-COMA NOS
80149	CMS CC	MS-DRG CC	CL SKULL BASE FX-CONCUSS
80150	CMS CC	MS-DRG MCC	OPEN SKULL BASE FRACTURE
80151	CMS CC	MS-DRG MCC	OPN SKL BASE FX W/O COMA
80152	CMS CC	MS-DRG MCC	OPN SKL BASE FX-BRF COMA
80153	CMS CC	MS-DRG MCC	OPN SKL BASE FX-MOD COMA
80154	CMS CC	MS-DRG MCC	OP SKL BASE FX-PROL COMA
80155	CMS CC	MS-DRG MCC	OP SKL BASE FX-DEEP COMA
80156	CMS CC	MS-DRG MCC	OPN SKL BASE FX-COMA NOS
80159	CMS CC	MS-DRG MCC	OPN SKUL BASE FX-CONCUSS
80160	CMS CC	MS-DRG MCC	OP SKL BASE FX/CEREB LAC
80161	CMS CC	MS-DRG MCC	OPN SKL BASE FX W/O COMA
80162	CMS CC	MS-DRG MCC	OPN SKL BASE FX-BRF COMA
80163	CMS CC	MS-DRG MCC	OPN SKL BASE FX-MOD COMA
80164	CMS CC	MS-DRG MCC	OP SKL BASE FX-PROL COMA
80165	CMS CC	MS-DRG MCC	OP SKL BASE FX-DEEP COMA
80166	CMS CC	MS-DRG MCC	OPN SKL BASE FX-COMA NOS
80169	CMS CC	MS-DRG MCC	OPN SKUL BASE FX-CONCUSS
80170	CMS CC	MS-DRG MCC	OP SKL BASE FX/MENIN HEM
80171	CMS CC	MS-DRG MCC	OPN SKL BASE FX W/O COMA
80172	CMS CC	MS-DRG MCC	OPN SKL BASE FX-BRF COMA
80173	CMS CC	MS-DRG MCC	OPN SKL BASE FX-MOD COMA
80174	CMS CC	MS-DRG MCC	OP SKL BASE FX-PROL COMA
80175	CMS CC	MS-DRG MCC	OP SKL BASE FX-DEEP COMA
80176	CMS CC	MS-DRG MCC	OPN SKL BASE FX-COMA NOS
80179	CMS CC	MS-DRG MCC	OPN SKUL BASE FX-CONCUSS
80180	CMS CC	MS-DRG MCC	OPN SKUL BASE FX/HEM NEC
80181	CMS CC	MS-DRG MCC	OPN SKL BASE FX W/O COMA
80182	CMS CC	MS-DRG MCC	OPN SKL BASE FX-BRF COMA

(Continued)

2008 ICD-9-CM	CMS DRG	MS-DRG	Short Title
80183	CMS CC	MS-DRG MCC	OPN SKL BASE FX-MOD COMA
80184	CMS CC	MS-DRG MCC	OP SKL BASE FX-PROL COMA
80185	CMS CC	MS-DRG MCC	OP SKL BASE FX-DEEP COMA
80186	CMS CC	MS-DRG MCC	OPN SKL BASE FX-COMA NOS
80189	CMS CC	MS-DRG MCC	OPN SKUL BASE FX-CONCUSS
80190	CMS CC	MS-DRG MCC	OP SK BASE FX/BR INJ NEC
80191	CMS CC	MS-DRG MCC	OP SKUL BASE FX W/O COMA
80192	CMS CC	MS-DRG MCC	OPN SKL BASE FX-BRF COMA
80193	CMS CC	MS-DRG MCC	OPN SKL BASE FX-MOD COMA
80194	CMS CC	MS-DRG MCC	OP SKL BASE FX-PROL COMA
80195	CMS CC	MS-DRG MCC	OP SK BASE FX-DEEP COMA
80196	CMS CC	MS-DRG MCC	OPN SKL BASE FX-COMA NOS
80199	CMS CC	MS-DRG MCC	OPN SKUL BASE FX-CONCUSS
8021	CMS CC	MS-DRG CC	NASAL BONE FX-OPEN
80220	CMS CC	MS-DRG CC	MANDIBLE FX NOS-CLOSED
80221	CMS CC	MS-DRG CC	FX CONDYL PROC MANDIB-CL
80222	CMS CC	MS-DRG CC	SUBCONDYLAR FX MANDIB-CL
80223	CMS CC	MS-DRG CC	FX CORON PROC MANDIB-CL
80224	CMS CC	MS-DRG CC	FX RAMUS NOS-CLOSED
80225	CMS CC	MS-DRG CC	FX ANGLE OF JAW-CLOSED
80226	CMS CC	MS-DRG CC	FX SYMPHY MANDIB BODY-CL
80227	CMS CC	MS-DRG CC	FX ALVEOLAR BORD MAND-CL
80228	CMS CC	MS-DRG CC	FX MANDIBLE BODY NEC-CL
80229	CMS CC	MS-DRG CC	MULT FX MANDIBLE-CLOSED
80230	CMS CC	MS-DRG CC	MANDIBLE FX NOS-OPEN
80231	CMS CC	MS-DRG CC	FX CONDYL PROC MAND-OPEN
80232	CMS CC	MS-DRG CC	SUBCONDYL FX MANDIB-OPEN
80233	CMS CC	MS-DRG CC	FX CORON PROC MANDIB-OPN
80234	CMS CC	MS-DRG CC	FX RAMUS NOS-OPEN
80235	CMS CC	MS-DRG CC	FX ANGLE OF JAW-OPEN
80236	CMS CC	MS-DRG CC	FX SYMPHY MANDIB BDY-OPN
80237	CMS CC	MS-DRG CC	FX ALV BORD MAND BDY-OPN
80238	CMS CC	MS-DRG CC	FX MANDIBLE BODY NEC-OPN
80239	CMS CC	MS-DRG CC	MULT FX MANDIBLE-OPEN
8024	CMS CC	MS-DRG CC	FX MALAR/MAXILLARY-CLOSE
8025	CMS CC	MS-DRG CC	FX MALAR/MAXILLARY-OPEN
8026	CMS CC	MS-DRG CC	FX ORBITAL FLOOR-CLOSED
8027	CMS CC	MS-DRG CC	FX ORBITAL FLOOR-OPEN
8028	CMS CC	MS-DRG CC	FX FACIAL BONE NEC-CLOSE

2008 ICD-9-CM	CMS DRG	MS-DRG	Short Title
8029	CMS CC	MS-DRG CC	FX FACIAL BONE NEC-OPEN
80300	CMS CC	MS-DRG CC	CLOSE SKULL FRACTURE NEC
80301	CMS CC	MS-DRG CC	CL SKULL FX NEC W/O COMA
80302	CMS CC	MS-DRG CC	CL SKULL FX NEC-BRF COMA
80303	CMS CC	MS-DRG MCC	CL SKULL FX NEC-MOD COMA
80304	CMS CC	MS-DRG MCC	CL SKL FX NEC-PROLN COMA
80305	CMS CC	MS-DRG MCC	CL SKUL FX NEC-DEEP COMA
80306	CMS CC	MS-DRG CC	CL SKULL FX NEC-COMA NOS
80309	CMS CC	MS-DRG CC	CL SKULL FX NEC-CONCUSS
80310	CMS CC	MS-DRG MCC	CL SKL FX NEC/CEREBR LAC
80311	CMS CC	MS-DRG MCC	CL SKULL FX NEC W/O COMA
80312	CMS CC	MS-DRG MCC	CL SKULL FX NEC-BRF COMA
80313	CMS CC	MS-DRG MCC	CL SKULL FX NEC-MOD COMA
80314	CMS CC	MS-DRG MCC	CL SKL FX NEC-PROLN COMA
80315	CMS CC	MS-DRG MCC	CL SKUL FX NEC-DEEP COMA
80316	CMS CC	MS-DRG MCC	CL SKULL FX NEC-COMA NOS
80319	CMS CC	MS-DRG MCC	CL SKULL FX NEC-CONCUSS
80320	CMS CC	MS-DRG MCC	CL SKL FX NEC/MENING HEM
80321	CMS CC	MS-DRG MCC	CL SKULL FX NEC W/O COMA
80322	CMS CC	MS-DRG MCC	CL SKULL FX NEC-BRF COMA
80323	CMS CC	MS-DRG MCC	CL SKULL FX NEC-MOD COMA
80324	CMS CC	MS-DRG MCC	CL SKL FX NEC-PROLN COMA
80325	CMS CC	MS-DRG MCC	CL SKUL FX NEC-DEEP COMA
80326	CMS CC	MS-DRG MCC	CL SKULL FX NEC-COMA NOS
80329	CMS CC	MS-DRG MCC	CL SKULL FX NEC-CONCUSS
80330	CMS CC	MS-DRG MCC	CL SKULL FX NEC/HEM NEC
80331	CMS CC	MS-DRG MCC	CL SKULL FX NEC W/O COMA
80332	CMS CC	MS-DRG MCC	CL SKULL FX NEC-BRF COMA
80333	CMS CC	MS-DRG MCC	CL SKULL FX NEC-MOD COMA
80334	CMS CC	MS-DRG MCC	CL SKL FX NEC-PROLN COMA
80335	CMS CC	MS-DRG MCC	CL SKUL FX NEC-DEEP COMA
80336	CMS CC	MS-DRG MCC	CL SKULL FX NEC-COMA NOS
80339	CMS CC	MS-DRG MCC	CL SKULL FX NEC-CONCUSS
80340	CMS CC	MS-DRG CC	CL SKL FX NEC/BR INJ NEC
80341	CMS CC	MS-DRG CC	CL SKULL FX NEC W/O COMA
80342	CMS CC	MS-DRG CC	CL SKULL FX NEC-BRF COMA
80343	CMS CC	MS-DRG MCC	CL SKULL FX NEC-MOD COMA
80344	CMS CC	MS-DRG MCC	CL SKL FX NEC-PROLN COMA
80345	CMS CC	MS-DRG MCC	CL SKUL FX NEC-DEEP COMA

(Continued)

2008 ICD-9-CM	CMS DRG	MS-DRG	Short Title
80346	CMS CC	MS-DRG CC	CL SKULL FX NEC-COMA NOS
80349	CMS CC	MS-DRG CC	CL SKULL FX NEC-CONCUSS
80350	CMS CC	MS-DRG MCC	OPEN SKULL FRACTURE NEC
80351	CMS CC	MS-DRG MCC	OPN SKUL FX NEC W/O COMA
80352	CMS CC	MS-DRG MCC	OPN SKUL FX NEC-BRF COMA
80353	CMS CC	MS-DRG MCC	OPN SKUL FX NEC-MOD COMA
80354	CMS CC	MS-DRG MCC	OPN SKL FX NEC-PROL COMA
80355	CMS CC	MS-DRG MCC	OPN SKL FX NEC-DEEP COMA
80356	CMS CC	MS-DRG MCC	OPN SKUL FX NEC-COMA NOS
80359	CMS CC	MS-DRG MCC	OPN SKULL FX NEC-CONCUSS
80360	CMS CC	MS-DRG MCC	OPN SKL FX NEC/CEREB LAC
80361	CMS CC	MS-DRG MCC	OPN SKUL FX NEC W/O COMA
80362	CMS CC	MS-DRG MCC	OPN SKUL FX NEC-BRF COMA
80363	CMS CC	MS-DRG MCC	OPN SKUL FX NEC-MOD COMA
80364	CMS CC	MS-DRG MCC	OPN SKL FX NEC-PROLN COM
80365	CMS CC	MS-DRG MCC	OPN SKL FX NEC-DEEP COMA
80366	CMS CC	MS-DRG MCC	OPN SKUL FX NEC-COMA NOS
80369	CMS CC	MS-DRG MCC	OPN SKULL FX NEC-CONCUSS
80370	CMS CC	MS-DRG MCC	OPN SKL FX NEC/MENIN HEM
80371	CMS CC	MS-DRG MCC	OPN SKUL FX NEC W/O COMA
80372	CMS CC	MS-DRG MCC	OPN SKUL FX NEC-BRF COMA
80373	CMS CC	MS-DRG MCC	OPN SKUL FX NEC-MOD COMA
80374	CMS CC	MS-DRG MCC	OPN SKL FX NEC-PROL COMA
80375	CMS CC	MS-DRG MCC	OPN SKL FX NEC-DEEP COMA
80376	CMS CC	MS-DRG MCC	OPN SKUL FX NEC-COMA NOS
80379	CMS CC	MS-DRG MCC	OPN SKULL FX NEC-CONCUSS
80380	CMS CC	MS-DRG MCC	OPN SKULL FX NEC/HEM NEC
80381	CMS CC	MS-DRG MCC	OPN SKUL FX NEC W/O COMA
80382	CMS CC	MS-DRG MCC	OPN SKUL FX NEC-BRF COMA
80383	CMS CC	MS-DRG MCC	OPN SKUL FX NEC-MOD COMA
80384	CMS CC	MS-DRG MCC	OPN SKL FX NEC-PROL COMA
80385	CMS CC	MS-DRG MCC	OPN SKL FX NEC-DEEP COMA
80386	CMS CC	MS-DRG MCC	OPN SKUL FX NEC-COMA NOS
80389	CMS CC	MS-DRG MCC	OPN SKULL FX NEC-CONCUSS
80390	CMS CC	MS-DRG MCC	OP SKL FX NEC/BR INJ NEC
80391	CMS CC	MS-DRG MCC	OPN SKUL FX NEC W/O COMA
80392	CMS CC	MS-DRG MCC	OPN SKUL FX NEC-BRF COMA
80393	CMS CC	MS-DRG MCC	OPN SKUL FX NEC-MOD COMA
80394	CMS CC	MS-DRG MCC	OPN SKL FX NEC-PROL COMA

2008 ICD-9-CM	CMS DRG	MS-DRG	Short Title
80395	CMS CC	MS-DRG MCC	OPN SKL FX NEC-DEEP COMA
80396	CMS CC	MS-DRG MCC	OPN SKUL FX NEC-COMA NOS
80399	CMS CC	MS-DRG MCC	OPN SKULL FX NEC-CONCUSS
80400	CMS CC	MS-DRG CC	CL SKUL FX W OTH BONE FX
80401	CMS CC	MS-DRG CC	CL SKL W OTH FX W/O COMA
80402	CMS CC	MS-DRG CC	CL SKL W OTH FX-BRF COMA
80403	CMS CC	MS-DRG MCC	CL SKL W OTH FX-MOD COMA
80404	CMS CC	MS-DRG MCC	CL SKL/OTH FX-PROLN COMA
80405	CMS CC	MS-DRG MCC	CL SKUL/OTH FX-DEEP COMA
80406	CMS CC	MS-DRG CC	CL SKL W OTH FX-COMA NOS
80409	CMS CC	MS-DRG CC	CL SKUL W OTH FX-CONCUSS
80410	CMS CC	MS-DRG MCC	CL SK W OTH FX/CEREB LAC
80411	CMS CC	MS-DRG MCC	CL SKL W OTH FX W/O COMA
80412	CMS CC	MS-DRG MCC	CL SKL W OTH FX-BRF COMA
80413	CMS CC	MS-DRG MCC	CL SKL W OTH FX-MOD COMA
80414	CMS CC	MS-DRG MCC	CL SKL/OTH FX-PROLN COMA
80415	CMS CC	MS-DRG MCC	CL SKUL/OTH FX-DEEP COMA
80416	CMS CC	MS-DRG MCC	CL SKL W OTH FX-COMA NOS
80419	CMS CC	MS-DRG MCC	CL SKUL W OTH FX-CONCUSS
80420	CMS CC	MS-DRG MCC	CL SKL/OTH FX/MENING HEM
80421	CMS CC	MS-DRG MCC	CL SKL W OTH FX W/O COMA
80422	CMS CC	MS-DRG MCC	CL SKL W OTH FX-BRF COMA
80423	CMS CC	MS-DRG MCC	CL SKL W OTH FX-MOD COMA
80424	CMS CC	MS-DRG MCC	CL SKL/OTH FX-PROLN COMA
80425	CMS CC	MS-DRG MCC	CL SKUL/OTH FX-DEEP COMA
80426	CMS CC	MS-DRG MCC	CL SKL W OTH FX-COMA NOS
80429	CMS CC	MS-DRG MCC	CL SKUL W OTH FX-CONCUSS
80430	CMS CC	MS-DRG MCC	CL SKUL W OTH FX/HEM NEC
80431	CMS CC	MS-DRG MCC	CL SKL W OTH FX W/O COMA
80432	CMS CC	MS-DRG MCC	CL SKL W OTH FX-BRF COMA
80433	CMS CC	MS-DRG MCC	CL SKL W OTH FX-MOD COMA
80434	CMS CC	MS-DRG MCC	CL SKL/OTH FX-PROLN COMA
80435	CMS CC	MS-DRG MCC	CL SKUL/OTH FX-DEEP COMA
80436	CMS CC	MS-DRG MCC	CL SKL W OTH FX-COMA NOS
80439	CMS CC	MS-DRG MCC	CL SKUL W OTH FX-CONCUSS
80440	CMS CC	MS-DRG CC	CL SKL/OTH FX/BR INJ NEC
80441	CMS CC	MS-DRG CC	CL SKL W OTH FX W/O COMA
80442	CMS CC	MS-DRG CC	CL SKL W OTH FX-BRF COMA
80443	CMS CC	MS-DRG MCC	CL SKL W OTH FX-MOD COMA

(Continued)

2008 ICD-9-CM	CMS DRG	MS-DRG	Short Title
80444	CMS CC	MS-DRG MCC	CL SKL/OTH FX-PROLN COMA
80445	CMS CC	MS-DRG MCC	CL SKUL/OTH FX-DEEP COMA
80446	CMS CC	MS-DRG CC	CL SKL W OTH FX-COMA NOS
80449	CMS CC	MS-DRG CC	CL SKUL W OTH FX-CONCUSS
80450	CMS CC	MS-DRG CC	OPN SKULL FX/OTH BONE FX
80451	CMS CC	MS-DRG CC	OPN SKUL/OTH FX W/O COMA
80452	CMS CC	MS-DRG CC	OPN SKUL/OTH FX-BRF COMA
80453	CMS CC	MS-DRG MCC	OPN SKUL/OTH FX-MOD COMA
80454	CMS CC	MS-DRG MCC	OPN SKL/OTH FX-PROL COMA
80455	CMS CC	MS-DRG MCC	OPN SKL/OTH FX-DEEP COMA
80456	CMS CC	MS-DRG CC	OPN SKUL/OTH FX-COMA NOS
80459	CMS CC	MS-DRG CC	OPN SKULL/OTH FX-CONCUSS
80460	CMS CC	MS-DRG MCC	OPN SKL/OTH FX/CEREB LAC
80461	CMS CC	MS-DRG MCC	OPN SKUL/OTH FX W/O COMA
80462	CMS CC	MS-DRG MCC	OPN SKUL/OTH FX-BRF COMA
80463	CMS CC	MS-DRG MCC	OPN SKUL/OTH FX-MOD COMA
80464	CMS CC	MS-DRG MCC	OPN SKL/OTH FX-PROL COMA
80465	CMS CC	MS-DRG MCC	OPN SKL/OTH FX-DEEP COMA
80466	CMS CC	MS-DRG MCC	OPN SKUL/OTH FX-COMA NOS
80469	CMS CC	MS-DRG MCC	OPN SKULL/OTH FX-CONCUSS
80470	CMS CC	MS-DRG MCC	OPN SKL/OTH FX/MENIN HEM
80471	CMS CC	MS-DRG MCC	OPN SKUL/OTH FX W/O COMA
80472	CMS CC	MS-DRG MCC	OPN SKUL/OTH FX-BRF COMA
80473	CMS CC	MS-DRG MCC	OPN SKUL/OTH FX-MOD COMA
80474	CMS CC	MS-DRG MCC	OPN SKL/OTH FX-PROL COMA
80475	CMS CC	MS-DRG MCC	OPN SKL/OTH FX-DEEP COMA
80476	CMS CC	MS-DRG MCC	OPN SKUL/OTH FX-COMA NOS
80479	CMS CC	MS-DRG MCC	OPN SKULL/OTH FX-CONCUSS
80480	CMS CC	MS-DRG MCC	OPN SKL W OTH FX/HEM NEC
80481	CMS CC	MS-DRG MCC	OPN SKUL/OTH FX W/O COMA
80482	CMS CC	MS-DRG MCC	OPN SKUL/OTH FX-BRF COMA
80483	CMS CC	MS-DRG MCC	OPN SKUL/OTH FX-MOD COMA
80484	CMS CC	MS-DRG MCC	OPN SKL/OTH FX-PROL COMA
80485	CMS CC	MS-DRG MCC	OPN SKL/OTH FX-DEEP COMA
80486	CMS CC	MS-DRG MCC	OPN SKUL/OTH FX-COMA NOS
80489	CMS CC	MS-DRG MCC	OPN SKULL/OTH FX-CONCUSS
80490	CMS CC	MS-DRG CC	OP SKL/OTH FX/BR INJ NEC
80491	CMS CC	MS-DRG CC	OPN SKUL/OTH FX W/O COMA
80492	CMS CC	MS-DRG CC	OPN SKUL/OTH FX-BRF COMA

2008 ICD-9-CM	CMS DRG	MS-DRG	Short Title
80493	CMS CC	MS-DRG MCC	OPN SKUL/OTH FX-MOD COMA
80494	CMS CC	MS-DRG MCC	OPN SKL/OTH FX-PROL COMA
80495	CMS CC	MS-DRG MCC	OPN SKL/OTH FX-DEEP COMA
80496	CMS CC	MS-DRG CC	OPN SKUL/OTH FX-COMA NOS
80499	CMS CC	MS-DRG CC	OPN SKULL/OTH FX-CONCUSS
80500	CMS CC	MS-DRG CC	FX CERVICAL VERT NOS-CL
80501	CMS CC	MS-DRG CC	FX C1 VERTEBRA-CLOSED
80502	CMS CC	MS-DRG CC	FX C2 VERTEBRA-CLOSED
80503	CMS CC	MS-DRG CC	FX C3 VERTEBRA-CLOSED
80504	CMS CC	MS-DRG CC	FX C4 VERTEBRA-CLOSED
80505	CMS CC	MS-DRG CC	FX C5 VERTEBRA-CLOSED
80506	CMS CC	MS-DRG CC	FX C6 VERTEBRA-CLOSED
80507	CMS CC	MS-DRG CC	FX C7 VERTEBRA-CLOSED
80508	CMS CC	MS-DRG CC	FX MULT CERVICAL VERT-CL
80510	CMS CC	MS-DRG MCC	FX CERVICAL VERT NOS-OPN
80511	CMS CC	MS-DRG MCC	FX C1 VERTEBRA-OPEN
80512	CMS CC	MS-DRG MCC	FX C2 VERTEBRA-OPEN
80513	CMS CC	MS-DRG MCC	FX C3 VERTEBRA-OPEN
80514	CMS CC	MS-DRG MCC	FX C4 VERTEBRA-OPEN
80515	CMS CC	MS-DRG MCC	FX C5 VERTEBRA-OPEN
80516	CMS CC	MS-DRG MCC	FX C6 VERTEBRA-OPEN
80517	CMS CC	MS-DRG MCC	FX C7 VERTEBRA-OPEN
80518	CMS CC	MS-DRG MCC	FX MLT CERVICAL VERT-OPN
8052	CMS CC	MS-DRG CC	FX DORSAL VERTEBRA-CLOSE
8053	CMS CC	MS-DRG MCC	FX DORSAL VERTEBRA-OPEN
8054	CMS CC	MS-DRG CC	FX LUMBAR VERTEBRA-CLOSE
8055	CMS CC	MS-DRG MCC	FX LUMBAR VERTEBRA-OPEN
8056	CMS CC	MS-DRG CC	FX SACRUM/COCCYX-CLOSED
8057	CMS CC	MS-DRG MCC	FX SACRUM/COCCYX-OPEN
8058	CMS CC	MS-DRG CC	VERTEBRAL FX NOS-CLOSED
8059	CMS CC	MS-DRG MCC	VERTEBRAL FX NOS-OPEN
80600	CMS CC	MS-DRG MCC	C1-C4 FX-CL/CORD INJ NOS
80601	CMS CC	MS-DRG MCC	C1-C4 FX-CL/COM CORD LES
80602	CMS CC	MS-DRG MCC	C1-C4 FX-CL/ANT CORD SYN
80603	CMS CC	MS-DRG MCC	C1-C4 FX-CL/CEN CORD SYN
80604	CMS CC	MS-DRG MCC	C1-C4 FX-CL/CORD INJ NEC
80605	CMS CC	MS-DRG MCC	C5-C7 FX-CL/CORD INJ NOS
80606	CMS CC	MS-DRG MCC	C5-C7 FX-CL/COM CORD LES
80607	CMS CC	MS-DRG MCC	C5-C7 FX-CL/ANT CORD SYN

(Continued)

2008 ICD-9-CM	CMS DRG	MS-DRG	Short Title
80608	CMS CC	MS-DRG MCC	C5-C7 FX-CL/CEN CORD SYN
80609	CMS CC	MS-DRG MCC	C5-C7 FX-CL/CORD INJ NEC
80610	CMS CC	MS-DRG MCC	C1-C4 FX-OP/CORD INJ NOS
80611	CMS CC	MS-DRG MCC	C1-C4 FX-OP/COM CORD LES
80612	CMS CC	MS-DRG MCC	C1-C4 FX-OP/ANT CORD SYN
80613	CMS CC	MS-DRG MCC	C1-C4 FX-OP/CEN CORD SYN
80614	CMS CC	MS-DRG MCC	C1-C4 FX-OP/CORD INJ NEC
80615	CMS CC	MS-DRG MCC	C5-C7 FX-OP/CORD INJ NOS
80616	CMS CC	MS-DRG MCC	C5-C7 FX-OP/COM CORD LES
80617	CMS CC	MS-DRG MCC	C5-C7 FX-OP/ANT CORD SYN
80618	CMS CC	MS-DRG MCC	C5-C7 FX-OP/CEN CORD SYN
80619	CMS CC	MS-DRG MCC	C5-C7 FX-OP/CORD INJ NEC
80620	CMS CC	MS-DRG MCC	T1-T6 FX-CL/CORD INJ NOS
80621	CMS CC	MS-DRG MCC	T1-T6 FX-CL/COM CORD LES
80622	CMS CC	MS-DRG MCC	T1-T6 FX-CL/ANT CORD SYN
80623	CMS CC	MS-DRG MCC	T1-T6 FX-CL/CEN CORD SYN
80624	CMS CC	MS-DRG MCC	T1-T6 FX-CL/CORD INJ NEC
80625	CMS CC	MS-DRG MCC	T7-T12 FX-CL/CRD INJ NOS
80626	CMS CC	MS-DRG MCC	T7-T12 FX-CL/COM CRD LES
80627	CMS CC	MS-DRG MCC	T7-T12 FX-CL/ANT CRD SYN
80628	CMS CC	MS-DRG MCC	T7-T12 FX-CL/CEN CRD SYN
80629	CMS CC	MS-DRG MCC	T7-T12 FX-CL/CRD INJ NEC
80630	CMS CC	MS-DRG MCC	T1-T6 FX-OP/CORD INJ NOS
80631	CMS CC	MS-DRG MCC	T1-T6 FX-OP/COM CORD LES
80632	CMS CC	MS-DRG MCC	T1-T6 FX-OP/ANT CORD SYN
80633	CMS CC	MS-DRG MCC	T1-T6 FX-OP/CEN CORD SYN
80634	CMS CC	MS-DRG MCC	T1-T6 FX-OP/CORD INJ NEC
80635	CMS CC	MS-DRG MCC	T7-T12 FX-OP/CRD INJ NOS
80636	CMS CC	MS-DRG MCC	T7-T12 FX-OP/COM CRD LES
80637	CMS CC	MS-DRG MCC	T7-T12 FX-OP/ANT CRD SYN
80638	CMS CC	MS-DRG MCC	T7-T12 FX-OP/CEN CRD SYN
80639	CMS CC	MS-DRG MCC	T7-T12 FX-OP/CRD INJ NEC
8064	CMS CC	MS-DRG MCC	CL LUMBAR FX W CORD INJ
8065	CMS CC	MS-DRG MCC	OPN LUMBAR FX W CORD INJ
80660	CMS CC	MS-DRG MCC	FX SACRUM-CL/CRD INJ NOS
80661	CMS CC	MS-DRG MCC	FX SACR-CL/CAUDA EQU LES
80662	CMS CC	MS-DRG MCC	FX SACR-CL/CAUDA INJ NEC
80669	CMS CC	MS-DRG MCC	FX SACRUM-CL/CRD INJ NEC
80670	CMS CC	MS-DRG MCC	FX SACRUM-OP/CRD INJ NOS

2008 ICD-9-CM	CMS DRG	MS-DRG	Short Title
80671	CMS CC	MS-DRG MCC	FX SACR-OP/CAUDA EQU LES
80672	CMS CC	MS-DRG MCC	FX SACR-OP/CAUDA INJ NEC
80679	CMS CC	MS-DRG MCC	FX SACRUM-OP/CRD INJ NEC
8068	CMS CC	MS-DRG MCC	VERT FX NOS-CL W CRD INJ
8069	CMS CC	MS-DRG MCC	VERT FX NOS-OP W CRD INJ
80700		MS-DRG CC	FRACTURE RIB NOS-CLOSED
80701		MS-DRG CC	FRACTURE ONE RIB-CLOSED
80702		MS-DRG CC	FRACTURE TWO RIBS-CLOSED
80703		MS-DRG CC	FRACTURE THREE RIBS-CLOS
80704	CMS CC	MS-DRG CC	FRACTURE FOUR RIBS-CLOSE
80705	CMS CC	MS-DRG CC	FRACTURE FIVE RIBS-CLOSE
80706	CMS CC	MS-DRG CC	FRACTURE SIX RIBS-CLOSED
80707	CMS CC	MS-DRG CC	FRACTURE SEVEN RIBS-CLOS
80708	CMS CC	MS-DRG CC	FX EIGHT/MORE RIB-CLOSED
80709	CMS CC	MS-DRG CC	FX MULT RIBS NOS-CLOSED
80710	CMS CC	MS-DRG MCC	FRACTURE RIB NOS-OPEN
80711	CMS CC	MS-DRG MCC	FRACTURE ONE RIB-OPEN
80712	CMS CC	MS-DRG MCC	FRACTURE TWO RIBS-OPEN
80713	CMS CC	MS-DRG MCC	FRACTURE THREE RIBS-OPEN
80714	CMS CC	MS-DRG MCC	FRACTURE FOUR RIBS-OPEN
80715	CMS CC	MS-DRG MCC	FRACTURE FIVE RIBS-OPEN
80716	CMS CC	MS-DRG MCC	FRACTURE SIX RIBS-OPEN
80717	CMS CC	MS-DRG MCC	FRACTURE SEVEN RIBS-OPEN
80718	CMS CC	MS-DRG MCC	FX EIGHT/MORE RIBS-OPEN
80719	CMS CC	MS-DRG MCC	FX MULT RIBS NOS-OPEN
8072	CMS CC	MS-DRG CC	FRACTURE OF STERNUM-CLOS
8073	CMS CC	MS-DRG MCC	FRACTURE OF STERNUM-OPEN
8074	CMS CC	MS-DRG MCC	FLAIL CHEST
8075	CMS CC	MS-DRG MCC	FX LARYNX/TRACHEA-CLOSED
8076	CMS CC	MS-DRG MCC	FX LARYNX/TRACHEA-OPEN
8080	CMS CC	MS-DRG MCC	FRACTURE ACETABULUM-CLOS
8081	CMS CC	MS-DRG MCC	FRACTURE ACETABULUM-OPEN
8082	CMS CC	MS-DRG CC	FRACTURE OF PUBIS-CLOSED
8083	CMS CC	MS-DRG MCC	FRACTURE OF PUBIS-OPEN
80841		MS-DRG CC	FRACTURE OF ILIUM-CLOSED
80842		MS-DRG CC	FRACTURE ISCHIUM-CLOSED
80843	CMS CC	MS-DRG CC	PELV FX-CLOS/PELV DISRUP
80849	CMS CC	MS-DRG CC	PELVIC FRACTURE NEC-CLOS
80851	CMS CC	MS-DRG MCC	FRACTURE OF ILIUM-OPEN

2008 ICD-9-CM	CMS DRG	MS-DRG	Short Title
80852	CMS CC	MS-DRG MCC	FRACTURE OF ISCHIUM-OPEN
80853	CMS CC	MS-DRG MCC	PELV FX-OPEN/PELV DISRUP
80859	CMS CC	MS-DRG MCC	PELVIC FRACTURE NEC-OPEN
8088	CMS CC	MS-DRG CC	PELVIC FRACTURE NOS-CLOS
8089	CMS CC	MS-DRG MCC	PELVIC FRACTURE NOS-OPEN
8090		MS-DRG CC	FRACTURE TRUNK BONE-CLOS
8091		MS-DRG MCC	FRACTURE TRUNK BONE-OPEN
81010		MS-DRG CC	FX CLAVICLE NOS-OPEN
81011		MS-DRG CC	FX CLAVIC, STERN END-OPN
81012		MS-DRG CC	FX CLAVICLE SHAFT-OPEN
81013		MS-DRG CC	FX CLAVIC, ACROM END-OPN
81110		MS-DRG CC	FX SCAPULA NOS-OPEN
81111		MS-DRG CC	FX SCAPUL, ACROM PROC-OP
81112		MS-DRG CC	FX SCAPUL, CORAC PROC-OP
81113		MS-DRG CC	FX SCAP, GLEN CAV/NCK-OP
81119		MS-DRG CC	FX SCAPULA NEC-OPEN
81200		MS-DRG CC	FX UP END HUMERUS NOS-CL
81201		MS-DRG CC	FX SURG NCK HUMERUS-CLOS
81202		MS-DRG CC	FX ANATOM NCK HUMERUS-CL
81203		MS-DRG CC	FX GR TUBEROS HUMERUS-CL
81209		MS-DRG CC	FX UPPER HUMERUS NEC-CL
81210		MS-DRG MCC	FX UPPER HUMERUS NOS-OPN
81211		MS-DRG MCC	FX SURG NECK HUMERUS-OPN
81212		MS-DRG MCC	FX ANAT NECK HUMERUS-OPN
81213		MS-DRG MCC	FX GR TUBEROS HUMER-OPEN
81219		MS-DRG MCC	FX UPPER HUMERUS NEC-OPN
81220		MS-DRG CC	FX HUMERUS NOS-CLOSED
81221		MS-DRG CC	FX HUMERUS SHAFT-CLOSED
81230		MS-DRG MCC	FX HUMERUS NOS-OPEN
81231		MS-DRG MCC	FX HUMERUS SHAFT-OPEN
81240		MS-DRG CC	FX LOWER HUMERUS NOS-CL
81241		MS-DRG CC	SUPRCONDYL FX HUMERUS-CL
81242		MS-DRG CC	FX HUMER, LAT CONDYL-CL
81243		MS-DRG CC	FX HUMER, MED CONDYL-CL
81244		MS-DRG CC	FX HUMER, CONDYL NOS-CL
81249		MS-DRG CC	FX LOWER HUMERUS NEC-CL
81250		MS-DRG MCC	FX LOWER HUMER NOS-OPEN
81251		MS-DRG MCC	SUPRACONDYL FX HUMER-OPN
81252		MS-DRG MCC	FX HUMER, LAT CONDYL-OPN

2008 ICD-9-CM	CMS DRG	MS-DRG	Short Title
81253		MS-DRG MCC	FX HUMER, MED CONDYL-OPN
81254		MS-DRG MCC	FX HUMER, CONDYL NOS-OPN
81259		MS-DRG MCC	FX LOWER HUMER NEC-OPEN
81310		MS-DRG MCC	FX UPPER FOREARM NOS-OPN
81311		MS-DRG MCC	FX OLECRAN PROC ULNA-OPN
81312		MS-DRG MCC	FX CORONOID PRO ULNA-OPN
81313		MS-DRG MCC	MONTEGGIA'S FX-OPEN
81314		MS-DRG MCC	FX UP ULNA NEC/NOS-OPEN
81315		MS-DRG MCC	FX RADIUS HEAD-OPEN
81316		MS-DRG MCC	FX RADIUS NECK-OPEN
81317		MS-DRG MCC	FX UP RADIUS NEC/NOS-OPN
81318		MS-DRG MCC	FX UP RADIUS W ULNA-OPEN
81320		MS-DRG CC	FX SHAFT FOREARM NOS-CL
81321		MS-DRG CC	FX RADIUS SHAFT-CLOSED
81322		MS-DRG CC	FX ULNA SHAFT-CLOSED
81323		MS-DRG CC	FX SHAFT RAD W ULNA-CLOS
81330		MS-DRG MCC	FX SHAFT FOREARM NOS-OPN
81331		MS-DRG MCC	FX RADIUS SHAFT-OPEN
81332		MS-DRG MCC	FX ULNA SHAFT-OPEN
81333		MS-DRG MCC	FX SHAFT RAD W ULNA-OPEN
81340		MS-DRG CC	FX LOWER FOREARM NOS-CL
81341		MS-DRG CC	COLLES' FRACTURE-CLOSED
81342		MS-DRG CC	FX DISTAL RADIUS NEC-CL
81343		MS-DRG CC	FX DISTAL ULNA-CLOSED
81344		MS-DRG CC	FX LOW RADIUS W ULNA-CL
81345		MS-DRG CC	TORUS FX RADIUS-CLOSED
81350		MS-DRG MCC	FX LOWER FOREARM NOS-OPN
81351		MS-DRG MCC	COLLES' FRACTURE-OPEN
81352		MS-DRG MCC	FX DISTAL RADIUS NEC-OPN
81353		MS-DRG MCC	FX DISTAL ULNA-OPEN
81354		MS-DRG MCC	FX LOW RADIUS W ULNA-OPN
81380		MS-DRG CC	FX FOREARM NOS-CLOSED
81382		MS-DRG CC	FRACTURE ULNA NOS-CLOSED
81383		MS-DRG CC	FX RADIUS W ULNA NOS-CL
81390		MS-DRG MCC	FX FOREARM NOS-OPEN
81391		MS-DRG MCC	FRACTURE RADIUS NOS-OPEN
81392		MS-DRG MCC	FRACTURE ULNA NOS-OPEN
81393		MS-DRG MCC	FX RADIUS W ULNA NOS-OPN
81410		MS-DRG CC	FX CARPAL BONE NOS-OPEN

(Continued)

2008 ICD-9-CM	CMS DRG	MS-DRG	Short Title
81411		MS-DRG CC	FX NAVICULAR, WRIST-OPEN
81412		MS-DRG CC	FX LUNATE, WRIST-OPEN
81413		MS-DRG CC	FX TRIQUETRAL, WRIST-OPN
81414		MS-DRG CC	FX PISIFORM-OPEN
81415		MS-DRG CC	FX TRAPEZIUM BONE-OPEN
81416		MS-DRG CC	FX TRAPEZOID BONE-OPEN
81417		MS-DRG CC	FX CAPITATE BONE-OPEN
81418		MS-DRG CC	FX HAMATE BONE-OPEN
81419		MS-DRG CC	FX CARPAL BONE NEC-OPEN
81510		MS-DRG CC	FX METACARPAL NOS-OPEN
81511		MS-DRG CC	FX 1ST METACARPAL BASE-OPN
81512		MS-DRG CC	FX METACARPAL BASE NEC-OPN
81513		MS-DRG CC	FX METACARPAL SHAFT-OPEN
81514		MS-DRG CC	FX METACARPAL NECK-OPEN
81519		MS-DRG CC	MULT FX METACARPUS-OPEN
81610		MS-DRG CC	FX PHALANX, HAND NOS-OPN
81611		MS-DRG CC	FX MID/PRX PHAL, HAND-OP
81612		MS-DRG CC	FX DISTAL PHAL, HAND-OPN
81613		MS-DRG CC	FX MULT PHALAN, HAND-OPN
8171		MS-DRG CC	MULTIPLE FX HAND-OPEN
8181		MS-DRG CC	FX ARM MULT/NOS-OPEN
8190		MS-DRG CC	FX ARMS W RIB/STERNUM-CL
8191		MS-DRG CC	FX ARMS W RIB/STERN-OPEN
82000	CMS CC	MS-DRG MCC	FX FEMUR INTRCAPS NOS-CL
82001	CMS CC	MS-DRG MCC	FX UP FEMUR EPIPHY-CLOS
82002	CMS CC	MS-DRG MCC	FX FEMUR, MIDCERVIC-CLOS
82003	CMS CC	MS-DRG MCC	FX BASE FEMORAL NCK-CLOS
82009	CMS CC	MS-DRG MCC	FX FEMUR INTRCAPS NEC-CL
82010	CMS CC	MS-DRG MCC	FX FEMUR INTRCAP NOS-OPN
82011	CMS CC	MS-DRG MCC	FX UP FEMUR EPIPHY-OPEN
82012	CMS CC	MS-DRG MCC	FX FEMUR, MIDCERVIC-OPEN
82013	CMS CC	MS-DRG MCC	FX BASE FEMORAL NCK-OPEN
82019	CMS CC	MS-DRG MCC	FX FEMUR INTRCAP NEC-OPN
82020	CMS CC	MS-DRG MCC	TROCHANTERIC FX NOS-CLOS
82021	CMS CC	MS-DRG MCC	INTERTROCHANTERIC FX-CL
82022	CMS CC	MS-DRG MCC	SUBTROCHANTERIC FX-CLOSE
82030	CMS CC	MS-DRG MCC	TROCHANTERIC FX NOS-OPEN
82031	CMS CC	MS-DRG MCC	INTERTROCHANTERIC FX-OPN
82032	CMS CC	MS-DRG MCC	SUBTROCHANTERIC FX-OPEN

2008 ICD-9-CM	CMS DRG	MS-DRG	Short Title
8208	CMS CC	MS-DRG MCC	FX NECK OF FEMUR NOS-CL
8209	CMS CC	MS-DRG MCC	FX NECK OF FEMUR NOS-OPN
82100	CMS CC	MS-DRG MCC	FX FEMUR NOS-CLOSED
82101	CMS CC	MS-DRG MCC	FX FEMUR SHAFT-CLOSED
82110	CMS CC	MS-DRG MCC	FX FEMUR NOS-OPEN
82111	CMS CC	MS-DRG MCC	FX FEMUR SHAFT-OPEN
82120		MS-DRG CC	FX LOW END FEMUR NOS-CL
82121		MS-DRG CC	FX FEMORAL CONDYLE-CLOSE
82122		MS-DRG CC	FX LOW FEMUR EPIPHY-CLOS
82123		MS-DRG CC	SUPRACONDYL FX FEMUR-CL
82129		MS-DRG CC	FX LOW END FEMUR NEC-CL
82130		MS-DRG MCC	FX LOW END FEMUR NOS-OPN
82131		MS-DRG MCC	FX FEMORAL CONDYLE-OPEN
82132		MS-DRG MCC	FX LOW FEMUR EPIPHY-OPEN
82133		MS-DRG MCC	SUPRACONDYL FX FEMUR-OPN
82139		MS-DRG MCC	FX LOW END FEMUR NEC-OPN
8220		MS-DRG CC	FRACTURE PATELLA-CLOSED
8221		MS-DRG CC	FRACTURE PATELLA-OPEN
82300		MS-DRG CC	FX UPPER END TIBIA-CLOSE
82302		MS-DRG CC	FX UP TIBIA W FIBULA-CL
82310		MS-DRG MCC	FX UPPER END TIBIA-OPEN
82311		MS-DRG MCC	FX UPPER END FIBULA-OPEN
82312		MS-DRG MCC	FX UP TIBIA W FIBULA-OPN
82320		MS-DRG CC	FX SHAFT TIBIA-CLOSED
82322		MS-DRG CC	FX SHAFT FIB W TIB-CLOS
82330		MS-DRG MCC	FX TIBIA SHAFT-OPEN
82331		MS-DRG MCC	FX FIBULA SHAFT-OPEN
82332		MS-DRG MCC	FX SHAFT TIBIA W FIB-OPN
82340		MS-DRG CC	TORUS FRACTURE OF TIBIA
82342		MS-DRG CC	TORUS FX TIBIA/FIBULA
82380		MS-DRG CC	FX TIBIA NOS-CLOSED
82382		MS-DRG CC	FX TIBIA W FIBULA NOS-CL
82390		MS-DRG MCC	FX TIBIA NOS-OPEN
82391		MS-DRG MCC	FX FIBULA NOS-OPEN
82392		MS-DRG MCC	FX TIBIA W FIB NOS-OPEN
8241		MS-DRG CC	FX MEDIAL MALLEOLUS-OPEN
8243		MS-DRG CC	FX LATERAL MALLEOLUS-OPN
8245		MS-DRG CC	FX BIMALLEOLAR-OPEN
8247		MS-DRG CC	FX TRIMALLEOLAR-OPEN

(Continued)

2008 ICD-9-CM	CMS DRG	MS-DRG	Short Title
8249		MS-DRG CC	FX ANKLE NOS-OPEN
8251		MS-DRG CC	FRACTURE CALCANEUS-OPEN
82530		MS-DRG CC	FX FOOT BONE NOS-OPEN
82531		MS-DRG CC	FX ASTRAGALUS-OPEN
82532		MS-DRG CC	FX NAVICULAR, FOOT-OPEN
82533		MS-DRG CC	FX CUBOID-OPEN
82534		MS-DRG CC	FX CUNEIFORM, FOOT-OPEN
82535		MS-DRG CC	FX METATARSAL-OPEN
82539		MS-DRG CC	FX FOOT BONE NEC-OPEN
8271		MS-DRG CC	FX LOWER LIMB NEC-OPEN
8280		MS-DRG MCC	FX LEGS W ARM/RIB-CLOSED
8281		MS-DRG MCC	FX LEGS W ARM/RIB-OPEN
8301		MS-DRG CC	DISLOCATION JAW-OPEN
83110		MS-DRG CC	DISLOC SHOULDER NOS-OPEN
83111		MS-DRG CC	ANT DISLOC HUMERUS-OPEN
83112		MS-DRG CC	POST DISLOC HUMERUS-OPEN
83113		MS-DRG CC	INFER DISLOC HUMERUS-OPN
83114		MS-DRG CC	DISLOC ACROMIOCLAVIC-OPN
83119		MS-DRG CC	DISLOC SHOULDER NEC-OPEN
83210		MS-DRG CC	DISLOCAT ELBOW NOS-OPEN
83211		MS-DRG CC	ANT DISLOC ELBOW-OPEN
83212		MS-DRG CC	POST DISLOC ELBOW-OPEN
83213		MS-DRG CC	MED DISLOC ELBOW-OPEN
83214		MS-DRG CC	LAT DISLOCAT ELBOW-OPEN
83219		MS-DRG CC	DISLOCAT ELBOW NEC-OPEN
83310		MS-DRG CC	DISLOCAT WRIST NOS-OPEN
83311		MS-DRG CC	DISLOC DIST RADIOULN-OPN
83312		MS-DRG CC	DISLOC RADIOCARPAL-OPEN
83313		MS-DRG CC	DISLOCAT MIDCARPAL-OPEN
83314		MS-DRG CC	DISLOC CARPOMETACARP-OPN
83315		MS-DRG CC	DISLOCAT METACARPAL-OPEN
83319		MS-DRG CC	DISLOCAT WRIST NEC-OPEN
83500		MS-DRG CC	DISLOCAT HIP NOS-CLOSED
83501		MS-DRG CC	POSTERIOR DISLOC HIP-CL
83502		MS-DRG CC	OBTURATOR DISLOC HIP-CL
83503		MS-DRG CC	ANT DISLOC HIP NEC-CLOS
83510		MS-DRG MCC	DISLOCATION HIP NOS-OPEN
83511		MS-DRG MCC	POSTERIOR DISLOC HIP-OPN
83512		MS-DRG MCC	OBTURATOR DISLOC HIP-OPN

2008 ICD-9-CM	CMS DRG	MS-DRG	Short Title
83513		MS-DRG MCC	ANT DISLOC HIP NEC-OPEN
8364		MS-DRG CC	DISLOCATION PATELLA-OPEN
83660		MS-DRG CC	DISLOCAT KNEE NOS-OPEN
83661		MS-DRG CC	ANT DISL PROX TIBIA-OPEN
83662		MS-DRG CC	POST DISL PROX TIBIA-OPN
83663		MS-DRG CC	MED DISL PROX TIBIA-OPEN
83664		MS-DRG CC	LAT DISL PROX TIBIA-OPEN
83669		MS-DRG CC	DISLOCAT KNEE NEC-OPEN
8371		MS-DRG CC	DISLOCATION ANKLE-OPEN
83819	CMS CC		DISLOCAT FOOT NEC-OPEN
83900	CMS CC	MS-DRG CC	DISLOC CERV VERT NOS-CL
83901	CMS CC	MS-DRG CC	DISLOC 1ST CERV VERT-CL
83902	CMS CC	MS-DRG CC	DISLOC 2ND CERV VERT-CL
83903	CMS CC	MS-DRG CC	DISLOC 3RD CERV VERT-CL
83904	CMS CC	MS-DRG CC	DISLOC 4TH CERV VERT-CL
83905	CMS CC	MS-DRG CC	DISLOC 5TH CERV VERT-CL
83906	CMS CC	MS-DRG CC	DISLOC 6TH CERV VERT-CL
83907	CMS CC	MS-DRG CC	DISLOC 7TH CERV VERT-CL
83908	CMS CC	MS-DRG CC	DISLOC MULT CERV VERT-CL
83910	CMS CC	MS-DRG MCC	DISLOC CERV VERT NOS-OPN
83911	CMS CC	MS-DRG MCC	DISLOC 1ST CERV VERT-OPN
83912	CMS CC	MS-DRG MCC	DISLOC 2ND CERV VERT-OPN
83913	CMS CC	MS-DRG MCC	DISLOC 3RD CERV VERT-OPN
83914	CMS CC	MS-DRG MCC	DISLOC 4TH CERV VERT-OPN
83915	CMS CC	MS-DRG MCC	DISLOC 5TH CERV VERT-OPN
83916	CMS CC	MS-DRG MCC	DISLOC 6TH CERV VERT-OPN
83917	CMS CC	MS-DRG MCC	DISLOC 7TH CERV VERT-OPN
83918	CMS CC	MS-DRG MCC	DISLOC MLT CERV VERT-OPN
83930		MS-DRG MCC	DISLOCAT LUMBAR VERT-OPN
83931		MS-DRG MCC	DISLOC THORACIC VERT-OPN
83950		MS-DRG MCC	DISLOC VERTEBRA NOS-OPEN
83951		MS-DRG CC	DISLOCAT COCCYX-OPEN
83952		MS-DRG CC	DISLOCAT SACRUM-OPEN
83959		MS-DRG MCC	DISLOC VERTEBRA NEC-OPEN
83961		MS-DRG CC	DISLOCAT STERNUM-CLOSED
83971		MS-DRG MCC	DISLOCATION STERNUM-OPEN
83979		MS-DRG CC	DISLOCAT SITE NEC-OPEN
8399		MS-DRG CC	DISLOCATION NEC-OPEN
8500	CMS CC		CONCUSSION W/O COMA

(Continued)

2008 ICD-9-CM	CMS DRG	MS-DRG	Short Title
85011	CMS CC	MS-DRG CC	CONCUS-BRIEF COMA < 31 MN
85012	CMS CC	MS-DRG CC	CONCUS-BRF COMA 31-59 MN
8502	CMS CC	MS-DRG CC	CONCUSSION-MODERATE COMA
8503	CMS CC	MS-DRG CC	CONCUSSION-PROLONG COMA
8504	CMS CC	MS-DRG MCC	CONCUSSION-DEEP COMA
8505	CMS CC	MS-DRG CC	CONCUSSION W COMA NOS
8509	CMS CC		CONCUSSION NOS
85100	CMS CC		CEREBRAL CORTX CONTUSION
85101	CMS CC		CORTEX CONTUSION-NO COMA
85102	CMS CC	MS-DRG CC	CORTEX CONTUS-BRIEF COMA
85103	CMS CC	MS-DRG CC	CORTEX CONTUS-MOD COMA
85104	CMS CC	MS-DRG CC	CORTX CONTUS-PROLNG COMA
85105	CMS CC	MS-DRG MCC	CORTEX CONTUS-DEEP COMA
85106	CMS CC	MS-DRG CC	CORTEX CONTUS-COMA NOS
85109	CMS CC		CORTEX CONTUS-CONCUS NOS
85110	CMS CC	MS-DRG MCC	CORTEX CONTUSION/OPN WND
85111	CMS CC	MS-DRG MCC	OPN CORTX CONTUS-NO COMA
85112	CMS CC	MS-DRG MCC	OPN CORT CONTUS-BRF COMA
85113	CMS CC	MS-DRG MCC	OPN CORT CONTUS-MOD COMA
85114	CMS CC	MS-DRG MCC	OPN CORT CONTU-PROL COMA
85115	CMS CC	MS-DRG MCC	OPN CORT CONTU-DEEP COMA
85116	CMS CC	MS-DRG MCC	OPN CORT CONTUS-COMA NOS
85119	CMS CC	MS-DRG MCC	OPN CORTX CONTUS-CONCUSS
85120	CMS CC	MS-DRG MCC	CEREBRAL CORTEX LACERAT
85121	CMS CC	MS-DRG MCC	CORTEX LACERAT W/O COMA
85122	CMS CC	MS-DRG MCC	CORTEX LACERAT-BRIEF COMA
85123	CMS CC	MS-DRG MCC	CORTEX LACERAT-MOD COMA
85124	CMS CC	MS-DRG MCC	CORTEX LACERAT-PROL COMA
85125	CMS CC	MS-DRG MCC	CORTEX LACERAT-DEEP COMA
85126	CMS CC	MS-DRG MCC	CORTEX LACERAT-COMA NOS
85129	CMS CC	MS-DRG MCC	CORTEX LACERAT-CONCUSS
85130	CMS CC	MS-DRG MCC	CORTEX LACERAT W OPN WOUND
85131	CMS CC	MS-DRG MCC	OPN CORTEX LACERAT-NO COMA
85132	CMS CC	MS-DRG MCC	OPN CORTX LACERAT-BRIEF COMA
85133	CMS CC	MS-DRG MCC	OPN CORTX LACERAT-MOD COMA
85134	CMS CC	MS-DRG MCC	OPN CORTX LACERAT-PROLN COMA
85135	CMS CC	MS-DRG MCC	OPN CORTEX LACERAT-DEEP COMA
85136	CMS CC	MS-DRG MCC	OPN CORTX LACERAT-COMA NOS
85139	CMS CC	MS-DRG MCC	OPN CORTX LACERAT-CONCUSS

2008 ICD-9-CM	CMS DRG	MS-DRG	Short Title
85140	CMS CC		CEREBELL/BRAIN STM CONTUS
85141	CMS CC		CEREBELL CONTUS W/O COMA
85142	CMS CC	MS-DRG CC	CEREBELL CONTUS-BRF COMA
85143	CMS CC	MS-DRG CC	CEREBELL CONTUS-MOD COMA
85144	CMS CC	MS-DRG CC	CEREBELL CONTUS-PROL COMA
85145	CMS CC	MS-DRG MCC	CEREBELL CONTUS-DEEP COMA
85146	CMS CC	MS-DRG CC	CEREBELL CONTUS-COMA NOS
85149	CMS CC		CEREBELL CONTUS-CONCUSS
85150	CMS CC	MS-DRG MCC	CEREBELL CONTUS W OPN WND
85151	CMS CC	MS-DRG MCC	OPN CEREBELL CONT W/O COMA
85152	CMS CC	MS-DRG MCC	OPN CEREBELL CONT-BRF COMA
85153	CMS CC	MS-DRG MCC	OPN CEREBELL CONT-MOD COMA
85154	CMS CC	MS-DRG MCC	OPN CEREBELL CONT-PROL COM
85155	CMS CC	MS-DRG MCC	OPN CEREBELL CONT-DEEP COM
85156	CMS CC	MS-DRG MCC	OPN CEREBELL CONT-COMA NOS
85159	CMS CC	MS-DRG MCC	OPN CEREBELL CONT-CONCUSS
85160	CMS CC	MS-DRG MCC	CEREBELL/BRAIN STEM LACERAT
85161	CMS CC	MS-DRG MCC	CEREBELL LACERAT W/O COMA
85162	CMS CC	MS-DRG MCC	CEREBELL LACERAT-BRIEF COMA
85163	CMS CC	MS-DRG MCC	CEREBELL LACERAT-MOD COMA
85164	CMS CC	MS-DRG MCC	CEREBELL LACERAT-PROLN COMA
85165	CMS CC	MS-DRG MCC	CEREBELL LACERAT-DEEP COMA
85166	CMS CC	MS-DRG MCC	CEREBELL LACERAT-COMA NOS
85169	CMS CC	MS-DRG MCC	CEREBELL LACERAT-CONCUSSION
85170	CMS CC	MS-DRG MCC	CEREBELL LACERAT W OPEN WND
85171	CMS CC	MS-DRG MCC	OPN CEREBELL LACERAT W/O COMA
85172	CMS CC	MS-DRG MCC	OPN CEREBELL LACERAT-BRF COMA
85173	CMS CC	MS-DRG MCC	OPN CEREBELL LACERAT-MOD COMA
85174	CMS CC	MS-DRG MCC	OPN CEREBELL LACERAT-PROL COMA
85175	CMS CC	MS-DRG MCC	OPN CEREBELL LACERAT-DEEP COMA
85176	CMS CC	MS-DRG MCC	OPN CEREBELL LACERAT-COMA NOS
85179	CMS CC	MS-DRG MCC	OPN CEREBELL LACERAT-CONCUSS
85180	CMS CC	MS-DRG MCC	BRAIN LACERAT NEC
85181	CMS CC	MS-DRG MCC	BRAIN LACERAT NEC W/O COMA
85182	CMS CC	MS-DRG MCC	BRAIN LACERAT NEC-BRIEF COMA
85183	CMS CC	MS-DRG MCC	BRAIN LACERAT NEC-MOD COMA
85184	CMS CC	MS-DRG MCC	BRAIN LACERAT NEC-PROLN COMA
85185	CMS CC	MS-DRG MCC	BRAIN LACERAT NEC-DEEP COMA
85186	CMS CC	MS-DRG MCC	BRAIN LACERAT NEC-COMA NOS

(Continued)

2008 ICD-9-CM	CMS DRG	MS-DRG	Short Title
85189	CMS CC	MS-DRG MCC	BRAIN LACER NEC-CONCUSS
85190	CMS CC	MS-DRG MCC	BRAIN LAC NEC W OPEN WND
85191	CMS CC	MS-DRG MCC	OPN BRAIN LACER W/O COMA
85192	CMS CC	MS-DRG MCC	OPN BRAIN LAC-BRIEF COMA
85193	CMS CC	MS-DRG MCC	OPN BRAIN LACER-MOD COMA
85194	CMS CC	MS-DRG MCC	OPN BRAIN LAC-PROLN COMA
85195	CMS CC	MS-DRG MCC	OPEN BRAIN LAC-DEEP COMA
85196	CMS CC	MS-DRG MCC	OPN BRAIN LACER-COMA NOS
85199	CMS CC	MS-DRG MCC	OPEN BRAIN LACER-CONCUSS
85200	CMS CC	MS-DRG MCC	TRAUM SUBARACHNOID HEM
85201	CMS CC	MS-DRG MCC	SUBARACHNOID HEM-NO COMA
85202	CMS CC	MS-DRG MCC	SUBARACHNOID HEM-BRIEF COMA
85203	CMS CC	MS-DRG MCC	SUBARACHNOID HEM-MOD COMA
85204	CMS CC	MS-DRG MCC	SUBARACHNOID HEM-PROLNG COMA
85205	CMS CC	MS-DRG MCC	SUBARACHNOID HEM-DEEP COMA
85206	CMS CC	MS-DRG MCC	SUBARACHNOID HEM-COMA NOS
85209	CMS CC	MS-DRG MCC	SUBARACHNOID HEM-CONCUSSION
85210	CMS CC	MS-DRG MCC	SUBARACHNOID HEM W OPN WOUND
85211	CMS CC	MS-DRG MCC	OPN SUBARACHNOID HEM-NO COMA
85212	CMS CC	MS-DRG MCC	OP SUBARACHNOID HEM-BRF COMA
85213	CMS CC	MS-DRG MCC	OP SUBARACHNOID HEM-MOD COMA
85214	CMS CC	MS-DRG MCC	OP SUBARACHNOID HEM-PROL COM
85215	CMS CC	MS-DRG MCC	OP SUBARACHNOID HEM-DEEP COM
85216	CMS CC	MS-DRG MCC	OP SUBARACHNOID HEM-COMA NOS
85219	CMS CC	MS-DRG MCC	OPN SUBARACHNOID HEM-CONCUSS
85220	CMS CC	MS-DRG MCC	TRAUMATIC SUBDURAL HEM
85221	CMS CC	MS-DRG MCC	SUBDURAL HEM W/O COMA
85222	CMS CC	MS-DRG MCC	SUBDURAL HEM-BRIEF COMA
85223	CMS CC	MS-DRG MCC	SUBDURAL HEMORR-MOD COMA
85224	CMS CC	MS-DRG MCC	SUBDURAL HEM-PROLNG COMA
85225	CMS CC	MS-DRG MCC	SUBDURAL HEM-DEEP COMA
85226	CMS CC	MS-DRG MCC	SUBDURAL HEMORR-COMA NOS
85229	CMS CC	MS-DRG MCC	SUBDURAL HEM-CONCUSSION
85230	CMS CC	MS-DRG MCC	SUBDURAL HEM W OPN WOUND
85231	CMS CC	MS-DRG MCC	OPEN SUBDURAL HEM W/O COMA
85232	CMS CC	MS-DRG MCC	OPN SUBDURAL HEM-BRF COMA
85233	CMS CC	MS-DRG MCC	OPN SUBDURAL HEM-MOD COMA
85234	CMS CC	MS-DRG MCC	OPN SUBDURAL HEM-PROL COMA
85235	CMS CC	MS-DRG MCC	OPN SUBDURAL HEM-DEEP COMA

2008 ICD-9-CM	CMS DRG	MS-DRG	Short Title
85236	CMS CC	MS-DRG MCC	OPN SUBDURAL HEM-COMA NOS
85239	CMS CC	MS-DRG MCC	OPN SUBDURAL HEM-CONCUSS
85240	CMS CC	MS-DRG MCC	TRAUMATIC EXTRADURAL HEM
85241	CMS CC	MS-DRG MCC	EXTRADURAL HEM W/O COMA
85242	CMS CC	MS-DRG MCC	EXTRADUR HEM-BRIEF COMA
85243	CMS CC	MS-DRG MCC	EXTRADURAL HEM-MOD COMA
85244	CMS CC	MS-DRG MCC	EXTRADUR HEM-PROLN COMA
85245	CMS CC	MS-DRG MCC	EXTRADURAL HEM-DEEP COMA
85246	CMS CC	MS-DRG MCC	EXTRADURAL HEM-COMA NOS
85249	CMS CC	MS-DRG MCC	EXTADURAL HEM-CONCUSS
85250	CMS CC	MS-DRG MCC	EXTRADURAL HEM W OPN WND
85251	CMS CC	MS-DRG MCC	EXTRADURAL HEMOR-NO COMA
85252	CMS CC	MS-DRG MCC	EXTRADUR HEM-BRIEF COMA
85253	CMS CC	MS-DRG MCC	EXTRADURAL HEM-MOD COMA
85254	CMS CC	MS-DRG MCC	EXTRADUR HEM-PROLN COMA
85255	CMS CC	MS-DRG MCC	EXTRADUR HEM-DEEP COMA
85256	CMS CC	MS-DRG MCC	EXTRADURAL HEM-COMA NOS
85259	CMS CC	MS-DRG MCC	EXTRADURAL HEM-CONCUSS
85300	CMS CC	MS-DRG MCC	TRAUMATIC BRAIN HEM NEC
85301	CMS CC	MS-DRG MCC	BRAIN HEM NEC W/O COMA
85302	CMS CC	MS-DRG MCC	BRAIN HEM NEC-BRIEF COMA
85303	CMS CC	MS-DRG MCC	BRAIN HEM NEC-MOD COMA
85304	CMS CC	MS-DRG MCC	BRAIN HEM NEC-PROLN COMA
85305	CMS CC	MS-DRG MCC	BRAIN HEM NEC-DEEP COMA
85306	CMS CC	MS-DRG MCC	BRAIN HEM NEC-COMA NOS
85309	CMS CC	MS-DRG MCC	BRAIN HEM NEC-CONCUSSION
85310	CMS CC	MS-DRG MCC	BRAIN HEM NEC W OPN WND
85311	CMS CC	MS-DRG MCC	BRAIN HEM OPN W/O COMA
85312	CMS CC	MS-DRG MCC	BRAIN HEM OPN-BRF COMA
85313	CMS CC	MS-DRG MCC	BRAIN HEM OPEN-MOD COMA
85314	CMS CC	MS-DRG MCC	BRAIN HEM OPN-PROLN COMA
85315	CMS CC	MS-DRG MCC	BRAIN HEM OPEN-DEEP COMA
85316	CMS CC	MS-DRG MCC	BRAIN HEM OPEN-COMA NOS
85319	CMS CC	MS-DRG MCC	BRAIN HEM OPN-CONCUSSION
85400	CMS CC		BRAIN INJURY NEC
85401	CMS CC		BRAIN INJURY NEC-NO COMA
85402	CMS CC	MS-DRG CC	BRAIN INJ NEC-BRIEF COMA
85403	CMS CC	MS-DRG CC	BRAIN INJ NEC-MOD COMA
85404	CMS CC	MS-DRG CC	BRAIN INJ NEC-PROLN COMA

2008 ICD-9-CM	CMS DRG	MS-DRG	Short Title
85405	CMS CC	MS-DRG MCC	BRAIN INJ NEC-DEEP COMA
85406	CMS CC	MS-DRG CC	BRAIN INJ NEC-COMA NOS
85409	CMS CC		BRAIN INJ NEC-CONCUSSION
85410	CMS CC	MS-DRG MCC	BRAIN INJURY W OPN WND
85411	CMS CC	MS-DRG MCC	OPN BRAIN INJ W/O COMA
85412	CMS CC	MS-DRG MCC	OPN BRAIN INJ-BRIEF COMA
85413	CMS CC	MS-DRG MCC	OPN BRAIN INJ-MOD COMA
85414	CMS CC	MS-DRG MCC	OPN BRAIN INJ-PROLN COMA
85415	CMS CC	MS-DRG MCC	OPN BRAIN INJ-DEEP COMA
85416	CMS CC	MS-DRG MCC	OPEN BRAIN INJ-COMA NOS
85419	CMS CC	MS-DRG MCC	OPN BRAIN INJ-CONCUSSION
8600	CMS CC	MS-DRG CC	TRAUM PNEUMOTHORAX-CLOSE
8601	CMS CC	MS-DRG MCC	TRAUM PNEUMOTHORAX-OPEN
8602	CMS CC	MS-DRG MCC	TRAUM HEMOTHORAX-CLOSED
8603	CMS CC	MS-DRG MCC	TRAUM HEMOTHORAX-OPEN
8604	CMS CC	MS-DRG MCC	TRAUM PNEUMOHEMOTHOR-CL
8605	CMS CC	MS-DRG MCC	TRAUM PNEUMOHEMOTHOR-OPN
86100		MS-DRG CC	HEART INJURY NOS-CLOSED
86101	CMS CC	MS-DRG CC	HEART CONTUSION-CLOSED
86102	CMS CC	MS-DRG MCC	HEART LACERATION-CLOSED
86103	CMS CC	MS-DRG MCC	HEART CHAMBER LACERAT-CL
86110	CMS CC	MS-DRG MCC	HEART INJURY NOS-OPEN
86111	CMS CC	MS-DRG MCC	HEART CONTUSION-OPEN
86112	CMS CC	MS-DRG MCC	HEART LACERATION-OPEN
86113	CMS CC	MS-DRG MCC	HEART CHAMBER LACER-OPN
86120		MS-DRG CC	LUNG INJURY NOS-CLOSED
86121		MS-DRG CC	LUNG CONTUSION-CLOSED
86122	CMS CC	MS-DRG MCC	LUNG LACERATION-CLOSED
86130	CMS CC	MS-DRG MCC	LUNG INJURY NOS-OPEN
86131	CMS CC	MS-DRG MCC	LUNG CONTUSION-OPEN
86132	CMS CC	MS-DRG MCC	LUNG LACERATION-OPEN
8620		MS-DRG CC	DIAPHRAGM INJURY-CLOSED
8621	CMS CC	MS-DRG MCC	DIAPHRAGM INJURY-OPEN
86221	CMS CC	MS-DRG MCC	BRONCHUS INJURY-CLOSED
86222	CMS CC	MS-DRG MCC	ESOPHAGUS INJURY-CLOSED
86229	CMS CC	MS-DRG CC	INTRATHORACIC INJ NEC-CL
86231	CMS CC	MS-DRG MCC	BRONCHUS INJURY-OPEN
86232	CMS CC	MS-DRG MCC	ESOPHAGUS INJURY-OPEN
86239	CMS CC	MS-DRG MCC	INTRATHORAC INJ NEC-OPEN

2008 ICD-9-CM	CMS DRG	MS-DRG	Short Title
8628		MS-DRG CC	INTRATHORACIC INJ NOS-CL
8629	CMS CC	MS-DRG MCC	INTRATHORACIC INJ NOS-OPEN
8630		MS-DRG CC	STOMACH INJURY-CLOSED
8631	CMS CC	MS-DRG MCC	STOMACH INJURY-OPEN
86320		MS-DRG CC	SMALL INTEST INJ NOS-CL
86321		MS-DRG CC	DUODENUM INJURY-CLOSED
86329		MS-DRG CC	SMALL INTEST INJ NEC-CL
86330	CMS CC	MS-DRG MCC	SMALL INTEST INJ NOS-OPN
86331	CMS CC	MS-DRG MCC	DUODENUM INJURY-OPEN
86339	CMS CC	MS-DRG MCC	SMALL INTEST INJ NEC-OPN
86340		MS-DRG CC	COLON INJURY NOS-CLOSED
86341		MS-DRG CC	ASCENDING COLON INJ-CLOS
86342		MS-DRG CC	TRANSVERSE COLON INJ-CL
86343		MS-DRG CC	DESCENDING COLON INJ-CL
86344		MS-DRG CC	SIGMOID COLON INJ-CLOSED
86345		MS-DRG CC	RECTUM INJURY-CLOSED
86346		MS-DRG CC	COLON INJ MULT SITE-CLOS
86349		MS-DRG CC	COLON INJURY NEC-CLOSED
86350	CMS CC	MS-DRG MCC	COLON INJURY NOS-OPEN
86351	CMS CC	MS-DRG MCC	ASCENDING COLON INJ-OPEN
86352	CMS CC	MS-DRG MCC	TRANSVERSE COLON INJ-OPN
86353	CMS CC	MS-DRG MCC	DESCENDING COLON INJ-OPN
86354	CMS CC	MS-DRG MCC	SIGMOID COLON INJ-OPEN
86355	CMS CC	MS-DRG MCC	RECTUM INJURY-OPEN
86356	CMS CC	MS-DRG MCC	COLON INJ MULT SITE-OPEN
86359	CMS CC	MS-DRG MCC	COLON INJURY NEC-OPEN
86380		MS-DRG CC	GI INJURY NOS-CLOSED
86381		MS-DRG CC	PANCREAS, HEAD INJ-CLOSE
86382		MS-DRG CC	PANCREAS, BODY INJ-CLOSE
86383		MS-DRG CC	PANCREAS, TAIL INJ-CLOSE
86384		MS-DRG CC	PANCREAS INJURY NOS-CLOS
86385		MS-DRG CC	APPENDIX INJURY-CLOSED
86389		MS-DRG CC	GI INJURY NEC-CLOSED
86390	CMS CC	MS-DRG MCC	GI INJURY NOS-OPEN
86391	CMS CC	MS-DRG MCC	PANCREAS, HEAD INJ-OPEN
86392	CMS CC	MS-DRG MCC	PANCREAS, BODY INJ-OPEN
86393	CMS CC	MS-DRG MCC	PANCREAS, TAIL INJ-OPEN
86394	CMS CC	MS-DRG MCC	PANCREAS INJURY NOS-OPEN
86395	CMS CC	MS-DRG MCC	APPENDIX INJURY-OPEN

(Continued)

2008 ICD-9-CM	CMS DRG	MS-DRG	Short Title
86399	CMS CC	MS-DRG MCC	GI INJURY NEC-OPEN
86400	CMS CC	MS-DRG CC	LIVER INJURY NOS-CLOSED
86401	CMS CC	MS-DRG CC	LIVER HEMATOMA/CONTUSION
86402	CMS CC	MS-DRG CC	LIVER LACERATION, MINOR
86403	CMS CC	MS-DRG MCC	LIVER LACERATION, MOD
86404	CMS CC	MS-DRG MCC	LIVER LACERATION, MAJOR
86405	CMS CC	MS-DRG CC	LIVER LACERAT UNSPCF CLS
86409	CMS CC	MS-DRG CC	LIVER INJURY NEC-CLOSED
86410	CMS CC	MS-DRG MCC	LIVER INJURY NOS-OPEN
86411	CMS CC	MS-DRG MCC	LIVER HEMATOM/CONTUS-OPN
86412	CMS CC	MS-DRG MCC	LIVER LACERAT, MINOR-OPN
86413	CMS CC	MS-DRG MCC	LIVER LACERAT, MOD-OPEN
86414	CMS CC	MS-DRG MCC	LIVER LACERAT, MAJOR-OPN
86415	CMS CC	MS-DRG MCC	LIVER LACERAT UNSPCF OPN
86419	CMS CC	MS-DRG MCC	LIVER INJURY NEC-OPEN
86500	CMS CC	MS-DRG CC	SPLEEN INJURY NOS-CLOSED
86501	CMS CC	MS-DRG CC	SPLEEN HEMATOMA-CLOSED
86502	CMS CC	MS-DRG CC	SPLEEN CAPSULAR TEAR
86503	CMS CC	MS-DRG MCC	SPLEEN PARENCHYMA LACER
86504	CMS CC	MS-DRG MCC	SPLEEN DISRUPTION-CLOS
86509	CMS CC	MS-DRG CC	SPLEEN INJURY NEC-CLOSED
86510	CMS CC	MS-DRG MCC	SPLEEN INJURY NOS-OPEN
86511	CMS CC	MS-DRG MCC	SPLEEN HEMATOMA-OPEN
86512	CMS CC	MS-DRG MCC	SPLEEN CAPSULAR TEAR-OPN
86513	CMS CC	MS-DRG MCC	SPLEEN PARNCHYM LAC-OPN
86514	CMS CC	MS-DRG MCC	SPLEEN DISRUPTION-OPEN
86519	CMS CC	MS-DRG MCC	SPLEEN INJURY NEC-OPEN
86600	CMS CC	MS-DRG CC	KIDNEY INJURY NOS-CLOSED
86601	CMS CC	MS-DRG CC	KIDNEY HEMATOMA-CLOSED
86602	CMS CC	MS-DRG CC	KIDNEY LACERATION-CLOSED
86603	CMS CC	MS-DRG MCC	KIDNEY DISRUPTION-CLOSED
86610	CMS CC	MS-DRG MCC	KIDNEY INJURY NOS-OPEN
86611	CMS CC	MS-DRG MCC	KIDNEY HEMATOMA-OPEN
86612	CMS CC	MS-DRG MCC	KIDNEY LACERATION-OPEN
86613	CMS CC	MS-DRG MCC	KIDNEY DISRUPTION-OPEN
8670	CMS CC	MS-DRG CC	BLADDER/URETHRA INJ-CLOS
8671	CMS CC	MS-DRG MCC	BLADDER/URETHRA INJ-OPEN
8672	CMS CC	MS-DRG CC	URETER INJURY-CLOSED
8673	CMS CC	MS-DRG MCC	URETER INJURY-OPEN

2008 ICD-9-CM	CMS DRG	MS-DRG	Short Title
8674	CMS CC	MS-DRG CC	UTERUS INJURY-CLOSED
8675	CMS CC	MS-DRG MCC	UTERUS INJURY-OPEN
8676	CMS CC	MS-DRG CC	PELVIC ORGAN INJ NEC-CL
8677	CMS CC	MS-DRG MCC	PELVIC ORGAN INJ NEC-OPN
8678	CMS CC	MS-DRG CC	PELVIC ORGAN INJ NOS-CL
8679	CMS CC	MS-DRG MCC	PELVIC ORGAN INJ NOS-OPN
86800	CMS CC	MS-DRG CC	INTRA-ABDOM INJ NOS-CLOS
86801	CMS CC	MS-DRG CC	ADRENAL GLAND INJURY-CL
86802	CMS CC	MS-DRG CC	BILIARY TRACT INJURY-CL
86803	CMS CC	MS-DRG CC	PERITONEUM INJURY-CLOSED
86804	CMS CC	MS-DRG CC	RETROPERITONEUM INJ-CL
86809	CMS CC	MS-DRG CC	INTRA-ABDOM INJ NEC-CLOS
86810	CMS CC	MS-DRG MCC	INTRA-ABDOM INJ NOS-OPEN
86811	CMS CC	MS-DRG MCC	ADRENAL GLAND INJURY-OPN
86812	CMS CC	MS-DRG MCC	BILIARY TRACT INJURY-OPN
86813	CMS CC	MS-DRG MCC	PERITONEUM INJURY-OPEN
86814	CMS CC	MS-DRG MCC	RETROPERITONEUM INJ-OPEN
86819	CMS CC	MS-DRG MCC	INTRA-ABDOM INJ NEC-OPEN
8690	CMS CC	MS-DRG CC	INTERNAL INJ NOS-CLOSED
8691	CMS CC	MS-DRG MCC	INTERNAL INJURY NOS-OPEN
8702		MS-DRG CC	LAC EYELID INV LACRM PAS
8703	CMS CC	MS-DRG CC	PENETR WND ORBIT W/O FB
8704	CMS CC	MS-DRG CC	PENETRAT WND ORBIT W FB
8708	CMS CC	MS-DRG CC	OPN WND OCULAR ADNEX NEC
8709	CMS CC	MS-DRG CC	OPN WND OCULAR ADNEX NOS
8710	CMS CC	MS-DRG CC	OCULAR LAC W/O PROLAPSE
8711	CMS CC	MS-DRG CC	OCULAR LACERA W PROLAPSE
8712	CMS CC	MS-DRG CC	RUPTURE EYE W TISSU LOSS
8713	CMS CC	MS-DRG CC	AVULSION OF EYE
8714	CMS CC		LACERATION OF EYE NOS
8715		MS-DRG CC	PENETRAT MAGNET FB EYE
8716		MS-DRG CC	PENETRAT FB NEC EYE
8719	CMS CC	MS-DRG CC	OPEN WOUND OF EYEBALL NOS
87212		MS-DRG CC	OPEN WND AUD CANAL-COMPL
87261		MS-DRG CC	OPEN WOUND OF EAR DRUM
87262		MS-DRG CC	OPEN WOUND OF OSSICLES
87263		MS-DRG CC	OPEN WND EUSTACHIAN TUBE
87264		MS-DRG CC	OPEN WOUND OF COCHLEA
87269		MS-DRG CC	OPEN WOUND OF EAR NEC

(Continued)

2008 ICD-9-CM	CMS DRG	MS-DRG	Short Title
87271		MS-DRG CC	OPEN WND EAR DRUM-COMPL
87272	CMS CC	MS-DRG CC	OPEN WND OSSICLES-COMPL
87273	CMS CC	MS-DRG CC	OPN WND EUSTACH TB-COMPL
87274	CMS CC	MS-DRG CC	OPEN WOUND COCHLEA-COMPL
87279		MS-DRG CC	OPEN WOUND EAR NEC-COMPL
87323		MS-DRG CC	OPEN WOUND NASAL SINUS
87333	CMS CC	MS-DRG CC	OPEN WND NAS SINUS-COMPL
8739	CMS CC		OPEN WND HEAD NEC-COMPL
87400	CMS CC	MS-DRG MCC	OPN WND LARYNX W TRACHEA
87401	CMS CC	MS-DRG MCC	OPEN WOUND OF LARYNX
87402	CMS CC	MS-DRG MCC	OPEN WOUND OF TRACHEA
87410	CMS CC	MS-DRG MCC	OPN WND LARY W TRAC-COMP
87411	CMS CC	MS-DRG MCC	OPEN WOUND LARYNX-COMPL
87412	CMS CC	MS-DRG MCC	OPEN WOUND TRACHEA-COMPL
8742		MS-DRG CC	OPEN WOUND THYROID GLAND
8743	CMS CC	MS-DRG CC	OPEN WOUND THYROID-COMPL
8744		MS-DRG CC	OPEN WOUND OF PHARYNX
8745	CMS CC	MS-DRG CC	OPEN WOUND PHARYNX-COMPL
8750	CMS CC	MS-DRG CC	OPEN WOUND OF CHEST
8751	CMS CC	MS-DRG CC	OPEN WOUND CHEST-COMPL
88020		MS-DRG CC	OPN WND SHOULDR W TENDON
88021		MS-DRG CC	OPN WND SCAPULA W TENDON
88022		MS-DRG CC	OPEN WND AXILLA W TENDON
88023		MS-DRG CC	OPEN WND UP ARM W TENDON
88029		MS-DRG CC	MLT OPN WND SHLDR W TEND
88120		MS-DRG CC	OPEN WND FOREARM W TENDN
88121		MS-DRG CC	OPN WOUND ELBOW W TENDON
88122		MS-DRG CC	OPN WOUND WRIST W TENDON
8822		MS-DRG CC	OPEN WOUND HAND W TENDON
8832		MS-DRG CC	OPEN WND FINGER W TENDON
8842		MS-DRG CC	OPN WND ARM NOS W TENDON
8870	CMS CC	MS-DRG CC	AMPUT BELOW ELB, UNILAT
8871	CMS CC	MS-DRG CC	AMP BELOW ELB, UNIL-COMP
8872	CMS CC	MS-DRG CC	AMPUT ABV ELBOW, UNILAT
8873	CMS CC	MS-DRG CC	AMPUT ABV ELB, UNIL-COMP
8874	CMS CC	MS-DRG CC	AMPUTAT ARM, UNILAT NOS
8875	CMS CC	MS-DRG CC	AMPUT ARM, UNIL NOS-COMP
8876	CMS CC	MS-DRG MCC	AMPUTATION ARM, BILAT
8877	CMS CC	MS-DRG MCC	AMPUTAT ARM, BILAT-COMPL

2008 ICD-9-CM	CMS DRG	MS-DRG	Short Title
8902		MS-DRG CC	OPN WND HIP/THIGH W TEND
8912		MS-DRG CC	OPN WND KNEE/LEG W TENDN
8922		MS-DRG CC	OPEN WOUND FOOT W TENDON
8932		MS-DRG CC	OPEN WOUND TOE W TENDON
8942		MS-DRG CC	OPN WND LEG NEC W TENDON
8960	CMS CC	MS-DRG CC	AMPUTATION FOOT, UNILAT
8961	CMS CC	MS-DRG CC	AMPUT FOOT, UNILAT-COMPL
8962	CMS CC	MS-DRG MCC	AMPUTATION FOOT, BILAT
8963	CMS CC	MS-DRG MCC	AMPUTAT FOOT, BILAT-COMP
8970	CMS CC	MS-DRG CC	AMPUT BELOW KNEE, UNILAT
8971	CMS CC	MS-DRG CC	AMPUTAT BK, UNILAT-COMPL
8972	CMS CC	MS-DRG CC	AMPUT ABOVE KNEE, UNILAT
8973	CMS CC	MS-DRG CC	AMPUT ABV KN, UNIL-COMPL
8974	CMS CC	MS-DRG CC	AMPUTAT LEG, UNILAT NOS
8975	CMS CC	MS-DRG CC	AMPUT LEG, UNIL NOS-COMP
8976	CMS CC	MS-DRG MCC	AMPUTATION LEG, BILAT
8977	CMS CC	MS-DRG MCC	AMPUTAT LEG, BILAT-COMPL
90000	CMS CC	MS-DRG CC	INJURY CAROTID ARTERY NOS
90001	CMS CC	MS-DRG CC	INJ COMMON CAROTID ARTER
90002	CMS CC	MS-DRG CC	INJ EXTERNAL CAROTID ART
90003	CMS CC	MS-DRG CC	INJ INTERNAL CAROTID ART
9001	CMS CC	MS-DRG CC	INJ INTERNL JUGULAR VEIN
90081	CMS CC	MS-DRG CC	INJ EXTERN JUGULAR VEIN
90082	CMS CC	MS-DRG CC	INJ MLT HEAD/NECK VESSEL
90089	CMS CC	MS-DRG CC	INJ HEAD/NECK VESSEL NEC
9009	CMS CC	MS-DRG CC	INJ HEAD/NECK VESSEL NOS
9010	CMS CC	MS-DRG MCC	INJURY THORACIC AORTA
9011	CMS CC	MS-DRG MCC	INJ INNOMIN/SUBCLAV ART
9012	CMS CC	MS-DRG MCC	INJ SUPERIOR VENA CAVA
9013	CMS CC	MS-DRG MCC	INJ INNOMIN/SUBCLAV VEIN
90140		MS-DRG MCC	INJ PULMONARY VESSEL NOS
90141	CMS CC	MS-DRG MCC	INJURY PULMONARY ARTERY
90142	CMS CC	MS-DRG MCC	INJURY PULMONARY VEIN
90181		MS-DRG CC	INJ INTERCOSTAL ART/VEIN
90182		MS-DRG CC	INJ INT MAMMARY ART/VEIN
90183	CMS CC	MS-DRG MCC	INJ MULT THORACIC VESSEL
90189		MS-DRG CC	INJ THORACIC VESSEL NEC
9019		MS-DRG CC	INJ THORACIC VESSEL NOS
9020	CMS CC	MS-DRG MCC	INJURY ABDOMINAL AORTA

(Continued)

2008 ICD-9-CM	CMS DRG	MS-DRG	Short Title
90210	CMS CC	MS-DRG MCC	INJ INFER VENA CAVA NOS
90211	CMS CC	MS-DRG MCC	INJURY HEPATIC VEINS
90219	CMS CC	MS-DRG MCC	INJ INFER VENA CAVA NEC
90220	CMS CC	MS-DRG MCC	INJ CELIAC/MESEN ART NOS
90221		MS-DRG MCC	INJURY GASTRIC ARTERY
90222	CMS CC	MS-DRG MCC	INJURY HEPATIC ARTERY
90223	CMS CC	MS-DRG MCC	INJURY SPLENIC ARTERY
90224	CMS CC	MS-DRG MCC	INJURY CELIAC AXIS NEC
90225	CMS CC	MS-DRG MCC	INJ SUPER MESENTERIC ART
90226	CMS CC	MS-DRG MCC	INJ BRNCH SUP MESENT ART
90227	CMS CC	MS-DRG MCC	INJ INFER MESENTERIC ART
90229	CMS CC	MS-DRG MCC	INJ MESENTERIC VESS NEC
90231	CMS CC	MS-DRG MCC	INJ SUPERIOR MESENT VEIN
90232	CMS CC	MS-DRG MCC	INJ INFERIOR MESENT VEIN
90233	CMS CC	MS-DRG MCC	INJURY PORTAL VEIN
90234	CMS CC	MS-DRG MCC	INJURY SPLENIC VEIN
90239	CMS CC	MS-DRG MCC	INJ PORT/SPLEN VESS NEC
90240	CMS CC	MS-DRG MCC	INJURY RENAL VESSEL NOS
90241	CMS CC	MS-DRG MCC	INJURY RENAL ARTERY
90242	CMS CC	MS-DRG MCC	INJURY RENAL VEIN
90249	CMS CC	MS-DRG MCC	INJURY RENAL VESSEL NEC
90250	CMS CC	MS-DRG MCC	INJURY ILIAC VESSEL NOS
90251	CMS CC	MS-DRG MCC	INJ HYPOGASTRIC ARTERY
90252	CMS CC	MS-DRG MCC	INJURY HYPOGASTRIC VEIN
90253	CMS CC	MS-DRG MCC	INJURY ILIAC ARTERY
90254	CMS CC	MS-DRG MCC	INJURY ILIAC VEIN
90255		MS-DRG CC	INJURY UTERINE ARTERY
90256		MS-DRG CC	INJURY UTERINE VEIN
90259	CMS CC	MS-DRG MCC	INJURY ILIAC VESSEL NEC
90281		MS-DRG CC	INJURY OVARIAN ARTERY
90282		MS-DRG CC	INJURY OVARIAN VEIN
90287	CMS CC	MS-DRG MCC	INJ MULT ABD/PELV VESSEL
90289		MS-DRG CC	INJ ABDOMINAL VESSEL NEC
9029		MS-DRG CC	INJ ABDOMINAL VESSEL NOS
90300		MS-DRG MCC	INJ AXILLARY VESSEL NOS
90301		MS-DRG MCC	INJURY AXILLARY ARTERY
90302		MS-DRG MCC	INJURY AXILLARY VEIN
9031		MS-DRG CC	INJURY BRACHIAL VESSELS
9032		MS-DRG CC	INJURY RADIAL VESSELS

2008 ICD-9-CM	CMS DRG	MS-DRG	Short Title
9033		MS-DRG CC	INJURY ULNAR VESSELS
9034		MS-DRG CC	INJURY PALMAR ARTERY
9035		MS-DRG CC	INJURY FINGER VESSELS
9038		MS-DRG CC	INJURY ARM VESSELS NEC
9039		MS-DRG CC	INJURY ARM VESSEL NOS
9040	CMS CC	MS-DRG MCC	INJ COMMON FEMORAL ARTER
9041		MS-DRG MCC	INJ SUPERFIC FEMORAL ART
9042		MS-DRG MCC	INJURY FEMORAL VEIN
9043		MS-DRG CC	INJURY SAPHENOUS VEIN
90440		MS-DRG MCC	INJ POPLITEAL VESSEL NOS
90441		MS-DRG MCC	INJURY POPLITEAL ARTERY
90442		MS-DRG MCC	INJURY POPLITEAL VEIN
90450		MS-DRG CC	INJURY TIBIAL VESSEL NOS
90451		MS-DRG CC	INJ ANTER TIBIAL ARTERY
90452		MS-DRG CC	INJ ANTERIOR TIBIAL VEIN
90453		MS-DRG CC	INJ POST TIBIAL ARTERY
90454		MS-DRG CC	INJ POST TIBIAL VEIN
9046		MS-DRG CC	INJ DEEP PLANTAR VESSEL
9047		MS-DRG CC	INJURY LEG VESSELS NEC
9048		MS-DRG CC	INJURY LEG VESSEL NOS
9049		MS-DRG CC	BLOOD VESSEL INJURY NOS
9251	CMS CC	MS-DRG CC	CRUSH INJ FACE SCALP
9252	CMS CC	MS-DRG CC	CRUSH INJ NECK
92800		MS-DRG CC	CRUSHING INJURY THIGH
92801		MS-DRG CC	CRUSHING INJURY HIP
9290	CMS CC		CRUSH INJ MULT SITE NEC
9340		MS-DRG CC	FOREIGN BODY IN TRACHEA
9341		MS-DRG CC	FOREIGN BODY BRONCHUS
9348		MS-DRG CC	FB TRACH/BRONCH/LUNG NEC
9405		MS-DRG CC	BURN W EYEBALL DESTRUCT
94130		MS-DRG CC	3RD DEG BURN HEAD NOS
94131		MS-DRG CC	3RD DEG BURN EAR
94132		MS-DRG CC	3RD DEG BURN EYE
94133		MS-DRG CC	3RD DEG BURN LIP
94134		MS-DRG CC	3RD DEG BURN CHIN
94135		MS-DRG CC	3RD DEG BURN NOSE
94136		MS-DRG CC	3RD DEG BURN SCALP
94137		MS-DRG CC	3RD DEG BURN FACE NEC
94138		MS-DRG CC	3RD DEG BURN NECK

(Continued)

2008 ICD-9-CM	CMS DRG	MS-DRG	Short Title
94139		MS-DRG CC	3RD DEG BURN HEAD-MULT
94140		MS-DRG CC	DEEP 3RD DEG BURN HEAD NOS
94141		MS-DRG CC	DEEP 3RD DEG BURN EAR
94142		MS-DRG CC	DEEP 3RD DEG BURN EYE
94143		MS-DRG CC	DEEP 3RD DEG BURN LIP
94144		MS-DRG CC	DEEP 3RD DEG BURN CHIN
94145		MS-DRG CC	DEEP 3RD DEG BURN NOSE
94146		MS-DRG CC	DEEP 3RD DEG BURN SCALP
94147		MS-DRG CC	DEEP 3RD DEG BURN FACE NEC
94148		MS-DRG CC	DEEP 3RD DEG BURN NECK
94149		MS-DRG CC	DEEP 3RD DEG BRN HEAD-MULT
94150		MS-DRG CC	3RD DEG BURN W LOSS-HEAD NOS
94151		MS-DRG CC	3RD DEG BURN W LOSS-EAR
94152		MS-DRG CC	3RD DEG BURN W LOSS-EYE
94153		MS-DRG CC	3RD DEG BURN W LOSS-LIP
94154		MS-DRG CC	3RD DEG BURN W LOSS-CHIN
94155		MS-DRG CC	3RD DEG BURN W LOSS-NOSE
94156		MS-DRG CC	3RD DEG BRN W LOSS-SCALP
94157		MS-DRG CC	3RD DEG BURN W LOSS-FACE NEC
94158		MS-DRG CC	3RD DEG BURN W LOSS-NECK
94159		MS-DRG CC	3RD BRN W LOSS-HEAD MULT
94230		MS-DRG CC	3RD DEG BURN TRUNK NOS
94231		MS-DRG CC	3RD DEG BURN BREAST
94232		MS-DRG CC	3RD DEG BURN CHEST WALL
94233		MS-DRG CC	3RD DEG BURN ABDOMN WALL
94234		MS-DRG CC	3RD DEG BURN BACK
94235		MS-DRG CC	3RD DEG BURN GENITALIA
94239		MS-DRG CC	3RD DEG BURN TRUNK NEC
94240		MS-DRG CC	DEEP 3RD DEG BURN TRUNK NOS
94241		MS-DRG CC	DEEP 3RD DEG BURN BREAST
94242		MS-DRG CC	DEEP 3RD DEG BURN CHEST WALL
94243		MS-DRG CC	DEEP 3RD DEG BURN ABDOM WALL
94244		MS-DRG CC	DEEP 3RD DEG BURN BACK
94245		MS-DRG CC	DEEP 3RD DEG BURN GENITALIA
94249		MS-DRG CC	DEEP 3RD DEG BURN TRUNK NEC
94250		MS-DRG CC	3RD DEG BRN W LOSS-TRUNK NOS
94251		MS-DRG CC	3RD DEG BURN W LOSS-BREAST
94252		MS-DRG CC	3RD DEG BRN W LOSS-CHEST WLL
94253		MS-DRG CC	3RD DEG BRN W LOSS-ABDOM WLL

2008 ICD-9-CM	CMS DRG	MS-DRG	Short Title
94254		MS-DRG CC	3RD DEG BURN W LOSS-BACK
94255		MS-DRG CC	3RD DEG BRN W LOSS-GENITALIA
94259		MS-DRG CC	3RD DEG BRN W LOSS-TRUNK NEC
94330		MS-DRG CC	3RD DEG BURN ARM NOS
94331		MS-DRG CC	3RD DEG BURN FOREARM
94332		MS-DRG CC	3RD DEG BURN ELBOW
94333		MS-DRG CC	3RD DEG BURN UPPER ARM
94334		MS-DRG CC	3RD DEG BURN AXILLA
94335		MS-DRG CC	3RD DEG BURN SHOULDER
94336		MS-DRG CC	3RD DEG BURN SCAPULA
94339		MS-DRG CC	3RD DEG BURN ARM-MULT
94340		MS-DRG CC	DEEP 3RD DEG BURN ARM NOS
94341		MS-DRG CC	DEEP 3RD DEG BURN FOREARM
94342		MS-DRG CC	DEEP 3RD DEG BURN ELBOW
94343		MS-DRG CC	DEEP 3RD DEG BRN UPPER ARM
94344		MS-DRG CC	DEEP 3RD DEG BURN AXILLA
94345		MS-DRG CC	DEEP 3RD DEG BURN SHOULDER
94346		MS-DRG CC	DEEP 3RD DEG BURN SCAPULA
94349		MS-DRG CC	DEEP 3RD DEG BURN ARM-MULT
94350		MS-DRG CC	3RD DEG BURN W LOSS-ARM NOS
94351		MS-DRG CC	3RD DEG BURN W LOSS-FOREARM
94352		MS-DRG CC	3RD DEG BURN W LOSS-ELBOW
94353		MS-DRG CC	3RD DEG BRN W LOSS-UPPER ARM
94354		MS-DRG CC	3RD DEG BURN W LOSS-AXILLA
94355		MS-DRG CC	3RD DEG BURN W LOSS-SHOULDER
94356		MS-DRG CC	3RD DEG BURN W LOSS-SCAPULA
94359		MS-DRG CC	3RD DEG BURN W LOSS ARM-MULT
94430		MS-DRG CC	3RD DEG BURN HAND NOS
94431		MS-DRG CC	3RD DEG BURN FINGER
94432		MS-DRG CC	3RD DEG BURN THUMB
94433		MS-DRG CC	3RD DEG BURN MULT FINGER
94434		MS-DRG CC	3RD DEG BURN FINGR W THUMB
94435		MS-DRG CC	3RD DEG BURN PALM
94436		MS-DRG CC	3RD DEG BURN BACK OF HAND
94437		MS-DRG CC	3RD DEG BURN WRIST
94438		MS-DRG CC	3RD DEG BURN HAND-MULT
94440		MS-DRG CC	DEEP 3RD DEG BRN HAND NOS
94441		MS-DRG CC	DEEP 3RD DEG BURN FINGER
94442		MS-DRG CC	DEEP 3RD DEG BURN THUMB

(Continued)

2008 ICD-9-CM	CMS DRG	MS-DRG	Short Title
94443		MS-DRG CC	DEEP 3RD BRN MULT FINGER
94444		MS-DRG CC	DEEP 3RD BRN FNGR W THMB
94445		MS-DRG CC	DEEP 3RD DEG BURN PALM
94446		MS-DRG CC	DEEP 3RD DEG BURN BACK OF HND
94447		MS-DRG CC	DEEP 3RD DEG BURN WRIST
94448		MS-DRG CC	DEEP 3RD DEG BRN HAND-MULT
94450		MS-DRG CC	3RD DEG BRN W LOSS-HAND NOS
94451		MS-DRG CC	3RD DEG BURN W LOSS-FINGER
94452		MS-DRG CC	3RD DEG BURN W LOSS-THUMB
94453		MS-DRG CC	3RD DEG BRN W LOSS-MULT FNGR
94454		MS-DRG CC	3RD DEG BRN W LOSS-FNGR/THMB
94455		MS-DRG CC	3RD DEG BURN W LOSS-PALM
94456		MS-DRG CC	3RD DEG BRN W LOSS-BK OF HND
94457		MS-DRG CC	3RD DEG BURN W LOSS-WRIST
94458		MS-DRG CC	3RD DEG BRN W LOSS HAND-MULT
94530		MS-DRG CC	3RD DEG BURN LEG NOS
94531		MS-DRG CC	3RD DEG BURN TOE
94532		MS-DRG CC	3RD DEG BURN FOOT
94533		MS-DRG CC	3RD DEG BURN ANKLE
94534		MS-DRG CC	3RD DEG BURN LOW LEG
94535		MS-DRG CC	3RD DEG BURN KNEE
94536		MS-DRG CC	3RD DEG BURN THIGH
94539		MS-DRG CC	3RD DEG BURN LEG-MULT
94540		MS-DRG CC	DEEP 3RD DEG BRN LEG NOS
94541		MS-DRG CC	DEEP 3RD DEG BURN TOE
94542		MS-DRG CC	DEEP 3RD DEG BURN FOOT
94543		MS-DRG CC	DEEP 3RD DEG BURN ANKLE
94544		MS-DRG CC	DEEP 3RD DEG BRN LOW LEG
94545		MS-DRG CC	DEEP 3RD DEG BURN KNEE
94546		MS-DRG CC	DEEP 3RD DEG BURN THIGH
94549		MS-DRG CC	DEEP 3RD DEG BURN LEG-MULT
94550		MS-DRG CC	3RD DEG BRN W LOSS-LEG NOS
94551		MS-DRG CC	3RD DEG BURN W LOSS-TOE
94552		MS-DRG CC	3RD DEG BURN W LOSS-FOOT
94553		MS-DRG CC	3RD DEG BURN W LOSS-ANKLE
94554		MS-DRG CC	3RD DEG BRN W LOSS-LOW LEG
94555		MS-DRG CC	3RD DEG BURN W LOSS-KNEE
94556		MS-DRG CC	3RD DEG BURN W LOSS-THIGH
94559		MS-DRG CC	3RD DEG BRN W LOSS LEG-MLT

2008 ICD-9-CM	CMS DRG	MS-DRG	Short Title
9463		MS-DRG CC	3RD DEG BURN MULT SITE
9464		MS-DRG CC	DEEP 3RD DEG BRN MULT SITE
9465		MS-DRG CC	3RD DEG BRN W LOSS-MULT SITE
9471		MS-DRG CC	BURN LARYNX/TRACHEA/LUNG
9472		MS-DRG CC	BURN OF ESOPHAGUS
9473		MS-DRG CC	BURN OF GI TRACT
9474		MS-DRG CC	BURN OF VAGINA & UTERUS
94810		MS-DRG CC	10-19% BDY BRN/3RD DEG NOS
94811		MS-DRG CC	10-19% BDY BRN/10-19% 3D
94820		MS-DRG CC	20-29% BDY BRN/3 DEG NOS
94821		MS-DRG MCC	20-29% BDY BRN/10-19% 3D
94822		MS-DRG MCC	20-29% BDY BRN/20-29% 3D
94830		MS-DRG CC	30-39% BDY BRN/3 DEG NOS
94831		MS-DRG MCC	30-39% BDY BRN/10-19% 3D
94832		MS-DRG MCC	30-39% BDY BRN/20-29% 3D
94833		MS-DRG MCC	30-39% BDY BRN/30-39% 3D
94840		MS-DRG CC	40-49% BDY BRN/3 DEG NOS
94841		MS-DRG MCC	40-49% BDY BRN/10-19% 3D
94842		MS-DRG MCC	40-49% BDY BRN/20-29% 3D
94843		MS-DRG MCC	40-49% BDY BRN/30-39% 3D
94844		MS-DRG MCC	40-49% BDY BRN/40-49% 3D
94850		MS-DRG CC	50-59% BDY BRN/3 DEG NOS
94851		MS-DRG MCC	50-59% BDY BRN/10-19% 3D
94852		MS-DRG MCC	50-59% BDY BRN/20-29% 3D
94853		MS-DRG MCC	50-59% BDY BRN/30-39% 3D
94854		MS-DRG MCC	50-59% BDY BRN/40-49% 3D
94855		MS-DRG MCC	50-59% BDY BRN/50-59% 3D
94860		MS-DRG CC	60-69% BDY BRN/3 DEG NOS
94861		MS-DRG MCC	60-69% BDY BRN/10-19% 3D
94862		MS-DRG MCC	60-69% BDY BRN/20-29% 3D
94863		MS-DRG MCC	60-69% BDY BRN/30-39% 3D
94864		MS-DRG MCC	60-69% BDY BRN/40-49% 3D
94865		MS-DRG MCC	60-69% BDY BRN/50-59% 3D
94866		MS-DRG MCC	60-69% BDY BRN/60-69% 3D
94870		MS-DRG CC	70-79% BDY BRN/3 DEG NOS
94871		MS-DRG MCC	70-79% BDY BRN/10-19% 3D
94872		MS-DRG MCC	70-79% BDY BRN/20-29% 3D
94873		MS-DRG MCC	70-79% BDY BRN/30-39% 3D
94874		MS-DRG MCC	70-79% BDY BRN/40-49% 3D

(Continued)

2008 ICD-9-CM	CMS DRG	MS-DRG	Short Title
94875		MS-DRG MCC	70-79% BDY BRN/50-59% 3D
94876		MS-DRG MCC	70-79% BDY BRN/60-69% 3D
94877		MS-DRG MCC	70-79% BDY BRN/70-79% 3D
94880		MS-DRG CC	80-89% BDY BRN/3 DEG NOS
94881		MS-DRG MCC	80-89% BDY BRN/10-19% 3D
94882		MS-DRG MCC	80-89% BDY BRN/20-29% 3D
94883		MS-DRG MCC	80-89% BDY BRN/30-39% 3D
94884		MS-DRG MCC	80-89% BDY BRN/40-49% 3D
94885		MS-DRG MCC	80-89% BDY BRN/50-59% 3D
94886		MS-DRG MCC	80-89% BDY BRN/60-69% 3D
94887		MS-DRG MCC	80-89% BDY BRN/70-79% 3D
94888		MS-DRG MCC	80-89% BDY BRN/80-89% 3D
94890		MS-DRG CC	90% + BDY BRN/3D DEG NOS
94891		MS-DRG MCC	90% + BDY BRN/10-19% 3RD
94892		MS-DRG MCC	90% + BDY BRN/20-29% 3RD
94893		MS-DRG MCC	90% + BDY BRN/30-39% 3RD
94894		MS-DRG MCC	90% + BDY BRN/40-49% 3RD
94895		MS-DRG MCC	90% + BDY BRN/50-59% 3RD
94896		MS-DRG MCC	90% + BDY BRN/60-69% 3RD
94897		MS-DRG MCC	90% + BDY BRN/70-79% 3RD
94898		MS-DRG MCC	90% + BDY BRN/80-89% 3RD
94899		MS-DRG MCC	90% + BDY BRN/90% + 3RD
9493		MS-DRG CC	3RD DEGREE BURN NOS
9494		MS-DRG CC	DEEP 3RD DEG BURN NOS
9495		MS-DRG CC	3RD BURN W LOSS-SITE NOS
9500		MS-DRG CC	OPTIC NERVE INJURY
9501		MS-DRG CC	INJURY TO OPTIC CHIASM
9502		MS-DRG CC	INJURY TO OPTIC PATHWAYS
9503		MS-DRG CC	INJURY TO VISUAL CORTEX
9509		MS-DRG CC	INJ OPTIC NERV/PATH NOS
9510		MS-DRG CC	INJURY OCULOMOTOR NERVE
9511		MS-DRG CC	INJURY TROCHLEAR NERVE
9512		MS-DRG CC	INJURY TRIGEMINAL NERVE
9513		MS-DRG CC	INJURY ABDUCENS NERVE
9514		MS-DRG CC	INJURY TO FACIAL NERVE
9515		MS-DRG CC	INJURY TO ACOUSTIC NERVE
9516		MS-DRG CC	INJURY ACCESSORY NERVE
9517		MS-DRG CC	INJURY HYPOGLOSSAL NERVE
9518		MS-DRG CC	INJURY CRANIAL NERVE NEC

2008 ICD-9-CM	CMS DRG	MS-DRG	Short Title
9519		MS-DRG CC	INJURY CRANIAL NERVE NOS
95200		MS-DRG MCC	C1-C4 SPIN CORD INJ NOS
95201		MS-DRG MCC	COMPLETE LES CORD/C1-C4
95202		MS-DRG MCC	ANTERIOR CORD SYND/C1-C4
95203		MS-DRG MCC	CENTRAL CORD SYND/C1-C4
95204		MS-DRG MCC	C1-C4 SPIN CORD INJ NEC
95205		MS-DRG MCC	C5-C7 SPIN CORD INJ NOS
95206		MS-DRG MCC	COMPLETE LES CORD/C5-C7
95207		MS-DRG MCC	ANTERIOR CORD SYND/C5-C7
95208		MS-DRG MCC	CENTRAL CORD SYND/C5-C7
95209		MS-DRG MCC	C5-C7 SPIN CORD INJ NEC
95210		MS-DRG MCC	T1-T6 SPIN CORD INJ NOS
95211		MS-DRG MCC	COMPLETE LES CORD/T1-T6
95212		MS-DRG MCC	ANTERIOR CORD SYND/T1-T6
95213		MS-DRG MCC	CENTRAL CORD SYND/T1-T6
95214		MS-DRG MCC	T1-T6 SPIN CORD INJ NEC
95215		MS-DRG MCC	T7-T12 SPIN CORD INJ NOS
95216		MS-DRG MCC	COMPLETE LES CORD/T7-T12
95217		MS-DRG MCC	ANTERIOR CORD SYN/T7-T12
95218		MS-DRG MCC	CENTRAL CORD SYN/T7-T12
95219		MS-DRG MCC	T7-T12 SPIN CORD INJ NEC
9522		MS-DRG MCC	LUMBAR SPINAL CORD INJUR
9523		MS-DRG MCC	SACRAL SPINAL CORD INJUR
9524		MS-DRG MCC	CAUDA EQUINA INJURY
9528		MS-DRG MCC	SPIN CORD INJ-MULT SITE
9580	CMS CC	MS-DRG MCC	AIR EMBOLISM
9581	CMS CC	MS-DRG MCC	FAT EMBOLISM
9582	CMS CC	MS-DRG CC	SECONDARY/RECUR HEMORR
9583	CMS CC	MS-DRG CC	POSTTRAUM WND INFEC NEC
9584	CMS CC	MS-DRG MCC	TRAUMATIC SHOCK
9585	CMS CC	MS-DRG MCC	TRAUMATIC ANURIA
9587	CMS CC	MS-DRG CC	TRAUM SUBCUTAN EMPHYSEMA
95890		MS-DRG CC	COMPARTMENT SYNDROME NOS
95891		MS-DRG CC	TRAUMA COMP SYND UP EXT
95892		MS-DRG CC	TRAUMA COMP SYND LOW EXT
95893		MS-DRG CC	TRAUMA COMPART SYND ABD
95899		MS-DRG CC	TRAUMA COMPART SYND NEC
9910		MS-DRG CC	FROSTBITE OF FACE
9911		MS-DRG CC	FROSTBITE OF HAND

(Continued)

2008 ICD-9-CM	CMS DRG	MS-DRG	Short Title
9912		MS-DRG CC	FROSTBITE OF FOOT
9913		MS-DRG CC	FROSTBITE NEC/NOS
9914		MS-DRG CC	IMMERSION FOOT
9920		MS-DRG CC	HEAT STROKE & SUNSTROKE
9933		MS-DRG CC	CAISSON DISEASE
9941		MS-DRG CC	DROWNING/NONFATAL SUBMER
9947		MS-DRG CC	ASPHYXIATION/STRANGULAT
9950		MS-DRG CC	ANAPHYLACTIC SHOCK
9954	CMS CC	MS-DRG CC	SHOCK DUE TO ANESTHESIA
99550		MS-DRG CC	CHILD ABUSE NOS
99551		MS-DRG CC	CHILD EMOTNL/PSYCH ABUSE
99552		MS-DRG CC	CHILD NEGLECT-NUTRITION
99553		MS-DRG CC	CHILD SEXUAL ABUSE
99554		MS-DRG CC	CHILD PHYSICAL ABUSE
99555		MS-DRG CC	SHAKEN INFANT SYNDROME
99559		MS-DRG CC	CHILD ABUSE/NEGLECT NEC
99560		MS-DRG CC	ANPHYLCT SHK FOOD NOS
99561		MS-DRG CC	ANPHYLCT SHK PEANUTS
99562		MS-DRG CC	ANPHYLCT SHK CRSTACNS
99563		MS-DRG CC	ANPHYLCT SHK FRTS VEG
99564		MS-DRG CC	ANPHYLCT SHK TR NTS SEED
99565		MS-DRG CC	ANPHYLCT SHK FISH
99566		MS-DRG CC	ANPHYLCT SHK FOOD ADDTV
99567		MS-DRG CC	ANPHYLCT SHK MILK PROD
99568		MS-DRG CC	ANPHYLCT SHK EGGS
99569		MS-DRG CC	ANPHYLCT SHK OT SPF FOOD
99580		MS-DRG CC	ADULT MALTREATMENT NOS
99581		MS-DRG CC	ADULT PHYSICAL ABUSE
99583		MS-DRG CC	ADULT SEXUAL ABUSE
99584		MS-DRG CC	ADULT NEGLECT-NUTRITION
99585		MS-DRG CC	OTH ADULT ABUSE/NEGLECT
99586	CMS CC	MS-DRG CC	MALIGNANT HYPERTHERMIA
99590	CMS CC	MS-DRG CC	SIRS, NOS
99591	CMS CC	MS-DRG MCC	SEPSIS
99592	CMS CC	MS-DRG MCC	SEVERE SEPSIS
99593	CMS CC	MS-DRG CC	SIRS-NONINF W/O AC OR DS
99594	CMS CC	MS-DRG MCC	SIRS-NONINF W AC ORG DYS
99600	CMS CC	MS-DRG CC	MALFUNC CARD DEV/GRF NOS
99601	CMS CC	MS-DRG CC	MALFUNC CARDIAC PACEMAKE

2008 ICD-9-CM	CMS DRG	MS-DRG	Short Title
99602	CMS CC	MS-DRG CC	MALFUNC PROSTH HRT VALVE
99603	CMS CC	MS-DRG CC	MALFUNC CORON BYPASS GRF
99604	CMS CC	MS-DRG CC	MCH CMP AUTM MPLNT DFBRL
99609	CMS CC	MS-DRG CC	MALFUNC CARD DEV/GRF NEC
9961	CMS CC	MS-DRG CC	MALFUNC VASC DEVICE/GRAF
9962	CMS CC	MS-DRG CC	MALFUN NEURO DEVICE/GRAF
99630	CMS CC	MS-DRG CC	MALFUNC GU DEV/GRAFT NOS
99639	CMS CC	MS-DRG CC	MALFUNC GU DEV/GRAFT NEC
99640	CMS CC	MS-DRG CC	CMP INT ORTH DEV/GFT NOS
99641	CMS CC	MS-DRG CC	MECH LOOSENING PROS JT
99642	CMS CC	MS-DRG CC	DISLOCATE PROSTHETIC JT
99643	CMS CC	MS-DRG CC	PROSTHTC JT IMPLANT FAIL
99644	CMS CC	MS-DRG CC	PERIPROSTHETC FX-PROS JT
99645	CMS CC	MS-DRG CC	PERIPROSTHETC OSTEOLYSIS
99646	CMS CC	MS-DRG CC	ARTICULAR WEAR PROSTH JT
99647	CMS CC	MS-DRG CC	MECH COM PROS JT IMPLANT
99649	CMS CC	MS-DRG CC	MECH COM ORTH DEV NEC
99651	CMS CC	MS-DRG CC	CORNEAL GRFT MALFUNCTION
99652	CMS CC	MS-DRG CC	OTH TISSUE GRAFT MALFUNC
99653	CMS CC	MS-DRG CC	LENS PROSTHESIS MALFUNC
99654	CMS CC	MS-DRG CC	BREAST PROSTH MALFUNC
99655	CMS CC	MS-DRG CC	COMP-ARTIFICIAL SKIN GRF
99656	CMS CC	MS-DRG CC	COMP-PERITON DIALYS CATH
99657	CMS CC	MS-DRG CC	COMPLCATION-INSULIN PUMP
99659	CMS CC	MS-DRG CC	MALFUNC OTH DEVICE/GRAFT
99660	CMS CC	MS-DRG CC	REACTION-UNSP DEVIC/GRFT
99661	CMS CC	MS-DRG CC	REACT-CARDIAC DEV/GRAFT
99662	CMS CC	MS-DRG CC	REACT-OTH VASC DEV/GRAFT
99663	CMS CC	MS-DRG CC	REACT-NERV SYS DEV/GRAFT
99664	CMS CC	MS-DRG CC	REACT-INDWELL URIN CATH
99665	CMS CC	MS-DRG CC	REACT-OTH GENITOURIN DEV
99666	CMS CC	MS-DRG CC	REACT-INTER JOINT PROST
99667	CMS CC	MS-DRG CC	REACT-OTH INT ORTHO DEV
99668	CMS CC	MS-DRG CC	REACT-PERITON DIALY CATH
99669	CMS CC	MS-DRG CC	REACT-INT PROS DEVIC NEC
99670	CMS CC		COMP-UNSP DEVICE/GRAFT
99671	CMS CC	MS-DRG CC	COMP-HEART VALVE PROSTH
99672	CMS CC	MS-DRG CC	COMP-OTH CARDIAC DEVICE
99673	CMS CC	MS-DRG CC	COMP-REN DIALYS DEV/GRFT

(Continued)

2008 ICD-9-CM	CMS DRG	MS-DRG	Short Title
99674	CMS CC	MS-DRG CC	COMP-OTH VASC DEV/GRAFT
99675	CMS CC	MS-DRG CC	COMP-NERV SYS DEV/GRAFT
99676	CMS CC	MS-DRG CC	COMP-GENITOURIN DEV/GRFT
99677	CMS CC	MS-DRG CC	COMP-INTERNAL JOINT PROS
99678	CMS CC	MS-DRG CC	COMP-OTH INT ORTHO DEVIC
99679	CMS CC	MS-DRG CC	COMP-INT PROST DEVIC NEC
99680	CMS CC	MS-DRG CC	COMP ORGAN TRANSPLNT NOS
99681	CMS CC	MS-DRG CC	COMPL KIDNEY TRANSPLANT
99682	CMS CC	MS-DRG CC	COMPL LIVER TRANSPLANT
99683	CMS CC	MS-DRG CC	COMPL HEART TRANSPLANT
99684	CMS CC	MS-DRG CC	COMPL LUNG TRANSPLANT
99685	CMS CC	MS-DRG CC	COMPL MARROW TRANSPLANT
99686	CMS CC	MS-DRG CC	COMPL PANCREAS TRANSPLNT
99687	CMS CC	MS-DRG CC	COMP INTESTINE TRANSPLNT
99689	CMS CC	MS-DRG CC	COMP OTH ORGAN TRANSPLNT
99690	CMS CC	MS-DRG CC	COMP REATTACHED EXTREM NOS
99691	CMS CC	MS-DRG CC	COMPL REATTACHED FOREARM
99692	CMS CC	MS-DRG CC	COMPL REATTACHED HAND
99693	CMS CC	MS-DRG CC	COMPL REATTACHED FINGER
99694	CMS CC	MS-DRG CC	COMPL REATTACHED ARM NEC
99695	CMS CC	MS-DRG CC	COMPL REATTACHED FOOT
99696	CMS CC	MS-DRG CC	COMPL REATTACHED LEG NEC
99699	CMS CC	MS-DRG CC	COMPL REATTACHED PART NEC
99700	CMS CC		NERVOUS SYST COMPLC NOS
99701	CMS CC	MS-DRG CC	SURG COMPLICATION - CNS
99702	CMS CC	MS-DRG CC	IATROGEN CV INFARC/HMRHG
99709	CMS CC	MS-DRG CC	SURG COMP NERV SYSTM NEC
9971	CMS CC	MS-DRG CC	SURG COMPL-HEART
9972	CMS CC	MS-DRG CC	SURG COMP-PERI VASC SYST
9973	CMS CC	MS-DRG CC	SURG COMPLIC-RESPIR SYST
9974	CMS CC	MS-DRG CC	SURG COMP-DIGESTV SYSTEM
9975	CMS CC		SURG COMPL-URINARY TRACT
99762	CMS CC	MS-DRG CC	INFECTION AMPUTAT STUMP
99771	CMS CC	MS-DRG CC	VASC COMP MESENTERIC ART
99772	CMS CC	MS-DRG CC	VASC COMP RENAL ARTERY
99779	CMS CC	MS-DRG CC	VASCULAR COMP VESSEL NEC
99799	CMS CC	MS-DRG CC	SURG COMPL-BODY SYST NEC
9980	CMS CC	MS-DRG CC	POSTOPERATIVE SHOCK
99811	CMS CC	MS-DRG CC	HEMORRHAGE COMPLIC PROC

2008 ICD-9-CM	CMS DRG	MS-DRG	Short Title
99812	CMS CC	MS-DRG CC	HEMATOMA COMPLIC PROC
99813	CMS CC	MS-DRG CC	SEROMA COMPLICTING PROC
9982	CMS CC	MS-DRG CC	ACCIDENTAL OP LACERATION
99831	CMS CC	MS-DRG CC	DISRUP-INTERNAL OP WOUND
99832	CMS CC	MS-DRG CC	DISRUP-EXTERNAL OP WOUND
9984	CMS CC	MS-DRG CC	FB LEFT DURING PROCEDURE
99851	CMS CC	MS-DRG CC	INFECTED POSTOP SEROMA
99859	CMS CC	MS-DRG CC	OTHER POSTOP INFECTION
9986	CMS CC	MS-DRG CC	PERSIST POSTOP FISTULA
9987	CMS CC	MS-DRG CC	POSTOP FORGN SUBST REACT
99883	CMS CC	MS-DRG CC	NON-HEALING SURGCL WOUND
99889	CMS CC		OTH SPCF CMPLC PROCD NEC
9989	CMS CC		SURGICAL COMPLICAT NOS
9990		MS-DRG CC	GENERALIZED VACCINIA
9991	CMS CC	MS-DRG MCC	AIR EMBOL COMP MED CARE
9992	CMS CC	MS-DRG CC	VASC COMP MED CARE NEC
99931	CMS CC		INFECT D/T CENT VEN CATH
99939	CMS CC		INFECT FOL INFUS/INJ/VAC
9994	CMS CC	MS-DRG CC	ANAPHYLACTIC SHOCK-SERUM
9995	CMS CC	MS-DRG CC	SERUM REACTION NEC
9996	CMS CC	MS-DRG CC	ABO INCOMPATIBILITY REAC
9997	CMS CC	MS-DRG CC	RH INCOMPATIBILITY REACT
9998	CMS CC	MS-DRG CC	TRANSFUSION REACTION NEC
V237	CMS CC		INSUFFICNT PRENATAL CARE
V2381	CMS CC		SUPRV ELDERLY PRIMIGRAV
V2382	CMS CC		SUPRV ELDERLY MULTIGRAV
V2383	CMS CC		SUPRV YOUNG PRIMIGRAVIDA
V2384	CMS CC		SUPRV YOUNG MULTIGRAVIDA
V2389	CMS CC		SUPRV HIGH-RISK PREG NEC
V239	CMS CC		SUPRV HIGH-RISK PREG NOS
V420	CMS CC	MS-DRG CC	KIDNEY TRANSPLANT STATUS
V421	CMS CC	MS-DRG CC	HEART TRANSPLANT STATUS
V422	CMS CC		HEART VALVE TRANSPLANT
V426	CMS CC	MS-DRG CC	LUNG TRANSPLANT STATUS
V427	CMS CC	MS-DRG CC	LIVER TRANSPLANT STATUS
V4281	CMS CC	MS-DRG CC	TRNSPL STATUS-BNE MARROW
V4282	CMS CC	MS-DRG CC	TRSPL STS-PERIP STM CELL
V4283	CMS CC	MS-DRG CC	TRNSPL STATUS-PANCREAS
V4284	CMS CC	MS-DRG CC	TRNSPL STATUS-INTESTINES

(Continued)

2008 ICD-9-CM	CMS DRG	MS-DRG	Short Title
V4289	CMS CC		TRNSPL STATUS ORGAN NEC
V4321	CMS CC	MS-DRG CC	HEART ASSIST DEV REPLACE
V4322	CMS CC	MS-DRG CC	ARTFICIAL HEART REPLACE
V451	CMS CC		RENAL DIALYSIS STATUS
V4611	CMS CC	MS-DRG CC	RESPIRATOR DEPEND STATUS
V4612	CMS CC	MS-DRG CC	RESP DEPEND-POWR FAILURE
V4613	CMS CC	MS-DRG CC	WEANING FROM RESPIRATOR
V4614	CMS CC	MS-DRG CC	MECH COMP RESPIRATOR
V4983	CMS CC		AWAIT ORGAN TRANSPLNT ST
V551		MS-DRG CC	ATTEN TO GASTROSTOMY
V6284		MS-DRG CC	SUICIDAL IDEATION
V850		MS-DRG CC	BMI LESS THAN 19,ADULT
V854		MS-DRG CC	BMI 40 AND OVER,ADULT

Appendix C

AHIMA Practice Brief: Developing a Physician Query Process

Principles of Medical Record Documentation

Medical record documentation is used for a multitude of purposes, including:

- Serving as a means of communication between the physician and the other members of the healthcare team providing care to the patient
- Serving as a basis for evaluating the adequacy and appropriateness of patient care
- Providing data to support insurance claims
- Assisting in protecting the legal interests of patients, healthcare professionals, and healthcare facilities
- Providing clinical data for research and education

To support these various uses, it is imperative that medical record documentation be complete, accurate, and timely. Facilities are expected to comply with a number of standards regarding medical record completion and content promulgated by multiple regulatory agencies.

The Joint Commission

The Joint Commission's *2000 Hospital Accreditation Standards* state, ". . . the medical record contains sufficient information to identify the patient, support the diagnosis, justify the treatment, document the course

and results, and promote continuity among health care providers" (IM.7.2).[1] The Joint Commission Standards also state, ". . . medical record data and information are managed in a timely manner" (IM.7.6).

Timely entries are essential if a medical record is to be useful in a patient's care. A complete medical record is also important when a patient is discharged, because information in the record may be needed for clinical, legal, or performance improvement purposes. The Joint Commission requires hospitals to have policies and procedures on the timely entry of all significant clinical information into the patient's medical record, and they do not consider a medical record complete until all final diagnoses and complications are recorded without the use of symbols or abbreviations.

Joint Commission standards also require medical records to be reviewed on an ongoing basis for completeness and timeliness of information, and they require that action is taken to improve the quality and timeliness of documentation that affects patient care (IM.7.10). This review must address the presence, timeliness, legibility, and authentication of the final diagnoses and conclusions at termination of hospitalization.

Medicare

The Medicare Conditions of Participation require medical records to be accurately written, promptly completed, properly filed and retained, and accessible.[2] Records must document, as appropriate, complications, hospital-acquired infections, and unfavorable reactions to drugs and anesthesia. The conditions also stipulate that all records must document the final diagnosis and that medical records must be complete within 30 days following discharge.

Relationship Between Coding and Documentation

Complete and accurate diagnostic and procedural coded data must be available in a timely manner in order to:

- Improve the quality and effectiveness of patient care
- Ensure equitable healthcare reimbursement
- Expand the body of medical knowledge
- Make appropriate decisions regarding health-care policies, delivery systems, funding, expansion, and education
- Monitor resource utilization
- Permit identification and resolution of medical errors
- Improve clinical decision making
- Facilitate tracking of fraud and abuse
- Permit valid clinical research, epidemiologic studies, outcomes and statistical analyses, and provider profiling
- Provide comparative data to consumers regarding costs and outcomes, average charges, and outcomes by procedure

Physician documentation is the cornerstone of accurate coding. Therefore, assuring the accuracy of coded data is a shared responsibility between coding professionals and physicians. Accurate diagnostic and procedural coded data originate from collaboration between physicians, who have a clinical background, and coding professionals, who have an understanding of classification systems.

Expectations of Physicians

Physicians are expected to provide complete, accurate, timely, and legible documentation of pertinent facts and observations about an individual's health history, including past and present illnesses, tests, treatments, and outcomes. Medical record entries should be documented at the time service is provided. Medical record entries should be authenticated. If subsequent additions to documentation are needed, they should be identified as such and dated. (Often these expectations are included in the medical staff or house staff rules and regulations.) Medical record documentation should:

- Address the clinical significance of abnormal test results
- Support the intensity of patient evaluation and treatment and describe the thought processes and complexity of decision making
- Include all diagnostic and therapeutic procedures, treatments, and tests performed, in addition to their results
- Include any changes in the patient's condition, including psychosocial and physical symptoms
- Include all conditions that coexist at the time of admission, that subsequently develop, or that affect the treatment received and the length of stay. This encompasses all conditions that affect patient care in terms of requiring clinical evaluation, therapeutic treatment, diagnostic procedures, extended length of hospital stay, or increased nursing care and monitoring[3]
- Be updated as necessary to reflect all diagnoses relevant to the care or services provided
- Be consistent and discuss and reconcile any discrepancies (this reconciliation should be documented in the medical record)
- Be legible and written in ink, typewritten, or electronically signed, stored, and printed

Expectations of Coding Professionals

The AHIMA Code of Ethics sets forth ethical principles for the HIM profession. HIM professionals are responsible for maintaining and promoting ethical practices. This Code of Ethics states, in part, "Health information management professionals promote high standards for health information management practice, education, and research." Another standard in this code states, "Health information management professionals strive to provide accurate and timely information." Data accuracy and integrity are fundamental values of HIM that are advanced by:

- Using practices that produce complete, accurate, and timely information to meet the health and related needs of individuals
- Following the guidelines set forth in the organization's compliance plan for reporting improper preparation, alteration, or suppression of information or data by others
- Not participating in any improper preparation, alteration, or suppression of health record information or other organization data

A conscientious goal for coding and maintaining a quality database is accurate clinical and statistical data.

AHIMA's Standards of Ethical Coding were developed to guide coding professionals in this process. As stated in the standards, coding professionals are expected to support the importance of accurate, complete, and consistent coding practices for the production of quality healthcare data. These standards also indicate that coding professionals should only assign and report codes that are clearly and consistently supported by physician documentation in the medical record. It is the responsibility of coding professionals to assess physician documentation to assure that it supports the diagnosis and procedure codes reported on claims.

Dialogue between coding professionals and clinicians is encouraged, because it improves coding professionals' clinical knowledge and educates the physicians on documentation practice issues. AHIMA's Standards of Ethical Coding state that coding professionals are expected to consult physicians for clarification and additional documentation prior to code assignment when there is conflicting or ambiguous data in the health record. Coding professionals should also assist and educate physicians by advocating proper documentation practices, further specificity, and resequencing or inclusion of diagnoses or procedures when needed to more accurately reflect the acuity, severity, and the occurrence of events. It is recommended that coding be performed by credentialed HIM professionals.[4]

It is inappropriate for coding professionals to misrepresent the patient's clinical picture through incorrect coding or add diagnoses or procedures unsupported by the documentation to maximize reimbursement or meet insurance policy coverage requirements. Coding professionals should not change codes or the narratives of codes on the billing abstract so that meanings are misrepresented. Diagnoses or procedures should not be inappropriately included or excluded, because payment or insurance policy coverage requirements will be affected. When individual payer policies conflict with official coding rules and guidelines, these policies should be obtained in writing whenever possible. Reasonable efforts should be made to educate the payer on proper coding practices in order to influence a change in the payer's policy.

Proper Use of Physician Queries

The process of querying physicians is an effective and, in the current healthcare environment, necessary mechanism for improving the quality of coding and medical record documentation and capturing complete clinical data. Query forms have become an accepted tool for communicating with physicians on documentation issues influencing proper code assignment. Query forms should be used in a judicious and appropriate manner. They must be used as a communication tool to improve the accuracy of code assignment and the quality of physician documentation, not to inappropriately maximize reimbursement. The query process should be guided by AHIMA's Standards of Ethical Coding and the official coding guidelines. An inappropriate query, such as a form that is poorly constructed or asks leading questions or overuse of the query process, can result in quality-of-care, legal, and ethical concerns.

The Query Process

The goal of the query process should be to improve physician documentation and coding professionals' understanding of the unique clinical situation, not to improve reimbursement. Each facility should establish a policy and procedure for obtaining physician clarification of documentation that affects code assignment. The process of querying physicians must be a patient-specific process, not a general process. Asking "blanket" questions is not appropriate. Policies regarding the circumstances when physicians will be queried should be designed to promote timely, complete, and accurate coding and documentation.

Physicians should not be asked to provide clarification of their medical record documentation without the opportunity to access the patient's medical record. Each facility also needs to determine if physicians will be queried concurrently (during the patient's hospitalization) or after discharge. Both methods are acceptable. Querying physicians concurrently allows the documentation deficiency to be corrected while the patient is still in-house and can positively influence patient care.

The policy and procedure should stipulate who is authorized to contact the physician for clarification regarding a coding issue. Coding professionals should be allowed to contact physicians directly for clarification, rather than limiting this responsibility to supervisory personnel or a designated individual.

The facility may wish to use a designated physician liaison to resolve conflicts between physicians and coding professionals. The appropriate use of the physician liaison should be described in the facility's policy and procedures.

Query Format

Each facility should develop a standard format for the query form. Sticky notes or scratch paper should not be allowed. Each facility should develop a standard design and format for physician queries to ensure clear, consistent, appropriate queries. The query form should:

- Be clearly and concisely written
- Contain precise language
- Present the facts from the medical record and identify why clarification is needed
- Present the scenario and state a question that asks the physician to make a clinical interpretation of a given diagnosis or condition based on treatment, evaluation, monitoring, and/or services provided. Open-ended questions that allow the physician to document the specific diagnosis are preferable to multiple-choice questions or questions requiring only a "yes" or "no" response. Queries that appear to lead the physician to provide a particular response could lead to allegations of inappropriate upcoding.
- Be phrased so that the physician is allowed to specify the correct diagnosis. It should not indicate the financial impact of the response to the query. The form should not be designed so that all that is required is a physician signature.

The query form should also include:

- Patient name
- Admission date
- Medical record number
- Name and contact information (phone number and e-mail address) of the coding professional
- Specific questions and rationales (that is, relevant documentation or clinical findings)
- A place for the physician to document his or her response
- A place for the physician to sign and date his or her response

The query form should not:

- Lead the physician
- Sound presumptive, directing, prodding, or probing, as though the physician is being led to make an assumption
- Ask questions that can be responded to in a "yes" or "no" fashion
- Indicate the financial impact of the response to the query
- Be designed so that all that is required is a physician signature

When Is a Query Appropriate?

Physicians should be queried whenever there is conflicting, ambiguous, or incomplete information in the medical record regarding any significant reportable condition or procedure. Querying the physician only when reimbursement is affected will skew national healthcare data and might lead to allegations of upcoding.

Every discrepancy or issue not addressed in the physician documentation should not necessarily result in the physician being queried. Each facility needs to develop policies and procedures regarding the clinical conditions and documentation situations warranting a request for physician clarification. For example, insignificant or irrelevant findings may not warrant querying the physician regarding the assignment of an additional diagnosis code. Also, if the maximum number of codes that can be entered in the hospital information system has already been assigned, the facility may decide that it is not necessary to query the physician regarding an additional code. Facilities need to balance the value of marginal data being collected against the administrative burden of obtaining the additional documentation.

Members of the medical staff in consultation with coding professionals should develop the specific clinical criteria for a valid query. The specific clinical documentation that must be present in the patient's record to generate a query should be described. For example, anemia, septicemia, and respiratory failure are conditions that often require physician clarification. The medical staff can assist the coding staff in determining when it would be appropriate to query a physician regarding the reporting of these conditions by describing the specific clinical indications in the medical record documentation that raise the possibility that the condition in question may be present.

When Is a Query Not Necessary?

Queries are not necessary if a physician involved in the care and treatment of the patient, including consulting physicians, has documented a diagnosis and there is no conflicting documentation from another physician. Medical record documentation from any physician involved in the care and treatment of the patient, including documentation by consulting physicians, is appropriate for the basis of code assignment. If documentation from different physicians conflicts, clarification from the attending physician should be sought, because he or she is ultimately responsible for the final diagnosis.

Queries are also not necessary when a physician has documented a final diagnosis and the clinical indicator, such as test results, do not appear to support this diagnosis. Although coding professionals are expected to advocate complete and accurate physician documentation and to collaborate with physicians to realize this goal, they are not expected to challenge the physician's medical judgment in establishing the patient's diagnosis. However, because a discrepancy between clinical findings and a final diagnosis is a clinical issue, a facility may choose to establish a policy that the physician will be queried in these instances.

Documentation of Query Response

The physician's response to the query must be documented in the patient's medical record. Each facility must develop a policy regarding the specific process for incorporating this additional documentation in the medical record. For example, this policy might stipulate that the physician is required to place the additional information to the body of the medical record. As an alternative, a form, such as a medical record "progress note" form, might be attached to the query form and the attachment is then filed in the medical record. However, another alternative is to file the query form itself in the permanent medical record. Any documentation obtained postdischarge must be included in the discharge summary or identified as a late entry or addendum.

Any decision to file this form in the medical record should involve the advice of the facility's corporate compliance officer and legal counsel, due to potential compliance and legal risks related to incorporating the actual query form into the permanent medical record (such as its potential use as evidence of poor documentation in an audit, investigation, or malpractice suit; risks related to naming a nonclinician in the medical record; or quality-of-care concerns if the physician response on a query form is not clearly supported by the rest of the medical record documentation).

If the query form will serve as the only documentation of the physician's clarification, the use of "open-ended" questions (that require the physician to specifically document the additional information) are preferable to multiple-choice questions or the use of questions requiring only a "yes" or "no" answer. The query form would need to be approved by the medical staff/medical records committee before implementation of a policy allowing this form to be maintained in the medical record. Also keep in mind that the Joint Commission hospital accreditation standards stipulate that only authorized individuals may make entries in medical records (IM.7.1.1). Therefore, the facility needs to consider modifying the medical staff bylaws to specify coding professionals as individuals authorized to make medical record entries prior to allowing query forms to become a permanent part of the medical record.

Auditing, Monitoring, and Corrective Action

Ideally, complete and accurate physician documentation should occur at the time care is rendered. The need for a query form results from incomplete, conflicting, or ambiguous documentation, which is an indication of poor documentation. Therefore, query form usage should be the exception rather than the norm. If physicians are being queried frequently, facility management or an appropriate medical staff committee should investigate the reasons why.

A periodic review of the query practice should include a determination of what percentage of the query forms are eliciting negative and positive responses from the physicians. A high negative response rate may be an indication that the coding staff are not using the query process judiciously and are being overzealous.

A high positive response rate may indicate that there are widespread poor documentation habits that need to be addressed. It also may indicate that the absence of certain reports (for example, discharge summary, operative report) at the time of coding is forcing the coding staff to query the physicians to obtain the information they need for proper coding. If this is the case, the facility may wish to reconsider its policy regarding the availability of certain reports prior to coding. Waiting for these reports may make more sense in terms of turnaround time and productivity rather than finding it necessary to frequently query the physicians. The question of why final diagnoses are not available at the time of discharge may arise at the time of an audit, review by the peer review organization, or investigation.

The use of query forms also should be monitored for patterns, and any identified patterns should be used to educate physicians on improving their documentation at the point of care. If a pattern is identified, such as a particular physician or diagnosis, appropriate steps should be taken to correct the problem so the necessary documentation is present prior to coding in the future and the need to query this physician, or to query physicians regarding a particular diagnosis, is reduced. Corrective action might include targeted education for one physician or education for the entire medical staff on the proper documentation necessary for accurate code assignment.

Patterns of poor documentation that have not been addressed through education or other corrective action are signs of an ineffective compliance program. The Department of Health and Human Services Office of Inspector General has noted in its Compliance Program Guidance for Hospitals that "accurate coding depends upon the quality of completeness of the physician's documentation" and "active staff physician participation in educational programs focusing on coding and documentation should be emphasized by the hospital." [5]

The format of the queries also should be monitored on a regular basis to ensure that they are not inappropriately leading the physician to provide a particular response. Inappropriately written queries should be used to educate the coding staff on a properly written query. Patterns of inappropriately written queries should be referred to the corporate compliance officer.

Prepared by

Sue Prophet, RHIA, CCS

Acknowledgments

AHIMA Advocacy and Policy Task Force
AHIMA Coding Practice Team
AHIMA Coding Policy and Strategy Committee
AHIMA Society for Clinical Coding
Dan Rode, MBA, FHFMA

Notes

[1] Joint Commission on Accreditation of Healthcare Organizations. 2000. *Comprehensive accreditation manual for hospitals: The official handbook*. Oakbrook Terrace, IL: Joint Commission.

[2] Health Care Financing Administration, Department of Health and Human Services. 2000. Conditions of participation for hospitals. Code of Federal Regulations. 42 CFR, Chapter IV, Part 482.

[3] Official ICD-9-CM Guidelines for Coding and Reporting developed and approved by the American Hospital Association, American Health Information Management Association, Health Care Financing Administration, and the National Center for Health Statistics.

[4] AHIMA is the professional organization responsible for issuing several credentials in health information management: Registered Health Information Administrator (RHIA), Registered Health Information Technician (RHIT), Certified Coding Specialist (CCS), and Certified Coding Specialist–Physician-based (CCS-P).

[5] Office of Inspector General, Department of Health and Human Services. 1998. Compliance Program Guidance for Hospitals. Washington, DC: Office of Inspector General.

References

AHIMA Code of Ethics, 1998.

AHIMA Standards of Ethical Coding, 1999.

AHIMA Coding Policy and Strategy Committee. 1996. Practice brief: Data quality. *Journal of AHIMA* 67(2).

Index